LIBERTY HYDE BAILEY

Liberty Hyde Bailey

A Story of
American Plant Sciences

BY *ANDREW DENNY RODGERS III*

PRINCETON, NEW JERSEY
PRINCETON UNIVERSITY PRESS

1949

To Dr. George Harrison Shull,
adviser and friend,
and to the memory of one most dear

CONTENTS

ILLUSTRATIONS

$\mathcal{L}IBERTY$ $HYDE$ $BAILEY$

CHAPTER I

A HOME IN A FOREST ON LAKE MICHIGAN

AN apple orchard in bloom in Michigan is unforgettably beautiful. Two generations or more ago, when Michigan was a forest, a young orchard of green leaves—growing amid that forest strong against high winds from Lake Michigan or Lake Huron—must have been marvelously enchanting. A hilly landscape, near seldom trodden roads and paths, perhaps merely a quiet fringe of ever changing luxuriance amid the tall splendor of pine, cedar, and hemlock, an orchard's white brilliance of spring or its rich red and yellow harvest of summer and autumn must have shone like a wonderland—a proud badge honoring man's arrival on the frontier.

It takes no stretch of the imagination to see in a Michigan orchard a living embodiment, a lasting symbol, of the history of American horticultural development. Located not far away, the garden supplied an adjunct, a partner with the orchard, in developing the art and science of growing vegetables, fruits, flowers, and ornamental shrubs and trees. Not far away the field and the woodlot also supplied landscape phases, dignified in learning by titles of agriculture and, in part, forestry. The whole are one in nature. There is a commonalty in the lives of plants, from the most sensitive to the most durable.

Michigan, it may be argued, was not the first state of the American union to develop and improve its plant life as part of its basic resources. It was perhaps not the first state to foster educational advancement in the study of the plant sciences. But it was among the first and it led in the great agricultural movement which made rural education more than learning in the classics and mathematics. A Michigan apple orchard will always be an emblem in America of a most worthy history in plant study and plant amelioration.

Liberty Hyde Bailey, junior, the subject of this biography, grew up amid the apple orchards and gardens of Michigan. His father and mother were among the first frontier people to take up permanent residence along the eastern shore of Lake Michigan, near South Haven.

In United States history during the frontier years of middle western settlement it was not unusual for persons of eastern and southern origins to marry. So it was in the marriage of Liberty Hyde Bailey, senior, of Townshend, Vermont, and Sarah Harrison, who, although born in Columbus, Ohio, was of a family who had moved north from one of the southern states. They met in Kalamazoo, Michigan, and were married on November 19, 1845, a young man twenty-five years of age and a young woman four years younger.

Liberty Hyde Bailey, senior, lived in Vermont until he was past twenty-one years of age. During his boyhood he had been raised on a farm, learning thoroughly the rigorous practice of New England farming, and had attended a school known as the Leland and Gray Academy. He was about twenty-two when he decided to migrate west. Going by way of Buffalo, he took the steamer *Madison* there across Lake Erie to Detroit. Railroad building was commencing to displace the canal and stage coach in the middle western states. In fact, in Michigan, the project of connecting Detroit and Chicago by a line of railroad through Niles was planned and, it is said, a few miles of track had already been laid. Young Bailey walked across the state to Kalamazoo where he settled and was employed by what is now known as the Michigan Central Railroad. Land, however, was his main interest. Indeed, he may have had a connection with a company known as the Vermont Land Company, and located some land for it in Michigan. Furthermore, it seems certain, even at this time, Bailey wanted to establish a farm and orchards. He was interested in apples, especially, as were many frontiersmen.

Where farming is learned in one's youth, mature years often increase a love of the soil and of orchards. In the instance of Bailey, this was so, but, even more, these were years of investing. Farming was the nation's greatest industry. Except as to pine, spruce, cedar, hemlock, walnut, cherry, maple and other forest and forest product resources, Michigan for years was to remain an agricultural state. Industrialization in the corporate sense was not to arrive until the automobile would begin to displace the ox-cart and horse and wagon. Young Bailey, of course, could not have foreseen all this but the forest wealth must have impressed him. He must have realized that, once cleared of the forest, the advantages of soil and climate would make the land a rich fruit-bearing and farm area. Migrants would come in large numbers and the land, especially along the waters of the Great Lakes, would grow in value. Already New England areas were depleted of much forest land. Soils there were becoming exhausted or abandoned because of the lure of fresh lands. Already New England capital talked aggressively of more investments in states of the Middle West. Tall, strong, and ambitious young Bailey gave ear to some of the great stories, and, on arrival in Michigan, he had opportunity to investigate for himself.

South Haven, situated where the Black River enters Lake Michigan, was represented to him as being a thriving town. Not far from there was a pioneer peach-growing region located near the Saint Joseph and Paw-Paw rivers, where the villages of Saint Joseph and Benton Harbor were—less than seventy-five miles from the Chicago markets. Regions on Mackinaw Island and along the Detroit River had had quite a history in apple and pear growing; and about eight years before Bailey's arrival a family named Abbee had planted in the Saint Joseph region improved varieties of peaches and apples, obtained from Rochester, New York. Though forested sand hills lined most of Lake Michigan's shore from Benton Harbor north to South Haven, the knowing eye realized that such land could make good sites for fruit growing. Perhaps Bailey went to the region and knew this. Perhaps he was told it before he left Vermont. Perhaps he decided to purchase "wild" government land sight unseen after his arrival in Michigan. In any event, Bailey, armed with a purchase agreement for which a patent would be signed later by President Polk, left Kalamazoo about 1843 and went to South Haven to find, not a thriving town, but a wilderness. Days were spent locating his land and at night he slept under trees with the nearest known white man thirty miles away. Probably he became acquainted with the Potawatomi, Ottawa, and Miami Indians who had inhabited the region for more than a century. From the very beginning his relations with them seem to have been cordial.

The land he chose was the west half of section 11 of South Haven township, Van Buren county.

Bailey, young as he was, must have visualized the possibilities of South Haven. He must have seen what excellent lake harbor facilities were there. To a shipper of fruit and produce, that would be very important. Moreover, it was said that South Haven was to be a western terminus of a great cross-state railroad. Practical and businesslike, Bailey must have believed that from the fruit-growing lands to the south speculation would extend northward. A desire to speculate was not the cause of his purchase. No man, however, overlooked boom prospects in potential agricultural regions, and wild speculation did visit the fruit-growing regions of Michigan at a comparatively early date. Nevertheless, he allowed his holdings to go back to the government.

In 1845 Bailey purchased another tract of land in Arlington township of the same county and there he took his bride Sarah Harrison, a distant relative of President William Henry Harrison and a daughter of Benjamin Harrison—a cousin of the Benjamin Harrison who was a signer of the Declaration of Independence. During the time that they lived on the Arlington township farm, a period of almost ten years, two sons, Dana Russell and Marcus Benjamin, were born.

Liberty Hyde Bailey, senior, was of English ancestry, a man of strong resolution and determination. His great-grandfather, Richard, was born in England, but as a young man had settled in the Massachusetts Bay Colony, becoming a soldier of the American Revolution. Dana Bailey, his grandfather, had moved with his parents from Massachusetts to Vermont, and during the War of 1812, he had also become a soldier. For over thirty years he served the legislature of Vermont and during the movement to abolish slavery he took an active part in the workings of the Underground Railroad. Betsy Walker Bailey, his grandmother, was also of English extraction. She was the daughter of a soldier who had served during the American Revolution at the siege of Yorktown and the surrender of Cornwallis. Liberty's own father was a selectman of Townshend, Vermont (his mother, Lucy Hyde Bailey, was of a prominent eastern Massachusetts family). He also was a strong Abolitionist. When a son was born on a wintry New England morning, and word of it was brought to him, he said, "Call him Liberty for all men shall be free." This son died and the same name, Liberty Hyde Bailey, was given a second son.

The resolution and determination characteristic of the family asserted itself. Bailey, senior, went again to the South Haven farm he had purchased from the government. Buying it up at eight dollars an acre, he built a log cabin in the forest to which he brought his wife, Sarah, and the two small sons. As the years of improvement went on, small structures of clean hemlock lumber were added to the cabin until by March 15, 1858, when yet a third son arrived, a small, comfortable, frame house was the family home of the owner of the west half of section 11 of South Haven township. To the third son was given the name Liberty Hyde Bailey, Junior.

Bailey had returned to the South Haven township farm about 1855. There he found Indians on the land. They renewed their friendship with him, exclaiming, "Suppose some white man had bought the land and we could not make maple sugar and trap pigeons." Some white settlement had taken place during the years. But for the most part the whites were a hardy and primitive group who lived much like the Indians—hunting, fishing, and making maple sugar. The cultivation of crops or the growing of improved varieties of fruit trees was neither extensive nor anticipated. The South Haven area was still a wilderness, a wild strip of land between Lake Michigan and the more populous region of Kalamazoo. What town there was was rough and uncouth. The harbor, utilized for the small but flourishing fishing industry, gave the community an outer semblance of civilization and of developing commercial enterprise. But underneath, a harsh, uncivilized law of survival of the fittest controlled.

Liberty Hyde Bailey, senior, however, was one of the fit. He wanted an orchard, an apple orchard. The great nursery of the time, the best on the continent, was that of Ellwanger and Barry of Rochester, New York. He ordered his apple trees from this nursery; the trees were shipped to him at Kalamazoo. From there to South Haven, a distance of forty miles, Bailey carried the trees on his back and planted them among the logs and stumps of his cleared land. His orchard became one of the most noted in Michigan's pomological history. Twice it received prizes for being the best orchard of its class in the state. Even today a few trees of the original lot are still standing.

Soon after Bailey planted his orchard, approximately in the year 1855, a neighbor, who also became prominent in early Michigan pomology, A. S. Dyckman, planted a peach orchard. These hilly lands, described a few years later as terminating "in a fine level bluff of clay subsoil and sandy and gravelly loam, interspersed with clay and rich black vegetable mold, averaging perhaps, 40 feet above the lake,"[1] had at last become a promising center of Michigan fruitgrowing.

Bailey was not content with one orchard. He planted another. On at least two different visits to his Vermont home he procured seedlings and seeds which he brought back to Michigan and planted among stumps and ash-heaps on the land behind his home. The "prize orchard," as the first orchard became known, was located to the north of the barn. To this Bailey gave the most studious and careful attention. Of the second orchard Bailey himself became the grower. His three small sons, especially the youngest, were his helpers. Liberty was about three or four years of age when the orchard began to bear. When he was a little more than ten years old, he began to top-graft the trees, in some instances grafting on new varieties, in others regrafting those already grafted. An old apple tree that failed to bear its own fruit was grafted so many times by the youth that at one time forty kinds of apples, and even pears, were growing on the tree.

The senior Bailey, always desirous of having the most improved varieties of fruit, sent for scions of stock from the renowned Hudson River valley horticulturist, Charles Downing, brother of Andrew Jackson Downing, author of the classic pomological work *Fruits and Fruit Trees of America* and first editor of the pioneer publication, *The Horticulturist*. Downing sent scions of the Surprise apple which the youthful Bailey grafted. The variety was preserved so well that years later the Bailey orchard became known as the only place where it could be found.

This was not all. So remarkable was the youth's talent that the whole countryside around South Haven employed the boy to do grafting. He would store leafless winter twigs and then in the spring carry them around in his pockets, on order grafting them into trees.

Nor were his interests confined to the orchard. All farms of the American frontier grew vegetables. The sturdy toil of wilderness farm life demanded most of the hours from dawn to sundown and not many

---

[1] See the "Digest of State Reports, Michigan," in the *Report of the Commissioner of Agriculture* for the year 1876 (Washington: Government Printing Office, 1877), p. 396, referring to Michigan State Board reports for 1873-1874.

had time to brighten their cabins with flower gardens. But a few refused to let the relentless frontier crush all aesthetic and intellectual pursuits. Occasionally, too, a well developed study of botany went with advancing western settlement. Sarah Harrison Bailey had always loved plants and almost from the beginning of her marriage she had maintained and cherished a flower garden.

But a grave tragedy now entered the lives of the Baileys. In the winter of 1860-1861 scarlet fever laid low all three sons, Dana, Marcus, and young Liberty. On February 13, at the age of fourteen and one-half years, Dana Russell died. Through a miracle the life of Liberty was spared. Marcus, not so ill as his brothers, weathered the crisis too, and lived.

Disaster often follows in the wake of such an ordeal as Sarah and Liberty, senior, had lived through. On December 16 of the next year the mother Sarah, grief-stricken and weakened, followed her son in death. Liberty, senior, still in the prime of life, was left with the care of two sons, Marcus, aged fourteen, and Liberty, four and one-half years old. On August 27, 1863, he married Maria M. Bridges, who quickly won the affection of young Liberty.

The heritage left by Sarah Bailey to her nature-loving son, Liberty, was a garden. For years he watched it, tended it, and kept the same plants growing in it. Indeed, when he became professor of horticulture at Cornell University, he took with him roots of some of the plants from this garden.

Furthermore, in his early youth, he resolved to have a flower garden of his own. As a boy about seven or eight years of age he began one. In this garden he developed a system of subirrigation. The inference is not unjustified that, furthered by his father's hearty love of gardening, from it came a fundamental inspiration for his devoted years of service in aiding the development of all branches of American horticulture, including floriculture.

Like many another boy, young Liberty early manifested an eager love of birds. Together with the robin, the crow, and the blue jay he would roam field and hill, observing wild plants and following the brooks to their seemingly limitless end. Years later to the robin, he wrote:

Robin! You and I were lovers when yet my years were few. We roamed the fields and hills together. We explored the brook that ran up into the great dark woods and away over the edge of the world. We knew the old squirrel who lived in the maple tree. We heard the first frog peep. We knew the minnows that lay under the mossy log. We knew how the cowslips bloomed in the lushy swale. We heard the first soft roll of thunder in the liquid April sky. Robin! The fields are yonder! You are my better self. I care not for the birds of paradise; for whether here or there, I shall listen for your carol in the apple tree.[2]

Also, telling of the brook, he explained:

As a boy I explored but never found the source. It came somewhere from the Beyond and its name was Mystery. . . . I felt that the brook was greater and wiser than I. It became my teacher. I wondered how it knew when March came, and why its round of life recurred so regularly with the returning seasons. . . . Many years have come and gone since then. My affection for the brook gave way to a study of plants and animals and stones. For years I was absorbed in phenomena. But now, mere phenomena and things have slipped into a secondary place, and the old boyhood slowly reasserts itself.[3]

A field behind the barn of Liberty's home was a veritable natural history museum. Water pools accumulating in places where felled trees had been torn up at the roots acquired with the years a semiaquatic life of tadpoles, minnows, turtles, frogs, and crickets. Large wild animals were not prevalent in the South Haven region. Hunting and the coming of more whites had either killed or driven most of the larger game away. But some were left and small life abounded. Their habits of life intrigued the youthful naturalist. He would go to their haunts and, lying on his stomach or back, watch and study them for hours, until his father became convinced that "young 'Lib' will never be worth his salt." Passenger pigeons interested him. Do they fly from the same rookery in Michigan every year, or every second or third year? In order to study them he would catch suckers as they came up to spawn, pursue an insect for hours to learn its ways, observe closely the growth of a plant, find a nest or hole or cave, study a snake, or fix his sight and hearing on a bird till it was lost to sound and vision. Growing older and donning cowhide boots, perhaps riding horseback to bring cattle to the barn, or accompanied by Indian friends, he would wander through woods and swamps, along marshes and brooks heavy with undergrowth, through fields piled high with brush or grown dense with thickets, always to find something new, to learn something new.

A taxonomic interest early asserted itself. He would gather specimens, carry them to an old shop, a kind of carpentry shop, and add to his store of wild life museum specimens. His father, knowing little of carpentry, seldom went to this shop; but one day he did, to discover a huge pile of "rubbish," frogs, snakes, turtles, lizards, and various other accumulations. His stepmother, Maria Bridges Bailey, never reacted unkindly to Liberty's passionate fondness for collecting natural history specimens.

[2] *Junior-Naturalist Monthly* III, no. 2 (March 1901). Published by the College of Agriculture of Cornell University.
[3] "An Outlook on Winter," *Country Life in America* (Doubleday, Page and Co.), I, no. 2 (December 1901), pp. 37 ff.

One day she went to an old stove, opened it, and screamed to "Lib" to come at once. He ran to her aid and, realizing that she had discovered some milk snakes he had hatched, explained, "Why, mother, I have been watching those eggs in there for days." Boyhood sports seldom enticed him, although once he was captain of a baseball team. His playgrounds were the woods, the farm, the fields, and the streams. Not many South Haven people followed him in his activities. A merchant, Charles Delemere, would ask him where he had been and what he had seen; but, until he commenced school, most of young Bailey's time was spent alone.

He quickly responded to schooling. Although his first teacher, Janet Hulbert, boxed his ears when she told him he must "toe the mark" and he asked "why," the small country school of South Haven village and the ungraded high school—in reality merely the room upstairs—gave the boy as sound an education as was afforded in communities dependent largely on agriculture and lake shipping for subsistence. The youth's education consisted chiefly of the subjects taught in most rural or village schools of the Middle West: spelling, grammar, reading, arithmetic. A most influential teacher was a Mrs. Field, a widow, who later went to England where she remarried, becoming Mrs. Field-King. She taught Liberty the value of direct observation of nature. "What did you see today, Liberty?" she would ask. "Did you notice how high were the trees you passed on the way?" Once, asking him what he wished to study, he replied, "Natural history." So with the aid of an old encyclopedia they began together a study of Latin grammar and various sciences. Comparisons of Latin names and descriptions with those of English were included. Bailey got from her both knowledge and inspiration, for the last of which he was so grateful that he later dedicated to her one of his books. Nevertheless, much of his amazingly large fund ot information was the product of self-education.

Youths in many homes were not permitted in those days to read novels. Corruption of the mind was never possible, so was the belief, when reading was confined to the truth, to what had actually happened. So, the few book shelves of the remote regions of western Michigan contained factual works for the most part. Liberty Hyde Bailey, senior, took great pride in his many prominent office holdings in the Masonic Order. Masonry was his church. First Master of the lodge at South Haven, first High Priest of the Chapter, thrice Illustrious of the Council, member of the Peninsular Commandery at Kalamazoo, holder of a thirty-second degree in the Ancient and Scottish Rite Masonry, member of the High Priesthood of Michigan, charter member of the Consistory at Grand Rapids, member of the Oriental Order of the Palm and Shell, and other distinctions, were enjoyed by him during his life. Annually he journeyed across Michigan to Detroit to attend the state lodge and always he bought a book for Liberty to read. One book, brought home in 1869, was *Explorations of the Nile Tributaries of Abyssinia,* a beautifully bound, stimulating volume with marvelous woodcuts. Young Bailey committed it almost to memory as he did every book given him. The result was that in South Haven it became noised about that on the Bailey farm outside of town there was a boy who read books. In the back end of a store of the village was a town library. Once in a while Liberty went there. One day he went to the shelves and took down a book that had been published ten or fifteen years before, *On the Origin of Species by Means of Natural Selection,* by Charles Darwin. Liberty's father supervised his reading. Consequently, when his son brought the book to the farm homestead, he took it from the boy. He gave it back to him, however, a few days later saying: "I do not know what this man is talking about. But I believe he is honest and wants to tell the truth. You may read the book." Young Liberty excitedly seized the volume, took it to a quiet corner of the small sitting room of their home, and fairly devoured its contents. For a number of years he had understood the difference between cultivated and wild plants. The plants of his garden, he had realized, were different from those of the field and wood. Habits and laws characteristic of the one were not altogether character-istic of the other. In Darwin's work he sensed a scientific interest in cultivated plants worthy of attention and study, and he was fascinated by the theory of natural selection.

Children of the Michigan wilderness knew nothing of the work of Asa Gray of Harvard University, who since about 1860 had taken up in the face of stern and strong opposition the defense of Darwin's theory of the origin of species by natural selection and his exposition of the law of survival of the fittest, "the preservation of favored races in the struggle for life." But when he was about fourteen years old Liberty went to the home of a friend whom he found reading Gray's *Field, Forest and Garden Botany.* This he found to be a book describing and classifying many kinds of plants, including both wild and cultivated ones. He borrowed the copy and through the winter months studied its contents, waiting anxiously for the first crocus of spring "to make the book real." When spring arrived he began collecting various plants, and soon a small herbarium was started. He found he enjoyed indenti-fying plants.

Observing plants of the field and garden had up to this time kindled the avidity of the student. But it was a studiousness akin to naturalness and to loving things of nature more as parts of creation than as para-graphs of booklore. It was a zeal, however, that visualized natural objects becoming more and more parts of book learning. By this time the world of science in growing numbers was following Darwin. But the concept of variation, though old, was not easy to learn. As Gray later expressed it in 1879,[4] Darwin taught that the *"Survival of the Fittest,* metaphorically . . . [natural selection], is in fact the destruction of all weaker competitors. . . . The hypothesis that the species of a genus have become what they are by diversification through variation is a very old one in botany, and has from time to time been put forward. But until recently, it has had little influence upon the science, because no clear idea has been formed of any natural process which might lead to such [a] result. . . ."

What Gray saw in Darwin's work—even though variation was not conceived as tending in any one particular direction—was a "working hypothesis" by which "all the facts in botany" might be coordinated and "a probable and reasonable answer [given] to a long series of questions which without it [seemed] totally unanswerable. . . ."

Gray's belief was predicated somewhat on another belief current at the time—and which for a while Bailey would follow—that each plant has a tendency or predisposition to vary. In other words, variation is a function of plants similar to growth and fructification. The essence of the belief was based on observation, not experimentation.

For a young, sharp-eyed naturalist what a wealth of thought was bound within the covers of *On the Origin of Species by Means of Natural Selection!* What a vision could open as one read Darwin's paper, "On the Variation of Organic Beings in a State of Nature," or Wallace's, "On the Tendency of Varieties to Depart Indefinitely from the Original Type" (both read in London at the famous Linnean Society meeting of July 1, 1858), or Darwin's *Variation of Plants and Animals under Domestication,* or Wallace's *Geographical Distribution of Animals!* What a revelation to read Gray's expositions, which appeared in popular and scientific magazines beginning in March, 1860, until they were gathered together in 1876 in *Darwiniana: Essays and Reviews Pertaining to Darwinism!* This was the vision that opened for Liberty Hyde Bailey, junior, although years would go by before it reached full maturity.

Nature study—living among, loving, and understanding the things of creation—came first. This one mastered as one became acquainted with laws and truths in nature. Science was not dry, Bailey found, although its teaching in many quarters was. Young Liberty early discovered that art and science combined as partners to make the open field, and books about the field and garden, of vast and consuming interest. With these were joined orchard and farm as places of delight—places which with the fields and woods were part of an immense eternal scheme which

[4] See Gray's *The Botanical Text-book* edition of that year, pp. 328, 661.

some called evolution. As Darwin said, a "view of life, with its several powers, having been originally breathed by the Creator into a few forms or into one; . . . from so simple a beginning endless forms most beautiful and most wonderful have been, and are being evolved."

Liberty, as he plowed the brown earth or strolled in sunlight over green hills, along the blue-watered lake, or into dark woods, began to wonder if all country life environment could not be made parts of a scheme of education that would enrich the lives of rural folk. He had listened to his father, had heard tales of his grandfather—both farmers —and tried to grasp their life view. Education benefiting rural communities would benefit the nation for of such was the nation strong.[5]

Liberty Hyde Bailey, senior, was one of the charter members of the South Haven and Casco Pomological Society. The society numbered among a distinguished membership such eminent Michigan pomologists as A. S. Dyckman, who was an authority on methods of pruning peach trees; H. E. Bidwell, who early in the 'seventies succeeded in raising figs in Michigan; and Bailey, whose orchard had more varieties of apples than anyone else's. At a fair given by the society, 320 varieties, all from Bailey's trees, were exhibited. This was before the years of experiment stations and testing grounds. But few, if any, experiment stations at any period could have shown as many varieties at one time. The practice of growing many varieties in an orchard is gone today. In those days, however, this testing was all important since the varieties were being selected which would later form the basis of the fruit industry. Liberty Hyde Bailey was not primarily a variety-tester, but an orchard grower. Considering the condition then of Michigan pomology, Bailey's accomplishment was rather remarkable:

In summarizing the present condition of pomology in the State, (1872) R. F. Johnstone, secretary of the State Agricultural Society, refers to the orchard-fruits and to the berries which are cultivated for profit with more or less success. There is yet no defined system in regard to the best methods of treating apple-orchards; no successful effort has been made to originate any new varieties from seedlings or by hybridization that would take precedence of those now regarded as the best for profitable culture. For new and old varieties dependence has been placed upon other States. Orchard-culture of the pear is limited, and it is doubted if the culture is well understood, or has been sufficiently experimented upon, or vigorously inquired into. The cultivation of the peach is confined for the most part to the shores of Lake Michigan, and as far inland as the influence of this body of water is supposed to extend. This fruit has not thus far sustained damage, to any appreciable extent, from diseases which have prevailed in other regions where the peach is raised. The varieties grown are those which have been introduced and found to be adapted to climate and soils. No variety has been originated that would supersede the sorts acclimated. As

[5] *Cornell Countryman*, IX, 8, p. 238.

an orchard-fruit the plum is not largely grown, the ravages of its great enemy, the curculio, having discouraged effort in that direction. Little attention has been paid to the cherry. The cultivation for market purposes of the currant, strawberry, raspberry, and blackberry is attracting more attention than formerly; the varieties now grown are not of Michigan origin. Several varieties of grapes have been raised with success, marketable for purposes of the table. The vineyards for wine-making are mostly confined to Monroe County, lying on Lake Erie. . . . There is nothing especially peculiar to grape-culture in the State, for the reason that dependence has been placed on other States for varieties and full confidence given acclimation. The fig grows and ripens to considerable perfection along the shores of Lake Michigan. . . . The cranberry and the whortleberry are indigenous and gathered and marketed largely. No attempt, however, has been made to improve either by culture or otherwise.[6]

Quite obviously, Michigan pomology was more concerned about problems of "acclimation" and quantity production of fruit varieties than about quality production and origination of new varieties suited to the soil and climate. The period was still one emphasizing practice. No long period of variety testing had taken place in western regions such as Michigan for the plausible reason that there were comparatively few, if any, new varieties to test. No great American entomologists had yet arisen. C. V. Riley in Missouri was doing some notable work, but Missouri was not Michigan. T. T. Lyon at Plymouth, Michigan, had become a leading pomologist, especially in peaches, and had made some investigations of insect ravages, devising a method to prevent depredations of the curculio in plum culture. In 1874 Lyon moved to South Haven and established a nursery and trial ground on land of the old Lake Shore Nursery Company of which he became president. The place is now used as an experiment station by Michigan State College. Altogether, an academic task of no small proportions confronted William James Beal when he took up a professorship of botany in the early 'seventies at Michigan Agricultural College, the first of the existing colleges in America dedicated to agricultural studies.

Beal occasionally visited South Haven and was the first botanist with whom Liberty made acquaintance. He came in connection with pomological society work. By 1872 the Michigan State Pomological Society had a membership of 507 persons and issued a "large, well-printed, and handsomely-illustrated volume [indicating] the energy and earnest work of the young society."

The South Haven and state societies gave young Bailey two forums in which to display his versatile talents. At the age of fifteen he gave a talk on grafting before the South Haven group. Before the state group on September 4, 1873, "Master L. H. Bailey, a lad of fifteen years,"

[6] "Digest of State Reports," *Report of the Commissioner of Agriculture for the year 1873*, op. cit., pp. 428-429.

spoke on the subject of "Birds." The previous December he had been made ornithologist of the South Haven society and had been presented with a cage of English sparrows brought from Central Park, New York City, where they had been recently introduced. Liberty's talk on "Birds" was an essay, subsequently published by the society.

The songs of birds meant much to the youthful Liberty. Neither poetry nor man-made music he thought could capture the full beauty of their songs. "When the rigors of winter are over, and the pleasant days of spring return," he exclaimed, "what is more charming and delightful than the presence of birds? . . . Their charming songs and beautiful plumage lend life and vivacity to the dullest place."

The service of birds to man also impressed him. He reminded his hearers that "nearly all the noxious insects which infest our fields and forests are devoured" by "these harmless songsters, yet the selfish man dooms them to destruction." He divided them into three classes, insectivorous, granivorous, and omnivorous, naming those of each class.

In the spring of his eighteenth year he heard of a botanist, Mrs. Lucy A. Millington, who had moved near South Haven beyond Dyckman's woods. "Will I now have someone to share my joy and to guide me through difficult parts of the book [Gray's *Field, Forest and Garden Botany*] I am reading?" he asked himself. The study of the book had occupied years. Liberty went to visit her. Mrs. Millington had come to South Haven with a brother who was to serve the village as a doctor for many years. She had purchased a small peach orchard and then returned to the East, but she came back, settling for a time in an eastern part of the village. His visits with Mrs. Millington were a delight to him. "She always received me pleasantly, calmly, without haste," he afterward related.[7] "She listened to my joys of wonderful discoveries, told me the names of my plants and pronounced the strange words as if they were her common speech. She told me of the trips and her collecting in the Adirondacks whence she had come." Together they walked through the pine woods and over the sand dunes near Lake Michigan. "One of [his] brilliant recollections was her remark about a broad-leaved grassy plant with a head of hanging stamens [he] had picked in Dyckman's Woods. She said it was a Carex, a very difficult group I should not then undertake to study." He said later, "I suppose it was *Carex albursina*. That old challenge has followed me through life." Mrs. Millington gave Liberty her tin collecting case which he used for many years, and, in fact, still possesses. Painted bright red, it had at one end a cup which held a bottle of water and at the other end was a compartment which carried moving or special things. The vasculum has a

[7] Liberty H. Bailey, "Lucy Millington," *Torreya*, xxxix (November-December 1939), pp. 159-163.

special interest for in it was carried the first specimen of spruce mistle-toe, *Arceuthobium pusillum*. Mrs. Millington was a discoverer of the plant. She possessed a microscope, a rarity in those years, especially in rural areas, and studied infusoria.

When a boy of twelve years Bailey had been treasurer of a group of young Americans—"Heroes" they styled themselves—sworn never to chew, smoke, drink, or swear. With the theological emphasis placed on specific morals in those sturdy times, members of such a group naturally interested a minister come to preach the gospel. Pastor E. A. Paddock organized a little society known as the Band of Hope. The Reverend Mr. Paddock, a young and fearless Congregationalist, belonged to that red-blooded lot of frontier preachers who believed that the lake front was as worthy of his stanchest efforts as the more refined and hardy owners of orchards and farms. Most of his life was spent on the edges of advancing American civilization. Once he commented: "I have worked on frontiers all my life and South Haven is the toughest of them all." At one time, long before young Bailey's years, South Haven's harbor had served ocean-going vessels and had consequently acquired some of the characteristics of a port town. If Pastor Paddock saw a young man go into one of the many saloons, he would go in also and, not drinking, talk to him. It was not strange, therefore, that he inspired the admiration of the rougher elements as well as of the orchard and farm folk. He said that South Haven needed a church. Men from lake front and farms went with him into the forest, hewed logs, excavated and gathered stones, carted them into South Haven, and built a church. Although more a Freemason than a churchman Liberty Hyde Bailey, senior, aided. Once he found the pastor on the roof of his church nailing down a chicken coop in which a bell was to be set. Bailey bought the bell and gave it to the church, where today this bell and the bricked over walls symbolize a transition from the past to the present. The bell unchanged still rings out a call to worship; the structure, altered from logs mortised together by toilers of earth and ships to a modern brick edifice, today serves an aristocratic center of fruitgrowing industry and a fashionable summer resort.

Pastor Paddock sensed the quality of young Bailey's mind. In him he realized was potential genius. The elder Bailey was a practical man with set ideas but he had respect for book learning. Maria Bailey, a real mother in every sense to the youth, was sure that the son was worthy of a college education. She and the pastor conversed, and he strengthened her in her conviction. Young Bailey's genius should not be wasted on the Michigan sand dunes. He was more than a grafter of orchard trees. More than a pruner of apple trees, more than a harvester and marketer of apples, peaches, and pears, more than a visionary naturalist, he was a student who discerned plants in their relationships, not only to each other but to climate, soil, and other environic factors. He had a vision for horticulture; he saw needs in agriculture; he was a young man for the schools and not for the hoe and plow only. Maria Bailey talked with her husband. He talked with his son. It was decided that young Liberty should go at once to the state agricultural college of Michigan before he had finished his course at the South Haven school.

Another man who influenced the college decision was Charles W. Garfield, an officer of the Michigan State Pomological Society. One year when it convened in South Haven he stayed in the home of the Baileys. Immediately becoming one of the most stimulating forces in Liberty's life—and such he remained for many years—he had an important part in persuading the young man to go to college. (He was foreman of the gardens during Bailey's freshman year and, although limited by lack of scientific training, his appreciation of the worth of such training and his foresight in matters horticultural, aided much in forming in the youth a predisposition toward developing scientific work in the gardens.)

So on September 8, 1877, the *South Haven Sentinel*, the town newspaper, recorded: "Master L. H. Bailey left here this week for a three months' sojourn at the Agricultural College, Lansing."[8] The long vacation at the college in those years was in the winter. It was planned, and the plan was carried out, that Bailey should return to the South Haven school in the winter and then take up his studies at Lansing again in the late winter or early spring. But he never graduated (in the sense that the term is used today), from the South Haven school. He merely studied there, and continued on in spring, summer, and autumn at college.

These were the last years of the age of homespun clothes. The first time young Bailey bought a ready-made suit he tried to get the crease out of the trousers. He was a tall, thin, young farmer, obviously serious minded, and had some appearance of strength and huskiness. Although not a ready "mixer," he at once earned respect. In him was the spirit of a poem he later wrote:

> Blow ye winds and lay on ye storms
> And come ye pests in rabble swarms
> And fall ye blights in legion forms—
> I am here: I surrender not
> Nor yield my place one piece or jot—

[8] Indebtedness is acknowledged for material, including this, to an unpublished term paper, "The Life and Accomplishments of Liberty Hyde Bailey, 'South Haven's Most Famous Son,'" prepared by Grace Howard at Michigan State Teachers College, Kalamazoo, Michigan.

For these are my lands
And these are my hands
And I am bone of the folk that resistlessly stands.

The blood of old ploughmen runs hard in my arm
Of axmen and yeomen and battlemen all
Who fought and who flinched not by marish and wall
Who met the bold day and chas'd ev'ry alarm;
    My father-kind sleep, but I hear the old call
    And fight the hot battle by forge and by farm—
For these are my lands
And these are my hands
And I am bone of the folk that resistlessly stands.

CHAPTER II

A COLLEGE ESTABLISHED IN THE MICHIGAN FOREST

MICHIGAN STATE AGRICULTURAL COLLEGE was provided for by the state constitution in 1850, organized in 1855, and opened in 1857. Among the agricultural colleges of the nation, its claim to precedence over Maryland Agricultural College, organized in 1856 by the state, and other colleges of agriculture, has on occasions been challenged. It would seem that claims to priority could be made by several institutions, but that Michigan is fairly secure in the merit of its assertion. Since agricultural colleges in the great preponderance of instances have been organized by the states, the year of organization, in the absence of complete reorganization, should be accepted as inaugurating the college. Sheffield Scientific School of Yale University was organized in 1847, but reorganized in 1860. Delaware College, moreover, was organized by the state in 1834, but reorganized in 1851 and 1871. Iowa State College of Agriculture and Mechanic Arts was organized by the state in 1858, but not opened to receive students until ten years later. Massachusetts Agricultural College was organized by the state in 1863 but not opened to students until 1867.

Agricultural colleges preceded the establishment of agricultural experiment stations by practically a quarter of a century. As we shall see, the first agricultural experiment station in America was established in 1875. By 1880 only four stations were operating. As late as 1887, some seventeen stations existed in fourteen states.[1]

By the year 1880, however, agricultural colleges to a number past forty had been organized in thirty-four states; approximately as many in the 1860's as in the 1870's; and a number were added in several states before the year 1888. Such important states as Alabama, Arkansas, California, Colorado, Connecticut, Delaware, Georgia, Illinois, Indiana, Iowa, Kansas, Kentucky, Louisiana, Maine, Maryland, Massachusetts, Michigan, Minnesota, Mississippi, Missouri, Nebraska, New Hampshire, New Jersey, New York, Ohio, Pennsylvania, South Carolina, Tennessee, Texas, Vermont, Virginia, West Virginia, Wisconsin,

---

[1] See an authoritative study, by A. C. True, "The Origin and Development of Agricultural Experiment Stations in the United States," *Report of the Commissioner of Agriculture* for the year 1888 (Washington: Gov't Print. Office, 1889), pp. 541-558. On pp. 553-558, may be found a "List of Agricultural Colleges in the United States," with data appertaining to the founding and inauguration of each. Also see E. W. Allen, "The Evolution of the Experiment Station," address delivered at the dedication of the Administration Building of the Ohio Agric. Exp't Sta., June 3, 1897, 16th *Annual Report of the Ohio Ag. Exp't Sta.* for 1897, and reprint, pp. xlii-l, at p. xlvi. Dr. Allen was assistant director of the Office of Experiment Stations, U.S. Department of Agriculture.

had taken the initiative in this regard before the year 1880; some states had organized more than one college; Georgia, several in different parts of the state; and during the 1880's Dakota, Florida, Nevada, and Rhode Island were added to the list. Oregon and North Carolina also organized agricultural colleges. The principal reason why each state took action and organized such a college was to take advantage of the beneficial provisions of the Morrill Act, so called, enacted by the federal Congress in 1862.

Until 1863, Michigan Agricultural College was supported entirely by the state. But in this year it began to receive from the federal government land-grant scrip, giving it title to some 235,673 acres of land,[1a] as provided under the law. The history of the Morrill Act embodied a movement to endow industrial colleges by the federal government. Revived in the midst of national fervor after years of states' rights controversy which culminated in civil war between states of the North and South, the act represented a forward-looking realization of the need of strengthening the federal compact. The establishment of the United States Department of Agriculture in independent status was another occurrence of the period which served to turn attention away from controversy and war to the goodness and plenty of the land and the nation's vast natural heritage. By the time young Bailey was a student, the federal department of agriculture and the land grant system provided to advance agricultural and mechanical arts education were firmly established. It is told that Professor Jonathan B. Turner of the Illinois Industrial University (now the University of Illinois) and Abraham Lincoln had often discussed the advantages of a nationally systematized education which would constitute agriculture and the mechanic arts members of the learned professions. Lincoln had promised that if elected to the presidency, he would sign such a bill, and, true to his promise, when elected, signed this legislation which inaugurated the land-grant college system.

The federal government, therefore, had authorized donations to the states of many thousands of acres of public lands to fix in each at least one college where the leading object would be, not excluding scientific or classical studies and including military training, the special

[1a] *Report of the Commissioner of Agriculture* for the year 1873, p. 338. Much of the factual data appertaining to the state agricultural colleges in this chapter are taken from the yearly "Digest of State Reports" and "Progress in Industrial Education." Concerning federal agricultural work, including early scientific research, during the half-century from its inauguration in the United States Patent Office in 1839 to the creation of a Department of Agriculture under a Cabinet officer appointed by the President, the reader is referred to Part I, the first four chapters, of *Two Blades of Grass* A History of Scientific Development in the U.S. Department of Agriculture, by T. Swann Harding (Norman: University of Oklahoma Press, 1947.) Pages 3-44 deal with the preliminary history of the subject.

teaching (as defined by state legislation) of such branches of learning as were directly related to agriculture and mechanic arts. Students in these colleges numbered several thousands and professors and assistants several hundreds. By far the largest number of colleges had farms, some of which were used to study experimentally plant and animal feeding and cultivation. Methods included examination of manures and fertilizers. The whole scope of the work will be disclosed as this book proceeds.

Agriculture as a member of the learned professions summoned forth quickly an able corps of leaders who responded with strength and enthusiasm to the new responsibility. A program of such national proportions often requires years, even decades, before the results show and the exact needs are defined. But vigor was not lacking. Such leaders as Samuel William Johnson of Sheffield Scientific School, Yale College; George Hammel Cook of Rutgers Scientific School at New Brunswick, New Jersey; Evan Pugh of the State College of Pennsylvania; Levi Stockbridge and C. A. Goessmann of Massachusetts Agricultural College at Amherst; Eugene Woldemar Hilgard of the University of California at Berkeley; Isaac Phillips Roberts and George C. Caldwell of Cornell University; Edward Lewis Sturtevant of Waushakum Farm of South Framingham, Massachusetts; Manly Miles of the Michigan and Massachusetts agricultural colleges; Norton S. Townshend of Ohio Agricultural and Mechanical College (now the Ohio State University) at Columbus; W. W. Daniels of the University of Wisconsin at Madison; and others realized not only that agriculture should be made scientific but also that the rural public should be convinced of the value of the scientific approach in terms of dollars and cents.

How these men went about their tasks has been revealed by Manly Miles, whom Dean Eugene Davenport (we shall refer to him again from time to time later) has described as not only the first professor of agriculture in America but also "the first of his kind in the world." While a student at Michigan Agricultural College, Davenport became acquainted with Miles, who then was retired from teaching and from his work as superintendent of the Houghton Farm at Mountainville, New York. He was living at Lansing, and, after recommending to Davenport that he read the Rothamstead Reports dating far back into the century, he advised as guides of practice:

"First: Agriculture has been practiced and taught as an *Art* because we did not know the *Principles* under which it operates. But it rests on facts and as soon and as fast as these facts can be discovered it will be taught and practiced as a *Science*. . . .

"Second: As you travel about you will be struck by some very queer practices, many of which will look absurd. However absurd they may look remember that either now or at sometime in the past there was a

Reason for it. It may not have been a good reason but it was the *Cause* of what you see and it will be wise to make a pretty careful study of the matter before attempting to advise a change.

"Third: When you address an audience be assured that if you do your best, there is at least one in the audience fully able to follow you at your best. Therefore, do your best and be not afraid of 'talking over their heads.' As you value your position never talk down to your audience. . . ."

Michigan State Agricultural College was not without its leaders. Among the foremost of them was William James Beal, professor of botany, a former student of Asa Gray and one strongly under the influence of Louis Agassiz. Agassiz's insistence that nature's own creations, not books about them, were the real instruments for study practically revolutionized methods of teaching science in America. Beal led in putting the Agassizian methods to work in botany. The new methods inaugurated in considerable part changes in horticulture, forestry, and other allied branches of the plant sciences. Needless to say, the methods established themselves also in the animal sciences—Agassiz's own strongholds—in zoology, entomology, and other biological branches.

Beal had been a student of Gray's at periods between 1862 and 1865 when, although laboratory methods of teaching were almost wholly undeveloped in America, the correspondence of Gray and Charles Darwin was attaining significant proportions. The botanical department at Harvard did not then own a compound microscope but borrowed one from the Lowell Institute. Gray would occasionally take favored students, among them, Beal, into his private laboratory.[2] The advanced student—Beal already held two degrees from the University of Michigan at Ann Arbor—must have learned of Darwin's studies in cross- and self-fertilization.[2a] Gray's own reviews at the time indicate clearly that he possessed a clear understanding of the subject of hybridization.

In any event, soon after going to Michigan Agricultural in the early 'seventies, Beal planned an experiment to test the grain yield of cross- and open-pollinated varieties of maize. By the year of Bailey's enrollment as a student, it was being announced and published that "experiments have been made in the garden by the botanist with two hundred and forty-four varieties of potatoes, and the yield of each is given. He has also conducted some interesting experiments in the production of new varieties. The seeds of fifty varieties were sown in boxes, hot-beds, and in the greenhouse, at the time of sowing seeds for early tomatoes.

[2] Ernst Bessey, "The Teaching of Botany Sixty-Five Years Ago," *Iowa State College Journal of Science,* IX, nos. 2, 3 (1935), p. 13.
[2a] W. Ralph Singleton, "Hybrid Vigor and its Utilization in Sweet Corn Breeding," *American Naturalist,* LXXV (January, February, 1941), p. 48.

When of sufficient size, a selection was made of the plants, and they were set two inches apart each way, and after danger from frost was passed were reset, two feet apart, in rows in the garden. About six hundred of them produced potatoes. The yield was surprising. Instead of a few little tubers the size of bullets, many of them were four to five inches long and of good size. In one instance a single plant produced eight pounds of potatoes, many of them being of good size. The yield in many cases was better than from old potatoes planted in the usual way. A test of their qualities will be made next year. From the many experiments which he has made with potatoes, he has come to the conclusion that new varieties must be originated every few years, as old ones degenerate in size and quality in most cases, and that the farmers will soon make it a common practice to raise them themselves. In his experiments with apple-trees he has found that applying manure close about the foot of the trees, or removing the grass and cultivating small circles about them, has very little beneficent effect. It is only by cultivating very large circles, equal to the extent of the branches, or the whole ground, that beneficial results can be obtained."[3]

As early as 1873 Beal had begun experiments in apple culture. About that time he directed Byron David Halsted and Garfield who made one hundred crosses from which about twenty fruits, some combining characters of both parents, resulted. Numerous recorded observations and results arrived at during this period, notably those on the effects of a change of climate on the growth of corn, have been since displaced by more thorough experimental study. Methods have been improved, and more exact instrumentation has been devised. Pages would be required to discuss them. The point of significance is that formal research, intensively pursued, had been started by Beal and others to improve and enrich the productions of the American farmer. Sturtevant criticized the smallness of Beal's plats from the farm standpoint. Tracts of at least one acre, he said, were required. But about 1878 he praised Beal's western pioneering work, saying, "The Michigan Agricultural College has done good service to agriculture in their field experiments. . . ." New studies were suggested and laws of plant growth learned. He wanted, however, the experiments to be continued over more years.

The horticulture which Beal taught was a botany of cultivated plants. Although he rejoiced that "pure science" enabled botanists to isolate bacteria as a cause of disease and death of plants (as shown by Thomas Jonathan Burrill's epoch-making study of pear and apple blight begun in 1877 at the University of Illinois) Beal attributed the accomplishment to botany and not to horticulture for Burrill was a botanist. The

[3] "Progress of Industrial Education," *Report of the Commissioner of Agriculture,* for the year 1876, pp. 338, 339.

ablest horticulturists, he said, those who had written on the science or theory of horticulture, Henslow, von Liebig, Lindley, Knight, Thomas, Warder, and Darwin, were many of them botanists.[4] As late as 1881, in an address before the State Horticultural Society of Michigan delivered at South Haven, Beal adopted the conclusions of Professor Tracy, which in large part were correct. Horticulture had advanced but very little in one hundred and fifty years except in two ways—one, due to the botanist, the origination of new varieties, and the other, due to the entomologist, the extermination or control of the ravages of insects. American mycology was in its infancy. Only a few years had passed since William Gilson Farlow had returned from study in European laboratories and begun at Harvard University his part in advancing scientific agricultural research at the Bussey Institution and the university's cryptogamic laboratory. Farlow's researches in mycology and plant pathology offered to youthful and ambitious American students the technical requisites by which to realize the establishment of a new science in this country. This work, and that of Burrill at the University of Illinois, then the Illinois Industrial University, will be further considered in this book. Right now, we should notice that both Farlow and Burrill were botanists by profession, Burrill a natural historian and Farlow a doctor of medicine. Beal may not have been pleading the cause of botany more than horticulture. But he did not make a special point of the fact that most of the valuable scientific study of plants, aside from taxonomy, was with horticultural species, plants of the garden and farm, and the orchard. Beal kept alive to advances, in fact, led. With Charles Edwin Bessey of Iowa Agricultural College at Ames, he was among the first to establish a botanical laboratory with compound microscopes for the teaching of undergraduate botany. This had been barely started when Bailey was a freshman although by the time he was ready for laboratory work compound microscopes had been obtained. Moreover, Beal's morphology was largely that of Gray—a morphology, idealized in character, that studied roots, stems, and leaves. Gray had begun to study the reproductive organs of plants before his retirement. In fact, his last series of lectures was on the subject, reproduction among lower plants being included in his considerations. Beal kept pace. He was among the first to see the merit of Julius Sachs's "grand text-book," of which Bessey made an American adaptation after an English model. Beal realized that with its appearance "vegetable physiology" became "the leading thing in botany." The medical progress achieved through microscopical research impressed him. With Professor A. J. Cook of

[4] "What Can Botany Do for Horticulture?" *11th Annual Report of the Secretary of the State Horticultural Society of Michigan,* 1881, pp. 122 ff.

Michigan Agricultural College, he advocated "the application of pure science to horticulture." But this was really not until 1881.

Bessey's *Botany for High Schools and Colleges* did not appear until 1880, Bailey's junior year, after his groundwork in botany had been laid. Indeed, Beal did not deliver his famous address before the Michigan State Teachers Association on "The New Botany" until after this time. The creative influence of Beal endured because he was among the first university scholars to coordinate in plant study a practical program of outdoor experimentation with the fundamentals of pure research. Beal brought together the garden, orchard, and farm field as object lessons both in the classroom and college laboratory. Throughout Bailey's years as an undergraduate student, Beal was professor of botany and horticulture and curator of the botanical museum.

Bailey entered Michigan Agricultural in the autumn term. The college, located on the banks of the Red Cedar River three miles east of Lansing, was situated on a rise of land in the midst of a purposely saved virgin forest. Three brick buildings, each three stories high, presented an imposing sight in those years. College Hall contained the chapel and recitation and lecture rooms. Williams Hall, the largest, was the dormitory, equipped with dining hall, kitchen, and laundry in the basement; parlors and steward's rooms on the first floor; and on the second and third floors rooms for about eighty students. Wells Hall, having the drill room and armory in the basement, was also a dormitory which could accommodate 128 students. In 1879 the college catalogue boasted, "There are walks, drives, rustic bridges, flower borders, groves, all together forming a park which for design and beauty is probably not excelled by that of any other College in the United States." In 1877, the year of Bailey's entrance, this description may well have been true. The trees of the spacious lawn—birches, alders, lindens, willows, beeches, cedars, pines, spruces, and various evergreens—were plainly labeled. A "good variety" of ornamental plants, including rhododendrons and azaleas, enhanced the beauty of the college flower garden. A greenhouse of four, and soon thereafter, seven, rooms was remarkably equipped with "a choice collection of best ornamental plants." Beal was especially interested, as a systematist, in grasses and clovers, and the "Sample Grounds for Timber-trees" with hedges of various plants, sweet herbs, and curiosities contained, it was said, 150 varieties. Beal had also a museum of vegetable products, "including sections of wood, samples of gums, bunches of grasses, bottles of seeds and grains, and a large number of microscopic slides selected and made to order." There were also a general museum, a museum of mechanical inventions, a chemical laboratory, and a library having about five thousand volumes and ninety periodicals. The college was especially proud of its Cooley herbarium, "a very valuable collection of plants." Albert J. Cook, professor of zoology and entomology and curator of the general museum, had a particular interest in bees and maintained an apiary containing Italian and German specimens. He became president of the American Bee Keepers Association. It was he who inspired Bailey to collect insects. The zealous collector's room before he finished his college work was filled with mounted specimens. These specimens, together with his South Haven collections, were given to the South Haven Pomological Society. Many not represented in the abundant museum collections of the college were also presented to that institution.

When Bailey took his entrance examinations, students were placed in a room seated in a semicircle. At the other end of the horseshoe was an attractive young girl, Annette Smith, daughter of James M. Smith, a prominent breeder of cattle near Lansing. Bailey took out his watch and his eyes fell on her. Her gaze met his. Which one noticed the other first was for years a matter of discussion and was never settled. They became acquainted after the examinations, and Bailey took careful note of the fact that her father's farm lay not far from Lansing and was in a region where most interesting plants and animals were observable. From that moment a friendship blossomed which was to ripen into love. She was to become the partner and helpmate of his life and career. Never was the original inspiration to fade and die. Annette Smith did much to develop the virile, persistent youth from South Haven.

Bailey's freshman class numbered fifty-eight students. The total number of students in the college was 154, including one resident graduate. The course of study in the first term consisted of algebra, history, and composition; in the second term, algebra, bookkeeping, and agriculture composed of lectures and a textual study of Waring on draining; and in the third term, geometry and French.

In nearly all American colleges at this time the text used in botany was Gray's *Botanical Text-Book*, the 1857 edition reprinted and revised once or twice and styled *Introduction to Structural and Systematic Botany*. Gray's *First Lessons in Botany and Vegetable Physiology* was also often used, and freshmen also studied Alphonso Wood's manual. At Michigan Agricultural instruction in botany under Beal was initiated in the second and third terms of the first year. As an aid to such study there was a wild garden containing by 1878, and probably before then, 500 to 700 plant species. Beal insisted on the study of the plant first by close observation alone. The textbook study thus became largely a matter of review. Botany was given special attention as a subject basic to agricultural study. Systems of classification; the orders most important in agriculture, horticulture, floriculture, and forest planting; the geographical distribution of plants; the agency of insects in plant pollination; the motion of plants; the history of botany and the work of noted botanists—all were subjects introduced during the freshman and sophomore years. A student began, however, with subjects such as the outline, margin, and venation of leaves; the morphology of stipules and leaves; the characteristics of stems and peculiar forms of vines, runners, tendrils, thorns, rootstocks; roots in soil, air, or water; inflorescence, that is, the forms and parts of the flower; buds, the kinds and the arrangement of parts; the arrangement of scales on cones and catkins; the peculiarities of fruits, seeds, and stages of germination. Even as late as Bailey's senior year, 1881-1882, this was the course in botany given freshmen and sophomores.

In Bailey's sophomore year—1878-1879—little, if any, formal study of botany was offered members of his class. The autumn term completed geometry and offered elementary chemistry under another noted and progressive professor of the college, Robert C. Kedzie. The spring term continued with organic chemistry and, together with French, extended to autumn and spring terms. Trigonometry and surveying were given. The summer term concluded with analytical chemistry using Kedzie's *Hand Book,* and began mechanics.

Not until Bailey's junior year, 1879-1880, was horticulture formally offered, and then it was given by lectures. Agricultural chemistry and anatomy were also taught by lectures; and the study of mechanics was completed. These subjects of the fall term were followed in the spring term by principles of human physiology, chemical physics, and principles of rhetoric; in the summer term, by English literature, meteorology, and work in Professor Cook's apiary. Owing to illness, Bailey was not a student during the school year 1880-1881. With a physical condition which would cause him to tip over and fall, and necessitated his going to bed for days, he was compelled to stay out of school for what otherwise would have been his senior year. He finally submitted to an operation. He returned for the terms of 1881-1882 and the courses offered were: in the autumn, zoology, geology, civil engineering, and logic under the college's president, Theophilus C. Abbott; and in the spring, psychology, the Constitution of the United States, political economy, and a two-hour laboratory course in botany in which the books of reference were Bessey's *Botany for High Schools and Colleges,* Sachs's *Lehrbuch der Botanik,* the *Treasury of Botany,* Cook's *Handbook of Fungi,* and John Lindley's famous work, *The Vegetable Kingdom.*

In May, 1906, John Craig wrote an editorial for the *Cornell Countryman,*[5] saying:

[5] Page 196.

Twenty-five years ago there were probably not more than half a dozen chairs of horticulture in the country. The teaching in the best of them consisted in obtaining from the student a certain amount of required manual practice work in orchard and garden, a study of the theory of horticulture as expounded by John Lindley accompanied by some training in the propagation of trees and shrubs. Botany was studied from the standpoint of economic plants, zoology from the systematic side, while the student was introduced to the great fields of plant physiology and economic entomology only through the medium of inadequate text-books. Mycology, especially along applied lines, was an unexplored field.

Of American conditions generally, this expression was for the most part true. Horticulture in practically every instance was bound with some other branch of plant study. What few classes there were in the subject were largely a part of agricultural or botanical work. The American investigator was busy finding what plants would grow in what soils and what climates, what kind of cultivation promoted the most effective growth, what increased yields, what feedings and what culture were required for various plants of various localities.

It was an era of practice and of testing, but it was also the beginning of the growth on its own footing of a science transplanted from Europe, where experiment stations were developed. The work and writings of Thomas Andrew Knight, Conrad Sprengel, van Mons, M. Louis Vilmorin, M. Naudin, Dean Herbert, Joseph Hayward, the De Candolles, and numerous others, amplified, refined, and enlarged by the work and writings of Darwin and Wallace, had long reached American shores. All that was lacking was strong and aggressive leadership to carry forward the task of naturalizing the European methods to American plant and animal study. For more than a century American investigation in the plant sciences had been occupied with the huge taxonomic task of learning and systematizing the plants of its two continents, in which process acquisition of knowledge of all the plants of the world was, of course, also required. The work of Muhlenberg, Eaton, Torrey, Schweinitz, Gray, Engelmann, Sullivant, Short, Tuckerman, Parry, Macoun, and a vast array of special talents have been given to the science of botany as it began to emerge victorious over this herculean task. Lesquereux, Newberry, Dawson, and a few others had initiated systematic study of the American paleobotanic flora.

Leadership in advancing an American science of horticulture could have been assumed by Asa Gray. The Gray Herbarium at Cambridge maintained one of the great gardens of the world and in each growing plant Gray took keen interest. Gray dominated the American plant science world as none before had and as no one probably ever will dominate it again. His point of view reflected the progress of the science to that time. Torrey had corresponded with, and been much influenced by, Sir William Jackson Hooker. As much so, and more, Gray was influenced by Sir William's son, the even more able Sir Joseph Dalton Hooker. The world-famous Kew Gardens, directed by the Hookers, divided the work of botany and horticulture. An iron wicket gate separated the sections devoted to the two subjects.

Torrey never urged Gray to establish a garden of cultivated plants. Comparatively little of their known correspondence dealt with cultivated plants as such; though he praised Engelmann for his interesting garden of western species collected by western explorers. Most of the rare species, however, had not attained a cultivated plant status.

Gray, following Torrey, sensibly stressed in his floral studies plants which nature had made relatively permanent and constant, at least sufficiently so to be subjects of a reasonably permanent and stable classification. He was deeply involved in his task when Darwin and Wallace came forward to show that cultivated plants were worthy of the attention and study of educated and scientific men. Gray wrote for agricultural journals and reviewed with astuteness the works of both botanists and horticulturists which dealt foremost with horticultural species. But Gray was not an agriculturist nor horticulturist, but a botanist. Yet his interest in agriculture and horticulture persisted to his last years as is shown by his visit to Rothamstead, England, in 1887, the year before his death, to view agricultural experiments there in progress. Gray's obligation was to complete the *Flora of North America.* This was enough of a task.

Prior to 1850 there had been established at Möckern, Saxony, the first agricultural experiment station in Germany. Even before its establishment, what has been referred to as the oldest agricultural station of the world, the Rothamstead station near London, had begun its renowned studies of plant nutrition. While pursuing work at Munich, a young American chemistry student, Samuel William Johnson, had had an opportunity to study the work of a number of stations that originated soon after the parent ones. Johnson returned to America. As professor of analytical and agricultural chemistry succeeding the venerable John P. Norton, he led in the pioneering agricultural work of Yale University, a program which as early as 1873 included lectures on forestry and tree culture.[6] His books, *How Crops Feed* and *How Crops Grow,* gave "a new impulse to scientific agriculture." In December, 1873, before the State Board of Agriculture of Connecticut, Johnson and Wilbur Olin Atwater launched a movement to establish an experiment station. Although this resulted at first in defeat of a bill before the legislature, Orange Judd, proprietor and editor of the *American Agri-*

[6] A course in forestry taught by William H. Brewer was listed in the 1878 Sheffield Scientific School catalogue.

culturist, offered, among other provisions, $1,000 to begin the work if the state would appropriate $2,800 for two years. About 1875, in the tenth annual report of Sheffield Scientific School, Johnson pointed out that seventy stations had been commenced in Europe, each of which employed one to five investigators trained in modern schools of chemistry and physiology. Thirteen stations studied chiefly cattle-feeding. Twenty-five stations investigated problems of vegetable growth and manures. Tobacco growing, grape culture, wine making, silk production, and seed tests for purity and vitality were included in the work. Serious attention was given the subject by the Connecticut legislature which granted the appropriation asked for, and scientific work began in October, 1875, Professor Atwater giving his services gratuitously. Within the space of a little more than a quarter of a century, Johnson and William H. Brewer had made a model of agricultural science work at Yale University. Soon would be linked to it the work of a land grant experiment station.[6a]

This, perhaps, was not the first American station established. Does the definition of an agricultural experiment station similar to those stations which were already functioning in Europe require, as its final prerequisites, legislative recognition of, and direct financial aid to, a formal organization, separately or conjointly employing technically educated personnel for the exclusive purposes of agricultural experimentation, and in furtherance thereof, maintained from year to year for these purposes alone, by the state? If so, there seems only a minimum of doubt that the traditional belief that the Connecticut station was first in point of time on the North American continent is firmly and forever established, since, more nearly than any other of the early American stations, the Connecticut station's history satisfies the requisites of the definition. If, however, the test is satisfied by agricultural work, predicated in planned experiments conducted by an official agency maintained by the state, irrespective of whether the agency's appropriations are made directly to it by the state legislature for the expressed and sole purposes of agricultural experimentation, a different conclusion might be arrived at. On the latter basis, other claims to priority of founding have been advanced.

It is necessary here to digress long enough to review the work of Eugene Woldemar Hilgard. Hilgard, it is said, was the first American scientist to interpret the results of soil analysis in relation to plant life and productiveness, the first to maintain that the physical properties of a soil are equal in importance to chemical properties in determining cultural values.

Samuel William Johnson in 1856 had published an article "On the

[6a] *Report of the Commissioner of Agriculture* for 1875, p. 472.

Physical Properties of Soils as Affecting Fertility." In approximately
the same year, Hilgard, also one who had received high honors at
European universities, perceived, during a geological survey of Mississippi, that development of the survey's service to agriculture was vastly
more important than merely delineating mineral discoveries. He perceived that plants were an essential in characterizing soils. Discerning
a "close connection between the surface vegetation and the underlying
formations," he began to trace out "the limits of adjacent formations, in
searching for outcrops, etc." He began to characterize "regions" on
the basis of "more or less uniformity of soil and surface features; and
each [was] considered in detail with respect to all natural features
bearing on agricultural pursuits. . . ." Already he had added to the
procedure of older geologists by making physical analyses of soils. He
extended his method by exploring the "intimate connection between the
natural vegetation and the varying chemical nature of the underlying
strata that have contributed to soil formation. . . ." Soil types were
elaborated correlating origins, natural vegetation, and the results of
cultivation. Differences in behavior and durability of soils under cultivation were noticed. As early as 1860, Hilgard published an official
soils map, correlating geological and agricultural resources. Two decades later, his report on the cotton crop, prepared for the United States
Census and in part based on soils study, was influential throughout the
nation, especially pointing new directions for scientific investigation.

Mississippi, however, had enabled him to get only a "one-sided idea
of the subject." Although for a while he served that state as state
geologist and as a professor of chemistry, geology, zoology, and botany
in the state university, when an opportunity to go to the University of
Michigan as professor of mineralogy, geology, and zoology was presented, he left the southern institution and went north. He remained at
the University of Michigan only a short time. The temptation to be
once more at work with "soil crucibles, beakers, funnels, soil solutions,
and soil problems" was too great. Sixteen years working with humid,
washed, and leached soils in the South had shaped for him a specialty in
agriculture and, although Michigan presented an opportunity to examine glacial soils, Hilgard accepted another professorship where agricultural and soils study were coordinately to be developed.

Though as late as 1873 the college of agriculture at the University
of California at Berkeley had not been made "a distinct department
with a separate course of study," provision had been made for agricultural study in the scientific course of the college. In 1873 the university regents had provided for the placement of an agricultural experiment station on the campus at Berkeley. Their decision was that the
station should specialize in soil study and Hilgard was invited to deliver

a course of lectures. It was then announced, in 1874, that Hilgard had been elected professor of agriculture and agricultural chemistry and that a practical course in agricultural instruction inclusive of orchard, nursery, botanical garden, and arboretum work, was being prepared. He was named California's first professor of agriculture. He left the University of Michigan and arrived with his family just before President Daniel C. Gilman resigned in 1875 to go to Johns Hopkins University.

Hilgard was so learned in all branches of science it was debated for a time what he should teach. Edward J. Wickson, professor of horticulture of that institution and for the rest of his life Hilgard's associate, is authority for the belief that the California station was the first in America. He said:

Hilgard opened his laboratory in the spring of 1875 and began an experiment to determine effects of deep and shallow plowing at the same time, and his rival for priority, Professor Atwater of Connecticut was prodding his legislature at that date, reaped a law in July and opened his laboratory in October, 1875, after Hilgard had his field in fallow.[7]

[7] "In Memoriam" addresses presented at a memorial service for Hilgard by Wickson and others, and printed by the University of California, page 16. The substance of Dr. Wickson's claims seems confirmed by Hilgard's first report as professor of agriculture, contained in *Report of the President of the University of California,* from the College of Agriculture and the Mechanic Arts, Sacramento, 1877, State Office, F. P. Thompson, Sup't State Printing, a report describing two seasons of laboratory and experimental work, pp. 11, 15, 16-18, and p. 20. Presumably Hilgard was primarily interested in developing the college's agricultural courses, his instruction in botany, structural and economic, including a garden "of general and economic botany," which claimed an important share of his attention. Hilgard wanted model and experimental farm work securely established. His program sought to institute an industrial survey of the state, and branch experimental stations over the state, as well as laboratory and experimental work on the university campus. The sum of $250 was provided for "a beginning of the work of an industrial survey and experiment station," but "the failure of the appropriations, asked of the last Legislature, in order to insure at least the continuation of the home work" prompted him to expend the sum with caution and care. Culture experiments were inaugurated during the years 1875 and 1876, and the effects of deep plowing in 1874 were observed during these years, and reported. Hilgard in his report referred to the "Connecticut Experiment Station" and its work. A. C. True and V. A. Clark in "Agricultural Experiment Stations in the United States," bulletin 80 of the Office of Experiment Stations, United States Department of Agriculture, 1900, p. 31, summarized the early history of experimental inquiries of the College of Agriculture at the University of California, and noticed that in 1875 the laboratory branch of the experiment station was inaugurated, the regents providing for the expenses thereof for the first two years. Preparations for planting, as a part of such experiments, were begun in 1874. See also A. C. True's "A Brief Account of the Experiment Station Movement in the United States," bulletin 1 of the Office of Experiment Stations, etc., in which 1876 is given as the year when "systematic experimental work in agriculture" was begun at the University of California.

The question, of course, presented, is: Are these facts sufficient to establish the claim that an experiment station, within the meaning of the phrase in use today, had been inaugurated, especially since the Connecticut station was accorded also in 1875 legislative recognition? Whereas the California legislature had refused an appropriation "to insure at least the continuation of the home work," the Connecticut legislature, on July 20, 1875, at the request of the state agricultural society, appropriated the sum of $700 per quarter ($2,800 annually) to Connecticut Wesleyan University for two years, the sum becoming available on October 1. In the *First Annual Report of the*

The principal reason why Hilgard chose California was that the far western state permitted him to develop a well rounded study of soils— the arid soils of the Pacific slope, in addition to the humid soil types in Mississippi and other southern states. The whole was related to climate and geological formation, to chemistry and plant nutrition, in a few words, to the chemico-physical properties and processes which underlie and determine the productive power of soils in vegetational growth. In California he differentiated humid and arid soils on the basis of their depth and physical and chemical characteristics. It is said that he was the first to explain drouth endurance by culture crops in the arid regions and "why sandy soils are the most productive in the arid and the least in the humid." He investigated alkali soils—the cause and occurrence of alkali salts—and their effects on vegetation as well as methods to utilize and reclaim these lands. Hilgard especially studied soil forming minerals, rocks, and plants. The place and the functional values of clay, humus, fertilizers, water, absorptive solids, gases, and other elements in the soil problem, including moisture and aeration, humification, nitrification, et cetera, were examined with a view to increasing the soil's productivity and improving the quality of production. Eastern soil types, tropical soils, in fact, soils of Europe and the world, were carefully studied and compared.

Hilgard envisioned soil study as bound up with the history of civilizations. It should be pointed out that the small tract of ground on which was erected the California station began as a laboratory or department of the college. Not until 1877 did it receive a direct appropriation from the state legislature—the same year that Hilgard pleaded for "knowledge of facts and principles and not the achievement of manual dexterity [as the] leading object" of agricultural instruction. Object teaching with manual exercise was to be "the pre-eminent method."

Connecticut Agricultural Experiment Station for 1876, pp. 9-10, may be found a brief history of the beginning of work at the Middletown station. "Early in October, soon after the opening of the college term," it is written, "a chemist was upon the ground, and two others were afterwards engaged; so that on the first of January, 1876, the work of the Station was fairly started." Professor Atwater was constituted the director. W. C. Tilden, chemist, W. Balentine, graduate of Maine State Agricultural College, and R. B. Griffin, from the University of Vermont, became assistants. On March 21, 1877, the act establishing the station at New Haven was passed, and on July 1, operations at the Middletown station ceased. See *Annual Report of the Connecticut Agricultural Experiment Station* for the year 1877, pp. 7-8; also, *Report of the year 1875*, p. 361; also W. O. Atwater's article, "The Experiment Station and Its Work," 10th *Annual Report of the Secretary of the Connecticut Board of Agriculture*, 1876-1877, published at Hartford, 1877, pp. 79 ff.; also, Elizabeth A. Osborne's *From the Letter Files of Samuel William Johnson*, Yale University Press, 1913, and previous reports of the Connecticut Board of Agriculture.

Facts of Hilgard's life and work are taken from many sources, including the foregoing and subsequently cited works. See, Eugene A. Smith, "Memorial of Eugene Woldemar Hilgard," *Bull. Geol. Soc. of Amer.* 28 (Mar. 31, 1917), pp. 40-67.

The Connecticut station was inaugurated with the use of the chemical laboratory of Orange Judd Hall of Natural Science at Wesleyan University in Middletown. When a larger appropriation was received in 1877 it was moved to New Haven and a land-grant institution established. The Middletown station labored "under the chronic ailment of lack of funds and [was] only kept running through the generosity of gentlemen who [gave] of their time and means." Its experimental work was little, most of its energies being expended in proving its worth to the state, by the saving made possible to farmers in the one item of fertilizers. With time, however, most important studies, such as acquisition of atmospheric nitrogen by plants, in fact, many methods of studying animal, human, and plant nutrition, physiological chemistry, and soil biology, would be developed at this station. Few, if any, American stations have contributed more to the advancement of American agriculture than the Connecticut agricultural experiment station at New Haven.

The soils question would be aggressively introduced in the neglected subject of forestry. As early as 1881, Bernhard Eduard Fernow, an inconspicuous foreign born and educated forester, would write from a remote Pennsylvania mining region where he was managing a forest property for an iron concern, and argue for "forest protection" and a conservative use of forest growth: "As in a well-settled country, the forest naturally will be assigned to the poorer soils (since forest trees *do not* need a chemically good soil,) so it will be proper that only those trees or parts of trees should be taken for charcoal, which cannot find any other use, namely, the branches and above all the coppice growth."

Edward Lewis Sturtevant was another leading advocate of American agricultural development. On January 27, 1877, presumably from his Waushakum Farm, he wrote:

The American book! The American agricultural book! Have we any such? The question is a pertinent one and must be answered with caution. Our ancestors brought with them to this land an European training, and an European method of thought, and taught their children the same.

For many years the minds of the cultured turned to Europe for their inspiration, and the United States achieved its political independence long before it did its intellectual independence. Hence our earlier literature is mostly founded on foreign models.

Our authors made books from foreign authority, or under foreign influences. The discussions of new methods usually originated abroad and were broadly transferred to our shores without discrimination and by an ambitious rather than a practical intellect. The motto of practice with science was either unknown, or quietly ignored, judging as we must, authors' results, rather than their claims.

Indeed, up to within comparatively a few years, our *American* agricultural books could be counted on the fingers of *one* hand, and even now scarcely would the *two* hands be required. Indeed, the majority of the American agricultural books which have issued from our home presses, have been esteemed too worthless for accumulation on our library shelves; of too little value even for the individual collector. A few works on fruits, a few books on the garden, a very few special treati[se]s on special subjects . . . [as] on the horse, a veterinary volume of recent issue, and our list is nearly complete. . . .

"I would that all could feel with me the necessity for a higher agriculture," urged Sturtevant. "I would that jealousy could be sunk in the nobler inspiration of true agricultural work. I would that our leading minds could act together for the common good, and that agriculture could occupy the position by right hers—the first of the arts, the first of the sciences. . . . The question must be not *can we do it*; but *do we wish it*. All rights are secured through knowledge."

Reports of agricultural boards and societies in some states encouraged Sturtevant. Those of the Connecticut board came, he said, "nearest to what we consider a report should be." Although a few individuals represented Michigan's higher agriculture, the strong influence of the agricultural college placed "Michigan in the front rank as an agricultural state." Sturtevant formed his opinion on "the efforts of the *leaders* of her agricultural thought." Scattered through New York volumes were "most valuable essays and contributions," especially certain notable dairy publications. Reports of the Ohio board parted "from the commonplace, not so much through the efforts of the farmers, but through the good judgment of the editor [John H. Klippart]." He published from miscellaneous sources educational materials for his readers. Certain translations of "valuable German experiments," and an abundant appendix containing "the cream of the annual agricultural literature," were held in high regard. In Massachusetts, work of its "influential and prosperous" horticultural society, of its honorable agricultural society, of the "purely scientific features" found in the Bussey Institution's bulletin, foreshadowed development of a "national literature, a literature adapted to American wants." Sturtevant believed that the Bussey Institution work had commenced "an era . . . of scientific agriculture."

Sturtevant in 1882 became the first director of the New York Agricultural Experiment Station at Geneva. This station was the sixth organized in the United States and "probably the fourth to be established through legislative action and direct State aid."[8] Organization in 1877 of the North Carolina station, the first of the southern states, of a faculty organized station in 1879 at Cornell University at Ithaca, New York, of a state station at Rutgers Scientific School at New Brunswick,

[8] W. H. Jordan, "The Station: its History and Work," *25th Anniversary Celebration* held August, 1907, p. 53.

New Jersey, in 1880, preceded the New York station at Geneva. The New York station, however, has certain special distinctions. It was to have an uninterrupted existence. Furthermore, it was to employ the first American station botanist, Joseph Charles Arthur, and horti-culturist, Emmett Stull Goff.

Special recognition should also be accorded the North Carolina station. If the test of a station's origin must be defined, as Dr. Jordan intimated, as legislative recognition and direct financial aid from the state, three stations apparently—the California, Connecticut, and North Carolina—vied for the honor of being America's first agricultural experiment station. Bailey, after a careful study, said, years later: "By act of the legislature, approved in March, 1877, the North Carolina Agricultural Experiment Station was established at Chapel Hill, in connection with the State University and as a division of the State Department of Agriculture. Dr. Albert R. Ledoux was made director. In 1887 the station was transferred to the North Carolina College of Agriculture and Mechanic Arts." During the school year 1869-1870, the college of agriculture and mechanic arts at the University of North Carolina was reported "not yet fully organized." For the next five years, the university was closed. Even as late as 1876, arrangements were still being completed to reestablish agricultural instruction on an adequate scale at the university. Use of an experimental farm was contemplated. A laboratory for quantitative and qualitative analysis had been installed. Laboratory work for the state agricultural depart-ment might have been done. However, it is doubted if such work could have been termed that of an agricultural experiment station. If work is the test of a station's origin, the California station, regarded at the time as an experiment station, may have been the first in America.

The year the New York station at Geneva was organized, stations were established in Massachusetts at Amherst, in Ohio at Columbus, and in Tennessee at Knoxville.

At Massachusetts Agricultural College some of the greatest pioneer-ing events of American agricultural study and teaching took place. Levi Stockbridge, a man who early envisioned the value of the experimental movement, had done much to persuade the legislature of his state to accept provisions of the Morrill law and establish in the 1860's an agri-cultural college at Amherst. Serving on the state board of agriculture in the company of distinguished men including Louis Agassiz, he had become a professor in the college and in January, 1878, had given $1,000 to finance for one year agricultural experiments at the station, a private venture at that time. Moreover, among the very first to be brought to Amherst was Charles Anthony Goessmann, a United States citizen of European birth and education, who was becoming recognized among the few leading American agricultural chemists. In 1870 Goessmann's field experimental studies in beet sugar culture were begun at Massachusetts Agricultural College, determining for Massachusetts comparative merits of various sugar producing plants, maple, sorghum, cane, and sugar beet—a study which in time included the early amber cane of Minnesota. These studies helped to inspire similar studies in other parts of the country and eventually culminated in the development of a great American plant industry. There are many reasons why this college is justly famous in American agricultural science history. For one thing this institution was among the first to recognize the claim of forestry to teaching and investigation status. The year 1887 marked the first year in America that a formal technically considered course of lectures on forestry was delivered by one lecturer. These were given at this college by Bernhard Eduard Fernow who, as America's first professionally trained forester, had so impressed leaders of the forestry movement that President Cleveland had appointed him in 1886 chief of a forestry division in the United States Department of Agriculture.

As early as 1882 Volney Morgan Spalding at the University of Michigan conducted a class teaching forestry principles. This class was mentioned approvingly at the American Forestry Congress held that year at Cincinnati. Other institutions, notably the University of Pennsylvania, early sought to establish a chair in forestry. But, funds lacking, the main sphere of plant investigation went to botany and horticulture. Several colleges and universities, many nurserymen, private woodlot owners, and owners of estates, conducted experiments in tree growing, all of which aided in demonstrating forestry as a practical art which might also be made another great American industry or business; one to aid, and not be hostile to, the flourishing American lumber industry. A few people had listened fascinated to Joseph Trimble Rothrock, a botanist, when each year beginning in 1877 he had delivered the historic Michaux lectures in Philadelphia. He did much to awaken Pennsylvania and the nation to the need of making the American public forestry and conservation conscious, cognizant of the immediate need of bringing forests into scholarly view as instruments related to economic welfare— forests which were being too rapidly and tragically decimated with little thought of replacement or restoration. With the dissemination of propaganda by American forestry organizations, particularly the American Forestry Congress (which became the American Forestry Association), and, most especially by importation of European practice and knowledge by Fernow and others, forestry became in the United States a national enterprise, one which might be placed on a scientific basis. It is interesting to observe that with the years the story of forestry development as a scientific entity has often followed or paralleled the story of the development of scientific study in botany, horticulture, and agriculture.

Fernow's insistence on a basic concept of the forest as an aggregate, as well as individual, collection of tree species, his advancement of functional study in the growth and development of forest species, especially his desire to effectuate such research as would investigate the subject of modifying and changing the behavior and elemental constituency—the structural and physiological properties and their relations—of forest species, was ahead of most plant science research. He emphasized forestry as a biological study—a scientific research field which, like agriculture, horticulture, and botany, has also economic and business phases. Had Fernow's and Roth's biologic conception of timber physics research endured uninterruptedly, a real forest pathology might have arrived sooner on this continent and the nation and the world been spared widespread forest disease scourges and consequent financial losses. However, in historical studies, there is small advantage in speculating on what might have taken place. Forestry, as a part of agriculture and with the aid of entomology and botany, has developed forest pathology on this continent, similar to the older science developed in Europe. Fernow and Roth studied the effects of tree diseases on timbers, and encouraged Hermann von Schrenk when he began to search out the causes of and remedies for the diseases. Indeed, even before Von Schrenk, Farlow had given the study of forest tree diseases some attention. Doubtless, as Fernow and Roth expanded their laboratory in timber physics and wood technology, they would have developed pathological research within the forest as well as in those laboratories more strictly confined to forest products investigations.

Another forestry phase has been dendrological and arboricultural research, work also largely furthered at the United States Department of Agriculture and, more especially, at the Arnold Arboretum at Harvard under Charles Sprague Sargent. In fact, Sargent's thorough and for that time exhaustive analysis of the forest resources of the United States for the 1880 census, also did much to awaken the American public to the alarming depletion of its forest resources, and to the need for extension of scientific study to include all plant life including trees and forests. Nevertheless, trees and forests, because of the long-time span required to attain their mature growth, were not quickly revenue-producing. Scholarly agriculture, to please a profit-seeking public, had to keep in view dollar-producing commodities of quick investment possibilities. Horticultural and agricultural plant species, therefore, occupied the major portion of the research student's interest at all institutions, including Yale and other schools which led. Great forestry schools were yet to be. Not until well into the twentieth century did forestry at an American college have a building made over or built for its own use, although Yale's great forestry school began in the home of Professor Marsh, who bequeathed the property to the university to establish a botanical garden. It has been asserted that a land-grant college—Pennsylvania State College—led the way, by devoting a small unpretentious building to forestry teaching and investigation. But, even there, in very early years, the emphasis was directed toward teaching the importance of forestry from an agricultural point of view. The reasons are plain. Agriculture, then as now, was the nation's basic industry. People could see with their own eyes the fields and harvests being increased and improved by quantity and quality crops. Only occasionally did a student sound warnings that the white pine and other timber resources were being consumed without intelligently planned programs of reforestation. The forests were regarded as inexhaustible.

Emulating the great example of the Rothamstead station in England, many studies at American agricultural colleges and stations were directed toward solving problems of plant nutrition. Animal nutrition problems also came in for a large share of investigation. To the tasks were summoned the aids of chemistry, biology, botany, and all branches of science. The public was slow to see that agricultural science was to treat farm crops and soils, the forests, and natural resources as a laboratory and not as a mine, to improve as well as utilize the products. Milk had to be tested for genuineness. Mass destructive animal plagues such as hog cholera, cattle fever, and pleuropneumonia had to be controlled. Reports of the Society for the Promotion of Agricultural Science attest to the early leadership of the Massachusetts, Connecticut, New York, and New Jersey stations, and the Bussey Institution of Harvard University in the east, of Hilgard and the California station in the west, of Beal and Bessey in the central west, of Burrill and other principals, whose precedence in given particulars remains unquestioned. The once prevalently used "Stockbridge manures" were efficient. At the Massachusetts station, a private venture in 1878 but granted legislative support in 1882, workers were prominent in securing passage of the first fertilizer law in the United States.[9]

The next year, 1883, another agricultural and mechanical college would have a station, this time again in the South, at Alabama Polytechnic Institute, located at Auburn. There, a number of years before, on an experimental farm at least indirectly part of the station, elaborate experiments in cotton culture had got under way, including within a few years crossing varieties of cotton.

[9] See *Charles Anthony Goessmann,* published jointly by the Corporation and the Associate Alumni of the Massachusetts Agricultural College, Cambridge, The Riverside Press, 1917.

The experiment station movement spread not only south but also to the west. In 1883 the regents of the University of Wisconsin established upon recommendation of the governor a station at Madison which was destined to become a great center of agricultural instruction. It was located in the midst of a fruit growing and farming region of wide orbit. William A. Henry, Cornell graduate and since 1881 professor of botany and agriculture there, was placed in charge of the agricultural college and became in 1887 the station's first director.

Henry, when he began his work, was outfitted with one pine table and a bottle of ink worth about $1.50. He had vision concerning farming in Wisconsin and was to aid in developing the state's great dairy industry. Tirelessly he worked for the farms and farmers. At this college he fathered the short winter course in agriculture. The station's and college's very able agricultural chemist, Stephen Moulton Babcock, invented at his request the celebrated Babcock milk test, a production which farmers themselves might operate, a production given to the world, and for which the state presented to Babcock a medal of honor. His true greatness is realized when one considers that from the test the inventor might have reaped an independent fortune. The ranks of agricultural education and research have many such heroic benefactors. Henry held Bailey in high esteem. He characterized Bailey as a "genius" and "the rest of us . . . plodders."

When Charles Edwin Bessey would be called from Iowa Agricultural College to head plant science work and agricultural development at the University of Nebraska, the experiment station movement would extend its sphere of influence into the farther prairie west. Bessey, one of the ablest botanists America has ever produced, a believer in science with practice, a man greatly inspired by the teaching and leadership of Gray and Farlow, had conducted some very noteworthy investigations on the growth of fungi and methods of destroying them. His discernment of the value of plant disease study followed the work of Burrill in Illinois, but his mycological investigations, which included study of rusts, smuts, molds, and parasitic forms, were practically contemporaneous with Burrill's. Like Burrill, Bessey was an early supporter of plant physiological study, a student of both wild and cultivated prairie flora, a participant in the western forestry movement which on the prairies at first consisted of tree-distribution studies and large-scale tree planting for growth, shelter, and conservation purposes. With his knowledge of foreign languages and his official position as state botanist of Nebraska he initiated in concrete terms, while surveying state plant resources with a brilliant corps of students, the beginnings of systematic modern ecological study in America. The debt of plant science study to this botanist is very great despite the fact that his study method was largely interpretation through observation and did not include many of the experimental practices—the application of methods in chemistry and physics to the analysis of protoplasm—in use today.

At Iowa Agricultural College about 1874 the department of horticulture and forestry was "distinctively established" from Bessey's aggressive work in botany, which included the opening of the first botanical laboratory for the teaching of undergraduate botany in an American college. A laboratory for botany! like that of chemistry and physics! jeered some of the professors who regarded it as "a mere bit of boasting or buncombe." Bessey, however, saw the fundamental relation of botany to agricultural study, and the crude sign "Botanical Laboratory" nailed in the spring of 1873 on the door of a little room made from a hallway was not taken down. When Bessey had arrived on the prairie campus of Iowa Agricultural, President Welch had placed him in charge of tree planting there. During 1870 the "uneven, treeless prairie [had been] made to give way to smooth lawns filled with trees and shrubs, the zigzag wagon track to the even and graceful carriage drive." Bessey believed the college should serve as a model to "future agriculturists" who were to "advance somewhat upon the old style farmers, and make their homes more beautiful by surrounding them with trees and flowers, and walks and drives. . . ."

Nor were pomological interests overlooked. An orchard, which supplied fruit to the college and which was also useful in teaching orchard management, was greatly expanded by the addition of "iron clad" varieties. A vegetable garden was changed from a plain open field to one with a "look of cultivation." It began to promise "many experiments of value and interest to the producer of Iowa vegetables." A vineyard of 400 "thrifty vines" promised a "rich harvest." Ten thousand strawberry plants made it seem certain "that best of all fruits [would] no more be a stranger" among them. The farm work went on "bravely." About 1875 experiments in the cultivation of potatoes, tomatoes, strawberries, grapes, and beans were being placed alongside investigations of wheats, oats, and other grains. One entire orchard of pears, cherries, and apples added to the always enlarging orchard area. By 1875 1,200 new forest-seedlings and 500 apple-grafts had been produced in the nurseries. By 1876 the 850-acre college farm had become a center of experiments with "varieties of grains and corn, and with grasses." Gardens, nurseries, orchards which included small fruit plantations, abundant forestry plantations, flower borders, hedges, and ornamental grounds provided practical bases for lectures and courses in horticulture, forestry, economic botany, landscape gardening, and other subjects. These made this college with its other important agricultural activities, which included stock breeding, one of the most progressive centers, educationally, in

America. It was particularly outstanding in the Middle West and West where for a number of years, and in some areas for decades, a migrating population had been rapidly filling up large unused and uncultivated land spaces.

During the great years of migration and settlement, however, scientific knowledge seldom accompanied the man who went west with a family, took up land, and began to farm. Consequently, for many years scholarly subjects such as botany, horticulture, and indeed agriculture as developed in the schools, were little more than names. Farming was practical; horticulture was largely a matter of the nursery business; and orchard and garden work were important only as incidentals of farms or ranches. The pioneer middle western agricultural colleges became aware of their responsibility. In November, 1873, all chairs at Iowa Agricultural College were declared vacant, the faculty was reorganized, and Bessey was appointed professor of botany, zoology, horticulture, and pomology. The appointee, however, declined the proffer, accepting a professorship of botany and zoology only, and Joseph Lancaster Budd[10] was placed in charge of horticulture, a profession comparatively new and untried in prairie regions except as it issued from well-established nurseries of which Budd himself was a product. At that time little exact knowledge of plant adaptation had accumulated there. Nearly all plants which were cultivated and not indigenous to Iowa prairies were old American varieties of common cultivation in the East which had moved westward with migration. This in large part included ornamental plants and most especially fruit trees. Because of varied conditions of soil and climate, the Middle West and West had staggering problems in the development of a scientific horticulture and agriculture. Texts of the Old World and, to a considerable extent, those of the East had little application to western conditions. Phytogeographical studies in botany were showing the varied characters of middle western and western floras, as distinguished from those of the East. This being so of the plants of wild nature, what of the cultivatable plants?

In the wide regions stretching westward from Minnesota and the Mississippi River basin there fortunately had been practical orchard and farm men, some very able, who, though seemingly unaware that they

[10] For an account of Budd and his work, see L. H. Pammel's *Prominent Men I Have Met*, published at Ames, Iowa, 1926, pp. 9-14. Henry H. McAfee, Captain Mathews, and Bessey had all taught phases of horticulture before Budd. Budd's departmental work on a professional basis began about 1877. Some of the materials of the foregoing paragraphs are based on unpublished writings by Dr. Bessey. Access to manuscript material was afforded the author of this book by Dr. Ernst A. Bessey, Dr. Bessey's son. On these points, see Dr. Ernst Bessey's "The Teaching of Botany Sixty-five Years Ago," *Iowa State Coll. Jour. of Sci.*, IX (2 and 3, 1935), pp. 13-19; Earle D. Ross, *A History of Iowa State College*, Iowa State College Press, Ames, Iowa, 1942. It seems that Budd became a lecturer at the college before he accepted the full time professorship of horticulture.

were contributing to the development of a science, had become immensely interested from a practical standpoint in developing new strains and races of plants for their native but none too hospitable soil. Among these were plant breeders of amazing versatility such as Charles G. Patten[11] of Charles City, Iowa, who developed the famous Patten's Greening apple, and the strange, mystic Peter M. Gideon of Minnesota who, along the shore of Lake Minnetonka, produced the excellent Wealthy apple. The alert and exemplary work of James Cabin Evans on his home plantation (now part of Kansas City) and later on his enterprising commercial orchard at Olden, Missouri, in the Ozark region supplied another leading instance of individual work which inspired and contributed directly to the advancement of scientific study in the Mississippi Valley. A peach, raspberry, and crab apple originated by him bore his name. Grapes, small fruits, and even the persimmon, received large shares of his attention. In early years these men, Gideon and Patten especially, experimented with thousands of seedlings in an effort to originate hardy and productive new varieties of orchard stock capable of withstanding the harsh hot or cold climates, varieties which would produce profitably under various soil conditions. These men did not fight the introduction of foreign varieties—especially those which were brought from Russia—of which "horticultural camp" Budd became some years later a leader. Budd was stimulated and aided financially by Charles Gibb, a Canadian who owned a widely known farm at Abbotsford, in the province of Quebec, where he grew hardy fruits and ornamental shrubs. Gibb stimulated the movement, both by financial aid to others and by his own efforts. Conceived as a movement of progressive importance to both forestry and horticulture—and, of course, agriculture—this work of foreign plant introductions (including ornamental and forest trees) spread over areas of Canada from Quebec and the maritime provinces to the prairies; and over the United States from New England to the far west. Agricultural colleges, particularly in Ontario, Iowa, and South Dakota, cooperated with the movement's leaders. A number of agricultural experiment stations became participants. During the early 1880's foreign journeys to northern Europe and Asia began. Reports were made to appropriate American societies. The trip of Gibb and Budd in 1882 to northern Europe and Asia, superimposed on the work initiated by the United States Department of Agriculture, might be said to have developed a new nomenclature of North American hardy trees and shrubs, including conifers.

About 1870 William Saunders of the United States Department of

---

[11] For an account of Patten and his work, see L. H. Bailey's "An Iowa Plant-Breeder, New Methods in Plant Production Contrasted with Old," *The Century*, LXXXI n.s., vol. 59 (1910-1911), pp. 392-401.

Agriculture introduced hardy Russian apples, and Budd accented the work by securing hardy fruit varieties adaptable to the northwest plains. In this he was aided by Bessey and other leaders. During his last teaching years Budd became an ardent advocate of plant breeding, as distinguished from regional adaptations of foreign varieties imported from seeds. Many of his students, inspired by his forceful personality as a speaker, naturalist, and scientist, became leaders in developing a prairie and northwest plains horticulture. Although he shared in its making, the principle that ultimately prevailed in the prairie regions was not wholly Budd's. It was that of growers such as Patten and Gideon who believed "that in regions demanding unusual qualities in fruit-trees and other plants, strains or races must be developed natively in the region," using where possible foundation stock improved and adapted to American uses.

Another place of consequential horticultural development in the Great Plains was Kansas State Agricultural College at Manhattan. About 1873 its nursery, occupying sixty-seven acres with 45,000 fruit and forest trees and 650 varieties of apples, was believed "the largest and most valuable west of the Mississippi." Farmers' courses and substantially all the general phases of horticultural and agricultural work had been inaugurated. Experiments similar to those undertaken at Iowa Agricultural were conducted in 1873 in wheat and corn cultivation. On a farm of more than 250 acres were grown wheat, rye, broomcorn, buckwheat, barley, oats, millet, flax, three varieties of potatoes, five varieties of sugar beets, two varieties of corn said to have yielded seventy-five bushels per acre, timothy, clover, hemp, and castor beans. In 1876, in addition, an experiment in 250 potato varieties, including those grown in eastern states, was conducted. A complete analysis of the progressive work of this institution is not necessary because of its general similarity to that of its neighbor in Iowa. A few distinctive departures should be noticed. One was that its regents early sought to develop a literary department with a four-year course that would be the equivalent of "the best literary institutions." Another was that about 1876 a one-story horticultural building was erected, equipped with lecture and recitation rooms, workshops, and cellars. Horticulture, including forestry, was stressed in the earliest years of the college. An experimental forest was, to say the least, pioneering; and in the college's early years thousands of trees were distributed to Kansas citizens. Nevertheless, not until about 1895 did horticulture acquire distinct recognition as a separate department in the college. Such prominent figures as Elbridge Gale, H. E. Van Deman, afterward pomologist of the United States Department of Agriculture, Edward A. Popenoe, and Silas C. Mason, a world authority on date palm culture who was also connected with the United States Department later, were at one time or another in charge of horticultural work at this college which has graduated many able scientists.

About 1875 Kansas State Agricultural College began large-scale experimental studies in grains and grasses to determine the most valuable Kansas forage plant resistant to heat and dryness. It was a work done with seeds furnished in part by the United States Department of Agriculture.

Seed distribution, including field, vegetable, flower, herb, tree, and evergreen seeds, occupied an important part of the federal department's activities, although as to its worth and efficacy there was much discussion. There were sectional localities, notably California and undeveloped western regions, whose agriculture, it was believed, had benefited practically from the department's services. Moreover, in the early 1870's the needs of the South were being studied and much effort was being expended to induce southern planters to cultivate jute. The Commissioner of Agriculture gave much space in his reports to the need for studying semitropical and tropical plants which might be cultivated in the United States. Widespread demand for forestry study was arising. Seed distribution and tests were a part of all plant study. Sturtevant, however, represented a point of view held by many. Said he in 1877: "The agricultural department should, while retaining the good will of farmers, treat them more as men than as children, and should treat agriculture as a great interest requiring development, rather than as a toy." As to the department's reports he urged:

Let the Department cease doing the work of the trader and seedsman, and spend its money to economize farming for the farmer. . . . It is a disgrace that with such expenditures as it makes that so few results should show. Our population is largely agricultural. The Department was established for their interest, and these books, misnamed reports, should clearly succeed in showing the benefit they are to American agriculture.

Really progressive, forward-moving American agricultural work, built on a well-organized architecture of plant science study, such as Sturtevant and other leaders sought, awaited the culmination of a national experiment station movement which attained maturity in 1888 with passage of the federal Hatch Act. During that year Iowa Agricultural and Kansas State, like many other state-founded institutions, established stations. Before this, however, many states had shared in the movement. In 1885 Maine and Kentucky and, it is said, Minnesota, established stations. That year Alabama began its Canebrake station and Louisiana a private sugar-planters' experiment station. In 1886 the states of Louisiana, Vermont, and, it is believed, New Hampshire also founded stations; in 1887 Indiana, South Carolina, and Pennsylvania were added to the list. Some were organized originally by the schools and some by the states.[12]

The task of educating the public to a realization of the value of more than just obviously practical work was difficult. Farmers at institutes could be shown the worth of matters such as seed selection and crop rotation. Proof of methods devised to destroy harmful insects and parasitic agencies was easily demonstrable. But the more elusive subjects of "pure science" investigation, proof of plant breeding as a potential science and not merely an art in which the more skilled excelled, the worth of scholarship and the progress to be obtained through microscopic analysis—experimentation in general—in these matters it took years to convince public spirited citizens that these were worthy of large money expenditures. Programs were planned by the leaders. Concerning one drawn by Bessey for Nebraska, Sturtevant wrote its author in 1884:

I recognize therein a breadth of view which is most encouraging for your future prospects. Your scheme for experimentation meets my approval so thoroughly that I must express my fear that your people are not as yet sufficiently advanced to appreciate it. To judge of the character and intent of agricultural experimentation requires careful thought and thorough consideration, and few come to the subject with the proper preparation. . . .

Although as early as 1885 the Michigan legislature appropriated funds to enable the state agricultural college to publish bulletins on experimental work, this college, too, waited until 1888 before an experiment station was available to aid its work. Scientific leadership, however, was not lacking, and, in the long years of waiting, agricultural and horticultural studies continued along the lines initiated by its early forward-looking leadership represented by men of such fiber as Beal, Cook, and Kedzie.

During these years the national movement to conserve the land's

[12] The official date of organization of several of the aforenamed stations is given as 1888. Considerable variance exists in the literature as to the exact dates of organization. In 1885 eight independent stations existed in Maine, Massachusetts, Connecticut, New York, New Jersey, Ohio, North Carolina, and Alabama, aside from Houghton Farm, New York. Systematic agricultural experiments were said, moreover, to be in progress, "and costing from $700 (Kansas) to $8,000 (California)" under G. C. Caldwell at Cornell University, W. H. Jordan at State College, Pennsylvania, John W. Glenn at the University of Tennessee, Knoxville, J. M. McBryde at the University of South Carolina, J. W. Sanborn at the University of Missouri, E. M. Shelton at Kansas State Agricultural College, H. C. White at the University of Georgia, Athens, and E. W. Hilgard at the University of California. To this was added, "There are others similarly engaged from whom no reports have been received." Wisconsin was not regarded as an independently organized station but one organized at the state university. Nearly all of them published either monthly bulletins, annual reports, or papers. Some became inactive for a period, others were reorganized, and some maintained an uninterrupted existence. See, "Agricultural Experiment Stations—Condensed Facts, 1885," *Proc. of 4th and 5th Meetings of the Society for the Promotion of Agricultural Science* held 1883 and 1884, published 1885, p. 95.

natural resources had not been organized. What realization of the growing need for conservational programs and propaganda existed in no way had brought about the commensurate activity demanded by the necessities of an increasing and expanding population. Here and there men argued and discussed such matters as the wise and right use of the forest and mineral resources. In Michigan, far-sighted students condemned the evils of excessive forest exploitation. They warned of the dangers to future agriculture, indeed to civilization itself, when the dearth from deforestation became widespread. Kedzie was one such student. Professionally, before becoming a teacher, he had been a doctor. Brought up on a farm near Monroe, Michigan, he had worked part of his way through Oberlin College, graduated with the first class of the medical department of the University of Michigan and, after years as a practicing physician in his home state and surgeon during the Civil War, he had begun to teach chemistry at Michigan Agricultural College in 1863. No man with his background could have failed to approach the study of plants and plant life without seeking to understand their physiological requirements, especially those requirements dependent on soils. It is true that the subject of fertilizers claimed a large share of his attention. It was very important in those years to obtain laws, making the licensing of agents compulsory and requiring vendors to analyze their preparations and label their products accordingly. Kedzie's name has lived more as an agricultural chemist than in any other one capacity. Other fields of accomplishment deserve consideration.

For more than a century, lands in the older or more populated sections of the country had begun to lose their fertility through long use or lack of proper care and cultivation. Lands were being abandoned, many times because it was easier to move to fresh, unused areas than to rehabilitate the old. Land erosion, the loss or destruction of fertile top soils, necessary water resources, and other slowly, sometimes imperceptibly, disappearing imperatives of good farming, followed often even the frontiersman and settler when no preventive, precautionary, or preservative measures were taken. As the number of frontiers and the amounts of untilled acreage fit for agriculture were reduced, movements and programs to rehabilitate the lost or damaged farm resource arose. Seeds of the movements for forest, soil, and water conservation planted during these and earlier years soon germinated and grew. In appraising the agricultural colleges' seeming tardiness of response to the new challenges, too often the role of the practical farmer, epitomized by the colleges of agriculture, was overlooked. For many years, farmers, with the zeal of conservationists, had devised methods and techniques to improve and conserve lands and crops. Many of their discoveries found their way to written columns and pages of agricultural journals and books. And many found their way to agricultural college classrooms. Professors took advantage of the experiential knowledge and furthered its usefulness by translating or elaborating practices in terms of experimental science.

Nevertheless, the main center of aggressive attention was to find what crops would grow in what soils and under what climates with what kind of treatment. Crop improvement, if it did not surpass, at least kept pace with, land improvement. Kedzie, for example, showed what kind of wheat was best suited to the soil and climate of Michigan. Through farmers' institutes he taught unlearned toilers of the soil much about agricultural chemistry. Moreover, he had much to do with introducing and expanding the beet-sugar industry in this country. One of his most widely known accomplishments was his contributions to the causes of state and national public health, an interest influentially expressed by holding high offices of prominence and by writings on the subject.

Beal, early an officer of the American Pomological Society, became first president of the Society for Promotion of Agricultural Science. Except as his instruction included lectures and experiments to increase yields, improve qualities, and breed new plants, his teaching in horticulture was essentially practical. His students studied pollination. They propagated fruit and ornamental trees, shrubs, and herbs by grafting, budding, layers, and cuttings. Beal's lasting contributions—those by which his name enduringly lives—were in what he regarded as botanical research. The annual catalogue for 1881-1882, Bailey's senior year, stressed practical phases of plant science learning. Horticultural instruction was by lectures, rather than laboratory research. The books of reference were Downing's *Fruits and Fruit Trees*, Henderson's *Floriculture and Gardening for Profit,* Hoope's *Book of Evergreens,* Warder's *American Pomology*, Barry's *Fruit Garden*, and others. The professor of horticulture, or his assistants, did spend some time each week with students in the orchard, vineyard, and gardens. Sections of classes met with the professor also in the greenhouse. The intention, however, was to give "practical instruction in operations which [could] not be well taught in the class-room," and the class-room lecture topics were described as follows:

Location of the garden; preparation of soil, grading, draining, laying out; sowing seeds; irrigation; modes of culture; mulching; tools,—care, structure, uses;. construction, composition, management of the compost heap; application of all kinds of fertilizers; rotation of crops; remedies for insects; construction, management, and use of hot-beds, cold frames, greenhouses; transplanting, harvesting, marketing, packing, shipping, storing fruits and vegetables; . . . best sites for orchards; kinds of trees to set out, and why; orchard culture; pruning; killing insects; thinning; harvesting; methods of classifying fruits by form, color, size, taste, twigs, leaves, flowers, and seeds; best management for each common large and small fruit. . . .

Special garden crops—onions, celery, cabbages, squashes, tomatoes, and others—were given consideration. Broader topics, such as double cropping and seed growing, were specially treated. Experimental research, however, was motivated more by practical than purely scientific objectives. Horticulture seems to have been regarded as primarily economic, utilitarian, and with no, or little, substratum of experimental science. The last belonged to botany.

Landscape gardening, also taught by lectures and illustrative material on the college grounds, was given "with a view to help students in ornamenting a home or public grounds in the best and most economical manner." Reference material of reputable authors—Downing, Kemp, Scott, and others—was included.

Farm work, of which the manual labor system in vogue in most agricultural colleges was a part, was dominant. Early collegiate agricultural education aimed to develop abler practical farmers. Compulsory practical labor in afternoons was required of all students. The college had a 676 acre farm, with barns for horses, cattle, and sheep, and with a piggery having ten pens. Students arose with the ringing of a morning bell at six o'clock and had breakfast a half hour later. At seven forty-five came the chapel exercises which preceded recitations, lectures, or study hours. At noon came dinner. After dinner students reported for work on the farm or in the gardens and grounds. This lasted until four o'clock in the afternoon. The library was then opened and, except for the supper period at six, it remained available to students during evening study hours. The historic feature was the manual labor system. Students earned eight cents an hour at the farm work, and there was much protest against the system.

Bailey enjoyed the garden work. One day a promising young American botanist paid a visit to Dr. Beal when the latter and Bailey were at work in a garden. He was William Trelease, a young man who from his earliest youth had taken a keen interest in out-of-door things. Born at Mt. Vernon, New York, Trelease was educated in a school system much like that of New York City. A strong religious adherence prevailed in his home. Often his family read aloud the Bible. He meditated much on things of nature. For example, a grass, Sisyrinchium, which flowers but a day, leaving a tender, fragile memory in the mind, related the world of nature with the realm of the eternal, not as a symbol of life and death, but as something of beauty vanished, and to return, with a kind of quiet splendor. From boyhood he was a student, though virile and fun-loving. Horsetail joints supplied materials for his fishing poles. Once he was punished for the noise some painted turtles made under his desk at school. He was overjoyed when under low shrubbery in moist ground he found a very beautiful little flower, Erythronium. His formative years had been spent in a small manufacturing town near New Haven, Connecticut, called Branford. There he came under the influence of Leonard Woods Parish, a Yale graduate, who was teaching in the little two-room high school of the village. He proved to be a real inspiration to the youth. His preparatory work finished in 1872, the next four years were spent getting ready for college with the aid of a tutor in French. Two terms after the opening of the school year in the spring of 1877 when he was twenty years of age, he presented himself for admission to Cornell University. He entered a class in French reading, studying Voltaire's "Charles XII." As the years went by he came under the influence of one of America's early great scientists, John Henry Comstock, a brilliant student already renowned as an entomologist. Through contact with him, he went into the field in his junior year. Comstock, who succeeded to a place, formerly held by C. V. Riley, with the Commissioner of Agriculture in the study of cotton insects sent Trelease into the work. Albert Nelson Prentiss had taught botany at Michigan Agricultural before Beal, but had left there and gone to Cornell. His instruction, together with that of W. R. Dudley in cryptogamic botany, had given Trelease "the high points of botany" and opened "little windows" into mycology. By the time of his graduation, Farlow at Harvard was back from his studies with De Bary and it was a difficult task for the young naturalist to choose between entomology and mycology. He chose the latter, however, and went to Harvard where he became acquainted with all the men in natural science there. In the spring of 1881 he began teaching at the University of Wisconsin and the next year while on a trip east, although not acquainted with Beal, he went by way of Lansing. Beal ushered him around his garden and soon a tall, lanky, young man put in an appearance. Beal said, "Oh, Trelease, there's a young man I want you to know. Come over here, Bailey." And then he added before Bailey arrived, "Bailey is a young genius studying here."

That school year, 1881-1882, the "young genius" had written an editorial for *The College Speculum*, of which he was the first editor-in-chief:

. . . Science is no longer synonymous with abstruse theories and vague, impractical hypotheses; it has discovered the laws which govern climate, vegetable growth, insect life and habits, the mutual relations of inorganic and organic nature, and the dependence of each branch of organic objects upon each other branch, and has contributed the practical results obtained from such discoveries to agricultural industries. Indeed, it was not until scientific education began to manifest itself that agriculture began its ascent from the slough of contempt in which it lay, and became at last sufficiently elevated to be thought a fit industry for talent and enterprise. . . . The farmer of today knows nothing of the drudgery which characterized his profession a hundred years ago. This change has been wrought by no other force than the systematic and scientific efforts of educated leaders. . . . The principles of science that underlie their labors will be applied vigorously. . . . If every county in the north had within its limits one business-like graduate of some scientific institution, and he a farmer, there would be just so many centers to which farmers would naturally look for leaders, and just so many centers of power for the elevation of agricultural industry.

CHAPTER III

EXCURSION INTO JOURNALISM. FRIENDSHIP WITH
ERWIN FRINK SMITH. YEARS AT HARVARD AND
A RETURN TO THE PLANT SCIENCES

YOUNG BAILEY had entered college with a pronounced liking for
botany, a lively interest in garden and farm, and an incidental flair
for journalism. No extracurricular activities had permitted much expression of his journalistic ambitions. But in June, 1881, after he had
returned for his senior year, a student movement got under way to
establish a college publication. This became one of the earliest, if not the
first, organized in a strictly agricultural college. Some of the larger
universities with schools or departments of agriculture had established
student publications, as, for example, in 1874 or thereabouts the Illinois
Industrial University at Urbana started *The Illini*. Michigan State
Agricultural College at this time had no technical schools and was in
no sense an engineering school. *The College Speculum* of Michigan
Agricultural, therefore, was a new venture in agricultural journalism
issuing from a college, a quarterly, which set from its first issue the
highest standards of journalism. In July, 1881, work began and on
August 1 the first number appeared. The immediate control of the paper
was placed with five collegiate societies: the Natural History Society
formed to pursue study in the natural sciences "with those of agriculture, horticulture," and rural engineering; Delta Tau Delta and Phi
Delta Theta, chapters of two national college fraternities; and two
literary societies, Union Literary and Eclectic. Each society elected its
own editor, and from one of these the students at large selected an
editor-in-chief. The paper announced it preferred "originality to literary
merit" and that its aims were to be "of general interest," to "contain
such college news and personals of former students as to at once draw
into a nearer relation the alumni and their alma mater," and to "give
to the public at large such scientific and general reading as may be interesting or useful." It was not to be an advertisement of the college.

A number of Michigan Agricultural's students came from states
other than Michigan. Some came from the East, especially from eastern
New York. They journeyed the long distance to Michigan because here
there was something different. The older eastern universities, Yale,
Harvard, Amherst, Rutgers, and other schools of strong classical traditions which somewhat condescendingly included noteworthy agricultural
instruction by a scientific school or department, shook their heads at a
school which did not place the classics, philosophy, and English literature

in the foreground of learning. A college without language and English requirements, they said, was no college at all.

Herbert W. Collingwood, from Massachusetts, who later became editor of the prominent agricultural journal, *Rural New-Yorker*, was the first business manager of *The College Speculum*. Dr. Beal was placed in charge of "Science" articles; J. W. Beaumont of "Literary Articles"; O. C. Howe of "Personals and Literary Notes"; and L. W. Hoyt was made secretary in charge of correspondence. Professor Samuel Johnson, professor of practical agriculture, became treasurer. On the cover of the *Speculum* appeared a quotation from Ruskin: "It is only by labor that thought can be made healthy."

The association of Collingwood and Bailey from the first was significant. For a period of almost half a century, Collingwood served as one of the most inspired agricultural journalists America has produced. He later described his impressions of Bailey as a student. "When I entered College as a Freshman, Bailey was a Junior," he said. "The upper classes were small in those days, and we Freshmen looked upon the upper students as great men, until we found how small some of them were. With one accord, I think our Freshmen decided that Bailey was the leading student in College. I never saw him play baseball, or engage in any of the rougher sports. His College power was derived entirely from his work as a student and the mastery of his subjects in the class room. At every College there are half a dozen men who seem to have an instinct for grasping the essential points of a subject. They do not seem obliged to grind out their work as many do, nor do the facts come to them in a flash of light, but somehow the instinct of study shows them just where to go and obtain the facts with the least effort. Bailey impressed me as a man of this type. He was always dignified. . . . From the first time I saw Bailey up to the present he has seemed to me to carry an immense power in reserve." Never once did he have the "big head" and he always "seemed to realize that after all the small slice of wisdom which one man can get hold of in the ordinary human life, is not worth bragging about. So far as I know Bailey never took the tongue out of a college bell, or shaved the gardener's cat, or emptied the barrel of water on a luckless Professor. I remember him rather as a studious, serious man, who knew what he went to College for, with fair training to take the course and the instinctive ability to go right to the heart of the subject and cover the essential fact."[1]

Bailey's own writing confirmed this point of view. He wrote, *"The Speculum* is not a boy's paper, into which the odds and ends of fun and nonsense may be thrown; it is published by a body of students who are earnest and desirous of making it a medium of instruction between

[1] "Bailey Number" *Cornell Countryman*, XI, 3 (December 1913), p. 74.

alma mater and alumni." His leadership was attested by the fact that on
September 15 he was elected president of "a permanent organization
which should have control of the new students' government, *The
Speculum*, and such other matters as relate to students in general."

Bailey wrote a column of "College News" and a number of editorials
for the *Speculum*. During the year the college was connected with
Lansing by telephone. That was an event. There was agitation for a
street railway between the two points. Bailey wrote an editorial favoring
its establishment. He also wrote on the subject of military training,
showing that agricultural colleges in Massachusetts, Maine, Alabama,
and Mississippi were ahead of Michigan in this regard. An editorial
favoring the establishment of a mechanical department at the college
was a rousing challenge:

> . . . There will be no friend of the College who will not heartily favor
> this measure. . . . Our total deficiency in mechanical instruction has caused
> much censure to be heaped upon us by other industrial institutions. . . .
> Our institution lays great stress upon its labor system—upon the great
> practical benefits which farmers' sons acquire by repeating on the College
> farm the many operations which they had already learned to do better at
> home. Of the thirty-five studies in our curriculum, only nine can possibly
> be practically applied in out-door labor, when as a matter of fact only four
> of these nine are so applied. The strenuous cry of practicality does not
> deceive the educationists of other states. At Iowa Agricultural College, at
> the Illinois Industrial University, and at Purdue they asked of us: "Why is
> Michigan Agricultural College so far behind the times?" "Why do you boast
> of practical instruction when you have not even the rudiments of essential
> mechanical discipline in the use and care of tools?" Along with these
> questions come similar ones regarding our lack of military discipline and
> our feeble grasp at veterinary instruction. These criticisms are well founded.
> Our own offspring among the agricultural colleges of the South and West
> are outstripping us. . . .

From the very beginning of his writing career, Bailey showed fear-
lessness when convinced he knew the right side of a question. The
Speculum sprang immediately into public notice. *The Michigan Farmer*,
the *New England Homestead*, the *Grange Visitor*, and alumni praised
its contents, and it became influential in the college and elsewhere. Even
departments did not escape the journal's censure, as illustrated by its
claim that the "labor system has become badly demoralized in the horticultural department. It is maintained at its old standard under the management of the farm department." There was praise as well as censure.
The whole farm department "never looked better than at present. There
is order and thrift apparent everywhere; everything shows thought and
good, practical management." Or, "There is no part of the College
premises which shows so much improvement as the vegetable garden."
Or, "One of the most interesting features of the College grounds is the

wild garden, maintained for purposes of botanical study. About five
hundred indigenous plants are now growing in the pond and rock work.
The arrangement of plants into natural orders is gradually being made."
The arboretum of two hundred species of trees and shrubs grew "more
and more interesting with age." Notice of the occupancy in the spring
of 1881 of the botanical laboratory, a "building . . . situated on the
west bank of the ravine, near the main drive, and northwest of the green
house, to which it is connected by a rustic foot bridge across the ravine,"
was received with genuine interest. Comments on Dr. Beal's small beds
of some 200 species of grasses and clovers for special students, established "some years ago" and being added to each year, and on prospective
orchard, garden, and farm crops, and reviews of current books or
treatises, such as Charles W. Garfield's *A Glimpse at Michigan Horticulture,* were included in Bailey's editorial scope. But the work which
obviously had captured his imagination most was the field and garden
experiments: the work in corn to ascertain the agricultural sources of
nitrogen and to test the value of foreign varieties in the locality; the
work in sugar cane and "Minnesota amber" to determine their value
as sugar crops; Cook's study of the army worm and insects injurious
to farm, garden, and orchard; Kedzie's chemical analyses of plant
products and his important meteorological observations including temperature, barometric pressure, pressure of vapor of water, relative
humidity or moisture of the atmosphere, direction and force of winds,
kinds and amounts of clouds, amounts of rain, snow, hail, etc., and
amount of ozone in the air—studies which had been continued for
eighteen years; and numerous other scientific projects, some crude, but
most of them farseeing.

In his notes Bailey told of the experiments that year under Beal, the
professor of botany and horticulture. They consisted of

the testing of the vitality of an assortment of vegetable seeds obtained
from 14 or more leading seedsmen; the testing of the seeds of all the clovers
and grasses in the markets; the testing for the fourth time of the growth of
Indian corn from seed of the upper ear on the stalk as compared with the
lower ear; the testing of dark colored seeds of red clover as compared with
light colored seeds; experiments with a view to improve the keeping
qualities of yellow Danver's onions by planting seeds from onions which
keep the latest in the spring, and experiments on the yield of corn as
influenced by root pruning. He has also begun an experiment in common
with several other professors in different States, on the yield and quality of
corn which has been brought from places one hundred miles apart, and
crossed with corn raised at Lansing, as compared with the same foreign
corn which has not been crossed. Many seedling fruits and wild plants from
seed supposed to be crossed are being grown and experiments begun in
former years are being continued.

As progressive as this work was, it, nevertheless, was not the most important research being done to advance American horticulture. That of greatest consequence was being done by Cook. This man performed in 1877 what may be described as one of the first successful sprayings of fruit trees in America. He realized that combating destruction was of equal, if not more, importance in developing garden and orchard science than originating or adapting varieties which might become preys of destroying agencies. Bailey's zealous support of this work may have stemmed from the fact that his father had been spraying the apple trees of his prize orchard many years before 1877. Where spraying as a practice began in America, probably no one will ever know. Certainly, Cook was among the very first to approach the subject as a matter of "pure science." Bailey commented:

Last year Professor Cook tried some experiments with a view to determining some better methods for the destruction of our most harmful insect pests. The results were very encouraging, and were embodied in a paper read before the American Association for the Advancement of Science at the Boston meeting. These experiments had reference to the use of London purple in fighting the codling moth, and bisulphide of carbon to destroy the various subterranean insects, such as bore into or eat the roots of plants. This year he is repeating these experiments, and is further seeking for some means to keep such insects as cannot well be destroyed while at work from making attacks. He is meeting with very encouraging results, and is making use of carbolic acid, which is one of the most offensive substances to all insects.

One of the greatest friendships of Bailey's life began at this period— that with Erwin Frink Smith. Smith was working in the office of the State Board of Health at Lansing, and as often as possible Bailey and he got together. At the July, 1881, meeting of the Natural History Society of the college, Bailey spoke in high terms of a new catalogue of Michigan plants. He exhibited plants of *Lemna minor* in blossom, and Wolffia, abundant around South Haven, and flowers of *Erythraea centaurium*, a plant introduced on the college ground. The reason for showing these plants was to rouse interest in Michigan plant study. Bailey's ardor had been greatly stimulated and one of the causes of his steadily sustained but now increasing enthusiasm was the new catalogue, compiled by Smith in collaboration with Charles F. Wheeler, and with the history of which for three years Bailey had had something to do. He had become a collector of plant and animal specimens for the college. Not unnaturally, he had found that the most novel and best plants and small animal life were in the direction of the farm owned by Annette Smith's father near Lansing. With the girl he had met on entrance examination day, an unbroken friendship had persisted. That was cause enough to justify his rambles and strolls to great distances around

Lansing, a state capital city rapidly enlarging its limits as a railroad and commercial center. Moreover, a now added reason was the new catalogue.

Bailey had roommates each of his college years. His favorite was Howard Holmes, "a noble chap in every way"; others were Alva Sherwood and Eugene Rauchfuss, both excellent friends. Another friend, though not a roommate, was C. B. Charles from Bangor, Michigan. In later years, to honor his friendship with Bailey, Charles's widow endowed a memorial, purchasing and presenting to South Haven the birthplace of Bailey. Enumerating all of Bailey's friends would require renaming the enrollment lists of each year at the college.

Probably anyway the most influential botanical friendships among his early years would not be found on the college rosters, aside from the name of Dr. Beal. As a boy Bailey had corresponded with Charles F. Wheeler. In fact, it was in Bailey's freshman year at college as he went to visit Wheeler at Hubbardston, Michigan, that he became acquainted with Erwin F. Smith. Wheeler and Smith were New Yorkers by birth, the former having been educated at Mexico Academy in that state, and at the University of Michigan, and, after service during the Civil War, settled in Michigan to pursue his profession as druggist. Smith had moved with his parents to Michigan at such an early age that practically all of his education was obtained in that state. Wheeler made of his small village drug store at Hubbardston a center of botanical study and activity. Since the store combined the incidental purposes of post office and church center, it was not surprising that a nature-loving youth sixteen years of age, who had just purchased a botany book which he described as "Gray's School and Field Book," heard of Wheeler and his learning in botany. Young Erwin journeyed from his father's farm situated in the Maple River valley three and one-half miles east of Hubbardston and the two soon formed a botanical partnership interested in preparing a catalogue of Michigan plants. When Bailey arrived to visit his erstwhile correspondent the partnership became a triumvirate; one not entirely dissimilar from an equally amateur quartet of botanists located at Hanover, Indiana, John Merle and Stanley Coulter, Charles R. Barnes, and Harvey Young, who at about this time were preparing their historic catalogue dealing with the flora of Indiana. Similarly, their production had gradually emerged from a beginning interest in exploring the local flora, a custom in those years and in some localities a thing of fashion, which expanded until a state-wide flora was planned.

Wheeler was not the scholar who prompted Smith to determine upon botany as a life profession. No less than the far-sighted and learned Professor Volney Morgan Spalding of the University of Michigan was later responsible for transforming Smith's original decision from that of becoming a doctor of medicine to that of applying his ingenious capabilities in plant science research to the study, then comparatively undeveloped, of the lower plant orders, particularly the parasitic fungi and the literature appertaining thereto. Smith's first work, after completing his undergraduate studies at the University of Michigan, some part of which was spent at Michigan Agricultural College during, at least, one summer, was principally mycological in character and illustrates the coordinated relationships between the strong and rapidly developing research in plant pathology, including diseases of agricultural crops caused by bacteria, which ensued during the last decade of the nineteenth and the first decade of the twentieth centuries. Nonetheless, Wheeler, who for twelve years served as an instructor in botany at Michigan Agricultural College and for a number of years was prominent in research at the state agricultural experiment station and with the United States Department of Agriculture, was the scholar, to use Smith's own words, who showed him "how to study flowering plants, opened [his] eyes to the wonders of wood and field and was [his] companion in a thousand delightful rambles." From Wheeler, Smith had also his first lessons in French, a knowledge which formed the basis for Smith's attainments as a linguist, a faculty which enabled him to keep abreast of the accomplishments of plant pathological investigations throughout the world, and in numerous ways stake out new paths with an authentic leadership. As early as 1888, Smith's evident ability came to the notice of William Gilson Farlow of Harvard University. One research triumph after another adorned the career of the skillful young scholar from Michigan. Before two decades had passed Farlow regarded Smith as America's greatest authority on plant diseases. Nor was his admiration and esteem unreciprocated. Smith ranked Farlow with Spalding as chief sources of inspiration and influence in his work. Indeed, on at least one occasion he expressed the belief that Farlow was America's ablest botanist.

Wheeler and Smith's catalogue was first published in an annual report of the state horticultural society, entitled, "Michigan Flora." The following year it was separately printed as a *Catalogue of the Phænogamous and Vascular Cryptogamous Plants of Michigan, Indigenous, Naturalized, and Adventive*.[2] In August, 1881, the *Botanical Gazette* reviewed the work, saying, "There could not well be a finer state, botanically, than Michigan. Cut up as it is into two peninsulas, with its diversified conditions, it seems rich in rare plants. The catalogue is confined to Phanerogams and Vascular Cryptogams and numbers 1,634 species."

Bailey aided his friends not only in explorations but also in preparation of parts of the catalogue. His earliest discoveries in the genus

---

[2] Lansing: W. S. George & Co., State Printers and Binders, 1881.

Rubus around South Haven, particularly along Lake Michigan, in 1880 were stimulated by and incorporated in this notable work.

In July, 1880, Bailey's article, "Michigan Lake Shore Plants," had appeared in the *Botanical Gazette*. Soon Bailey began to publish other articles. "Limits of Michigan Plants" was printed in the *Gazette* in the summer of 1882.

Smith in these early exploratory years had not begun the studies which eventually constituted him the "Dean of American plant pathologists,"[3] an unquestioned authority in fungous and bacterial diseases, and whose investigations and writings in diseases now classed in the virus group became fundamentally significant and pointed the way to more conclusive research. When Smith began to relate his study of botany to agriculture and horticulture, more especially to the study of parasitic fungi and plant diseases, bacterial diseases among plants were scarcely recognized except in a few maladies even by such leading European authorities in cryptogamic botany as Anton De Bary, Robert Hartig, and others. European biology was enjoying a world leadership, thanks to the work of Darwin, Huxley, and other great students of the continent. Only a few decades had passed, however, since such natural phenomena as fermentation, putrefactions, organic decomposition and decay, nitrification, origin of microscopic life, and, indeed, the germ theory of disease had begun to be understood with the requisite exactness to produce a real pathology, whether in humans, animals, or plants. Smith's introduction to the biological world almost coincided with the spread and advancement of knowledge of the role of microorganisms in fermentation and disease, which issued from the great laboratories of Louis Pasteur, Robert Koch, Lister, and dozens of other lesser known experimental scientists in Europe and other parts of the world.

Correlating disease to systematic and experimental studies of lower plant forms presented a challenge which, in a most prominent part, Farlow brought to botanical science in this country when, through instruction and writing, he disseminated knowledge of De Bary's interpretation of the role of fungi in pathology. Smith's departure from taxonomy coincided with a period of years, when more and more the belief was confirmed it was possible to control destructive fungous diseases by recognizing a pathogene and studying out measures to counteract it or them, as the case might be. Environmental studies, stressing soil, climate, etc., were indicated, and before Smith began in 1886 an active employment the most celebrated of pronouncements that certain diseases could be controlled by spray and seed treatments—that of

[3] Herbert Hice Whetzel, *An Outline of the History of Phytopathology* (Philadelphia and London: W. B. Saunders Co., 1918), frontispiece.

Millardet's discovery of bordeaux mixture—would have reached American shores.

Books and study increased Smith's understanding of the natural sciences, stimulating more with every year his interest in its pathology. As early as January, 1869, Professor Thomas Jonathan Burrill had addressed an agricultural conference in Illinois and called attention to the possibilities and need of study in vegetable diseases and the importance of developing increased facilities for microscopic observations of insects and parasitic fungi and their influences in plant disease. The next year he introduced a course of instruction, called "Cryptogamic Botany," at what now is the University of Illinois, and in this course parasitic fungi were made part of the work. In 1873, among other writings of this pioneering period, Burrill published a paper in the *Transactions of the Illinois Horticultural Society* (VII, p. 217) entitled "Aggressive Parasitism of Fungi," in which he advanced a claim, about which there was prevalent dispute for many years, that vegetable parasites were the cause and not simply the results of diseases.

Smith seems to have read the Europeans before he did the Americans. 1884 was the year in which Koch published his model papers on the cause of tuberculosis and his discovery of the cause of Asiatic cholera. "What a year that was!" later confided Smith, "and what enthusiasm these two papers evoked! I remember it all as if it were yesterday, and much of the old thrill comes back! I knew very little about Pasteur in those days, but Robert Koch was my hero, and his influence more than that of any other man decided me to enter pathology and bacteriology." One need but read Smith's paper, "Fifty Years of Pathology," delivered in 1926, and published in 1929 as part of the *Proceedings of the International Congress of Plant Sciences*, to see that Smith's original interest was centered around the great discoveries in human and animal diseases, although the slowly paced forward movements and accomplishments in plant disease study were by no means neglected. Smith in 1884 was still employed by the Michigan Board of Health. He was looking forward to a career as either a teacher of natural sciences or a doctor of medicine. Through the medium of continued work on the *Flora of Michigan*, he had become closely acquainted with Professor Spalding, and frequently while yet living at Lansing he wrote to the learned doctor. His proximity to Michigan Agricultural College was distinctly helpful, as night after night he indefatigably pursued the study of natural sciences, using books borrowed or purchased in this country or ordered from abroad. Utilizing foreign botanical texts and treatises of A. Duchartre, Julius von Sachs, Anton de Bary, Karl von Goebel, and others, to learn the French and German languages, he was preparing himself to satisfy the requirements in natural sciences and linguistics, preliminary to getting in 1886 after one year of university residence a degree of Bachelor of Science in biology at the University of Michigan. While in attendance at the state agricultural college in the summer of 1880, he had been taught plant histology by Dr. Beal, and entomology and zoology by Dr. Cook, whose courses directed to the study of insect pests and their significance economically and practically in agriculture, had been pioneering in American universities and with whom Smith had conducted an entomological correspondence since his youth.

Before 1884, therefore, Smith was not without some university experience and schooling. Furthermore, among his numerous correspondents in systematic botany, both in America and abroad, were other university men, among them, Joseph Charles Arthur, Charles Reid Barnes, John Merle Coulter, and, of course, Bailey and Wheeler, as well as Charles Sprague Sargent, Byron David Halsted, Albert Nelson Prentiss, William A. Henry, Lester F. Ward, and Sereno Watson.

Why animal and human pathology and bacteriology at first attracted Smith more than plant pathology and bacteriology is explained in an address, "Plant Pathology: A Retrospect and Prospect," (*Science*, n.s., xv, no. 381, pp. 601-612), delivered in 1902 as president of the Society for Plant Morphology and Physiology. Smith confided, "Plant pathology was not an attractive profession in those days. When he first desired to make the diseases of plants, or mycology, as we called it, his chosen profession, the speaker well remembers casting his eye over the field very dubiously. There were no places for such workers, and, from the pecuniary side, it was a barren and unsatisfactory prospect." Laboratory methods for the study of fungi and bacteria were "not well developed." No exact and convenient method for obtaining pure cultures existed. "The main thing considered," he said, "was the parasite rather than the host plant, and the technique for the study of both was of the simplest sort. We had no precise fixing and staining methods, no fine microtomes with their yards of serial sections, no synthetic culture media, no elaborate sterilizing ovens and brood chambers, and no apochromatic glass for lenses. 'Pure cultures' were practically unknown, and photography and photomicrography had not yet become arts of daily use in the laboratory. . . ." Except for the work of Dr. Burrill at the University of Illinois and Dr. Farlow at Harvard, and their students, at a few agricultural experiment stations in this country, plant pathology—books, critical studies, teachers, and students—belonged to Europe, quite like, but much less advanced than, medical pathology. In each, the laboratory method of instruction and experimentation was yet to attain its fullest development.

During the early 1870's, matters of national public health had begun to enlist the attention of talented doctors and scholars.[4] The American Public Health Association was formed, and, since the leadership of various state boards of health contributed to promote interests of the national movement, Dr. Robert C. Kedzie, president of the Michigan board for many years after 1877 and a former president of the state medical society in 1874, was prominent in both the American Public Health Association, in fact, its president in 1882, and in the American Medical Association. Smith, while in Lansing, became acquainted with Robert Kedzie, one of Dr. Kedzie's brilliant sons, and, forming a "high opinion both of his manly qualities and of his scholarly attainments," doubtless became acquainted also with Dr. Kedzie. The latter may have been the first person to interest Smith in the work of the state board of health. The first article which Smith contributed to *The School Moderator*, a journal inaugurated in the early 1880's at Grand Rapids, and of which Smith later became editor of a department of science and sanitation, was a review of the state board's report for the year 1880. Since Smith from boyhood was intensely interested in chemistry, attended Michigan Agricultural College during the summer of 1880, where Dr. Kedzie was professor of chemistry, the inference seems not unjustified.[5]

The complete story of the origins of Smith's interest in pathology and bacteriology, strongly influenced and stimulated, as it was, by such leaders in the national public health movement as Dr. Kedzie, Dr. Victor C. Vaughan, Dr. Henry B. Baker, Dr. J. H. Kellogg, and other Michigan scientists and doctors struggling to establish public health, sanitation, and hygiene on a scientific and enduring basis, and with each of whom Smith came in contact during his years at Lansing, will be told in a biography of Smith being prepared by the author of this book.

Substantive origins antedated even the years at Lansing. While a small boy, Erwin's scientific precocity had been evidenced by his purchasing with small savings, and reading, scholarly books on medicine. True, these were years before modern preventive medicine had come into being. Erwin "longed to be a physician," because, to quote his words, "it seemed such a divine thing to relieve pain and prolong life." While a high school student, he had expressed with as much maturity

[4] Wilson George Smillie, *Public Health Administration in the United States*, New York, The Macmillan Company, 1940, pp. 16-18, concerning the founding of the American Public Health Association in 1870-1872 and citing and quoting from M. P. Ravenel, *A Half Century of Public Health*, Amer. Pub. Health Assn., 1921, and Stephen Smith's "A Half Century of Public Health," edited by Ravenel.

[5] Concerning Robert Clark Kedzie, see the *Dictionary of American Biography* x, p. 277, the *National Cyclopedia of Biography*, viii, p. 488, concerning Smith's acquaintance with the Kedzies, *The School Moderator* (Grand Rapids, Michigan) ii, p. 24, concerning Dr. Kedzie's presidency of Am. Pub. Health Assn., *American Public Health Association Year Book*, 1930-1931 (New York), "Past Presidents," p. 8, *Michigan School Moderator* iii, p. 9, *The College Speculum*, April 1, 1882, p. 44.

as his elders, his beliefs with reference to the interdependence and interrelationship of the animal and vegetable kingdom; that "the life principle" in forest, field, and stream was manifested in "a thousandfold variety of forms from the mute gray lichen on the rock, to the god-like forms and capacities of the man who bends over it in admiration"; and that the study of their mechanisms and endless forms in the "broad arms" of the great sciences which wrapped up all that had been said or could be said in relation to plants and animals was "intensely interesting." Darwinian evolution, to this high school pupil, had wrought a scientific revolution, and, in less than two decades since the *Origin of Species* was published, this youthful student, whose entire life thus far had been spent in remote towns and on farms along civilization's frontier, was insisting that the study of "beast and bird and fish," as well as plants and crops, must be reinterpreted in the new light and in "intimate relation to one all wise God whose work we are."

Young Erwin graduated in 1880 from the high school at Ionia, Michigan, having earned part of his way by serving as a guard at the Ionia State Reformatory. For a while he taught at a district school, and for a year or more, was keeper of the reformatory, where prison conditions accentuated his already formed interest in sanitation and hygiene.

Science thrilled him. The microscope revealed to him "a strange diminutive wonderland" more startling than the fairy tales of Grimm, the travels of Gulliver, or Aladdin and the Arabian nights.

When Louis Pasteur discovered and demonstrated the cause of "splenic fever" in animals, the anthrax bacillus distributed by earthworms, and produced an immunological remedy in a vaccine made from an attenuated culture, Smith, still a resident of Ionia and not yet formally employed by the Michigan Board of Health, hailed the triumph as an anticipation that in time "a multitude of trained observers both in America and Europe," followers in the "great field" which Pasteur had opened, would "discover and stamp out the germs of yellow, typhoid and miasmatic fevers, by and by, and . . . reduce the dreadful mortality of diphtheria and scarletina." For, Pasteur was "evidently on the right track. . . ."

The International Medical Conference of London held in August, 1881, honored Pasteur. The study of bacterial diseases of animals had real beginnings with the anthrax researches of Pasteur and Robert Koch. Pasteur climaxed his series of epoch-making triumphs over chicken cholera, anthrax, measles of swine, and boils, to name a few, by vaccinating and saving the life in 1885 of the boy Joseph Meister, bitten severely by a mad dog and suffering from hydrophobia. But, until then, their direct application to the saving of human life, within the hopes and prediction which Smith expressed, was not proven, except to doctors and students who allowed some scientific imagination and logic to function. At the London Conference, furthermore, was demonstrated before Pasteur, John Lister, and other dignitaries, what Smith later characterized as perhaps the most potent contribution, however simple it was, which advanced bacteriology as a science—Koch's poured plate method of obtaining pure culture of microorganisms.

Michigan, still an agricultural and forested state, was harassed with numerous epidemics of human diseases. These were frontier years and the state had neither an abundant nor thoroughly organized medical profession. The Michigan Board of Health, therefore, concentrated what strength and influence it had in warring foremost with human diseases. Appropriations were small; indeed, during the 1880's the board had to fight to survive, and, because of its limited personnel, its activities had to be somewhat restricted. Sometime about the middle of the year 1882, Smith left Ionia and became correspondence clerk of the board at Lansing. In his new position, he collected and systematized useful data concerning the state's medical profession, gathered statistical information concerning diseases most prevalent and their location throughout the state, taught a class in human physiology, wrote on sanitary and hygienic subjects, participated in meetings of the state teachers' association, and in many other activities, the while finding time outside of work hours to study science and keep pace with the new knowledge at home and abroad. The board's secretary, Henry B. Baker, saw in Smith a forceful, upright character of strong capabilities. Baker sensed the value of the new European discoveries to the state's economy and progress. On good authority, it is said, he in part was instrumental in sending Dr. Victor C. Vaughan, a member of the board, and Frederick V. Novy in 1888 to Berlin to study bacteriology under Koch with a view to opening a laboratory of hygiene and develop the notable program in medical bacteriology at the University of Michigan, for which each today is famous.

As early as 1882, Baker's report as secretary took notice of recent experiments of Koch and others which "made it appear very probable that consumption is caused by a microscopic bacillus," a reproducing organism, which communicates the disease "from one person to another, and from one animal to another," by means of this bacillus. In time American research would differentiate human from bovine tuberculosis, and the scientist responsible for the achievement would be one of Smith's closest friends, Theobald Smith. It is likewise to be noticed that Novy, a classmate of Erwin Smith during his year at the University of Michigan, became one of several persons who urged Erwin Smith to study plant diseases—peach yellows, specifically—from the bacterial stand-point.

Smith in 1882 definitely had begun to study the bacteria. During his high school years, a wise principal, Anson DeWolf, had permitted him wide latitude in his studies. This unprecedented but sagacious policy must have been followed by Dr. Baker during Smith's years at Lansing, and later, by the faculty of the University of Michigan, when, because Dr. Spalding regarded Smith "a rare man, one of the very few genuine investigators who turn up in the course of a decade," the faculty agreed to examine Smith and accredit him with three years of college work. Smith had become acquainted with Dr. J. B. Steere of the university faculty, in fact, had published in his department of science and sanitation of the *School Moderator* some articles entitled "Lessons in Zoology," on birds and reptiles, and papers on other species were planned for publication, but in 1883 Smith resigned from his position with the *Moderator*. On June 5, 1885, Dr. Vaughan of the university's medical school faculty informed Smith, "I can pass you on the course in Sanitary Science," and that year, 1885-1886, Smith entered the university for his senior year. That summer he spent much time in preparatory study and of a number of books ordered, at least three were on bacteria and yeast fungi, on microorganisms and disease. In February, he had ordered a new German botany by Eduard Strasburger. Physiological botany, and the study of parasitic fungi, in relation to agriculture, were to prepare him someday to occupy a chair in natural history "in some first class institution." He, however, did not neglect his earlier formed interest in bacteriology.

For the October, 1885, issue of *Michigan Horticulturist*, he reviewed "Recent literature concerning pear blight," a summary of results of Burrill's and Arthur's researches on the first plant disease proved in this country or the world to be of bacterial origin. Two years earlier, in the May 31, 1883, issue of the *School Moderator*, Smith had reviewed a "very satisfactory account" in English "of the nature and organization, effects, and classification of" the bacteria. Over in Germany in 1880 a treatise on bacteria by Georg Winter had appeared as a part of the total publication of Die Pilze of Rabenhorst's Kryptogamen flora, a volume bearing date of 1884. Burrill had translated a portion of this and included it in a paper entitled, "The Bacteria," presented in 1882 as a part of the eleventh report of the Illinois Industrial University. Interestingly enough, Burrill styled "Anthrax of fruit trees" a paper on "Fire Blight of Pear and Twig Blight of Apple Trees," given in August, 1880, before Section B, Natural History, of the American Association for the Advancement of Science; and this was his first paper on this subject to a national scientific organization, his first two communications being made to the Illinois State Horticultural Society. For the July number, 1881, of the *American Naturalist* (xv, p. 527). Burrill prepared an article, "Bacteria as a Cause of Disease in Plants." In this, after describing the bacterial origin of pear and apple twig blight, he added, "I am now able to add the 'yellows' of the peach with much confidence, without, however, the full investigation given to the former disease." Burrill's scientific caution was astute. Peach yellows, of which later Smith uncovered much new knowledge but few final conclusions and no solution, is known now to be a virus, and not bacterial, origin. Virus diseases of plants then were not established in science. Burrill, like Smith, possessed a good reading knowledge of German and French. Naturally, therefore, little that was later published in Europe in bacteriology, animal or plant, escaped them. Unfortunately for science, but to the advantage of the university and its instruction in science, particularly the development of experimental laboratory facilities, Burrill's abilities were much required for administrative matters. Nevertheless, the two great names linked with the history of plant bacteriology and pathology in America are Burrill and Smith.

That Smith's study of the bacteria began soon after his employment by the Michigan Board of Health is shown not only by his journal but also by his published writing. In the November 30, 1882, issue of the *School Moderator*, he included a short account of these microorganisms, in which he observed that the question of spontaneous generation of living forms could be regarded as "settled in the negative by the researches of Tyndall and Pasteur." The adult, mature scientist Smith would qualify conclusions, authenticate or cite authority for his every belief, and require the most conclusive proof before asserting the microorganic origins and dissemination of diseases. Smith commended to his readers a translation by Dr. George M. Sternberg of Antoine Magnian's book on the bacteria, written in French, the translation published in 1880. Smith cautioned that new discoveries had been made since then. Sternberg later became surgeon-general of the United States Army, president in 1887 of the American Public Health Association, and in 1897 president of the American Medical Association.

In 1886 Adolf Mayer in Holland disclosed that tobacco mosaic was a communicable disease and, although this was later, like the peach yellows, shown to be due to a filterable virus—the first virus disease elaborated, Smith believed—as late as July 23, 1892, Mayer had to admit that no microorganism had been isolated from affected plants. Virus diseases, including curly top of sugar beet, were written about during the last two decades of the century. But research well into the twentieth century was required to arrive at anything like a complete understanding of their exact nature, origin, and dissemination. Mayer's paper of 1886 on tobacco mosaic created little stir among the small group of plant pathologists in the United States during the 1880's. Even far-seeing botanists had "generally overlooked" so important a disclosure as Mayer's. Smith wrote to him and, receiving a reply, reviewed the former's work of some six years previous in the fourth volume of the *Journal of Mycology*, published by the section of vegetable pathology of the United States Department of Agriculture. Other diseases in wheat, oats, barley, clover, potatoes, corn, sorghum, hops, beets, grasses, and other farm crops, including one or two of claimed bacterial origin, provided impetus to the study and treatment of plant diseases. Their story must be omitted from this book, because each has its own narrative and individual workers selected specialties even during these years, although it must be added that the era of real scientific specialization in plant disease study had not begun. Students specialized in a few diseases more because of a scarcity of specialists than specialties.

While at the university, Smith took for study "an interesting group of parasitic fungi"—*Peronosporaceae*. In December, 1885, in the *Michigan Crop Report*, he published an article on the potato rot, a part of which was reprinted the following year in the annual report of the Wisconsin Agricultural Experiment Station. By May, 1886, he had ready to publish a paper on grape rot. Spalding and he met together once or twice a week and read German and French literature. In November, 1885, in addition to studying trigonometry and advanced physics, he was spending much time in the botanical laboratory examining fungi microscopically "in fresh and alcoholic material," and, in his spare time continuing research on "the relations of sewerage and water supply to the death-rate in cities"—a subject on which he had written and gathered data while in Lansing with the State Board of Health.

The science of plant pathology during the late 1880's in the United States, hardly as many years as medicine was centuries old, though with not more than a half dozen real specialists and not much literature to draw on from Europe where workers were more numerous and research facilities better, could list, according to a public utterance by Spalding, some three dozen diseases of cultivated plants in which the structure, habits, and mode of attack by a parasite, and its effects, were known, and means of combating them indicated. The conclusions were based on Felix von Thümen's *Die Bekämpfung der Pilzkrankheiten unserer Culturgewächse*, published in Vienna in 1886, and Spalding believed the book illustrated how definite scientific knowledge, both in America and abroad, had begun to replace "vague theories and uncertain experiments."

Most important among the diseases of farm crops were rusts and smuts of grains; diseases of the grape vine; diseases of orchard crops, the pear, apple, and peach; and in garden crops such destructive maladies as spot disease of strawberry leaves, the orange rust of raspberry and blackberry leaves, the cane rust of raspberry and blackberry, had been studied in the United States, and definite progress achieved. Results were both creditable and encouraging for the future.

Several principal centers of scholarly instruction came into prominence during this pioneering period of plant disease research, each center combining the two chief trends—that which stressed taxonomy and life histories of parasitic fungi and algae, and that which leaned more decidedly to the study of treatments for diseases of cultivated plants. Should anyone maintain that Dr. Farlow at Harvard emphasized the former trend to the exclusion of the latter, the list of his students, and his published writings, should be examined. Among his students were such leaders in experimental research as Byron David Halsted, Charles Edwin Bessey, William Trelease, Louis Hermann Pammel, Joseph Charles Arthur, Hermann von Schrenk, and others, each of whom, when in the employ of a university or experiment station, or both, helped to make the study of "insect pests" and fungi scientific, practical, and of economic significance, the while not failing experimental phases of the work. The work of each of these men will be referred to in this book. One of them, Von Schrenk, after obtaining his Bachelor of Science degree under Atkinson at Cornell University in 1893, and his Master of Arts degree in 1894 under Farlow at Harvard, became instructor in plant diseases at the Shaw School of Botany in St. Louis. In this, there was also a connection with Washington University, and when the Mississippi Valley Laboratory of the United States Bureau of Plant Industry was located in that city, Von Schrenk was constituted pathologist in charge. In 1895 he had studied in Europe with Robert Hartig, and there is much reason for regarding Von Schrenk as the first forest pathologist of America. Certainly his studies of cypress and pine, and diseases of conifer races, as well as the changes of wood fibers and cells due to fungous agencies, were both pioneering and of much value economically and from the standpoint of scientific advancement in forestry.

Spalding had been trained both in zoology and botany at the University of Michigan. During these years no one questioned the American leadership of Harvard University in botany. Farlow's leadership in cryptogamic botany was practically the equivalent of Gray's in phanerogamic botany, which says much. Some very important contributions, recognized as sustaining all the qualities of leadership, had issued from the cryptogamic laboratory under Farlow's direction. During the last half of the 1870's, Farlow wrote on the potato rot, the American grape-vine mildew, on onion smut, on diseases of fruit-bearing trees, of forest trees, and fungous diseases generally, not to exclude his researches continued over many years on species of Peronospora and Cystopus, and other subjects. Farlow's study of the black knot of plum and cherry impressed Spalding as having traced for the first time the life history, nature, and development of the disease and offered methods of combating it.

Most notable, however, from a scientific as well as practical standpoint, a research evoking the high praise and enthusiasm of Burrill and other students, was Farlow's paper published in 1880 in the anniversary memoirs of the Boston Society of Natural History as the leading contribution, "The Gymnosporangia or cedar apples of the United States." Notes on this and kindred subjects followed during a number of years, especially in 1885, when he concentrated study on the same group. Halsted during 1886-1887 supplemented Farlow's work, and the results of his research were published by a bulletin of the Iowa Agricultural College. Roland Thaxter, who, before becoming mycologist of the Connecticut Agricultural Experiment Station from 1888-1891, was an assistant in biology at Harvard and associated with Farlow, obtained additional results in 1887 and 1889, and by the end of the decade the connection between several species of Gymnosporangium and Roestelia were established, to which was later added work by Pammel, and by his students G. W. Carver, and F. C. Stewart who also took graduate study under Farlow. By the time of Spalding's appraisal of Farlow's completed study, the facts were fairly well before him. Spalding regarded Farlow's contribution on the black knot of plum and cherry as "one of the most complete and satisfactory" studies which had appeared in America. But still more important were Farlow's researches on the orchard rusts.

Careful culture study to determine the life histories of fungi and their development cycles was brought to America in Farlow's first experiments with the Gymnosporangia. In a few words, the methods by which De Bary and Woronin had arrived at their epoch-making results in the study of the potato blight and club root of cabbage were introduced to American research. The roles fungi play in the production of two obscure plant diseases were made known to American scientists. And Farlow explained away another puzzling circumstance. Orchard rusts in some parts of the country had proven highly destructive to apple trees, and the fungi responsible were found to infest cedar trees during a period of their cycle of development, and to pass from these to apple trees. Certain varieties of crab apple, especially wild varieties, were found to be more subject to infection than others. Farlow, demonstrating the merit and influence of study under Anton De Bary, thus by establishing from many years of research the infectious agency's life history, the source and time of infection, was enabled to recommend preventive measures. Either, he advised, cut out the red cedar trees growing near apple orchards, or select for orchard planting apple varieties resistant or those least susceptible to attack by the infection. If the situation revealed the presence of wild and/or infected crab apples, these should be removed.

Doubtless, this study influenced Erwin F. Smith. In July, 1887, he was appointed a special agent of the United States Department of Agriculture to investigate and report on peach yellows. Each of Farlow's recommendations, and more, since Smith's researches on the peach yellows lasted almost a decade and followed numerous angles of field and laboratory investigation, were included in Smith's recommended procedure. Farlow was dealing with a fungous disease; Smith, with a disease caused by a virus, which, though he budded and grafted peach tree stock and reproduced the disease, failed to be isolated, for reasons similar to the failure thus far to prove a causal parasite of tobacco mosaic. Smith also proved the communicability of peach yellows.

Smith's work with the United States Department of Agriculture began in 1886 as assistant mycologist to F. Lamson Scribner, in charge of the section of mycology in George Vasey's division of botany. At first, Smith was employed to work on fungous diseases of plants. Within a few months, however, he requested to be, and was, placed in charge of the most difficult problem confronting the work of the department in the study of plant diseases—the peach yellows—a problem much more difficult than the rusts and mildews, in extreme need of solution because of its threat to whole peach-growing industries in certain northern states, definitely a challenge to the most confidently ambitious scientist.

Scribner was a graduate of the Maine State College of Agriculture and Mechanic Arts. In May, 1885, he had entered the department as assistant botanist and soon thereafter was placed in charge of the mycological section referred to in the preceding paragraph. Presently, we shall review briefly the departmental history[6] leading to the establishment of the section of vegetable pathology on a recognized legal basis, with its own appropriation, chief, and personnel, and which won for the department world-wide recognition. The section of mycology under Scribner, indeed, the section of vegetable pathology since under his regime the name was changed, was created in response principally to

---

[6] See a recently published book on the entire subject, by T. Swann Harding, *Two Blades of Grass*, A History of Scientific Development in the U.S. Department of Agriculture, University of Oklahoma Press, Norman, 1947.

a memorial of the American Association for the Advancement of Science. At its Ann Arbor meeting, a committee presented its historic report, "The Encouragement of Researches on the Health and Diseases of Plants," and Smith may have heard this and visualized immediately the tremendous potentialities in plant disease work by the federal government. If so, he never lost this vision, for, his entire working life thereafter was spent with the United States Department of Agriculture. Scribner specialized in the study of viticultural diseases, in 1887 accompanying Pierre Viala on a considerable part of his exploration of the continent made for the same purpose in the interest of his native land, France.

It was the remedial and control methods, adduced from exact research and study of every reported and important plant disease, research utilizing field exploration and outdoor and indoor laboratory study, by state agencies as well as the federal government's work under Scribner and later Beverly T. Galloway—including improvements in apparatus to apply insecticides and fungicides, notably Millardet's bordeaux mixture—which gave rise to a chief point of difference between the old and the "new horticulture," the cause of which Bailey later would so capably espouse both in research and writings. Bailey was a product of Michigan Agricultural College and Smith of the same college and the University of Michigan. Although the two men were never formally associated together, the bond of their botanical friendship, founded in Michigan and influential throughout the entire career of each, had provided scientific horticulture and agriculture with one of its greatest boons.

Bailey's college years added abundantly to his factual knowledge. His capacity for observation was enlarged. His excellent sense of discernment was sharpened. During his senior year the Natural History Society, with a proud list of past presidents which included the Kedzies, Byron David Halsted, Beal, Garfield, Cook, George T. Fairchild, and others, elected Bailey president. Faculty and students joined in the maintenance of this society. It possessed a museum and library, and held regular meetings on the second Friday of each month. Practically every honor possible was conferred on Bailey. Many times he spoke before the society, as he had done previously before the pomological societies of South Haven and the state. At times he read papers, as, for example, one given before the October 21, 1881, meeting on "How Certain Plants Prepare for Spring."

At this time Bailey began to travel, going south into Kentucky and beyond. Always he observed any agricultural improvements or needs.

Finally came the writing of his last important editorial for the

Speculum. He chose as his subject the results of agricultural education. In strolls around South Haven when he had pondered the possibilities of an educational scheme which might enrich more fully the lives of rural folk, he had thought in terms of country life. But little of a specific and concrete nature had been contemplated. During his college years, however, he had begun to reflect on points of practical application. In 1879, when Bailey was a junior, George T. Fairchild, father of David Fairchild, was professor of English literature and college librarian.

Eugene Davenport, the great dean who from the years 1895-1922 developed the college of agriculture at the University of Illinois, when a member of the senior class at Michigan Agricultural, was assigned by Professor Fairchild to correct freshman themes. He has related, "One day I stumbled upon a freshman essay beautifully written, a rarity indeed. After a few minutes I remarked that here was something out of my class. [Fairchild] reached for it across the desk, read it through without a word, looked up and asked if I happened to know that freshman. I replied that I did not know him and had never seen him but once when I sold him a chair for his room in the dormitory. 'Well,' he remarked, 'that boy will either make a great man or he won't amount to shucks.' 'That boy,' was L. H. Bailey. . . ."

Fairchild later went to Kansas State Agricultural College as president. But before his departure Bailey often conversed with him. Why couldn't matters of agricultural education be presented in terms of statistics? Bailey would say. Fairchild would answer there were no such statistics in existence. Bailey importuned him to write a book and illustrate it with agricultural notes and statistics. Years later when Dr. Fairchild wrote *Rural Wealth and Welfare,* he attributed to Bailey a large share of credit for suggesting the book's plan and contents.

Bailey's flair for gathering statistical information showed itself more than once and was evident in his last important *Speculum* editorial:

Agricultural colleges are founded for the purpose of imparting a knowledge of those sciences which pertain especially to agriculture and the industrial arts related to it. The extent to which this purpose is carried out determines the value of these schools as educators of the farmer and gardener. One of the best means of judging of the merits of a college and its work is by noting the extent and efficiency with which the graduates practice the principles that have been taught them. Let us, then, examine the list of the alumni of this College and see how well it has filled its mission. . . . Sixty-two per cent of them are pursuing those professions which are subjects of special study in this College. Of the graduates, forty per cent are farmers, who are doing much to elevate their class of work by making it more remunerative—in a financial way by practicing the most improved methods of farming; in an intellectual way, by making further experiments in their work. No other school of its kind can show so favorable a result. . . .

Liberty Hyde Bailey, 1882   Walter Tennyson Swingle, 1893

David G. Fairchild, 1893   Herbert John Webber, 1899

Four Young Scientists

The editorial concluded by a statistical analysis of similar figures representing other colleges and one university.

In 1881 the United States Department of Agriculture, under a new commissioner, was initiating its great program of bringing together all important agricultural agencies. The new commissioner had continued his predecessor's work—investigating agricultural conditions of the Pacific coast, developing artesian well work in Colorado, experimenting with the cultivation of the tea plant, concluding the study of the manufacture of sugar from sorghum, observing contagious diseases in cattle, estimating needs and opportunities of forestry, testing textile fibers, investigating injurious insects, and other projects. The new commissioner had summoned delegates of state societies and land-grant colleges to convene in Washington and consider topics such as agricultural education, animal husbandry, and horticulture. Experimental culture or propagation of the pineapple, banana, guava, chocolate, cinnamon, coffee, pepper, ginger, arrowroot, "and many fiber-producing and starch-yielding plants" was advocated. Soon orange importations of the department would be regarded as the best raised in California. Grape growers of Texas, Florida, and other southern states, in increasing numbers, were finding "good promise of success" with foreign importations. New varieties of citrus were being sought with a view to introduction. By 1883 the Japanese persimmon was regarded as successfully introduced;[7] and by 1886 "Kafir corn," a grain sorghum eventually to give rise to a thriving industry in the western dry land areas, was being distributed by federal and state authorities.[8]

Since 1862 William Saunders had served the United States Department of Agriculture as botanist and superintendent of propagating gardens. Plant introduction work which he inaugurated in many directions improved agriculture, quantitatively and qualitatively, east, south, west, and north, throughout the United States. His work, when contrasted with the later world scope of the Office of Seed and Plant Introduction, was a miniature anticipation of what was to follow; but it was foundational, pointed the way to what might be accomplished from large scale, systematic, coordinated efforts in this direction. The first bulletin issued by the department was prepared by Saunders and reported the objects and aims of the propagating garden, also cataloguing the plant material available for distribution. Not content with building up a propagating garden, Saunders gradually established an arboretum on the mall at Washington—an extensive collection of trees

[7] Commissioner's Report, pp. 1-16; also the Commissioner's Report of Nov. 25, 1881, p. 5.
[8] Carleton R. Ball, "The Grain Sorghums," *Yearbook*, U.S. Dep't of Agric., 1913, pp. 221-225.

and shrubs adapted to the climate and soil of the middle-Atlantic tide-water region, and for many years its prestige vied favorably with the Arnold Arboretum of Jamaica Plain, Massachusetts. Forest studies, as well as horticulturists, came to the department grounds to study growth rates of tree species and their uses and adaptability to various purposes. So important was this regarded by the commissioner of agriculture in 1876, the year of the Philadelphia Centennial Exposition and about when Congress appropriated funds to constitute a forestry agent within the department, that the commissioner reported on these matters specially to the President.

In 1876 Saunder's report as superintendent of gardens, in addition to discussing many ornamental plants, elaborated the "fitness for cultivation" or lack of it in the United States of varieties of coffee, india-rubber, cinchona, eucalyptus, European olive, Japan persimmon, vanilla, paraguay tea, chinese tea, and hedge plants; in 1878, figs, apricot, native and foreign grapes, orange, lemon, and other citrus varieties, as well as orchard planting;[9] and during the 1880's his official title became horti-culturist, pomologist, and landscape gardener, as well as superintendent of gardens and grounds.

David Fairchild, to whom belongs a principal share of credit for the notable further development of the department's coordinated work in plant introduction and plant breeding, and whose first shipment of foreign plants to America was of Corsican citron scions and took place in later years of the century, has written books, appropriately dealing with his life and the later development of this work. Two paragraphs, from one of his articles bearing on history, relate the older and later effectively:

There is nothing more picturesque in agriculture than the role played by the discovery or introduction of a new variety. The vines of the Chautauqua grape belt, producing annually 200,000,000 pounds of grapes, come almost entirely from cuttings of a seedling planted in Concord, Mass., 68 years ago. Both the Elberta and Belle varieties of the peach, which have earned many millions for fruit growers since the fall of 1870, originated in Georgia from the same tree of an imported Chinese cling peach. The founding of miles of orange groves such as the world never saw before is the result of the importation of a single bunch of scions from Bahia, Brazil.

These are familiar examples of discoveries in the agricultural world comparable to the inventions of the telephone and the typesetting machine in the world of technology. And yet Ephraim Bull, who discovered the Con-

[9] Reports, U.S. Dept. of Agric., 1876, pp. 61-73; *idem*, 1878, pp. 194-207; 1883, pp. 181-196. Concerning William Saunders, his life and work, see "William Saunders," by the editor, George William Hill. Saunders's picture as the frontispiece, a brief chronology of principal events of his life, and a note of his death are set forth. *Yearbook, idem,* for 1900, pp. 625-630, and p. 42. The stories of many of Saunders's plant introductions are contained in the article. See, also, William Alton Taylor's biographical account of Saunders in the *Dictionary of American Biography,* and authorities cited.

cord grape; the Rumph brothers, who originated the Elberta and Belle peaches; and William Saunders, who introduced the Bahia navel orange, received no financial advantage from their discoveries. . . .[10]

In 1869 Saunders introduced into this country the trifoliate orange, *Citrus trifoliata*.[11] As a writer on garden and farm subjects, as a landscape architect of many famous American grounds, including Gettysburg cemetery, as the introducer to American cultivation of many economically valuable plants and varieties of tree species brought from almost every part of the globe (notably, the kaki or Japan persimmon during the middle 1870's; *Eucalyptus globulus*, the Australian blue-gum tree; and species of camphor), the name of this Scotchman, who, for a while after arriving in the United States, was a partner of the far-seeing and studious Thomas Meehan, is deservingly illustrious in the history of American plant science study. A feat of pioneering importance of the early 1870's was his already referred to importation from Russia, and later distribution through the northern states, of hardy apple varieties, some 300 at least. It is said that as early as 1868 he recommended sulphur dusting of grapes to control mildew and rot and thus aroused interest in therapeutical remedies. Saunders, as a student, was prolific, indulging in many types of garden, field, and landscape work, and authoring during his career some 3,000 titles.

These were years when the United States Department of Agriculture was shaping its future courses of action. Not every section of the Union agreed on matters of federal sovereignty, and what could, as well as what should, be done had to be decided. Little question existed as to whether diseased plants were within the federal province of research. The principal impediment has been shown to have been the lack of available trained personnel. Consequently, plant pathological, rather, mycological, investigation moved forward slowly. In the Commissioner's Report for 1873 had been set forth results of some "Microscopic Investigations" conducted by Thomas Taylor, microscopist. These had a horticultural bearing, but not too much recognition as such from such authorities as Farlow, Smith, Burrill, and other scholars. Taylor selected diseases of cultivated plants, prepared a report of about 26 pages on hawthorn-blight, potato blight and rot, black-knot, orange blight, apple-speck, or rot, and onion rust, each disease important enough in itself, but requiring a student of plants as well as microscopes to describe or solve them.

Encouragement that a national service of plant disease investigation

[10] "Plant Introduction for the Plant Breeder," *Yearbook, idem,* for 1911, pp. 411-422, quotation at p. 412.
[11] Herbert J. Webber and Walter T. Swingle, "New Citrus Creations of the Department of Agriculture," *Yearbook, idem,* for 1904, p. 224.

would become adequately established found little basis in fact year after year during the 1880's. When the commissioner of agriculture, Norman J. Colman, published his annual report in 1885, the assistant botanist, F. Lamson Scribner, presented a "chapter," which outlined "certain fungous diseases of plants, with remarks upon the application of remedies." The information contained, however, drew heavily upon the learning of Dr. Farlow and a corps of his students, Trelease in Wisconsin, Bessey in Iowa, Halsted, Peck, and others. Just the same, botanist George Vasey of the Department of Agriculture appointed Scribner to take charge of the section of mycology and investigate "diseases of fruits and fruit trees, grains and other useful plants, caused by fungi." Arthur and others, more interested in experimental than herbarium research among diseases of plants, lost heart, and thought the years of their efforts within the American Association for the Advancement of Science to secure establishment of a bureau or division to study plant diseases "tabled." In July, 1885, a "convention of influential agriculturists" at Washington, plus the memorial of the association which sought federal action on behalf of vegetable pathological research, made Commissioner Colman thoroughly aware of the national demand, and in Beverly T. Galloway the needed leader to serve as chief of the section was found.

Scribner by no means was finished with his constructive contributions to plant science work of the federal government. After a period of teaching at the University of Tennessee, during which time also he served as botanist and director of the Tennessee Agricultural Experiment Station, Scribner, as a recognized leading authority on grasses, returned to Washington in 1894 to take charge of the important duties of agrostologist, including investigations of forage plants. As a part of his work as chief of the division of agrostology, he maintained a garden of economic plants, became a hearty supporter of plant introduction work, was noted as one of America's ablest arrangers of produce exhibits and, of course, was principally responsible for building the celebrated grass herbarium, commenced by his former superior, George Vasey. Scribner was an able taxonomist and, later, developing a pronounced interest in tropical horticulture and agriculture, extended his work to the Philippine Islands.

The scientific immaturity of "vegetable pathology" in America during the early 1880's can perhaps be best portrayed by an illustration. It seems almost incredible that not until the years 1883-1884 was the word "fungicide," as a descriptive term in scientific research, known in American pathological literature. Insecticides, notably Paris green, London purple, and arsenious acid or white arsenic, were known and used, in large part through the efforts of entomologists, C. V. Riley most prominently. But the story of currency given the word "fungicide" has been related by so representative a worker among plants as Byron David Halsted in a letter to Galloway and dated April 5, 1893:

. . . While in the editorial office of the *American Agriculturist*, and after having studied fungi to some extent with Dr. Farlow, I endeavored to carry out certain recommendations, particularly the use of sulphur for the powdery mildews. During that time I had used with myself the word fungicide taking the cue from the word insecticide. In 1883 at the request of the American Pomological Society I prepared a paper entitled "The white mildews," which was another name for the Erysipheae. This was for the meeting held in Philadelphia . . . and in it I used the word fungicide, and underscored it so that it appeared in italics. . . . Like many other of the papers at that meeting mine was not read, in fact almost no papers were read at the meeting, the time being taken with discussions of various and new fruits, etc., and I remember asking some of the horticulturists present if they had ever seen or used the word fungicide, and none of them knew of such a word. It was new to me and I used it with that understanding. . . .

It may be added, furthermore, that Halsted, in his historic paper, "A Tomato Disease," presented at the fifth annual meeting of the Society for the Promotion of Agricultural Science held at Philadelphia, September 1-2, 1884, was quoted as having said: "If it is established that the rot first appears upon the foliage, some fungicide may be applied to the leaves with the desired results. It would certainly do no harm to use flowers of sulphur in much the same manner that it is applied to grape-vines, roses, etc., as an effective remedy for the mildew."

Of course, in greatest view, these years were being utilized by leaders more to invade every corner of the continent with the movement which made for a progressive and scientific agriculture in broadest scope. Experimental field researches had been inaugurated. Some experimental laboratories had been established. But the new knowledge of agricultural science was still being organized, still being promoted. One might point to the appeals of Eugene Woldemar Hilgard in California. In 1882 the *Atlantic Monthly* published an article by him on "Progress in Agriculture by Education and Government Aid." The seed and plant distribution of the department, Hilgard maintained, had been enormously overdone. More attention should be given plant introductions from foreign countries—"new species and varieties of valuable culture plants adapted to varied conditions of different portions of the Union." He praised the department's excellent crop and commercial statistics, their worthy monographs and treatises. Its special work, involving experiment and investigation, in entomology was useful and commendable. The chemical, sorghum, and forage investigations were valuable. However, he observed, "It is curious that examinations of soils have been almost entirely excluded from the list of subjects, under a somewhat antiquated impression of the inutility of wasting one's efforts on so complex and difficult a matter. . . . Considering that the question of soil exhaustion and maintenance of fertility by the cheapest means is fast becoming the prominent one in the States east of the Mississippi River, it can hardly be doubtful that the examination of this subject is among the most important services the Agricultural Department could render to practical agriculture."

Forestry, too, should be given continued and close attention. Incidentally, he praised Charles Sprague Sargent's work in the census taking of 1880. The agricultural department of the national government, Hilgard urged, should lead in "practical and scientific experiments" as defined in the congressional act creating the department. It should become "the leading centre of agricultural information and progress, gathering up all the disconnected threads, now scattered from the Atlantic to the Pacific, into a radiating net-work, conveying back and forth messages of mutual information and encouragement, by deed as well as by word. . . ."

What a prophet Hilgard was! A man of scientific and practical vision. He was the cousin of George Engelmann, the son of a Bavarian chief justice at Zweibrücken. Raised on an Illinois farm, educated in America and Europe, he became a chemist of great ability and a professor at both the universities of Mississippi and Michigan.

It was into a remarkable comradeship of scientific men that as an agriculturist Liberty Hyde Bailey, junior, graduated from Michigan Agricultural College in 1882, the same year and almost to the same month as the publication of Hilgard's article. Years would pass before the work of Hilgard and other soils men would receive official government recognition, and not always would Hilgard and government scientists agree entirely on matters of soil study. Yet friendship and cordial relations always continued. The differences were scientific, never personal.

Nationalization of the experiment station movement in 1888 elevated all scientific experimental work to an enterprise of nation-wide proportions, although the state units were retained and no central national station was ever organized. The function of the federal government would remain coordinative and directive. Paternalism in government would bring together the work of the great agricultural agencies—the experiment stations and colleges—from which developed the Association of American Agricultural Colleges and Experiment Stations.

Membership in Phi Beta Kappa was not conferred on Bailey until later—at Cornell University. Phi Beta Kappa had no chapter at Michigan Agricultural College. Bailey's social fraternity had been Phi Delta Theta, the same fraternity which his friend, Erwin Frink Smith, joined while at the University of Michigan.

After graduating from college, Bailey returned to South Haven to decide finally what was to be his future life work. Should journalism, a subordinate interest, prevail over his devotion to agriculture? Much was to be said in favor of the choice of journalism. It was more practical and in some respects more certain. Bailey had found that he enjoyed writing. Giving expression to his talent for presenting both the spoken and written word he had discovered was pleasurable.

His brother, Marcus, was living in Illinois. In September, 1882, Bailey wrote to Smith that he had left Michigan and was exploring botanically in Wisconsin while on his way to Springfield, Illinois. By October, he had crossed into Illinois, and from Belvidere he wrote Smith of his visit with Michael Schuck Bebb, the American authority on willows:

> . . . I was over to Rockford the other day, where . . . I had the pleasure of making the acquaintance of M. S. Bebb. That reminded me of Carex Bebbii, etc., but more especially of endlessly-entangled Salix. Nothing seemed tangled to him however. He took me through his great, beautiful *Herbarium Salicum*,[12] explaining its intricacies in the most masterly but commonplace manner. Mr. Bebb is a man of pleasing countenance, medium height, sandy whiskers and auburn hair, evidently about 40 or 45 years of age. I sat in mute astonishment, with gaping jaws, as he poured slug after slug of unadulterated Salix into my hungry maw-*brain*, excuse me. Of course, I enjoyed the visit. One always meets a congenial soul when he meets a botanist, one who sees in Nature a constant, intricate, friendly beauty, and who is ever aching to convey his happy associations and acquaintances to others.
>
> I hope to soon cease my nomadic life and take up pen and pencil elsewhere. I shall enjoy the constant excitement of the reporter's daily round, shall find, no doubt, new traces of Elysium. But I must not circumlocute. . . .

Sometime before, while visiting his brother, Marcus, Bailey had accepted a position on the Springfield *Monitor*. For a while he was a general reporter and dramatic critic. But Captain Kidd, the publisher, sensed in him an ingenuity at politics and soon he was placed at the state capitol building to report proceedings of the legislature. This experience was to prove valuable to Bailey in later years. He lived in a home which backed up to one in which Abraham Lincoln had lived. However, just as he was being promoted to become city editor of the paper at the fabulous salary of twenty dollars a week, a letter arrived from Dr. Beal enclosing one from Dr. Asa Gray of Harvard University. On October 24, 1882, Bailey wrote to Smith:

[12] This herbarium is today the property of the Chicago Natural History Museum.

. . . You are no doubt somewhat puzzled as to the "news" you are to receive. Well, here it is: I have accepted a salaried position in the botanic gardens and herbaria at Cambridge! Dr. Gray writes, "we want for a year or two a man who has the making of a botanist in him." Through some undeserved good fortune I was selected. Rejoice with me!"

By February 25, 1883, Bailey was settled at 4 Wallace Street, Cambridge, Massachusetts, and he confessed his earnestness and determination to work, in another letter to Smith:

. . . Dr. Gray wrote me while in Springfield that I'd be continued if I proved of sufficient usefulness, and he says now that I am doing well. I also heard him say to my landlady when she asked him how long I was going to stay, "Oh, forever." . . . I took a stroll today all alone. . . . I went to Arlington Heights and looked away to the south to the summits of fir-clad hills, over the wide valleys in which Cambridge sleeps cosily. I saw much to interest me. . . .

And on April 3, he received good news, and immediately shared his happiness with Smith:

I've been hired for two years! Life begins to seem great and earnest to me. My duties are distinctly defined, as follows:
1st. Assistant Curator of the Harvard University Herbarium.
2nd. Entire charge of the nomenclature of the gardens and greenhouses.
3rd. Entire charge of the Students' Herbarium.
4th. Entire charge of the Garden Herbarium.
5th. Assistant in physiological experiments.
That places a great deal upon my shoulders. I am already worked down to a thinner point than ever before, I think, but I am bearing up admirably. . . . I begin to see the clouds lifting from my golden "Island of Sometime," and its shores present a most pleasing appearance. . . . The botanical dep[artmen]t is poor and there is no prophesying as to future salaries. . . . I am to have one of my winter months all to myself. I'll crowd that to bursting with the odds and ends of plans and studies. But every day I am to have to myself sufficient time to carry on my private studies and speculations. My debts bothered me so much that I gave up my German . . . and devoted my nights to writing for the press. I've worked late and hard, and am about exhausted. . . . I have a score of things on my hands, and the minutes and hours are too short for them. I have the privilege of attending Dr. Goodale's lectures to his students. I find it profitable both in rest and acquisition. . . . I was invited to Dr. G[ray]'s a third time a few nights since, but declined. . . . I also had the honor of shaking hands with Pres-[ident] McCosh of Princeton. . . .

Bailey enjoyed the literary life of Cambridge, attending lectures of scholars of the school and church, and meeting celebrities. But he had been brought to Harvard University to perform a specific task. G. C. Joad of Wimbledon, England, a noted world collector of plants, had bequeathed to the Kew Gardens his large collections on condition that if Kew did not want them, this valuable accumulation of a lifetime would go to the Gray Herbarium. In the spring of 1882 Sir Joseph Dalton

Hooker on behalf of the Kew Gardens received a large rock plant collection given by Joad, but the herbarium found its way to America
and the Cambridge institution. Bailey had realized what a marvelous
opportunity was presented to study plants gathered in all parts of
Europe and those collected in Marocco by John Ball. During these
years, the honor of being an assistant to Dr. Gray would have satisfied
the most ambitious young botanist in America anywhere. Bailey, therefore, with alacrity, yet not without often suffering moods of conscientious despair at the meticulous weight of responsibility placed with him,
arranged the large collection into sets, one of which went to the Missouri Botanical Garden at St. Louis and another to the United States
National Museum at Washington. Gray, impressed with the work of
Bailey, told the aspiring young botanist, a third set was "yours." On
June 9, 1884, Gray wrote to Hooker, "The Joad herbarium was a real
bonanza."

Soon after his arrival at Cambridge, Bailey addressed a letter to
James M. Smith, father of Annette Smith, of the farm near Lansing,
and asked the hand of his daughter in marriage. Smith was a taciturn
man and his reply was brief:

"My dear Mr. Bailey,
"You are both of age."

After one-half year of work at the Gray Herbarium at an annual salary
of three hundred and forty dollars, Liberty Hyde Bailey, junior, was
married to Annette Smith on June 6, 1883. Thus years of happiness
and labor, interspersed with reading valuable literary productions of
European masters in physiological and taxonomic botany, were begun.

When the herbarium work was concluded, Bailey was put to naming
all of the plants of the garden and greenhouses, one of which was
filled with acacias from Australia. Bailey took advantage of his time in
Boston, then without question the leading American horticultural center.
He went through all its famous greenhouses and studied carefully all
the plants he saw. The famous Arnold Arboretum, established by a
bequest of James Arnold in 1872 and given over largely to arboricultural
study, was available. During the early 1880's, the city of Boston aided
the arboretum by road placements, repairs, lighting, and policing. It was
to become a part of the city's park system, yet still remaining an integral
part of Harvard University. Its great student of arboriculture and
horticulture, Charles Sprague Sargent, was to plant thousands of trees
and shrubs. Its large acreage gradually provided a world center for the
study of woody plants. Sargent's remarkable interest in floriculture, and
his magnificent estate devoted in part to floricultural study, was of itself
an inspiration. There were also the greenhouses and scientific agri-

cultural work of the Bussey Institution as well as the famous market garden lands of Arlington near Boston—arid wastes when British soldiers had marched on Lexington, and even fifty years before called "poverty plains," sandy soil in need of humus, fertilizer, and good management—and by 1883 the richest garden land Bailey had ever seen.

Moreover, there was the famous Cambridge botanical garden where Gray would spend hours each day with Bailey discussing the plants. In those years the Harvard garden enjoyed a world-wide reputation which, combined with the largest American collection of living plants, gave to the university's botanical work its prestige as effectively as its large library and renowned herbarium. Both beautiful and valuable, the garden served a very useful function in American botany. Gray, in his teaching, had stressed study of the living plant as well as analysis of the dried specimen. Physiology, even in its early years as a laboratory subject, concerned itself with the live plant. The study of interior structures and their functions made this imperative. Research in morphology would intensify the whole of botanical investigation. But the herbarium sheet and the dried plant remained fundamental. Botany was approaching a wonderful new era of expansion. The entire research range in the improvement and amelioration of plants of the wild and the plants of cultivation would coordinate the descriptive and functional study of plant life, in health and disease. Gray's vision embraced a preparation for the future. The truth of this conclusion is confirmed not only in his reviews of literature but also in his last edition of the *Botanical Text-Book* made available as early as 1879.

On February 26, 1882, after his and Mrs. Gray's return to Cambridge from an extensive European tour during which he had his last visit with Charles Darwin and traveled with Sir Joseph and Lady Hooker in Italy, Gray had written to Sir Edward Fry:

I have settled down to my work with enjoyment, but with a growing sense of discouragement growing out of an *embarras de richesses*. It was natural to find here a great accumulation of collections of North American plants, all needing examination; but unfortunately, they continue to come in faster than I can study and dispose of them. This comes from the increasing number of botanical explorers, and the new facilities offered to them by new railroads along our south-western frontiers and other out-of-the-way regions. The consequence is, that while new and interesting things are pouring in, which one must attend to, and which are very enjoyable, I do not get ahead with the steady and formidable work of the "North American Flora." I begin to think it were a happier lot to have the comparatively completed botany of an old country, in which your work "were done when it were done," and in which, even if it were not done quickly, you were not called on to do it over and over, to bring the new into shape and symmetry with the old.

Gray was conscious "of the new mode of thought," of the change of "the face of geology and philosophical natural history" brought about by Sir Charles Lyell, Darwin, Wallace, and others. He was alive to the new investigations issuing from German laboratories devoted to "scientific botany," and also to the important new studies coming from American quarters in botany, paleobotany, and other sciences. But his was the task of completing what had been commenced years earlier in association with his great friend John Torrey, the *North American Flora,* and to the accomplishment of this task all his energies were united.

Gray did not have the fire of youth any more, although his health was excellent. When outbreaks of "ill-humor" occurred, Mrs. Gray would excuse him as being "in the valley of the shadow of the Asters." In 1883 he sent George Bentham "Trumbull's (mostly) and my annotations on DeCandolle's 'L'Origine des Plantes Cultivées' " and told Bentham he was "busy with an article on DeCandolle's 'Nouvelles Remarques sur la Nomenclature.' " These were matters in which Bailey afforded some aid. In 1884 Gray prepared and delivered his scholarly address before the botanists of the British Association for the Advancement of Science at Montreal on "Characteristics of the North American Flora." He contrasted certain outlines of vegetation of the United States and Canada with those of Europe. He also treated "causes or anterior conditions to which much of the actual differences between the two floras may be ascribed." This address more or less climaxed a list of studies made over several decades on a topic which Gray, along with Sir Joseph Hooker, brought to world attention—the relations of continental floral distributions. Beginning in 1859 Gray had sustained a hearty interest in continental plant distributions, as shown by his "observations upon the relations of the Japanese Flora to that of North America, and of other parts of the Northern Temperate Zone." Cultivated plants had been included in the study. Gray's reviews of such works as Hooker and Thomson's *Flora Indica,* Naudin's "Researches into the Specific Characters and the Varieties of the Genus Cucurbita," published in the *Annales des Sciences Naturelles,* Louis Vilmorin's *Notice sur l'Amélioration des Plantes par le Semis et Considérations sur l'Hérédité dans les Végétaux,* and Francis Parkman's "The Hybridization of Lilies," attested to his substantial interest in plants of the garden and cultivation.

Despite the fact that the subjects were interpreted from the standpoint of taxonomy, the remarkably complete knowledge shown and the evident grasp of the intricacies of the subjects were bound to influence a great deal a man such as Bailey who was more interested in the garden and farm by training than in exploring. Giving due consideration to the state of knowledge at that time, one need only examine Gray's article in the *American Journal of Science and Arts,* "Naudin on the Nature of Heredity and Variability in Plants,"[13] or his discussion for the New York *Tribune* on "Do Varieties Wear Out or Tend to Wear Out?"[14] for further proof of Gray's knowledge of agricultural and horticultural species.

In 1883 botanical instruction at Harvard covered at least two years. Gray's structural botany was the basis of the course, which included microscopic study and all points. The second year instruction was given in the lower orders, the cryptogamia. The treatment was biological, tracing plant life in evolutionary development from lowest to highest forms, histological phases being considered. Gray for many years had been the leading American exponent of evolution. Farlow, with the foresight of genius, was extending evolutionary study to "vegetable parasites." (In his New York address in 1887 he gave an epitome of the subject, receiving wide commendation therefor.) With much originality George Lincoln Goodale was developing the much needed subject of "vegetable physiology." His renowned text, applauded even in Europe, was published in 1885 as the second volume of Gray's *Botanical Text-Book.* In 1883, after a trip abroad to visit the famous laboratories of Sachs, Pfeffer, Pringsheim, Wiesner, Frank, and others, Goodale imported the most valuable and expensive apparatus for physiological investigation that America theretofore had known. He established a laboratory center unexcelled at the time on this continent. While Goodale did not have either Farlow's training or ability in research, as a teacher and inspirer of students few in the history of American botany were more able. A doctor by education, a biologist, a natural historian, and for many years the director of the botanic garden, he had vision in botany, was entertaining, and kept his classroom students alert in a fashion similar to some of the great European masters. Many of his researches were of a purely scientific character, and his great influence on students was unquestionably in the direction of pure, as well as applied, science. Bailey attended his lectures and received much stimulation and inspiration from him. It was only to be expected that one of independent mind and vision should see the need of developing a "new horticulture" in America. Beal at Michigan Agricultural was, by this time, advancing the claims of a "new botany."

Later, traveling around the world, Goodale became impressed with the possibilities of improving economic plants in the service of man. He turned aside from physiological botany, let dust gather on his valuable laboratory apparatus, and developed a course in botany, taxonomic in character, but with an economic slant. The botanical museum with its superb collection of Blascha glass models of plants, the central building

[13] Third series, XI, pp. 153 ff.   [14] December 8, 1874, semiweekly edition.

of the Museum of Comparative Zoology, the Harvard botanical gardens on the Soledad estate at Cienfuegos, Cuba, with its station for tropical research and sugar cane investigation, a pioneering work, are all memorials to this noble character. He was part of a movement that surged through American colleges in the 1890's—a movement unafraid of developing botany as a science stressing economic and useful phases. It made no claim to displacing horticulture. Indeed, it could not have since horticulture was too firmly established as one of the oldest of arts. The development of plant physiology, pathology, and other branches of botany which ceaselessly refined techniques of investigation gave rise to a new vision even in horticulture.

Gray's predilection was toward the development of "scientific botany" as distinguished from ornamental phases. This was shown by Engelmann's and his correspondence prior to Engelmann's death in 1884. Scientific botany, issuing as it did from European laboratories, was bound to affect the course of American botany. Gray, Goodale, Farlow, and Engelmann, all doctors of medicine, visualized the new movement in terms of physiology. Horticulture to them was, as it had been, an ornamental art with practical phases in the vegetable garden and orchard. The horticulturist was a gardener, a man of the soil with manure on his boots, and his shirt-sleeves—if any—rolled high. If he created a new plant, if he introduced from seed or seedling a foreign plant, if with feeding and fertilizer he induced a plant to grow where it had not before, it was to sell, to make money or enrich the national domain, in other words, horticulture was the elegant part of agriculture. Horticulture was a business. Men did not don overalls to be academic. Horticulture had no experimental laboratories. If garden or orchard products became experimental subjects, the investigation was regarded as botanical for it then became a part of "scientific botany," whether or not taxonomy took first place in botany. Virtually, therefore, botany was the white-collar part of plant science work. Bailey gave expression to his view that —whether a branch of agriculture or botany—horticulture had great potentialities. This implies no disagreement with Gray, Engelmann, Hooker, or anyone. It merely advances the belief that Bailey was looking to the future.

In the spring of 1884 Gray took counsel with Henry Shaw, a wealthy Englishman of St. Louis who planned to endow a great garden, the Missouri Botanical Garden. Gray had in mind, as he expressed to Hooker, "the right development of [a] Mississippian Kew . . . a grand foundation" and a proper disposition of Engelmann's invaluable herbarium. Gray wanted to learn whether Shaw's ample fortune was "likely to be quite wasted, or was in condition to be turned to good account for botany and horticulture. . . ." The selection of William Trelease as di-

rector and Gray Professor in the new Shaw School of Botany organized
in connection with Washington University and the garden was due
largely to Gray. Trelease attributed his selection to Gray. It really was
a triumph of experimental research. Shaw's conception of botany differed from that of both Engelmann and Trelease. But he listened to
Gray. More than to maintain a beautiful ornamental garden, the institution was to continue the tradition set by Engelmann in taxonomy
and include in its scope the new order of experimentation. Trelease's
completion of work with Farlow was a significant event in American
botanical history. His participation in a Wisconsin natural history survey, in the course of which he assembled a valuable cryptogamic herbarium, had demonstrated value in study of the lower orders of plants;
in much the same way as Burrill's participation in an Illinois survey
had shown the importance to agriculture and horticulture of acquiring
a knowledge of fungi, and destructive plant diseases. To study forces
required first a knowledge of what the forces were—the building of
herbaria and development of intelligent literature on the subject. Gray
must have recommended someone be placed in charge who had
technical training in general botany, entomology, and mycology. Trelease was such a man.

January 1, 1885 Michigan State Agricultural College found itself in
need of a professor of horticulture and landscape gardening. It needed
a superintendent of the horticultural department. James Satterlee, a
farmer from near Greenville, Michigan, and former member of the
executive committee of the State Horticultural Society had tendered his
resignation from the positions. Often agricultural colleges in early years
selected a man influential in horticultural society ranks. Beal believed in
Bailey. He had shown his confidence during Bailey's student years and
after his graduation. So had the college believed in Bailey. The position
was offered him and he accepted. Now there was a chance to put in
practice his dreams for horticulture, a horticulture of science. He went to
Gray. "But, Mr. Bailey," said Gray, "I thought you planned to be a
botanist." Bailey, seeking to palliate the great botanist's seeming disappointment, urged that "a horticulturist needs to be a botanist." To
which Gray replied, "Yes, but he needs to be a horticulturist, too." John
Merle Coulter prophesied when Bailey told him of his appointment:
"You will never be heard from again."

Bailey was to demonstrate fully as great a leadership as that shown by
Gray and Coulter. The world of a "new horticulture" lay before Bailey.
He was to develop the thesis that the biological phase of horticulture is
botany; the business phase is agriculture.[15]

---

[15] "What is Horticulture?" *Proceedings of The Society for Horticultural Science*,
1905, pp. 53, 54 ff.

CHAPTER IV

THE FIRST PROFESSORSHIP.
A "NEW" HORTICULTURE

SINCE Bailey's graduation from Michigan Agricultural College, a state-wide insistence that a separate department of horticulture be created had culminated in its establishment in 1883. Under Professor Satterlee, the college grounds, gardens, and walks had been kept trim and neat, orchards had been enlarged and made to look thrifty, the college and professors' tables were abundantly supplied with vegetables and farm produce. Satterlee was a good, able farmer, and practical man. But the instruction—book learning and the best available farming practice was the most that could be said for it. What research there was, was incidental. Certainly this program could not exist harmoniously with the quality of botanical research which Beal had established, and always sought to improve. Crop improvement, land rehabilitation and improvement, the conquest of plant diseases, the introduction of new plantable varieties, and, in a few words, the whole range of plant research, were known by leading agriculturists to bring larger and more lasting profits. Gardeners, nurserymen, and farmers wanted, therefore, a young man of vision, a scientist, one who could sustain the college's traditional leadership in horticulture as well as in other branches of study.

Bailey brought with him the fresh inspiration of his Harvard years. He could remember his youth in South Haven, when he had read the *Origin of Species* and seen evolution at work in the garden. Charles Darwin was to him the world's greatest horticulturist. While Darwin had not addressed his work to horticulturists alone, had not most of his epoch-making conclusions been derived from study of horticultural species? Bailey could remember Dr. Beal's horticultural instruction and his vision for botany blending happily the evolution view and the best of the Agassizian concepts. Researches in the fundamental biology of plant life, along with taxonomic study, needed the stimulating enthusiasm which the college graduate from South Haven, and the advanced student at Harvard, could, and did, bring to his task. Bailey was vigorous, alert, and healthy, a sturdy son of Michigan.

Darwin's view had prevailed over Agassiz's theory of a special and local creation of forms. Only the great contribution of Agassiz was left—direct observation of things in nature to discern nature's laws. Botany was now a greatly enlarging study with a new morphology, a new physiology, a new cytology and anatomy coming into being. Horticulture, being its research partner, was also to enlarge its compass. Darwin, Wallace, Hooker, and Gray had dwelt on the great changes that had occurred through the ages. Their work, and that of the paleontologist and paleobotanist, had changed the cosmic horizon to epochs and ages, millions and millions of years in time. The garden had become a miniature cosmos where evolutionary study might proceed with exactness. There were the far reaching problems of plant origins, modifications, changes, and development. There were the more immediate problems of understanding and interpreting the methods and causes of change induced and controlled by the agency of man. Bailey moved into a new house situated in an oval on the college campus. He cut down some trees to improve the view from his dining-room window and went to work.

The college apple orchard, coming under Bailey's immediate control, presented a discouraging appearance. A hard winter had destroyed many of the large trees on the lower land. He conceived a plan to renovate by pruning, scraping, thinning, plowing, and recultivation. He refused to take the advice of some farmers that the orchard ought to be cut down. Eventually was to issue from several years' experimenting the summary, "Till. Feed. Prune. Spray." New drainage, sod removal, and general renovation did its work.

A new fruit garden with a thorough system of tile drainage and comprising four acres was set out before the end of the summer. It was to be a testing ground for new varieties of small fruits. Most of the fruits were set out in the spring—strawberries during the previous fall— and a catalogue of these and other fruits was prepared and published as a bulletin. Including raspberries, blackberries, strawberries, currants, gooseberries, quinces, grapes, pears, and cherries, apricots, mulberries, and seedlings of "promising wild fruits," the project formed a student garden where under Bailey's supervision, and that of his foreman, the nature and culture of the plants were studied and taught.

Special attention was given the vineyards growing sixty-three named varieties of grapes, and a number of hybrids and seedlings. For them Bailey erected "an illustrative system of trellises to represent to students all the methods of out-door training."

A seven acre vegetable garden was maintained by the foreman as a market garden. Bailey soon began to assemble collections of vegetables, especially tomatoes. His foreman was Charles S. Crandall. (Crandall later went to the University of Illinois where he remained more than a quarter of a century bringing together the world's largest collection of apple materials. At one time it is said he had about 30,000 potential new varieties. He did much experimental breeding.) Bailey and he constructed in Michigan an experimental hotbed and a forcing house heated by hot air from a homemade furnace.

On August 19, 1885, Edwin Willits had become president of the college, and a condition of his acceptance had been that the school go to the state board of agriculture and the state legislature and secure an appropriation to broaden its facilities and cover adequately all activities contemplated in the Morrill Act of 1862.

Bailey hoped to inaugurate experiments of more general value, of wider application, than the mere testing of varieties. He was ambitious and he wanted to make an exact record of the whole visible biography of our cultivated plants from sowing to maturity. He wanted to record in tabulated form the seasons of germination and maturity, the period of the plant's greatest and least vigor, the exact external influence of culture and weather, the detailed characteristics of leaves, flowers, and fruits, and many highly important experimental features. He wanted means to store or evaporate fruits and vegetables, to collect and preserve specimens for class illustration. He wanted facilities for greenhouse and forcing house instruction, facilities for carrying on indoor work in cold weather. Classroom instruction in horticulture covered four and one half months.

Bailey's courses in horticulture and landscape gardening were described during his first year as a teacher:

The course in horticulture includes four general topics: Pomology, vegetable gardening, floriculture, seed growing. The instruction is given both by lecture and by practical operations in the fields. Of the two methods of instruction, it is intended that the field work shall be the more important. The Juniors are given instruction by the Professor in sections or squads, in budding, grafting, pruning, tilling, harvesting, marketing, and storing fruits and vegetables. All vegetables which are suited to this climate are grown in the vegetable garden, and all desirable small fruits in the fruit garden. An apple orchard, pear orchard, plum orchard, cherry orchard, and two vineyards are invaluable aids to the observing student. The diligent student who desires to follow fruit growing or vegetable gardening can secure here the necessary practical training. The classroom lectures also cover the practical points of the subject and enable the student to enter at once upon his field work. The lectures also treat of the principles of plant growth and their relation to cultivation, of the classification and nomenclature of fruits and vegetables, of hybridization and cross-fertilization, and of plant diseases. Instruction is given in the care of hedges, ornamental trees and flowers, and upon the characters and value of native wild fruits. A few lectures are also given upon the history and the literature of horticulture.

Landscape Gardening is treated as a fine art, and its study is introduced by a discussion of the principles of art in general. Unity, harmony, and variety are discussed at length, and abundant illustrations are drawn from the picturesque views upon the college premises. The principles of the art of ornamental gardening once understood, they are applied to the ornamentation of parks and large estates, after which practice the student is able to discriminate the features which can be judiciously applied to the embellishment of country homes. In practical rural embellishment the subject finds its greatest expansion. Finally, the student is given instruction in rural architecture, in the making of walks and drives, in sodding, grading and in the selection of trees. All these subjects are illustrated in walks which the Professor takes with his class over the beautiful and extensive grounds of the college.

When Bailey became professor he held only a bachelor of science degree. In 1886 the degree master of science was conferred on him by the college. Satterlee, his predecessor, an alumnus, for all his acknowledged reputation of being a skillful handler of horticultural crops, a lawn landscaper of ability, had nevertheless been an uninteresting teacher. Bailey had all his predecessor's accomplishments and was moreover "like a breeze" to the students for he had a viewpoint which fired their imaginations. He began his lectures as he entered the room and commanded attention throughout the entire lecture period. He was an orator of ability and he became immensely popular. His talent at interpreting and writing poetry was also an attraction. (He was most enthusiastic about Poe and Milton and he enjoyed versification.) As soon as students could elect his course, they did.

The consequence was that his classrooms were always filled. It seems to have made no difference whether the student was preparing for medicine, law, engineering, or other training. Invariably, horticulture was included at some time during his college experience. With his foreman and assistant Crandall, a nephew of Manly Miles, Bailey had almost immediately an enviable department.

In October of the first year he published a synopsis of horticultural experiments:

Series A. Acclimation and adaptation of fruits and vegetables. Fruits and vegetables of acknowledged merit in one or more directions, both exotic and from foreign portions of the United States, will be grown and tested, and their acclimation will be attempted in some cases.

Series B. Improvement of native wild fruits.

Series C. Improvement of fruits and vegetables by crossing and hybridizing.

Series D. Experiments to determine limits of manipulation and best methods of manipulation.

Series E. Mutual relations between stock and scion, and limits within which grafting is possible and profitable.

Series F. Experiments upon methods and possibilities of propagation by all methods of making cuttings, layers, etc. These experiments will have especial reference to the propagation of native wild plants. This subject, and that outlined in Series G, although old, are very imperfectly understood.

Series G. Germination experiments, concerning behavior of seeds and germination especially in wild plants. Experiments to determine the effect of cold upon seeds are now in progress.

Series H. Improvement of native wild plants for ornamental purposes.

Series I. Effects of soils, selection and culture upon variability of plants.

Series J. Studies upon Classification, Terminology, and Nomenclature of fruits and vegetables.

Series K. Synonymy. It is a conspicuous fact that many or most of the seedsman's novelties are old varieties or very slight and unimportant modifications of them under new names. It becomes the business of experimenters to test all varieties of every product side by side, and to determine some standard or measure for each variety. It is impossible to undertake experiments in this line upon more than one kind of vegetable at a time with ordinary facilities. All American varieties of tomatoes are being grown this year. [76 so-called varieties]

Series L. Special observations upon the behavior of individual plants and varieties.

Series M. Studies concerning the influence of latitude upon vegetation; also observation for determining minimum and maximum periods of plant activity.

Series N. Methods and modifications of grafting and budding.

Series O. Testing commercial varieties of fruits and vegetables.

Series P. Tools and methods of culture.

Botany had a laboratory, why should not horticulture have one too? Subjects such as potting and handling plants; making and repairing tools; making mats for hotbeds, mats for forcing houses; making cuttings; and all the wide variety of experimental subjects demonstrated the need for one. Bailey wanted horticulture taught as a basic course, along with agriculture—not to have its teaching delayed until the second half of the college course.

At the second annual meeting of the Society for the Promotion of Agricultural Science, held at Cincinnati, Ohio, August 15-16, 1881, Beal in his presidential address had elaborated fifteen objectives, many of which by the years 1886-1887 were well on the way to attainment. In his 1881 address, "What Can Botany Do for Horticulture?" Beal, moreover, had pointed out that Asa Gray had made the "dominant feature" of American botanical science the study of "How plants behave," and this had led into foundations for research and study in vegetable physiology and pathology, as well as systematic efforts to originate new plant forms. Plants were studied both biologically and taxonomically. By the years 1886-1887, Beal was more near sixty than fifty years of age. Botany and horticulture were two separate departments of the college. Beal was at work on his great two volume book, *Grasses of North America*, a taxonomic study of value even today. Systematics was still the most important branch of American botany. Grasses were fundamental to agriculture. Beal realized that Bailey had talent in "agricultural science," and represented a new, youthful, aggressive leadership. A laboratory for horticulture was needed to advance researches in "pure science," and improve and supplement the teaching of practical applications.

To convince the progressive members of the faculty of Michigan Agricultural College of this need was not as much of a task as to convince other officials. Agricultural college faculties for many years met with student bodies who knew little more than business phases of farming. The tasks of the agricultural colleges, as Bailey conceived them to be, were to improve the rural areas as well as the agricultural industry. Hardheaded farmers sat on college boards of trustees, and, since the pleas of the enlightened leadership in academic circles went for many years and in many places unheeded, although through periodicals and public gatherings the pleas were read or heard, rural progress remained at the levels of the various state agricultural boards and state horticultural societies. Michigan was progressive in both, and so immediately, through writing and addresses, Bailey began to present his cause and his views to them as well as the college officials. The annual reports of these organizations for the years 1885-1888 contain a number of articles by Bailey covering points of approved practice, and also what was being accomplished at the college. In some is seen the emergence of a creative horticultural vision.[1] In some the intention was more plainly instructional.[2]

Rural ornamentation, Bailey argued, did not call for lavish expenditure; rather, the whole subject challenged study and attention. Agriculture, characterized by bareness, could not progress. Rural life should and could be picturesque and beautiful. Nature's fresh attractiveness should and could be preserved: at sources of streams, "along all steep and broken banks and sinuous water-courses," along highways, in open fields, and in rocky and inarable lands—without interference with the farmer's work. Attractive, convenient, and economical plantings of shrubbery and flowers, attractive arrangements of windbreaks and woodlots, of walks and drives, could beautify and preserve natural landscapes. "Style in farming"[3] (in a paper read before the farmers' institute of Grass Lake and Quincy), he urged, should consist of more than adornments. Picturesqueness and beauty should portray color harmony and contrast, form and perspective, and appeal to the mind. The student's task was to learn the laws and relationships of attractive, useful ornamentation.[4] Bailey prepared lists of hardy ornamental plants which

---

[1] *26th Ann. Rep. St. Bd. Agric. of Mich.*, 1886-1887, p. 64. "Illustrations of Intensive Horticulture," *14th Ann. Rep. of Sect. St. Hort. Soc. of Mich.*, p. 321.

[2] "Harvesting Apples," *idem*, p. 275.

[3] *25th Ann. Rep. of Sect. St. Bd. of Agric. of Mich.*, 1885-1886, pp. 56 ff., at p. 58.

[4] "Things in a New Country Not Generally Appreciated," *15th Ann. Rep. Sect. St. Hort. Soc. of Mich.*, 1885, p. 52. In the report of the third year of the department of horticulture and landscape gardening, was set forth brief synopses of lectures on horticulture and landscape gardening, *24th Ann. Rep. Sect. St. Bd. of Agric. of Mich.*, 1884-1885, p. 71.

might be used in rural adornment.[5] Vines, shrubs, conifers, evergreens, and deciduous trees were often preferable in rural areas.[6] In a few words, during these heroic years in agricultural education, he sought to improve the farming business on which rural life depended, yes, *and also*, rural living itself.

"I like the common things of life," confided Bailey. He enjoyed the contrast of planting flowers along with more practical plantings of beets and cabbages. Especially he enjoyed bringing wild plants—scenes of natural beauty—into his yard. "Many wild plants, and especially some of the shrubs," he wrote, "are worthy of cultivation in the dooryard. Some of our attractive swamp shrubs thrive on any garden soil. One never appreciates the beauty of many common plants until he sees well grown specimens in a garden." Even pasture land could be planted with shrubbery and attractive wild plants.

Bailey distinguished between landscape gardening, the fine art, essentially a mind-ideal, and landscape horticulture, the more economic and mechanical phases of ornamental gardening which required use of spade and hoe, the road maker, and the student of trees, shrubs, and flowers. City and village horticultural societies, he said, should direct and foster ornamentation.

The United States Department of Agriculture had long distinguished in its work between plants "of mere ornamental value and those that represent economic products."[7] In September, 1862, when William Saunders, who for eight years had been a partner of Meehan of Germantown, Pennsylvania, in landscape gardening and horticulture, was appointed horticulturist of the department, he prepared a statement of his objects and aims. His program, always kept in view during his many years with the department, provided that seeds, cuttings, bulbs, and plants from foreign and domestic sources should be transmitted to the department, their possibilities and comparative merits for growth in the United States and in various localities of the nation be experimentally tested and studied, and by "hybridizing and special culture, products of a superior character to any now existing" should be procured.[8] The

[5] The list of hardy ornamental plants was contained in the college's Bulletin 12.

[6] See "Windbreaks for the Fruit-Grower," *27th Ann. Rep. Sect. St. Bd. Agric. of Mich.*, 1887-1888, p. 350. "Climbers and Their Uses," *15th Ann. Rep. St. Hort. Soc.*, p. 284. "Native Flowering Shrubs," *16th Rep.*, p. 501. "Lombardy Poplar," *idem*, p. 493. Rules for planting and lists of plants were given in many of the foregoing.

[7] *First Report of the Secretary of Agriculture*, 1889 (Washington: Government Printing Office, 1889), p. 29. Notice, however, the distinction applied more with regard to plant propagation. The secretary's comments on gardens and grounds are found at pp. 28-29.

[8] In his report in charge of the division of gardens and grounds, for 1889, *idem*, pp. 111-134, under a subheading, "Horticulture in the Department," Saunders incorporated "a brief recital of some, at least, of the operations of this division since its establishment in the organization of the Department." The statement referred to may be found

effects of pruning and other manipulation and influences on growth were
to be examined. Plant diseases and the insects that destroy plants should
be investigated. Hedge plants and choice shrubs to decorate "gardens
and landscape scenery" were to be cultivated. Glass structures were to
be built to provide facilities to cultivate exotic fruits and plants, and
to demonstrate their best and most effective construction and management. Moreover, in experimental farm tracts, the "best fruit trees and
plants, such as grapes, apples, pears, peaches, strawberries, raspberries,"
were also to be grown. Within a very few years, test experiments in
cereals, forage plants, garden fruits, and vegetables, had substantially
progressed. A conservatory, planned to house "economic and useful"
plants, was completed and occupied by 1871. Lands were graded, roads
built, and that year was planted an arboretum of "every tree and shrub
capable of existing in the climate . . . in strict accordance with a botanical
system, and at the same time produce a high degree of effective landscape gardening and pleasure ground scenery—a combination not
hitherto attempted on a similarly extending scale." Already we have
considered, and will again refer to Saunders' work of introducing to the
American plant economy new or rare plants from other world regions.
Saunders's program no more explained in entirety Bailey's horticultural vision and the program he inaugurated at Michigan Agricultural
College than did the work of Beal or any other plant scientist in American agriculture. Bailey's work was his own. But he was too smart not
to profit occasionally by the mature experience and wisdom of his
elders. The fruitful results of the older scientific agriculturists had
succeeded in building already an American agricultural tradition from
which younger men might benefit, and Bailey's program was in harmony with its broad compass. J. M. Rusk was the first regularly appointed United States secretary of agriculture. Norman J. Colman, the
last commissioner of agriculture, held the office until the next president,
Benjamin Harrison, appointed Rusk to the new cabinet position.
Secretary Rusk, in his report for the year 1889, describing Saunders'
work as horticulturist, landscape gardener, and superintendent of the
division of gardens and grounds, and horticulture, with reference both
to the reservation at Washington and the Arlington estate, observed
that the "main feature of interest in the ornamental portion of the
grounds is the method employed in grouping trees and shrubs. . . ." The

---

at pp. 118-119, the data concerning variety testing, the arboretum, and the conservatory, as well as the work with many of the species, pp. 128-131, and pp. 119-128,
concerning grapes, pear trees, peaches, Japan persimmons, cinchonas, Chinese tea
plant, coffee, oranges, lemons, and other citrus fruits, apples, olives, eucalyptus, figs, at
p. 130, concerning pineapples, p. 131, hedges, and pp. 132-134, miscellaneous plants. A
point worthy of notice was that 45,000 and more plants were distributed during the
year 1889.

United States possessed several notable, historic gardens, many privately owned and in the larger and older cities of the nation. However, the history of landscape gardening as a phase of agricultural development in the United States, seems, although an adjunct, distinguishable from the older history of landscape gardening as an art and science which emerged from the work of the great ornamental gardens. Harvard and other leading eastern universities, colleges, and special schools, developed and taught this, and its kindred subject, landscape architecture, although for reasons already noticed, their undergraduate curricula, especially during their early years, emphasized learning in the classics more than the promotion of scientific agriculture.

Bailey centered attention on one specific phase. Natural beauty should be preserved, he believed, and so he interested himself in bringing wild plants into cultivation—wild roses of the plains of Oscoda County, a white flowered species of New Jersey tea, and other plants of esthetic and economic value, could and should be cultivated.[9]

Plant variation, however, seems to have been the subject that absorbed his attention. In an address on "The Multiplication of Plants," given at the Hanover and Charlotte institute, with a large chart on plant propagation prepared by B. M. Watson, Jr., of the Bussey Institution and magic lantern slides, he said:

. . . The successful multiplication of plants lies at the foundation of all success in horticulture. . . . This matter is not commonly understood in its details among those who have not been especially trained in it. . . . The acquirement of taste and skill in this direction usually leads to successful practice and more enjoyment in other horticultural operations. . . .[10]

Improvement possibilties in many of Michigan's native fruits impressed him and he wrote an article for *The College Speculum*,[11] urging:

. . . The Northern States abound in indigenous fruits which promise to the patient pomologist great rewards in the way of hardy and palatable varieties. Those plants which vary most widely in a state of nature improve most readily under the influence of cultivation.This principle is illustrated in our strawberries, blackberries, raspberries, and grapes. All our cultivated blackberries have sprung from one wild plant, the Rubus villosus of our copses and tangles. Many of our varieties, prominent among them being the old Lawton, are natural sports which were picked up in fence-rows or clearings. Nearly all hardy raspberries, and all the black-caps, have originated from one or other or both of our native species, the black and the red. . . . All of our leading strawberries are varieties of our common Fragaria Virginiana, or perhaps are modified by crosses with other

[9] *18th Ann. Rep. Sect. St. Hort. Soc. of Mich.*, 1888, p. 56. See also the 17th report, *idem*, 1887, p. 443.
[10] *26th Ann. Rep. St. Bd. Agric. of Mich.*, 1886-1887, p. 429.
[11] XVI, June 15, 1885, p. 6.

species. . . . Most of our grapes are also natural varieties which were picked up in the woods.

. . . Why not improve more extensively all our wild fruits. We have a wild black currant, Ribes floridum, which is naturally better than the Old World Ribes nigrum that is in common cultivation. The variety known as American Black is a natural sport of this wild species. The common wild gooseberry varies exceedingly and is worthy of close attention. The attractive Missouri currant which is planted in various places upon our grounds is the parent of two or three very good varieties. Two wild plums give promise of great capabilities. The Wild Goose and Miner are nearly pure native Chickasaws, Prunus Chicasa. The dwarf sand cherry of the beaches and dunes of our Great Lakes bears a sweet and attractive fruit which deserves the attention of every pomologist. Our wild crab apple needs attention. All our wild nuts are awaiting the labors of the horticulturist. The pecan must have the bitter matter bred out of its inner shell; walnuts, butternuts, chestnuts and hickory nuts are waiting for thinner shells and plumper meats. Our common walnut has greater capabilities than had the parents of the English walnuts of the confectioners. There are no less than twenty-five fruits, of various kinds, natives of Michigan, which present attractive problems to all lovers of botany and horticulture.

The Horticultural Department desires to undertake the solution of a few of these problems. Our present method must be to plant the seeds of the finest wild fruits and await results. We desire the cooperation of students and others in securing seeds of the largest, smoothest and sweetest of all kinds of native fruits.

Bailey did not quarrel with the board. He pleaded for increased facilities. As much as Dr. Beal, or any board member, he appreciated the value of discovering new varieties of plants, of improving quantity and quality yields, of the value of taxonomic work. He had recently been in Boston—as a part of Carex studies he continued correspondence with Gray and increased an already established correspondence with Dr. George Vasey of the United States Department of Agriculture at Washington. Unquestionably, these two centers had more intelligent horticulturists than any others. In reality, Boston was more and more coming to be regarded as "the most active centre of associated horticulture in America."[12]

Bailey planned to place most of the garden and orchard work with Crandall. He saw the need, first, of a modernized literature in horticulture. He planned a book and wrote Bessey about it. On November 9, 1885, after receiving Bessey's answer, he wrote again:

I am now preparing a lecture on the "Garden Fence" which I am to deliver in Massachusetts this winter. In that I shall make a plea for the "new horticulture." I am enthusiastic over botany in the garden. I like that phase of the science. My leading motive in proposing that book is to find out

[12] *The American Garden* and Floral Cabinet, edited by Edgar H. Libby, VIII, 1887, old series XV, p. 248.

some of the laws of plant variation and dissemination, especially in relation
to climate and latitude. If I have the facts collated we might be able to get
at some general principles.

Although he realized it would not be an easy task, Bailey proposed to
"go at the science of horticulture" himself.

"The Garden Fence"[13] was a lecture read at the country meeting of the
Massachusetts state board of agriculture at Framingham in December.
It was so well received that it was later separately published. The garden fence was the relative "fence which stands between theory and practice. . . . It exists and does not exist." In the work of Thomas Andrew
Knight, even before Darwin, horticulture had become a science. In his
work, science itself had climbed the garden fence. A few had surmounted
the fence "at some of its highest points, and of these, none [stood] out
so clearly as Charles Darwin." "It is not the man who tills the soil who
is necessarily the best horticulturist," said Bailey, "it is rather he who
knows nature best, and who can put his knowledge into form for others
to use." He referred to Burrill's and Arthur's studies in pear blight as
a "type of successful investigation regarding the diseases of plants."
"Horticulture, the art, is old; horticulture, the science, is new," he affirmed. "To get our science from the field and the laboratory into the
garden, is the problem of the age. We must demand it there. . . . We fail
to catch the butterfly if we chase its irregular flight over the meadow,
but the still hunt beside a thistle will bring us a captive." Experiments
must be conducted by scientific as well as by practical men.

Taxonomy of horticultural species interested Bailey from the first.
We must "ask ourselves what a species is," we must define our concepts,
he said. At the New York experiment station races of dwarf plants and
each year all varieties of one vegetable were being grown, and the use of
Paris green against the codling moth was being demonstrated (important studies of Sturtevant and E. S. Goff). In reference to these Bailey
stated:

The classification and the method of naming are such that the diligent
botanist can hold in his mind the names and the kinship of thousands of
plants with no tax upon the memory. There is no system of arrangement so
complete, no logical method of subordinating a lesser character to a greater
so thorough, as the system of classification and nomenclature which we
apply to wild plants and animals. On the other hand, there is no system
more bungling, none more thoroughly haphazard, than that which we apply
to the plants of the garden. Is there not some way to get our classification
and nomenclature over the garden fence? . . . In the Station report for
1883, fifty eight varieties of beans are accurately described and compared.
Progressive horticulture demands that some efficient system of classification
be worked out for each of our orchard and garden plants.

[13] Boston, Wright & Potter Printing Co., State Printers, 1886.

In this classic address was also contained a significant set of observations which would persist many years in Bailey's philosophy of plant origination and development:

We sow with the confidence that like produces like, that as we sow so shall we reap; but the keen observer sees in the offspring of almost any seed, when sown in considerable quantity, a wide variation. Indeed, no two individuals are alike, although they spring from seeds grown in the same fruit.

From these concepts, formed as early as 1885, can be discerned something of a reaction from the teachings of Gray who sought to show order, plan and design in creation. Gray, primarily always the systematist, in his reviews of European literature stressed a theory of like begetting like in hybridization, allowing, of course, for wide diversity and plant variation. Bailey, however, found in the course of experimental studies that unlike begets unlike, that there is a certain inheritance of similarities but never sameness. Bailey's view was a challenging one in these early years of philosophical speculation. He admired Gray's reviews, studied them carefully for directness, conciseness, and simplicity of style. He knew that Gray was not merely a closet botanist but that he was vitally interested in living plants of the garden. Darwin had accepted the concept of design in universal creation, but in a qualified sense. Darwin could not view things of creation as wholly products of chance, nor wholly as products of a great scheme of universal order or design. Gray claimed no more for design than a probability unsusceptible of absolute proof. Evolution loomed as an immense study, insight into which would grow. Knowledge of the first cause would not be included in its scope. Gray's religious adherence naturally created a bias in favor of teleological concepts. Proof or disproof of the truth of the concepts of development awaited exact experimentation. Perhaps Bailey's view of unlike begetting unlike would prove experimentally qualifiable. Certainly it was not to become the prevalent view in all quarters. Bailey had not sat as a classroom student of Gray. But he had discussed matters with him; and had carefully studied his writings. Time would be the arbiter. Neither Mendel or De Vries had arrived on the American scene. Even with the arrival of their immensely valuable and tremendously significant contributions, time is still the arbiter of the truth or falsity of the great, fundamental concepts.

Still dear to Bailey's heart was nature study. He had seen the need for interpreting truths of science to large masses of people. His *Talks Afield about Plants and the Science of Plants*,[14] published in Boston in 1885, was such a book. There were scientists ahead of Bailey who insisted on the application of scientific principles to horticulture. There

---

[14] Houghton, Mifflin and Co., IX, 173 pp., illus.

were botanists ahead of Bailey in experimental work. But who, among them, appreciated with such foresight the great educational need, the need of including all peoples in schemes of teaching? Who realized with greater awareness the need of vitalizing science for the young? Science was rife with a "dry as dust" method of teaching. Materials were taught with small regard to relationships. Science teaching was filled with a bookish learning that drove more students away from the subjects than attracted them. Rural teaching in science was full of an antiquated knowledge. In fact, for the young in many places, there was little or no science teaching. Bailey decided that he would take the subjects as far as they were developed and put them in pedagogical form. He would put them in such form that even the young could apply the learning in the daily work of life on the farm and in the garden. In his *Talks Afield* he tried to convey to others the pleasure he had had from botanical study.

The year following the appearance of *Talks Afield about Plants and the Science of Plants* there was published another book by Bailey, this one designed for orchard men's use, *Field Notes on Apple Culture*.[15]

Bailey was elected president, for the year 1886, of the Ingham County Horticultural Society. He seized every opportunity to urge horticulture to advance scientifically. "The materials for study are everywhere. No science has more of them than has horticulture. This science is new, fresh, bracing. It invites us all out of doors, and challenges us to ask questions."[16] Nomenclature was the beginning of the pathway. In a note on "Nomenclature of Garden Plants," he pointed out perplexities which were remediable. "There are three fertile sources of confusion," he said, "carelessness and ignorance of gardeners; the indisposition of floriculture to keep pace with botanical science; the lack of any code for horticultural nomenclature." Again he advanced claims:[17]

. . . That a beautiful and simple system of nomenclature can be stripped of all its power and meaning to suit the convenience, or to satisfy the whim, of the user, is a patent and deplorable fact in floriculture. It should be impressed upon the public mind that botanical names, once properly made, should be forever fixed. Indeed, upon the fixity of names must rest the whole superstructure of systematic biology. If the confusion now rampant in the use of garden names is ever reduced to harmony, the change must be made upon a recognition of this principle. Names are not a common property, to be used or discarded at pleasure. Once made, they become a part of the machinery of science, which only the master workman may change, and then under strict rules. . . . It is the sole object of nomenclature to secure

15 New York, Orange Judd Co., 90 pp. incl. front. illus. 1886.
16 *16th Ann. Rep. Sect. St. Hort. Soc. Mich.*, 1886, p. 299.
17 *Ibid.*, p. 546.

for the plant an enduring and distinctive name. Embellishments are minor matters.

Bailey had studied nurserymen's catalogues since his youth. While at Harvard, and really before then, he had come to deplore the way in which gardeners changed names in their catalogues at their own convenience and pleasure. He had observed that botanists refused to trust garden and horticultural publications for this reason. He pointed out this fact to the horticulturists.

When William Saunders founded, at least was one of the founders of, the Patrons of Husbandry, the national grange, he served as its Master for its first six years. One of the strongest and most influential agencies for agricultural improvement America has known was established when this was organized. Bailey early became an enthusiastic supporter of the grange in Michigan, often taking his students with him to meetings and participating in programs. Often the state horticultural societies met in grange halls and also to their meetings he took his students. At the summer meeting of the society, which convened at Capital Grange Hall at Lansing in June, 1886, Bailey presided on the second night and introduced members of his class who read papers, one of which by A. Pettet on "Some Experiments in Grafting,"[18] was of especial interest. Bailey told the gathering that his aim in teaching horticulture was to lead young men to see, investigate, and think for themselves. At a farmer's institute at South Haven in January, 1888, where he was extended "the heartfelt welcome accorded to the child returning to his old home," Bailey convinced his audience that he and President Willits who accompanied him were there not to teach them but to take up that in which they were interested. He spoke on commercial horticulture stressing good cultivation; good locations; good, honest packages of best varieties; good marketing; good pedigrees in fruit; succession of crops, double cropping; and adapting "ourselves" to market facilities. "We must know something of insects in order to know how to combat them," he argued. "Our insect pests are increasing and as the forests are destroyed they come from thence into the orchard. The flat-headed apple borer has been transferred from the oak to the apple. Professor Cook will not tell you so, but he was the first to discover the way to destroy the codling moth. He saw that the blossom stands erect and the moth lays her egg in the blossom. If, now, the tree is sprayed with Paris green, it holds the poison and kills the moth, and later, as the blossom turns down, they fall out. . . ."[19]

[18] *16th Ann. Rep. Sect. St. Hort. Soc. of Mich.*, 1886, p. 98.
[19] *18th Ann. Rep. Sect. St. Hort. Soc. Mich.*, 1888, pp. 214 ff., at p. 219.

Bailey had already laid down rules for placement of windbreaks, more and more needed as deforestation increased:

1. In general a windbreak presents a great advantage to the fruit grower.
2. The windbreak should not obstruct atmospheric drainage.
3. The windbreak should never be dense enough to force the buds on fruit trees in those localities which are subject to late spring frosts.
4. As a rule, in localities where atmospheric drainage will not be seriously checked, the windbreak should have a comparatively dense bottom, formed by undergrowth or low-branching trees.
5. So far as practicable the windbreak should be planted at a distance of six rods or more from the fruit plantation.
6. Native trees are preferable for windbreaks.[20]

These rules were formulated by the "Horticulturist of the Experiment Station." Prosperity had come to Bailey's department of horticulture at the college. During the school year 1887-1888 for the first time things had been put "in respectable running order. Two good teams, good tools, and the subjugation of certain areas within the limits of the horticultural department make the work," reported Bailey, "much more satisfactory than it has been before. Many rough and troublesome portions of the grounds have been brought into good condition, and sufficient drainage has been done to make the land, both in lawn and crops, easy of manipulation. In short, most of the pioneer work upon the department has now been done." An important announcement was made:

The horticultural building is nearly completed. Upon the whole the building is well planned, although certain minor changes made by the architect from our original plans impair its utility in some directions. This is the first distinctively horticultural laboratory in this country. Many inquiries concerning the details of its plans have been received, and it therefore seems worth while to add here an outline plan of the building. The building is about 36 x 68 feet, two stories and basement, veneered with brick. Its cost is $6,000. . . .[21]

Bailey's first "laboratory" had been a pine board and glass greenhouse, heated by a stove located near the door and equipped with a terra cotta flue which carried the smoke to an upright pine board chimney. When he had arrived, finding a small amount of money available for a "laboratory," he had done what he could with the funds at his disposal. Notwithstanding, not even by the year 1887-1888, was the college greenhouse made a part of the horticultural department. And much "scavenger and errand work of the institution" was still required of the department. "It has been impossible, heretofore," said Bailey, "to conduct consecutive experiments requiring close application because of the unprofessional work heaped upon the department, and, even with the

---

[20] *27th Ann. Rep. Sect. St. Bd. Agric. Mich.*, 1887-1888, p. 350; also *Garden and Forest* I (1888), p. 46.
[21] *27th Ann. Rep. Sect. St. Bd. Agric. Mich.*, 1887-1888, "Report of the Professor of Horticulture and Landscape Gardening," p. 36.

present improved facilities, this difficulty is far from being removed. There has not been time to devote to any of the niceties of gardening."

President Willits was Bailey's admirer and friend. He sought on all occasions possible to aid him. When board members complained that edges of the walks were not as trim as they had been under Satterlee, when they maintained there were many things not as well cared for, Willits answered, "That's true, but Bailey is a genius, and you mustn't hitch a race horse to a plow."

In the years 1886-1887 Bailey began his fascinating hybridization studies in Cucurbita, in pumpkins, squashes, melons, and gourds, plants to which he has always attached not only economic importance but also aesthetic value. There were still few hybridizers in American colleges.

In his report for the division of botany of the United States Department of Agriculture, George Vasey presented a paper on cross-fertilization "and another on pollination" which, he commented, "will provoke research and investigation." Presented in 1887, when Bailey wrote a letter on the subject, it included an observation of A. A. Crozier, assistant botanist and author of the papers, to the effect:

In 1887 Prof. L. H. Bailey crossed Hyslop crab with the Oldenburg apple, and another variety of crab with Sweet Romanite, but no change in the fruit was observed. He also crossed the Spiny-fruited *Datura stramonium* with pollen of the Smooth-fruited *Datura inermis* without observing any change in the character of the pods. . . .[22]

Reference was made to Bailey's letter which read:

I have performed many crosses this year between such plants as would give unmistakable evidence of the immediate effect of pollen should effect occur. I crossed Hyslop crab with Duchess of Oldenburg and got no effect in any way, not even in season of maturity or texture. I crossed another crab with Sweet Romanite and obtained no immediate effect.

By the way, I made a singular incidental experiment on these varieties. Of five crabs I removed four of the pistils and crossed the remaining one. From these crosses I got two mature apples, but they had seeds in only one cell!

I crossed many Crookneck squashes with the White Scallop or Summer Turban. The squashes are now nearly mature, but there is no immediate effect whatever. In order to test the matter more fully I hybridized two plants which have exceedingly dissimilar fruits. These are *Datura stramonium* [Jamestown weed] and *D. inermis*. The former has very prickly pods, the latter very smooth ones. I have made reciprocal hybridizations, but there is no immediate effect of pollen. *I have never yet seen any immediate effect of pollen.* I am very careful in making my crosses and I know that I have made no mistake. I do all the work myself. I use manila bags on both pistillate and staminate flowers, and I leave them on the pistillate flowers a week after the operation is performed.

[22] *Report of the Commissioner of Agriculture* for 1887, p. 314.

At Iowa Agricultural similar experiments in apples had been made by Joseph L. Budd and B. D. Halsted. There, also, Niels E. Hansen, a student, collected evidence showing that foreign pollen "does sometimes exert an immedate effect on the fruit." Goff at the New York experiment station and William R. Lazenby at the Ohio experiment station had tested the matter using varieties of strawberries; Goff also had fertilized black and white grapes. Crozier, S. M. Tracy, Sturtevant, and a few others had experimented with corn. But there were not many men in colleges and experiment stations doing hybridization work.

The primary reason for this was, of course, that it was an undeveloped science. Also in many instances the importance of such experiments was interpreted taxonomically. Botanists in many quarters had not got over the belief that such work was "radical" and of not much importance academically. What significance they could see in the work was from the practical standpoint. The men to whom these garden and orchard experiments principally belonged, in their view, were the men of practice— farmers with aptitudes for the work, nurserymen, gardeners by trade, and others linked commercially, who had the requisite field facilities and greenhouses to enable them to conduct the experiments on the scale required. Many, if not most, botanists did not have access to sufficiently adequate gardens, orchards, and indoor facilities, to pursue such experiments. Nor the money or time. Bailey, Goff, and a few other advanced thinkers initiated a movement to undermine this old belief. On January 12, 1887, Bailey wrote Sereno Watson of the Gray Herbarium:

I am giving considerable attention of late to the nomenclature and terminology of cultivated plants. Among other things it occurs to me that the stringing together of Latin adjectives for the names of garden varieties should be remedied. The names of many of our garden plants are longer than the pre-Linnean names. Should there not be some means of distinguishing by the name the garden varieties from natural varieties? I have in mind two methods of doing this: by using the word *forma* (forms) for variety or else the word *hortensis* (hort.). Thus, Juniperus Sabina *form.* variegata or *hort.* variegate. I incline to the latter word. Will you please let me know which word you would prefer?

Bailey was not the first to concern himself with the origins of cultivated plants. Years before Edward Lewis Sturtevant had written Bessey and others about his very valuable work in origins. DeCandolle in Europe before him had devised modernized methods for the study. Sturtevant began his studies in an effort of heroic proportions to enlist the interest of botanists in cultivated plants. In this Bailey and he were in accord.

In Bailey's "Origin of the Tomato from a Morphological Standpoint,"[23] he maintained the thesis, "There are two methods by which the cultivator can determine the origin of vegetables which have been long in cultivation. He can follow the history of the plant back to its introduction to gardens and may then be able to identify it with a wild species, or he may reason from inference from the morphology and direction of variation of the plant at hand." In the instance of the tomato, Bailey inferred red to have been the plant's original color but admitted, "How far man may have influenced these colors by selection, however, is unknown." Variability lay in size, form, and number of cells, and his discussion went along these lines. At the foot of the article, an interesting editorial note signed by "A[sa] G[ray]" appeared: "It would be interesting to compare the above study with work of Dr. Sturtevant, of the New York Experiment Station, on his new agricultural botany." If the assumption that Gray edited this article is correct, it is not difficult to understand his point of view on this subject. Botany included both an "agricultural botany" and a "scientific botany." It would be difficult to say in which branch Gray placed horticulture. Probably what was meant by this was that one branch was impressed with an economic and business use; the other, with the purposes of biologic study.

Bailey began a series of studies in "Horticultural Terminology."[24] "Horticultural terms," he said, "are for the most part poorly defined and loosely used. Good English, considerately employed, is requisite to great advancement in horticultural literature. Some of the current technical literature is nearly worthless because of inattention to the terms employed." He illustrated by pointing to a number of terms improperly "confounded." Principally concerned with horticultural classification, he wrote:

The horticultural classificatory terms are of necessity poorly defined. Nature is not uniform nor methodical in the making of groups or associations of plants. She has given us no unit of classification. Hence it comes that some thinkers discard the idea of species, saying that specific types do not exist. But there must be classification of natural objects before we can have science concerning them and it therefore becomes necessary to fix upon some unit, even though it be an arbitrary one from which we build an ascending or a descending series. This unit is the species. The idea of species is conventional. It is therefore not definite. The horticulturist does well to allow the botanist to construct the limit of species. The species given, the horticulturist finds tolerable ease in constructing his minuter classifications. . . .

Such articles explanatory of how a horticultural taxonomy was to be constructed met instant approval. *The American Garden* and Floral Cabinet commented that Bailey's "recent articles in these pages have attracted much attention,"[25] and announced that in the next issue would

[23] *The American Garden* and Floral Cabinet, pp. 116, 117.
[24] *Ibid.*, pp. 157, 200, 219.   [25] *Ibid.*, p. 248.

appear a study by him on "Acclimatization. Does It Occur?"[26] With
the work's appearance, the author sought to establish several fundamental concepts in answer to H. E. Van Deman, pomologist of the
United States Department of Agriculture, who had asked, "Is there such
a thing as acclimatization?" Bailey said:

It must be borne in mind that the essential idea of both acclimation and
acclimatization is the overcoming of a climate which is at first injurious to
the plant or the species. It must also be remembered that the difference
between acclimation and acclimatization lies in the fact that the former is a
process of wild nature, while the latter takes place under the guidance or
supervision of man. The processes, methods, in the two are essentially the
same.

The literature of the subject is in most cases valueless, because the idea
of overcoming climate is not kept in view. . . . Increase in hardiness is by no
means the only proof of acclimatization, although common opinion seems
to consider it so. . . .

A slight change, as well as a great one, is acclimatization. . . .

The issue, not a very serious one it must be said, was what was sufficient to characterize a given situation as an instance of acclimatization
or acclimation. Some persons were unreasonable in their demands.
Bailey drew examples from wild plants and cultivated plants. He discussed the work of Beal taking corn from Michigan to Kansas and
bringing corn from southern states to Michigan. He referred to work of
Charles Gibb and Budd of Iowa Agricultural in American importation
of Russian fruit and ornamental varieties. This was a very important
enterprise which was later also taken up by Frederic William Taylor,
the University of Nebraska's first professor of horticulture, an un-
schooled but trained nurseryman selected by Bessey from the state's
horticultural and agricultural ranks. Indeed, so important a subject was
American importation of Russian fruit varieties for the western prairies,
especially apples, we must digress and consider the work of the experimental farms of Canada which participated in the work and which
beginning in 1886 were being established under leadership of William
Saunders.[27]

The work of this William Saunders, for a quarter of a century director of experimental farms of the Dominion and with whom was entrusted the task of selecting sites and choosing officers for farms

[26] *Ibid.*, pp. 295, 325, ff.
[27] The material used in this book concerning William Saunders of Canada has been
taken from Bailey's *Cyclopedia of American Horticulture*, an article by C. J. S. Bethune
in *The Canadian Entomologist*, XLVI, 10 (October 1914), pp. 333-336, and a collection
of newspaper clippings gathered together in book form at the public library of London,
Ontario. Members of the Saunders family have given the author some aid. Attention
may be called to a pamphlet, prepared by Blodwen Davies and published in 1930 by
The Ryerson Press of Toronto, Ontario, *The Story of Agriculture*, Canadian History
Readers, pp. 17-28, devoted principally to elaborating the work of Dr. Saunders and
his sons, Percy and Charles, in wheat improvement.

established from the Atlantic to Pacific coasts, must not be confused with the work of William Saunders of the United States Department of Agriculture.

William Saunders of Canada was an economic entomologist, author of the classic *Insects Injurious to Fruits*, a botanist, and one, as agriculturist and horticulturist, to perform some of the most useful hybridization experiments in American scientific history. He produced cold resistant apples of good quality and size and high grade cereals. Nor were William Saunders' attentions confined to fruits and cereals. During his celebrated career, he brought to Canada much that was beautiful and useful among trees, shrubs, and flowers. Foreign importations played a vital part in the work, as will be seen.

Born in Devon, England, June 16, 1836, Saunders came to Canada at the age of twelve years. Studious by nature and persistent, he acquired sufficient knowledge of chemistry to set himself up between the years 1860-1865 as a manufacturing chemist. For twenty-five years he remained in business at London, Ontario. A love of nature, however, early led him into collecting wild plants and insects around London. Because he always did thoroughly whatever he did, almost before he realized it he was becoming a student of botany and entomology.

In 1862 Saunders and C. J. S. Bethune organized an Entomological Society and six years later began publishing the *Canadian Entomologist*, to the first numbers of which they were the only contributors. Bethune served as editor for five years and Saunders held the position from 1873 to 1886. To these interests Saunders joined his sharp insight in fruit growing. In 1868 he had purchased a farm near London, a farm which today is deserving of high historical rank in Canadian science: because there Saunders began his significant hybridization experiments in small fruits—gooseberries, currants, raspberries, and grapes.

Saunders was fortunate in the happiest of marriages. His wife was an ardent nature lover, also a botanist, and an intelligent practical gardener. From this union were born sons of exceptional ability, at least three of whom in science and the arts and as teachers have contributed greatly to the world's knowledge, productivity, and pleasure.

In 1881 Saunders' scientific abilities were recognized by an official appointment as Fellow of the Royal Society. This honor as a founder of the society was to be superseded only by his election in 1906 to Canada's greatest scientific distinction, the presidency of the society. Space does not permit elaboration of all the honors accorded him. Suffice it here to record events of the following year, 1882.

In 1882 he participated in an eventful botanical exploration of southern Ontario with T. J. W. Burgess and John and James Macoun, another family which has contributed greatly to the natural history of

Canada. In 1882 Saunders was elected president of the Ontario Fruit Growers' Association, an organization in which for years he took a most active part. That same year he became professor of materia medica of Western University, a position which he held three years. This added to his fame as the founder of the Ontario College of Pharmacy of which he was president for two years. His book *Insects Injurious to Fruit* was published in 1882 and, forming the basis for an enlarged work, served as a standard text for many years in schools and colleges of the United States and Canada. This year also Saunders attended the American Forestry Congress held in Cincinnati, Ohio, as one of three delegates from the Dominion. His paper on "Forest Insects" won him recognition and as years went on he became a leading authority on Canadian tree and forest planting. "Here is the man," wrote one magazine, "who has done more for Canada than all the politicians."

During the 1880's, that vital artery between the Atlantic and Pacific coasts in Canada—the Canadian Pacific Railway—was laying its tracks westward for the increased migration that soon went west. Timber lands were abundant in the West. In the far west one of the finest timber stands of the world invited industrial growth. But agriculture on the prairies presented a sorry sight. The coldness of the winters and the short growing season discouraged agricultural development. Finding fruit and cereal varieties that would ripen early enough, that would be of sufficiently good and hardy quality, that would thrive on the hot arid lands in summer and make living possible there, presented a challenge which William Saunders and his corps of workers accepted and won after a long valiant struggle. In their battle, techniques of soil and water conservation, the control of overgrazing by domesticated animals, erosion control, in brief, range management supplemented by programs of forestry practice adapted to farms, have played prominent parts; and the origins of some of these and other techniques applied to develop a prairie horticulture, agriculture, and forestry, similar to that developed in like situations in the United States, date to early years of the founding of these stations. At least, their utilization on a scientific basis in Canada in large part emanated from these stations.

In the early 1880's the whole of Canada suffered from an agricultural depression, so much so that Parliament acted. A House appointed committee circulated a questionnaire, among numerous other inquiries, asking:

Would the establishment of an experimental farm or garden where varieties of foreign grain, fruits, trees and fertilizers might be tested, and whence such seeds, plants, etc. might be distributed throughout the Dominion be advisable?

Among other matters, the committee recommended the placement of experimental farms similar to experiment stations of the United States and Europe. The trouble, said the report in effect, was not in Canadian agricultural resources but in the farming methods employed.

Sir John Carling was then Dominion minister of agriculture. In 1885 he selected his fellow townsman Saunders to go to Europe and study the work of stations there. Saunders went, returned and made his report, and in 1886 a resolution and bill conforming substantially to his urgings received Parliamentary and royal approval.

Saunders by this time was in his fifty-first year. At the height of his capabilities he was taken in the autumn of 1886 from London to Ottawa to develop, as director, perhaps the most extensive governmentally authorized and financed program for agricultural advancement the world had yet known. When the first site—the central farm—was selected, a bare tract of land had to be leveled, stumps and boulders dynamited, houses and buildings constructed, hedges and an arboretum planted. To this farm Saunders transferred eight hundred seedlings of grape, gooseberry, raspberry, and currant varieties created on his London farm. Immediately importation of foreign varieties was officially commenced— crab apples from Siberia; wheats from northern Russia, northern India, Japan, the United States, and elsewhere—and cross breeding and acclimatization studies of wide variety were begun. It is said that in 1887 Saunders had introduced brome grass from Russia. Earlier work had made available a western rye grass on a large scale. At the Colonial Exhibition held in London, England, in 1886, Saunders' Emerald grape had come into highest recognition. Wheats, oats, barleys, field peas, and numerous other plants of utility and value were developed under his period of directorship. The introduction of labor saving implements and machinery was both needed and valuable in developing a Dominion-wide agriculture. In the West, the elaboration of dry-farming techniques became very useful. Saunders and his sons, A. F. and C. E.—the last named was knighted for the accomplishment—almost alone, practically transformed western Canadian agriculture from a frontier farming of hogs and corn to cattle and wheat by crossbreeding Red Fife wheat with other foreign grains, thereby presenting to Canada early ripening northern harvests of the celebrated wheats, Marquis, Garnet, Reward, "and the present favorites, Red Bobs and Thatcher. . . . By allotting such grains to the varying regions in terms of their efficiency when measured against the known drought, insect, disease and frost risks," comments John Bartlet Brebner in *North Atlantic Triangle*,[28] "first-class wheat could be grown over most of the plains from their semiarid margins to the Peace River district at 56° north latitude. . . . The 42

[28] "The Interplay of Canada, the United States and Great Britain," pp. 217, 231-232. Yale University Press, 1945.

million bushels of 1891 [became] 132 million by 1911, doubled in the next five years, and . . . reached the 400-million-bushel level by 1922, the crop year in which for the first time Canadian wheat exports exceeded those of the United States. This tenfold growth in thirty years gave Canada an entirely new place in the world economy. . . ." Moreover, these triumphs gave tremendous impetus to industrial research in plants on the North American continent, furthering greatly the cause and work of agricultural experimentation.

Saunders, it is said, spent three months continuously traveling to locate the branch farms. The central farm was located near Ottawa on the boundary line of the provinces of Ontario and Quebec. So the first branch was also located on the boundary line of Nova Scotia and New Brunswick at Nappan. The second branch farm was placed in the Northwest at Brandon, Manitoba. For the work of open prairies, a site at Indian Head, Saskatchewan, without a tree or bush, was selected. Within four years, forest clumps, shelter belts, hedges, small fruit plantations, and vegetable and flower gardens were thriving. Even a few young apple trees, which had not been winter-killed, were growing. At Agassiz, British Columbia, the problem was fruit and nut growing. Only a few years passed, and the work at each place was proving its worth. The movement would expand to include many more branch farms and stations, including forest nurseries, a horse-breeding station, a fox farm, and experimental substations. To this would be linked a chain of illustration stations. All phases of farm life would receive attention. "Acclimatization" studies in those years may seem crude in the light of modern progress. Cross breeding of those years may seem more products of chance than science. But they were real and they were fundamental.

In 1887, when Bailey wrote his article on "Acclimatization. Does It Occur?" the Canadian experimental work had not really been organized. His attention, therefore, was centered mostly on results obtained in the United States.

It was in this year, 1887, that Bailey urged, "We need to study our plants in the field rather than in the herbarium to acquaint ourselves with their entire history, and their habits. The constrast between our wild red currant and the wild red currant of Europe, unobservable in the herbarium, is an illustration in point."[29] The study of plant life histories has been going on in America for a number of years. But only within the past year on any formal scale of consequence had ecological studies been pursued. Study of geographical plant distributions had been some time in progress. Gray and Hooker had these subjects well developed. However, study of plants in their habitats, of their physical and biological factors, had not really commenced on any formal plane.

[29] "The Wild Currant a Sketch," *The College Speculum,* April 1, 1887 issue, pp. 6, 7.

The year before, as part of his state survey of the Nebraska flora, Bessey had commenced semi-ecological studies including practices, indefinite and not fully organized, which anticipated the later more thorough and exact phytogeographical work of the University of Nebraska department. Practically at the same time Bailey and Bessey were urging more study of plants in their habitats.

Since his years at the Gray Herbarium, Bailey had been studying the genus Carex. Appearing as notes on the genus, since 1884, studies had been published in the *Botanical Gazette*[30] edited by John Merle Coulter, Charles R. Barnes, and Joseph Charles Arthur. On May 28, 1885, Bailey had written George Vasey:

> Yours of the 14th inst[ant], together with the very welcome and interesting pamphlet on grasses, came during my absence from home, hence the delay of this response. You will please accept thanks for your catalogue. I enclose you four of my Carex catalogues. If you should wish more they are at your disposal. . . .
> It has long been my desire to prepare a considerable pamphlet on the sedges—their general character, distribution, uses, histories, etc. Does the department of agr[iculture] ever undertake such work?

Labrador and Grinnell Land species were obtained. Access was permitted to more important collections, at the University of Michigan, Charles R. Orcutt's at San Diego, California, Turner's, and many others. Bailey wished "to take in all Cyperaceae" but for some time he was confined to species within Carex. In 1884 was published *A Catalogue of North American Carices*, compiled as an exchange list, a check list for herbaria, and as a contribution to American caricography. That same year began to appear the supplements or catalogues. Not until 1887 did another large-sized presentation take place. This was published as a *Proceeding of the American Academy of Arts and Sciences*, as a contribution from the herbarium of Harvard University, "A preliminary synopsis of North American carices including those of Mexico, Central America, and Greenland, with an American bibliography of the genus."[31] During 1888 appearance of the studies continued.

Bailey often had to go to Boston. In September, 1887, he attended there the twenty-first session of the American Pomological Society, at which he spoke on "The Relation of Seed Production to Cultivation," stating in the course of his speech the following conclusions:

1. Seed production has increased, as a rule, in those plants which are cultivated for their seeds.
2. Seed production has decreased, as a rule, in those plants which are

[30] I-VI, *Bot. Gaz.* IX, X, 117-122, 137-141, 203-208, 293-296, 317-319, 379-382. Pls. iii-viii. (1884-1885.) VIII-IX, *ibid.*, XI, 328-330. Pl. xi. 1886. XIII, 82-89. (1888.)
[31] VII, *Proc. Amer. Acad.* XXII, 59-157. (1886.)

propagated exclusively or nearly so by parts, other than seeds, which nature uses in their propagation.

3. Seed production bears no immediate relation to cultivation in those plants which are cultivated for the flesh or pulp of their so-called fruits.[32]

Bailey maintained that seed production in all fruits falling under the third caption, is an incidental variation, the same as form, color, size, texture, and other characters.

Joseph Charles Arthur was born in upper New York state—of distinguished New England lineage. He was in the direct line of descent from Governor Bradford of Massachusetts and John and Priscilla Alden. Raised in Iowa where he had gone to the agricultural college, Arthur had become one of Charles E. Bessey's first students, and had achieved in three years an enviable reputation in physiological botany at the New York Experiment Station at Geneva. On February 9, 1885, he had written Bessey, "I am greatly interested in my investigations, and I am to take my doctor's degree at Cornell a year from June." This doctorate, D.Sc., the first conferred in botany at Cornell University, together with Bessey's adequate foundation, prepared Arthur for a life work in the study of "the life and habits of some of the plants that cause diseases of cultivated crops, such as the rusts etc." A decision to specialize in these subjects was the result of a visit to Farlow's herbarium at Cambridge in 1884. Although Arthur lacked money to purchase exsiccatti or any collections for study, he began his investigations studying with Albert Nelson Prentiss, Bessey's teacher at Michigan Agricultural, who had been appointed in 1868 to the chair of botany, arboriculture and horticulture at Cornell. Of course, Arthur continued his work at the experiment station. But at the university he had the added advantages of laboratory facilities which had been developed over a period of several years—from meager beginnings about 1875 and added to in the department's quarters in the south wing of Sage College.

Not only was Arthur's doctorate the first conferred in Botany at Cornell University, it was possibly the first doctor's degree ever conferred by any university for a thesis on the pathological aspects of a plant disease. Certainly it was the first dealing with a bacterial disease of plants, and employing modern pure culture methods. Burrill, who first discovered living bacteria in the blighted bark ("cambium of the blighted branch, where the trouble first shows itself," he said) had transmitted successfully the disease by direct inoculation—first, by introducing on a knife-point "minute moving particles" contained in a viscous fluid or exudate of the diseased trees and, later, by use of bits of diseased tissue. Thus he established presumptively a strong casual relation between his *Bacillus amylovorus* and the disease. Arthur, however,

[32] Proceedings of the society, p. 120.

set out to find "absolute proof that pear blight is due to bacteria."
On January 30, 1885, he wrote Bessey, "I have just begun the
cultivation of bacteria on solid substratum and hope soon to arrange
culture tubes for their cultivation in fluids. I only today planted my
pear bacteria and so do not yet know how I shall succeed with them." A
half year later he was convinced he had such "absolute" proof. But
his studies continued for more than a year longer,[33] in the course of
which the Cornell doctorate was conferred on him, notwithstanding the
fact that a large part of the work was performed at the Geneva station.
Arthur's doctorate diploma now hangs on the walls of the plant science
building at Cornell University, his gift to the first department of plant
pathology to be established in an American university.

In 1885 Arthur received an appointment as botanist of a Minnesota
geological and natural history survey and wrote Bessey:

> My engagement in Minnesota is to have control of the whole botanical
> survey. Unfortunately I am only engaged for at the most three months in
> the year. The pay is $100 per month, and field expenses. I had planned to go
> on in a week or two and remain till the meeting at Ann Arbor, and expected
> to lay out the survey and get the work well under way in this time. This was
> upon the contingency of my getting a position elsewhere that would permit
> me to resign my present place. Now that this has failed I shall be obliged to
> give up my visit to Minnesota this year. How this will suit Prof[essor]
> Winchell and the authorities, I do not yet know. I am having the blues over
> it myself, but see no alternative. . . .

Arthur's and Sturtevant's relations at the New York station were
none too cordial; at least, from Arthur's point of view, relations were
strained. Sturtevant, he believed, was not giving him full credit for his
work. He had consulted Bessey in an effort to find a position elsewhere.
None, however, had materialized. The Minnesota work, spread through

---

[33] Another worker, Merton B. Waite, a student of Burrill at the University of
Illinois, conducted while in the employ of the United States Department of Agriculture further research on "pear blight," to which reference later will be made in
the text. For present purposes, no less an authority than Erwin F. Smith may be quoted
to describe Waite's contribution: "Waite finally isolated the right organism, reproduced the disease with pure cultures, worked out his cultural characters, proved by
painstaking experiments that it was distributed by bees and other insects in the orchard,
proved that the main danger to the orchard lies in hold-over blight, and demonstrated
on a large scale in Georgia and California that the orchards could be saved by the
rigid elimination of this hold-over blight." During the year 1899 Smith wrote several
articles published in the *Centralblatt für Bakteriologie* on bacterial diseases of plants.
In these, Arthur's work on pear blight was considered, and on December 30, 1899,
Arthur wrote to Smith, "I want to thank you for the excellent and discriminating
statement regarding my contribution to the subject of pear blight which I find in your
answer to Dr. Fischer in a recent *Centr. f. Bak.* Of course I have known for some
time that I had confounded in my published accounts a non-pathogenic with the true
pear blight bacillus, but that chiefly affected the morphological part of my work. What
you have said of my work is certainly true, and could not have been better stated by
myself." Waite's work was also considered in these articles. The above quotation
concerning Waite's work is taken from a letter of Smith to L. R. Jones, dated February 24, 1914.

a year under Professor N. H. Winchell's direction, would have been sufficient. A summer's work was not. Arthur, despite his suspicion that an "internal eruption" at the station would occur at any time, held his place. The following summer the work in Minnesota came to fruition and Arthur went to study the flora, assisted by Bailey, Warren Upham, and E. W. D. Holway.

On July 1, 1886, Bailey wrote Gray:

. . . I am going with the botanical party of the geological survey of Minnesota on a collecting trip in the vicinity of Vermillion Lake, N[orthern] Minnesota, about 30 miles from the British boundary. The country is entirely unexplored. I will be out about three weeks. Is there anything in particular I shall look for for you? I start July 10. Mrs. Bailey will go as far as Minneapolis with me.

In 1887, published as the survey's third bulletin, appeared the "Report on Botanical Work in Minnesota for the Year 1886"[34] by Arthur, Bailey, and the two special assistants, Upham and Holway. After completing his work on the survey, Bailey, escorted by some Ojibway Indians, went on to the termination of Hunter Island on the line of the Ontario boundary. Returning, he wrote a book of his explorations, a manuscript which was never published.

This was not the only exploration which Bailey made during his years at Michigan Agricultural. On July 4, 1888, he wrote Watson:

I take the liberty to send you by express, prepaid, a small parcel of plants for examination. Dr. Beal, C. F. Wheeler, and myself have made a botanizing trip across Michigan in the jack pine plains region, and the few things I send are mostly from this collection . . .

On the previous April 19 he had written Watson:

I have in my possession a valuable and handsome paper on American Grapes by Professor Munson. He says that you wish to see it. I shall make an abstract of it for my own use, and then send it to you—in two or three weeks. Or if you need it sooner, will try to make my abstract at once.

I have accepted the new chair of horticulture at Cornell.

As a matter of fact, Bailey had been offered the directorship of the agricultural experiment station located at Cornell University. He had refused the offer, however, since he preferred to remain in research rather than go into administration. On March 7, 1888, he confided to Erwin F. Smith, ". . . I have not yet decided as to Cornell . . . ," and then, in another letter, dated May 16, attempting to persuade Smith not to accept the directorship of a station in another state, Bailey explained: ". . . To my way of thinking, a directorship is not a sinecure, and is not a desirable place for a specialist in any line. Too much of one's time is

[34] St. Paul, Pioneer Press Company, 56 pp. 1887.

consumed in purely executive matters. I was offered directorship at Cornell, but would not have it. . . ."

In March, 1887, President Cleveland had approved a congressional act which established an agricultural experiment station in every state of the Union, and appropriated therefor the sum of fifteen thousand dollars for use by each state. New York state had two stations—the firmly established one at Geneva and the one at Cornell University maintained by the university. Under provisions of the law, the famous "Hatch Act," and under terms of the state laws distributing the funds, Cornell was to receive nine-tenths of the New York state fund for federalization of the station—that is, it was to become a state station, aided by the federal government similar to other state stations—and the Geneva station was to receive the other one-tenth to enable it to secure the franking privileges on its publications. With money available, Cornell University decided to establish a chair of horticulture. In this, it became the first American university or college to recognize permanently horticulture as a subject distinct from botany and other branches of plant science.

Charles W. Garfield, it is said, was the first man considered by Cornell for the place. Garfield, however, was not a scientist but a banker who through years of interest in horticulture and forestry had maintained a very forward-looking attitude. Able and individualistic, he had watched with dismay Michigan's vast forest resources being depleted by commerce and fires, by advancements made in agriculture and the fruit-growing industry. It can be said that Garfield in a very real sense fathered the notable forestry work established later at the University of Michigan at Ann Arbor. Michigan Agricultural's board had been impressed by his vigorous writings and driving strength in state agricultural and horticultural circles. As a consequence, he had become a member of the college's governing board. Indeed, it is not improbable that he had had much to do with returning Bailey from Cambridge, Massachusetts, and botany under Gray, to Michigan Agricultural College in a professorial capacity in horticulture. He realized then that what was needed was a young man of thorough scientific vision and capability.

Cornell University, contemplating systematic development of a too much neglected horticulture, invited Garfield to lecture at Ithaca. Ithaca, like Lansing, was located in a great horticultural region of grapes, apples, peaches, and other pomological products. Agriculture at Cornell, however, was organized only as a department of the university. Its small corps of experiment station workers, like those of nearly all other stations, were compelled to confine their labors to feeding and fertilizer experiments stressing chemical phases of investigation. They had ambitiously planned an organization which would have assured cooperation of all state agricultural societies. But the plan had failed. Consequently, workers, few in number, gave voluntarily of their time from teaching and with no specific remuneration. To learn farming was to do farming, it was believed. Emphasis was placed on animal care and crop production and other aspects of practical agriculture. Had not the presence of certain leaders in American agriculture been afforded Cornell, its rank as an agricultural center, educationally, would probably have been inconsiderable. Despite the fact that instruction began eleven years after Michigan Agricultural College had opened its doors, such men of eminence as Isaac Phillips Roberts, professor of agriculture, who had come to Cornell in 1874 from Iowa Agricultural, G. C. Caldwell, professor of chemistry and its "offspring," agricultural chemistry, James Law, professor of veterinary science, a graduate of good Scotch, English, and French schools and regarded one of the ablest men in his science; Prentiss, in botany; John Henry Comstock, in entomology with his Insectary erected from station funds in 1887-1888, the first known building devoted to such study; and W. R. Dudley in cryptogamic botany who initiated studies, more or less mycological in nature, but quite definitely anticipating later more exact plant disease work, constituted an array of educational greatness not excelled by any American university. Their work and instruction were the chief glories of Cornell's agricultural department, not its experiment station. William Rose Lazenby had been an instructor in horticulture but in 1881 resigned to accept a position as Ohio State University's first professor of horticulture and forestry. Needless to say, with poor experimental facilities and practically no special instruction in horticulture, Cornell's work in not only practical but also experimental phases of horticulture instruction was devastatingly lacking.

Pomology as a neglected but potential science was attracting interest everywhere. In these transitional years, when scientific experimentation was coming to the foreground with almost the swell of a tidal wave, two years were more than sufficient to set in motion new strong currents of scientific thought. Although late in establishment, two years before, on July 1, 1886, a division of pomology had been created in the United States Department of Agriculture. Theretofore, only such attention as William Saunders, superintendent of gardens and grounds, had been able to give voluntarily to pomological study had been practically all the notice paid by government services to a fruit-growing industry approaching an annual value of between two and three hundred million dollars. On August 6, 1886, H. E. Van Deman had left his home at Geneva, Kansas, gone to a Central Texas horticultural society meeting, later proceeded to Cleveland, Ohio, to attend sessions of the American Horticultural Society and visit nearby places of interest in Ohio and

Michigan including the Michigan state fair, still later attended a fair of the Arkansas State Horticultural Society and a meeting of the State Horticultural Association of Pennsylvania, and in January of the next year viewed the work of "one of the oldest and most active horticultural societies in the United States," the Western New York Horticultural Society. In the course of his investigations as the newly appointed pomologist of the federal division, Van Deman, aided by agricultural colleges, concluded that at least another two or three hundred million dollars were annually "lost by insect depredations, by mistakes made in planting unsuitable varieties, and in ignorantly caring for the fruit-bearing trees, vines, and plants of the United States, a great share of which might be saved by our people with comparatively little outlay of means and labor if intelligently applied." Van Deman proposed that his division should gather information and distribute it. Pomologists and horticulturists endorsed the contemplated work. Value in learning under what conditions and with what measure of success Japanese plums were being grown in California, what pears were being cultivated in the South, what oranges in Florida and California, what Russian apples in Iowa and Wisconsin—quite certainly, the new varieties of each—was obvious. Leading fruit growers and "life-long experimenters in practical pomology" offered use of their grounds and their personal labors.[35]

In 1891, one of Bailey's most able students, an editor-in-chief of *The College Speculum* in 1887, William Alton Taylor, would become assistant pomologist of the division, to continue a general and systematic study of American and world fruit. Taylor had grown up on the edge of the woods. His father, a Congregational minister and graduate of Union and Princeton theological seminaries, and his mother, a graduate of Mount Holyoke College, had moved from a New York state home to the orchard lands near the mouth of the Kalamazoo River on the eastern shore of Lake Michigan not far from South Haven, because of his father's ailing health. There William had been born. Educated in his home state of Michigan, Taylor came to the division with a thorough knowledge of pomological conditions in middle western areas of the United States. Incidentally, he arrived with a thorough knowledge of Bailey's teaching and a thorough admiration for his ability as a pomologist and general horticulturist.

The movement to coordinate American agricultural experimentation had had a slow but steadily progressive growth projected to a goal set at least two decades before—and probably earlier. Dr. Manly Miles, America's first professor of practical agriculture and at the time at Michigan Agricultural College, had been a principal initiator of the

35 *Report of the Comm. of Agric.* for 1886, "Report of the Pomologist," pp. 259 ff.

movement. With the aid of W. C. Flagg of Illinois Industrial University, Miles had assembled a convention which had met in Chicago in August of 1871 and considered experiments which different institutions might conduct similarly. The best methods of conducting experiments having regard to raising standards of farm products and domestic animal breeds were discussed. Attempt was made, as far as possible, to find ways to experiment on uniform plans, particularly with reference to size of plats, continuance of experiments year after year, crop rotation—agricultural matters primarily but which included horticultural phases. Many years passed and the movement to establish stations extended to all corners of the nation. A convention of agricultural college delegates in 1883 endorsed college stations created and financed in part by money from the national treasury. Again in 1885 a convention of delegates from agricultural colleges and experiment stations advocated similarly and went on record as favoring establishment of means of intercommunication and a periodical showing results of agricultural progress. In October, 1887, the Association of American Colleges and Experiment Stations was organized in a convention assembled for the purpose; and in October of the next year the Commissioner of Agriculture set up an Office of Experiment Stations as a branch of the United States Department of Agriculture. Each development brought nearer the long-fought-for realization of coordination of work between the stations and a central office in the charge of an able director, W. O. Atwater. The enactment of Congress introduced by William H. Hatch of Missouri represented the culmination of a struggle which on at least two occasions had been defeated. Twice, recommended legislation had been rejected. The "Hatch Act," as it became known, proved to be the enabling act to well-knit organization. An arrangement was effected under which the stations worked for many years, pursuant to the landgrant college objectives of the Morrill Act of 1862.[36] A strong current of authority holds that Norman J. Colman, governor of Missouri, and later United States Commissioner of Agriculture, was the "virtual sponsor" of the Hatch Act, although Representative Hatch introduced it and saw it through Congress.

Bailey did not become acquainted with Hatch. Nor did he appear before any legislative committee hearings in the course of Congressional proceedings. But for Michigan State Agricultural College he made up a program for a station to be placed there. It is more than likely that a copy of this found its way to Washington. At the state fair held at Jackson in September, 1887, Bailey reported for a committee on the

[36] For further elaboration of most of the points of this paragraph, see A. C. True's "Origin and Development of Agricultural Experiment Stations in the United States" with a list of the stations, *Report of the Commissioner of Agriculture* for 1888, pp. 541-547; and 547-558.

subject prior to the station's organization on February 21, 1888, with President Willits as director:

Recognizing the great importance of horticultural interests in the State of Michigan and appreciating the demand constantly made by intelligent fruit-growers and gardeners for experimental aid to their business, we recommend that the State Horticultural Society present to the State Board of Agriculture and others in authority the importance and necessity of applying a liberal portion of the funds to accrue from the operation of the Hatch bill to horticultural experiments. As an indication of the experiments needed by practical horticulturists, we submit the following synopsis, and suggest that some one or more of the topics indicated may be chosen as a basis of continuous labor in the forthcoming experiment station:

I. Experiments in the organization of new varieties of fruits, vegetables and ornamental plants.
a. By ordinary seedage.
b. By selection.
c. By crossing and hybridizing.
II. Improvement and maintenance of old varieties.
a. By methods of tillage.
b. By fertilizers.
c. By change of stock, crossing and hybridizing.
III. Introduction and testing of new varieties and species.
a. Promising wild fruits and ornamental plants.
b. Japanese and Chinese plants.
c. Russian plants.
d. Domestic cultivated plants.
IV. Physiological researches.
V. Pathological researches; investigations concerning diseases of plants, especially in Michigan, peach yellows, rotting of plums and cherries, falling of the plum leaf, apple scab, tomato rot, potato rot, blackberry and raspberry rust, grape rots and mildews, strawberry rust, gooseberry mildew, lettuce mold, celery rust.
VI. Experiments upon the relative cost of methods of culture and upon manipulations, tools, etc.[37]

Because of pressure of college duties, Bailey's horticultural department during his last year had not been able to undertake experiments such as would be "leading features of true experiment station work."[38] The work was turned over to President Willits and L. R. Taft and his assistant U. P. Hedrick. During Bailey's years as professor at Michigan Agricultural, it is said that not one foot of space under glass was provided for vegetable growing. Bailey was ambitious to study greenhouse work experimentally.

Bailey's acceptance of a position at Cornell meant an increase in salary. It was not this reason, however, that prompted his leaving the school of his own instruction. Charles Kendall Adams was president

[37] 17th Ann. Rep. Sect. St. Hort. Soc. Mich., pp. 471, 472.
[38] 27th Ann. Rep. Sect. St. Bd. Agric. Mich., 1887-1888, p. 233.

of Cornell at this time, having succeeded Andrew Dixon White who had been made United States ambassador to Russia. The professorship of practical and experimental horticulture, created as a result of a committee recommendation framed by President Adams and professors Roberts, Caldwell, Prentiss, Comstock, and Williams as one means of carrying out at Cornell the purposes of the Hatch Act, was offered Bailey. Charles W. Garfield told Roberts that Bailey was the young man for whom they were looking. The Cornell authorities wrote President Willits asking his opinion of Bailey and Willits replied that he scarcely knew what he thought because he had never been able to move fast enough to catch up with him.[39]

President Adams went to Lansing and interviewed Bailey at the Michigan capital's leading hotel. In the course of their "chat," Willits happened in and, recognizing Adams and Bailey, said to Adams, "You're plowing with my heifer." Adams acknowledged it, and next day Bailey went to Willits and told of Cornell University's offer to him. Bailey said that for money only he would not leave Michigan Agricultural. But Adams had topped the offer by saying that Cornell would send Bailey to Europe to study what was going on in horticultural research and education. Willits answered, "In that event you must go. You can do more for the advancement of M. A. C. than if you stay here at what we can do for you." To this members of the faculty also agreed. So Bailey accepted the offer made by Cornell.[40]

Another Michigan Agricultural graduate went at this time from the Middle West to the East. At Iowa Agricultural College also, an experiment station was established under provisions of the Hatch Act. In March, the new director arrived. Byron David Halsted's mind at that time was on what was expected of him in the work there. Zealously he had kept on with scientific investigations—a naturalist of proven ability—interested in physiological and pathological studies. As Farlow's first graduate student, he contributed to the development of American mycology. It was probably this fact, along with some original studies conducted at Iowa Agricultural, that caused his removal to the new station, established with the state station, at Rutgers College, New Brunswick, New Jersey. On December 26, 1888, he wrote Farlow:

Yesterday I received a telegram announcing my appointment as Professor of Botany and Horticulture at Rutgers College. The work will be very largely in the Experiment Station. The position it seems to me will be much better than the one here aside from the greatly added facilities for the consulting of libraries and herbaria and the advance in salary. The

[39] "L. H. Bailey as a Co-worker," by I. P. Roberts, *Cornell Countryman*, xi, 3 (December 1913), p. 80.
[40] This account is based on President Willits' account as related to William A. Taylor.

position came to me and one month ago I had no idea of leaving here. The appointment is for February first . . . I owe you so much already that thanking seems useless. . . .

Some time was consumed before the station building was completed. But by June of the next year Halsted would be in his work room, and teaching would be almost finished for the first term. Halsted did owe much to Farlow.

However, the man at Harvard to whom Bailey was so deeply indebted—Asa Gray—was gone. To the great loss of the entire plant science world, Asa Gray died on January 30, 1888, from what Dr. Goodale described as an "attack of hemiplegia."

CHAPTER V

PROFESSOR OF HORTICULTURE
AT CORNELL UNIVERSITY

ON JUNE 9, 1888, from the horticultural department of the Cornell University Experiment Station, Bailey addressed a letter to Sereno Watson of the Gray Herbarium:

Returning from an absence I find yours of June 1st.

I will attempt the revision of Carex for the much needed new Manual. I doubt, however, if I shall be able to get the copy into your hands by Jan[uary] 1st., as I do not expect to return from Europe until well into December. I cannot complete the article before I go, for a part of my mission abroad is to see the originals of our older species. I hope to see the herbaria of Wahlenberg, Schkuhr, Willdenow, Steudel, Boott, and others, and I shall be surprised if some of the American species do not prove to have been misunderstood. Boott did not see all these originals. I shall not get settled at Ithaca until about Jan[uary] 1st. I shall hope to get the copy ready by the middle of January, if that will do. My collection of Carex is growing very rapidly, the American species being represented by between 3000 and 4000 mounted specimens.

Before I sail for Europe I shall want to ask you for introduction to two or three individuals.

The family is well, and Mrs. Bailey wishes to be remembered.

The Baileys were a family now. They had two daughters, Sara May and Ethel. It was planned that the entire family should go to Europe. There work for the new edition of Gray's famous *Manual* could be done.

Bailey realized, from his experience in Michigan, that his first work at Cornell would be to secure equipment. Accordingly, he planned his European tour with a view to acquainting himself with new methods and to acquire information pertaining to experiments. On August 1, 1888, *Garden and Forest*, edited by Charles Sprague Sargent of the Arnold Arboretum, announced:[1]

Prof. L. H. Bailey Jr., of Cornell University sails for Europe the last of August to visit experiment stations and study the horticulture of the countries he visits. A leading object of his trip is to collect data for the completion of text-books of horticulture, which he now has partly written.

An international horticultural exhibition was to be held at Cologne, Germany. Altogether the trip promised every prospect of satisfactory accomplishment.

For example, while in Ireland, Bailey went out to the Dixon Nurseries. There he was impressed with the quantity of plants being grown to protect game. "There is my word for green manuring in orchards,"

[1] I, 1888, p. 276.

said Bailey, "I'll give it a new name, 'cover crop.' " Sod mulch for some time had been in use. "Cover crop" and "plant breeding" were two of a number of terms which Bailey would place in circulation. "Open country," a long list of others, were to follow.

From London, on September 19, Bailey wrote Watson again:

I am now getting well to work at Kew, and I am finding many of the originals of carices which I have long needed to see. I shall want to publish some of my notes as soon as I return, especially as I hope to visit the important herbaria on the continent. These notes will be too long for Bot[anical] Gaz[ette] and of such a nature as to unfit them for it. I should like to publish them in the American Academy, if a second publication is not taking too many liberties for a stranger. The notes should be published before the new Manual comes out.

Professor Oliver is placing everything at my disposal. I am also making the acquaintance of C. B. Clarke, who is preparing Cyperaceae for DeCandolle.

"Carex notes from the British Museum," presented in the *Journal of Botany* in 1888 was to issue from this. Preparation of Bailey's much praised "Studies of Some Types of the Genus Carex," published as the first article of a memoir series initiated in 1889 by the Torrey Botanical Club, was soon to be well under way. For the balance of the century additional notes on Carex would appear from time to time in various publications.[2] Bailey was without doubt the American authority on the genus at this time.

On October 10, Bailey wrote Watson from Stockholm, Sweden:

I am just in receipt of a note from Dr. Beal giving your determinations of some of our plants from the pine barrens of Michigan. I am particularly interested in the little violet, because it appears to be a very distinct variety, at least. It is confined to the sands, and occurs over many miles of territory —across the state, in fact—and appears always to hold its characters. If you think it worthy a variety name, please call it Wheeleri, for Mr. Wheeler first collected it, and he deserves to be remembered in our state flora.

I am aware of the interest attaching to our roses, and I have thought to make a systematic study of them at Cornell by growing them. Being ornamental, they come strictly within the limits of horticultural work.

I have been to Upsala to see Wahlenberg's carices, and am disappointed

<hr/>

2 x, *Journal of Botany*, XXVI, 321-323, 1888; XI, *Mem. Torrey Botanical Club* I, 1-85, 1889; XII, XIII, *Bulletin Torr. Bot. Club*, XVI, 218-220, 1889; XVII, 61-64, 1890; XV, *Bull. Calif. Acad. Sci.*, s. 2, 3, 104-106, 1891; XVI, *Botanical Gazette*, XVII, 148-153, 1892; XVII, *Bull. Torr. Bot. Club*, XX, 417-429, 1893; XVIII-XIX, *Botanical Gazette*, XXI, 1-8, pl. 1, 1896; XXV, 270-272, 1898.

NOTE: XII is entitled "Carex umbellata, Schkuhr; XIII is entitled "The Carices of the Upper Half of the Keweenaw Peninsula."

In 1890 Bailey would publish "Carex rigida Gooden, and Its Varieties," *Journal of Botany*, XXVIII, 171-173.

Besides doing Carex for Coulter and Watson's 6th edition of Gray's *Manual of the Botany of the Northern States,* Bailey also did Carex for Coulter's "Manual of the Phanerogams and Pteridophytes of Western Texas," published as a *Contrib. from the U.S. National Herbarium,* in 1894, as the third and last part.

not to find his American species. Some of these species have made much trouble and no one, I think, has studied the specimens. They are said to be somewhere in Stockholm, and I shall look them up. I hope to see the originals of all American species before I prepare the genus for the Manual. On my way south I shall spend a few days at Copenhagen, and shall see the plants of Drejer, Liebmann, and Lange. At Berlin I shall see Willdenow's, Boeckelers, Sheele's, and others; at Halle, Schkuhr's; at Prague, Presl's; at Paris, Michaux's, Lamarck's, and Steudel's. I have already seen the carices of Rob[er]t Brown—one of which is a Kobresia!—Rudge, Gay, Drummond, Goodenough, and others, and of course I saw Boott's and Carey's.

As soon as I return to America, I expect to examine those of Muhlenberg, Schweinitz, and Dewey. Some of Dewey's later species are not yet disposed of. I hope, also, to see Elliott's, but do not know where they are.[3]

During the first part of November Bailey was in Berlin, Germany. All the "old Carex puzzles [were] clearing up nicely." He was "seeing much that [he] came to see" and enjoying himself. He wrote, "I am confident that the future difficulties in North American carices will be those concerned with the merits of species and varieties, for we shall now have accounted for all the names which have been applied to our species. I have seen or expect to see, all the types which Drs. Torrey, Gray, and Boott did not see, except those at St. Petersburg, and there is little need of seeing those. My trip is proving pleasant and profitable. I go today to Halle, thence to Maeorkern and Therandt and Prague, and thence south to Turin."

Bailey, therefore, inspected leading European experiment stations as well as Carex herbaria. He returned to America, his missions accomplished, and well fortified for the future with a plan for Cornell which he immediately put into words:

It is expected that the work of the department will be various, although there are few experiments which can receive great attention. The leading investigation will be the endeavor to originate new varieties of cultivated plants. This attempt is to be made in a purely scientific spirit. All the laws

[3] On October 21, 1888, Bailey at Copenhagen, Denmark, wrote to Erwin F. Smith: ". . . I am having a very successful and profitable trip, although a very hurried one. But I am here simply to observe in many countries, not to study, and my flight does not so much matter. I have had a pleasant trip in Norway and Sweden. I am hoping to get to Italy in late November, and I will look at the peach orchards if any are in my region. I will also bear in mind the orchard at Montreuil.

"I am considerably disappointed in the horticulture of Europe, so far as I have seen it. The poor man's orchard does not exist in any of the six or seven countries I have yet visited. Fruit growing is confined to a few trees in cramped gardens, and the great mass of the people know nothing of it, not so much, even, as in Amerika.

"I am getting anxious to get home again and get to work. I want to sail from Hamburgh about the first of December . . ."

After his arrival at his "new home" in Ithaca, New York, Bailey again wrote to Smith, in his letter describing his trip as an "instructive one," and adding that he had "found it impossible to visit the orchards at Montreuil." Reluctantly he had been compelled, owing to time limitations, to visit only northern Italy during the last part of his trip.

which are known to govern the improvement of plants, by variation in culture and management, by acclimatization, by selection, and pollination, will be applied so far as possible. Large quantities of selected seeds of raspberries, blackberries, gooseberries, and currants were secured last season for sowing this spring. The work will be undertaken on a large scale, as the prospects of usefulness in this direction of investigation are great, and the need of scientific attention is urgent. In connection with this work, the testing of new varieties placed annually upon the market will be undertaken, largely, however, as a means of making record of the horticultural progress of the day. It is not the intention to pronounce upon the commercial value of all varieties, as, by mutual agreement, this important labor is left largely to the State Experiment Station at Geneva. Efforts are also being made to secure all wild species which give promise of capability of improvement in useful directions.

Many minor investigations will be undertaken as we find opportunity to conduct them without interference with the larger experiments in hand. The department is ready and anxious to give any attention within its power to difficulties which attend the various horticultural industries. At the present moment, there are under contemplation various studies in germination, experiments upon methods of culture of several plants, and the testing of many new fruits as to hardiness.

Bailey did not announce an intention to deal with insect depredations. That work was being ably studied under Comstock in "economic entomology." The study of fungi and fungous growths was regarded at Cornell, as it had been at Michigan Agricultural, work of the cryptogamic botanist—irrespective of whether the species affected were cultivated or wild plants.

After his return from Europe, while frost was yet in the ground, he began building in a clay hillside a forcing house with an exposure to the south. Filling trenches with water, he located his beds over them, placed planks on stilts, and commenced work.[4] A comparison of his 1888 and 1889 reports summarized his early accomplishments and facilities. In his 1888 report, he said:

The equipment of the department consists of a good assortment of the best tools, a large line of seed-bags,—some of them prepared with special reference to use in pollination experiments,—seed-cases with tin drawers, herbarium cases, an excellent compound microscope with attachments, a large number of carefully selected books, and many office aids and conveniences. An ample barn and the necessary contents are also provided. A forcing-house of improved construction, 20 x 60 feet, is now building. This is to be heated by steam, and hot beds in connection are to be heated in the same manner. It is contemplated to add a companion house to the present structure next summer. Some twenty-five acres are at the disposal of the department for purposes of experiment.

By 1889 the "forcing house of improved construction," mentioned in the foregoing report, was completed, as well as other "good" facili-

4 I. P. Roberts, op. cit., p. 80.

ties. Bailey initiated a study of vegetables and their cultivation under glass—an experiment to determine the influence of the electric light on the growth of plants. The forcing house was divided into two parts, at night one part was lit with an arc-light, while the other part was left in total darkness. This, one of the first important university researches in vegetables growing under glass, began, also, Cornell University's notable work in "electro-horticulture." The results were not disappointing, although not all that was contemplated was proved. Studies of plant growth under conditions of continuous illumination and within different ranges of proximity between the plant and the light had, however, their first known American beginnings. This work, while anticipatory, must not be confused with modern studies of plant growth under controlled conditions. Modern studies are the outgrowth of long years of physiological and agronomic investigation. For example, the apparatus devised by Charles F. Hottes at the University of Illinois to reproduce plant growth under controlled physical conditions—soil, temperature, water, light, et cetera—is an illustration. The effect of light, and the absence of light, on plants—and the relation between the two—were among the earliest subjects studied by American experimental physiologists. Eventually study related light and the chemical composition of plants. There was a somewhat different motivation behind Bailey's study. Glass coverings for many years were rarities, especially where experimentation had a mixed pure and practical intention. His professorship was that of experimental and practical horticulture, and the word "practical" was construed by everyone except the most far-sighted students as almost synonymous with immediate results. Fundamental groundwork in academic greenhouse practice was being laid. Owners of greenhouses were interested in the study from this standpoint. Those who knew Bailey knew there was more than this. There was an academic exploration in his mind, one that studied the behavior and response of the plant under strong illumination and under glass, under weak illumination, even in darkness. Bailey could initiate no such studies in so well equipped an institution as Michigan Agricultural College. At Cornell, facilities made such studies possible and he took advantage of the first opportunity. The studies, similar to ones being pursued in Europe, were to last for years. We will discuss this further later on.

Bailey's hybridization studies in the cucurbita tribes, begun at Michigan Agricultural, were continued at Cornell. Seeds were brought from Michigan. Within a year a large number of acres was required to grow the crosses and selections. Conducted over a period of years, more than 1,000 experiments were performed, including several hundred hand crosses. Later Bailey estimated that "probably as many as

126 Liberty Hyde Bailey

2,000 nondescript forms of pumpkins and squashes were produced."[5] The results were notable from the student standpoint, although their practical worth was not at once so clearly evident.

Bailey became "convinced that the production of good new varieties was not by means of hybridization. I then," he related, "undertook plain selection from promising fruits as they appeared in the field of commercial kinds and followed the work attentively through hundreds of examples. Again there was no practical result; but this set of experiments really did not differ from my hybridizings except that in this case the parents were not known." Nevertheless, the extensive tests verified the specific lines laid down years earlier by Duchesne; crossing limits were demonstrated; the notion that straight selection could produce new and stable varieties was upset; and the experiments showed definitely that any worth while breeding must recognize the species in nature. Knowledge concerning the plants themselves was enlarged. An old common belief that all kinds of pumpkins, melons, squashes, and others of the cucurbits mix in the field was done away with. Superstitions that pumpkins "spoil" squashes and that muskmelons become insipid and worthless when grown near cucumbers were disproved. As consequential as any result was the proved fact that domestic plants were amenable to botanical study.

Historically considered, however, it must be remembered that formation of a fundamental philosophy of plant breeding, a pre-Mendelian genetics, enunciated with great clarity by Bailey a few years later, arose in part from principles deduced as a result of these experiments covering a number of years and performed in two states. Soon he would commence bringing in roots of plants of the wild, especially in the genus Rubus, to study not only their variations but also their behavior under different conditions.

Aside from an experimental interest in cucurbits, Bailey studied tomatoes and egg plants. In these, and in the small fruit orchard studies, his interest was in varietal improvement and not variety testing except as the latter was an aid to the former or, because of circumstances, necessary. Bailey early announced that the Cornell station could distribute many kinds of currants, gooseberries, raspberries, and blackberries. All new varieties of small wild fruits still interested him, particularly those promising improvement. At this time, evidently, he planned no systematic studies of synonymy of small fruits. Of the large fruits, he planted all species suited to the climate in considerable variety but insisted, "The primary object in the setting of the fruit is the determination of certain points of culture and treatment rather than the mere testing of varieties." An orchard of pears and plums was set on land

[5] *Gentes Herbarum*, ii, 2, p. 67; also, vi, 5, pp. 271 ff.

which had never had stable manure. Not yet had Bailey commenced his great surveys of western New York pomological needs.

The reason was quite simple. The work of the department in the university had to be inaugurated first. Although Bailey brought with him from Michigan an interest in dahlias—and there was already a widespread interest in the chrysanthemum—his central concern was the vegetable garden. Depth of planting and transplanting; prevention and cure of vegetable diseases; effect on yield, for example, by detasseling corn; and other experiments received attention. "Kitchen-garden vegetables" were a subject of nomenclatural interest. In fact, the Association of Agricultural Colleges and Experiment Stations had appointed a committee (Bailey, E. S. Goff, and W. H. Green) to report on their nomenclature. They had drafted a set of rules which was published by the United States Department of Agriculture and by *Garden and Forest*. At the Geneva station Goff was still working with Sturtevant at classifying garden vegetables. Bailey admired their work, the breadth of their research, their high standards of performance, and their skill. Each emphasized origination of new varieties and improvement of varieties by domestication. Goff and Bailey believed that many new species of plants, fruits particularly, would come into use during the next century.

The garden fence of this subject, however, was to prove high and stubborn of access. In his 1889 report, Bailey announced, "The Ignotum tomato, a superior variety, which originated with the writer in 1887, has been further selected and tested, and this year it has been put upon the market." The product was a beautiful thing, large and round. When originated, not recognizing the variety, it had been called "ignotum." Seedsmen heard of it, offered seventy-two dollars for seed of the patch, the money went into Cornell's treasury, and it was introduced. Although it was found later that the plant had not been sufficiently tested to determine whether its characters were fixed, this product had an historical significance. In 1895 in *Garden and Forest*, Goff made a strong plea for more attention to plant breeding at the experiment stations. "The Ignotum Tomato, introduced by Professor Bailey," said Goff, "has become a standard variety, but Professor Bailey has never claimed that he originated this Tomato. Besides this, I do not recall a single variety of fruit or vegetable that has been disseminated from a state or government experiment station that has attained any prominence. It has been said that Mr. Luther Burbank, of California; Mr. E. S. Carman, of New Jersey; and Mr. T. V. Munson, of Texas, have each of them done more for horticulture in the way of improving varieties than all of the experiment stations combined. It would seem that the trained horticulturists of our station, with all the needed appliances and with help at their command, ought to be able to accomplish as good work in this field as private horticulturists, who must take the time from their own business and develop the varieties at their own expense." Bailey added to what Goff had written:

The Ignotum Tomato which Professor Goff is kind enough to mention, was introduced by me in 1889; but the form which I introduced is probably nowhere in cultivation at the present time; it has passed out by variation into poorer and probably into better forms. Now, the person who centres his attention upon the mere production of new varieties is likely to forget the importance of the underlying principles and forces which are capable of uplifting the vegetable kingdom. We need a general uplift more than an occasional spasm. We must make more of the varieties which we have and by doing so we push forward the progeny year by year in a gradual and enduring evolution. . . . I look upon new varieties as so many new starting-points for still further development, not as final or permanent things in themselves. . . . the amelioration of the vegetable kingdom is a slow unfolding of the new out of the old, through the simple and quiet agencies which man employs in cultivation and selection.[6]

There were few, if any, fundamental differences in the points of view of Goff and Bailey. In 1889 Goff left the New York station at Geneva and went to the University of Wisconsin. He was a research man—a patient, untiring worker—who sought unostentatiously to improve horticultural crops by established and new methods. Goff studied plants at all periods and seasons of development, from their seed to fruitage. The problems of the proper depth of planting seeds and the spread of root systems—their development in the earth—fascinated him. Root systems were early utilized by him to discern plant relationships. He gathered roots of horticultural plants, including tree and small fruits, and displayed them in cases. Goff was among the first of early American scientists to examine the influence of heredity on vigor, pursuing this study with special application to the potato. Potato varieties were the subject of a long time research. Among many other phases of investigation, he studied conditions which affect starch content in this vegetable. The research, however, of widest and most enduring interest and influence, and for which he is most known today, sought in widest scope to trace the origin and development of flower buds and flowers in such valuable tree species as the cherry, plum, apple, and pear. He studied the fertility of flowers of the native plum. He was a student of morphology. The development of autumnal leafage in fruits and ornamental plants and the resumption of growth in spring were closely observed. Goff persistently studied the conditions under which fruit set. In a word, he adopted a functional point of view when investigating and interpreting plant life.

[6] L. H. Bailey, "Plant Breeding," *Garden and Forest*, VIII, p. 318.

He did his job for the state of Wisconsin, testing and growing varieties of fruits, vegetables, and crops. He made culture experiments, aiming to improve horticultural species. He maintained at the same time his strong plant breeding interest. Potatoes, tomatoes, corn, oats, grapes, strawberries, raspberries, and other commodities were objects of his researches. Even tobacco culture for his state received attention. He attacked plant pests vigorously, inventing the kerowater spray pump, a tar paper disk and tool, and other devices to control the spread of disease producing agencies. In certain noteworthy instances, he conducted researches in plant diseases. American horticulture has produced few, if any, research students who have had a more lasting influence than Goff.[7]

West of Wisconsin, in the fall of 1895, Niels Ebbesen Hansen arrived at the South Dakota State College of Agriculture and Mechanics at Brookings to grow hardier fruits and agricultural crops for the northwest plains. Inspired at Iowa State Agricultural College by Bessey, Budd, and L. H. Pammel, Hansen took with him a practical program. In his senior year at college, he had written a thesis which promulgated a comprehensive plan to improve American fruits grown in the prairie West. He set about now to apply it. He did not represent himself as being a botanist, although he had had graduate study under Pammel and had spent several years in large commercial Iowa nurseries, and although he used his botanical knowledge as a basis for each experiment. Hansen studied the writings of Darwin and DeCandolle, but he could not find here the final answers to his problems. What answers there were did not settle matters as to the prairie regions. In effect, he saw that on the prairies one could not wait for nature to bring choice harvests to South Dakota. Man must aid nature.

Hansen saw the geographical problem as the central problem. He decided that he must find plants which grew and thrived in a similar or like climate to his, plants which might be improved and ameliorated to northwest plains conditions. The geographical approach to problems to increase the agricultural resources of a region was distinguishable from the approach which stressed physiological investigation. However, it must be borne in mind that all the more able horticulturists used both methods. The one was denominated "applied science." The other, "pure science." Some idea of the scope of Hansen's work was conveyed in a letter to Galloway of August 4, 1900:

... I shall be much pleased to receive bud-sticks and scions of the Siberian crabs you mention, especially as I obtained them for plant-breeding experiments and for stocks while in Russia. If you secure plants or seeds of hardy fruits from any source, please remember that I am making a specialty of

[7] For much of the material concerning Goff's work, I wish to acknowledge aid from James G. Moore, Chrm. Dept. of Hort., the University of Wisconsin.

improving the native and other fruits of the Northwest. I have a great many thousand seedlings coming on of various wild fruits, many of them from seedlings selected on the College grounds for size of fruit. The main work so far has been with the western sand cherry, of which I have now several thousand seedlings coming on from seed picked from the best of over 5,000 seedlings fruited here under cultivation. . . . I also have a lot of seedlings of the wild black currant, golden currant, gooseberry, grape, chokecherry, raspberry, etc. In this state the prairie settlers use the native form of *Solanum nigrum* for sauce, preserves, etc., and I am working quite extensively with this species also. Work with the wild strawberries was made a specialty the past winter in the greenhouse, and now I have at least over 10,000 seedlings growing, one of the parents in all cases being the wild strawberry of Manitoba, North or South Dakota, and the other parent some choice cultivated sort, including the new everbearing varieties from France. We are also working for an extra early tomato by crossing and selection. . . .

In 1888 Hansen had been offered a position as an agricultural explorer for the United States Department of Agriculture. He, however, wanted to do his work as a "lone eagle." The prairie Northwest he characterized as an "American Siberia." So most of his important discoveries were of Russian origin. Hansen became a well known explorer. His chief exploring fields were Russia and Siberia, but he made at least eight tours of Europe, Asia, and Africa. Hansen has aided in giving hardy plums, cherries, pears, apricots, apples, and small fruits, grapes, and specific industrial products to the Northwest. *Prunus Besseyi*, the sand cherry, which Bessey studied and which Bailey named in his honor, was combined with other plants by Hansen. From Kansas north to Saskatchewan, and west to eastern Oregon, millions of acres have been sown in crested wheat, an introduction of Hansen's. Historically, he is known also for other reasons. In 1897 he built the first known fruit-breeding greenhouse. Another technique, now widely used—raising fruits under glass to secure seeds for sowing—was early employed by him. Hansen has been an ardent worker. His fruits are grown in dry climates, similar to that of South Dakota, and extend, it is said, from Texas to Manitoba. Bailey admired his work as practical and later included in his book on plant breeding an article in which Hansen described breeding hardy fruits for the northwest plains.[8]

An awareness of the growing difference in the directions of plant breeding study was bound to develop. Botany was emerging from its herbarium dens and its preoccupation with study of plants of the wild. Botany in some quarters was studying more intensively the cultivated plants to develop, possibly, new industries. In 1894, however, the *Botanical Gazette* complained:

[8] See also Mrs. H. J. Taylor's *To Plant the Prairies and the Plains* The Life and Work of Niels Ebbesen Hansen, Bios, Mount Vernon, Iowa, 1941.

. . . But the transformation is not complete. . . . There are still good botanists who will not admit that there is any actual change. They are content that the study of the food of plants should be carried on by chemists, the investigation of the laws of breeding and practical treatment of diseases by horticulturists, the relation of plants to heat, light and electricity by physicists, the study of bacteria by pathologists, the examination of fossil plants by geologists, and so on. . . . It is more difficult to obtain ten dollars to equip a laboratory for vegetable physiology than a thousand dollars for a laboratory of chemistry because Baron von Liebig and others long ago fully convinced the popular mind that a knowledge of chemistry was essential to an intelligent pursuance of most of the arts and industries. . . . A Liebig is needed in botany. . . .

Plant physiology, consequently, was to have a long, slow growth to complete effectiveness. Physiological botany laid the foundation for the growth of scientific horticulture. But it had waged a long, uncertain struggle for recognition. Commending an editorial of the *Experiment Station Record*, the *Gazette* quoted, " 'The systematic investigation of the physiology of particular species of plants throughout their life history is greatly needed. The practical, as well as the scientific, importance of such researches in the case of cultivated plants is very great. . . .' " At the conclusion of the year 1893, there were fifty-five stations in the United States, employing thirty-seven botanists, of whom seventeen gave attention also to other work. Half of the stations employed no botanist at all.[9]

Bailey had strong convictions on the subject. In the July 22, 1892, issue of *Science*, he made a "Plea for a Broader Botany":[10]

Strictly speaking, botany is the science of plants, but by general consent it appears to have dwarfed itself into a science of wild plants; or if it deals with cultivated plants they are such as fall to the care of botanical gardens, or, in other words, those which are cultivated for the sole purpose of maintaining a collection. It is not strange that in the earlier days botanists should have eliminated from their domain the whole realm of cultivated plants, for cultivation then meant little else than the maintenance and improvement of plants for mere economic purposes, and there was little science of cultivation. But now that the teachings of evolution have thrown a new purpose into the study of all natural objects, cultivated plants have acquired a fascinating interest from the abundant light which they throw upon variation and descent. In fact, aside from paleontology, there is no direction in which such abundant material can be found for the study of evolution as in cultivated plants, for in nearly all of them the variation is fully as great as in domesticated animals, while the species are very many times more numerous; and by the fostering aid rendered by man, the accumulative

[9] *Botanical Gazette*, xix, pp. 160-161, at p. 161; *idem*, p. 85, and *Experiment Station Record*, v (1893), pp. 270-271 for quoted editorial; *Bot. Gaz.*, xix, p. 425, concerning botanists in experiment stations and based on report of director of office of experiment stations for 1893.
[10] xx, p. 48. See also reprint in *American Gardening*, xiii, 10 (October, 1892), pp. 584-585.

effects of modified environment and selection are much more quickly seen—and therefore more intelligible—than in wild plants.

. . . Just now, mycology is making important additions to horticultural practice, but there are greater fields for the application of an exact science of plant physiology, whenever that science shall have reached a proportionate development. In short, the possibilities in horticulture, both in science and practice, are just as great as they are in the science of botany upon which it rests. . . . Horticulture belongs to botany rather than to agriculture.

The ideal chair or department of botany, therefore, should comprise in material equipment, laboratories, botanic gardens, greenhouses, orchards, vegetable and ornamental gardens, all of which should be maintained for purposes of active investigation rather than as mere collections. . . .

"I have yet to find a variation in cultivated plants," Bailey urged, "which cannot be explained by laws already announced and well known. It is strange that one can ever believe that any variation of natural objects is unnatural."

Nor was he unaware of the difficulties of horticultural classification. For many years he had liked to take difficult genera, grow plants of the species, and make records of those of which there were no records and no herbaria. He saw that, because of certain horticultural characters— drooping flowers, erect double flowers, et cetera, and these increased as knowledge widened—their classification was made necessary as a basis, if for nothing else, of evolutionary study.

The horticultural industries were growing. More and more they were becoming interested in the new possibilities revealed by science. Practical men of skill, artists in their line, no longer controlled.

Bailey saw the real need—a need for trained investigators. Horticulturists were getting together as experiments demonstrated again and again that cooperative action brought more results than independent action.

In a sense the same snobbery that had long been leveled at the agricultural student by the classical academician was directed, in a milder form, by the botanist who worked at a table toward the worker, student though he was, who labored with farm products and cultivated plants. Bailey, Hilgard, and other leaders saw that manual labor that put dust, mud, and straw on breeches was not beneath the dignity of scientific men. They saw that horticulture was more than the income factors. They saw that a traditional chasm had to be bridged. Nurserymen, dealing in propagation, salesmanship, and other phases of their business, capitalized. Benefit to the public welfare was direct, but secondary. Horticulture as a work of educated men could put the public welfare first. Money considerations could become subordinate, and secondary. From his boyhood Bailey had thought in terms of public welfare, more particularly, rural welfare.

However, what a task lay ahead! Innumerable experimental problems to be solved, inadequate facilities with which to solve them, few up-to-date books, unsympathetic attitudes grown out of long years of isolated toil in remote farm areas, hostility of men of the trades toward men of education were a few of the shadows that dimmed the bright picture. But the size of the challenge never daunted Bailey. The larger the work, the more zest he brought to it. Men do not rise above their aspirations, he said. Education does not make men but it does influence them.

Floriculture was almost wholly undeveloped. Variety testing dominated experimental practice. Forestry was yet an art with little real systematic forest practice and very few, if any, trained foresters. Winter-grown vegetables under glass as a common practice was only commencing, and this was due principally to recently improved methods of building and heating greenhouses. Only now were greenhouses becoming prevalent. Two decades before they had been decided luxuries. Such matters as rest periods in plants were not commonly understood. Only about 250 species of important cultivated plants were used for food purposes among civilized people, although a little more than a thousand had been recorded. There was no certainty as to whether the predominantly used process of root grafting was good in all departments of horticulture. Such discoveries, as Bailey's, that the chokeberry could be used to dwarf apples, were not generally known. There was debate whether grafting was devitalizing to the plants, or strengthening.

In fact, the entire fabric of special education in horticulture was undergoing questioning. Not even improved transportation facilities and new methods of refrigeration, tying "the ends of the earth together," dispelled all doubts. During 1889, 1890, and 1891, some 380 plant species not in commercial cultivation in North America were introduced from foreign and home sources. In 1891 of itself, 219 species were introduced. Not even these facts dispelled doubts as to an imperative necessity of a new horticultural education. In 1889 at Buffalo, New York, the American Chrysanthemum Society was organized. The "sudden popularization" of this flower would become one of the marvels of horticulture, due largely to the facts that in 1889 some 39 varieties were introduced, in 1890 some 57 varieties, and in 1891 some 121 varieties. The chrysanthemum, Bailey regarded as "the princess of flowers." Organization, however, was not confined to floral industries. By 1892, North America led "the world in the extent, variety, and excellence of its canned products, and much of the material [was] the product of orchards and gardens. In 1891, the sweet-corn pack of the United States and Canada," said Bailey, "was 2,799,453 twenty-four-can cases, and the tomato pack was 3,405,365 cases."[11] About 20,000 canning factories employing about one million persons in canning season placed this industry, for its remarkably rapid development, alongside the evaporating fruit industry. Was there any wonder that one, viewing the whole plant growing and distributing enterprise, saw a new world in which education would play increasingly a most important role?

World plans were being laid for plant introduction work. Russia, Japan, China, and Mediterranean areas would not be the only regions most frequently visited. Botanical exploration, already more than a century old, had not reached all regions of the globe; in fact, many totally unexplored United States regions remained.

By this time, the United States Department of Agriculture was in the midst of its epoch-making and pioneering decade, 1885-1895, in the study of plant diseases, and their treatment. Beverly Thomas Galloway has pointed out that in "1885 there were only three institutions besides the Department of Agriculture making an organized effort in the way of teaching or in experimental work of this character. Ten years later there were fifty colleges and stations engaged in the work and no less than one hundred special investigators were devoting their time to it."[12]

Plant disease study throughout the nation, therefore, somewhat eclipsed plant introduction work, although progress in physiological and pathological research made more and more evident the imperative necessity of plant introductions both for their own value and to breed resistant varieties against diseases. Galloway was a Missourian, a graduate of the state university at Columbia. Recommended by its faculty after he had served a period from 1884-1886 as assistant in the horticultural department under George Husmann, viticulturist of German birth and training, Galloway was appointed by Commissioner Colman as assistant pathologist under Scribner's regime, and, when the latter resigned to go to the University of Tennessee at Knoxville to work with Charles W. Dabney and Charles Sumner Plumb, Galloway, on November 1, 1888, was promoted to chief of the section of vegetable pathology. He had grown up near the University of Missouri, in a region where a valuable vineyard and wine producing industry had been threatened by phylloxera.

Numerous times the story has been told how Pierre Marie Alexis Millardet, quite by accident, came across a fundamental observation

[11] "Recent Progress in American Horticulture," read before the Agricultural and Experimental Union of Ontario, at the Ontario Agricultural College, Guelph, December 23, 1892. *Science*, n.s. XXI, pp. 20 ff. (January 13, 1893); and in *18th Ann. Rep. Ontario Agric. College*, 1892, pp. 300 ff.
[12] "Progress in the Treatment of Plant Diseases in the United States," *Yearbook of the U.S. Dept. of Agric.*, for 1899, pp. 191-200, at p. 199.

which led to his creation of the remedy, another epoch-making triumph, of Bordeaux mixture. In 1883, this great French pathologist initiated ingenious experiments following a discovery made the year before in the historic vineyard of St. Julian in Medoc. It is told that, while engaged on a commission to combat two vine pathogenes introduced from America into France, he became aware of the possibilities of the use of copper as a fungicide by noticing effects against one pathogene, a downy mildew fungus, when, to prevent fruit pilfering along a roadside, he sprinkled a mixture of copper sulphate and lime on the grapevines. He had saved the vineyards from the other pathogene, the phylloxera, by introducing and grafting resistant American vines, wild species doubtless, on the European varieties. Determined to solve the other problem, he set about and developed Bordeaux mixture which so effectively destroyed the mildew fungus that the wine industry for that year was saved.

Millardet reported his discovery in 1885, and the next year his article, translated probably by Erwin F. Smith, was published by the United States Department of Agriculture. Very soon this fungicide was employed in America against *Phytophthora infestans*, a fungus on potatoes, and against *Fusicladium dendriticum*, fungus of apple scab, and to find the over-wintering stage and life history of which required so many years of field and laboratory research. "The discovery and introduction of this mixture," Herbert Hice Whetzel in his valuable *Outline of the History of Phytopathology*[13] has said, "more than any other one thing influenced and shaped the development of the science of plant pathology during the quarter century following its discovery."

Bailey's principal interests were in other phases of study than treatment of plant diseases. More, his interests lay with originating new races and varieties of cultivated plants, and the formulation of methods for their taxonomic study. Soon he would become aware of the significance of the discovery of Bordeaux mixture and initiate a program to apply its uses horticulturally. Workers in other state experiment stations did likewise.

Galloway and his corps of workers which he brought together in the section of vegetable pathology, immediately went to work to explore the multitude of applications found possible in this and other remedial substances known of and being improved, or, together with useful apparatus, being developed. Perhaps it may be said that these remedies made more friends for the federal work in plant pathology than any other original enterprise. The section's membership, however, was comprised of practically minded students, each a leading scholar from a leading university, and the industrious work of the federal govern-

13 W. B. Saunders Co., Phila. and London, 1918, pp. 58-63, at p. 59, and notes.

ment in every direction of plant study progressed, growing by leaps and bounds every year, until, with the first years of the new century, the department's great bureau of plant industry was established.

On July 25, 1889, David Grandison Fairchild was appointed, after taking examinations, assistant chief of the section. Arriving a few months after Merton Benway Waite, Fairchild held both Bachelor of Science and Master of Science degrees from Kansas State Agricultural College, of which his father was president. He was appointed while at the New Jersey station where his uncle, Byron D. Halsted, was now firmly established and aggressively pursuing elaborate and valuable researches in diseases of agricultural and horticultural crops. By 1892, disease investigations were being pursued at state agricultural experiment stations over the entire nation, some of the most notable of which were Sturgis's studies in tobacco at the Connecticut station, Atkinson's and Pammel's studies in cotton in Alabama and Texas, Pammel's studies at the Iowa station at Ames including in its scope bacterial investigations in field and garden crops, Humphrey's work in Massachusetts, Chester's in Delaware, Bolley's in North Dakota, and others whose work more specially will be or has been considered. The mycological and pathological work of the federal government took some of its most able men from the state stations. Witness the fact that Fairchild, Swingle, and Carleton each began their experimental researches at the Kansas station. Walter Tennyson Swingle, a profound and brilliant scholar, gifted with a knowledge of several foreign languages, was brought to Washington by Smith and Galloway from Kansas Agricultural College where, schooled with William Ashbrook Kellerman, he had performed pioneering mycological investigations and breeding experiments in cereals.

Merton B. Waite, born in Oregon, Illinois, in 1865, and graduated from the University of Illinois in 1887, went to the United States Department of Agriculture after having enjoyed the distinction for a year of being Dr. Burrill's assistant. Growing up in the Illinois corn belt section and with an aroused interest in pomaceous fruits and their diseases, including, of course, bacterial forms, he studied phases of cross pollination and hybridization. His demonstration of insect transmission of a plant disease, the results of which were presented in a paper read before the American Association for the Advancement of Science in 1891, almost paralleled the demonstration by Theobald Smith and others of the Bureau of Animal Industry that the protozoan of southern cattle fever is transmitted by a tick. Thus, another great advance in scientific research—discoveries of carriers of other plant, animal, and human diseases—began. In 1891, beets of a high sugar content were shown to grow in many western states, including even arid ones where irrigation or moisture conservancy could be utilized. By 1891, moreover, it seemed certain that alcohol could be utilized in the making of sorghum sugar and that the process would practically double the amount of crystallized sugar obtained from quantities of cane at small cost. None of these accomplishments, however, attracted the attention and merited praise that research in the functions of bacteria and extension of the knowledge of pathogenic bacteria received. Waite, aside from furthering his own celebrated researches in the field, participated incidentally in attracting and arousing Erwin F. Smith to interest himself in the comparatively new and undeveloped subject in America.

On May 7, 1889, Bailey had written to Smith and encouraged him to continue his efforts to solve the baffling problem of the peach yellows. Bailey said, "I am much interested in your proposed experiments. You are doing the best, most practical, work in a plant disease of anyone in this country. . . ." He confessed that he was not a student of mycological subjects but he was much interested in the *Journal of Mycology* which the Department was publishing and Galloway and his assistants were editing and preparing. November 11-13, 1890, the Association of American Agricultural Colleges and Experiment Stations held its fourth annual convention at Champaign, Illinois, and Bailey presented in general session a paper on the subject, "The Work of Experiment Stations in the Reform of Vegetable Nomenclature." Bailey realized as much as anyone that the nomenclature in mycology, particularly as fungology and bacteriology extended its research to crops of the garden and field, would more and more need to be standardized. So did Smith, for that matter. In the autumn of 1889 Smith came in from his field work and immediately became interested in the equipment which Waite had gathered together to study plant diseases—an array of apparatus so imposing that today it is regarded by excellent authority as having constituted the "first bacteriological laboratory for the study of plant diseases at Washington or east of the Alleghany Mountains." Smith, it is said, saw in this another way to attack the peach yellows problem. To no final avail had his many methods of approach solved the mystery of this inscrutable disease which today is regarded, like the mosaic disease of tobacco, as in the virus group. Smith went to work to search for bacteria as the cause of peach yellows, and for years he stubbornly refused to surrender although, of course, he soon learned that neither peach yellows or peach rosette were caused by bacteria. That Smith failed to discover a bacterial explanation of peach yellows is relatively unimportant. The resolution of epoch-making proportions and potentialities was Smith's determination to study real bacterial plant diseases, a work on which he was wholeheartedly engaged within a few years, and by which the science of plant pathology was revolutionized so that elder workers in the field and laboratory—Burrill, Bessey, Arthur, Farlow, and others—deferred to him. No less than the originator of plant bacteriological research in this country—T. J. Burrill—wrote to Smith as early as 1902: "to no one is the forward movement due, and the presentation of the same in print, more directly traceable than to yourself."

Nor were Smith's energies confined to bacteriological subjects. He collaborated with each and every one of the noted federal workers in the section of vegetable pathology and with practically every outstanding investigator in the state stations. Illustrations are far too numerous to describe here. The important pathological work of Newton B. Pierce and later P. H. Dorsett at the government substation at Santa Ana, California, in the California vine disease, which, incidentally, also has been shown to belong to the virus group and transmitted by an insect vector, in diseases of the almond, and other produce grown in the far west, deserves reference. The story of this work must be reserved for another book. Later we shall discuss further another subject, which we shall merely make mention of here. Smith became convinced that in respect to certain diseases, plant breeding for disease resistance provided the most efficient, and perhaps the only, solution. In 1899 he prepared and read before the Columbus, Ohio, meeting of the American Association for the Advancement of Science a paper entitled, "On the Fungous Infestation of Agricultural Soils in the United States," and then selected a promising student at the University of Vermont, William A. Orton, to forward this work. Orton secured highly resistant cottons, melons, and cowpeas, plants capable of thriving on Fusarium infested soils in the South, regions where in the middle 1890's Smith studied diseases of the species and for which no substantially satisfactory remedy or method of prevention or control had been found. The period between 1888 and 1895 was characterized in the last year of the century as epoch-making because of the rapid strides which were made in discovering the causes of plant diseases and methods for their prevention. Outstanding were the results obtained in combating grape diseases, nursery stock diseases, and diseases of cereals, and other plant groups (to be discussed later). From the beginning of the period, division laboratory work included such special subjects as diseases of celery, lettuce, cucumbers, parsnips, and other garden crops; diseases of cereals, including rusts of wheat, rye, and oats; blights and rots of the Irish potato; sweet potato diseases; tomato blight and rot; and diseases affecting floricultural interests. The research scope was widened as the years progressed so that nearly all forms of agricultural and horticultural crops, and even forest trees, were included. The disease producing organism searched for was more than a fungus, more than a parasitic alga, bacterium, or other lower plant form; at times, it was discovered that the disease was produced by an indiscernible agency, at least agencies which required microscopes of the highest power and the most exact and painstaking procedure to isolate and examine. The division's brilliant constituency collaborated with other laboratories.

Under the progressive leadership of Beverly T. Galloway as chief, the division of vegetable pathology gradually enlarged its policy of cooperation with state agencies, including experiment stations and individuals, until, together with its own working force and experimental stations—substations, or experimental areas—the program was nationwide in effectiveness. A few instances will illustrate this. Collaborating with the division, E. S. Goff conducted experiments on the fruit farm of A. L. Hatch near Ithaca, Richland County, Wisconsin, in the treatment of apple scab, and fungous diseases of small fruits, raspberry and blackberry, and vegetable crops, most important, the potato rot. Similar programs of cooperation and collaboration were conducted with other state experiment station workers. The work of Halsted, for example, was not confined to New Jersey, although, of course, most of his pathological work was concerned with diseases prevalent in his state. Halsted was invited to study in the Middle West and in the southern states as well. Cooperative programs were initiated with authorities of the Dominion Experimental Farms, in special agricultural problems and forest pathology. At times, an authority was issued to study special industrial problems, as, for example, Lucien M. Underwood's report, as special agent of the division, on "Diseases of the Orange in Florida," the notes for which were gathered together during February, March, and April of 1891. The importance of this report ranked with Atkinson's studies of nematode root-galls, and anthracnose of cotton, or Pammel's examinations of fungous root diseases.

The division's own workers also contributed notably to progress. David G. Fairchild, for instance, after demonstrating with Galloway valuable fungicidal treatments for black rot of grapes at Vienna, Virginia, was sent to Lockport, and other regions in New York state, to study grape diseases. In 1891-1892, with the New York Agricultural Experiment Station at Geneva, he studied with effect leaf blight control of nursery stock—pear, cherry, plum and quince—and powdery mildew of the apple, and the influence of treatments on growth and reproduction. Fairchild also participated in the experimental treatments of pear leaf-blight and scab conducted in the celebrated orchards of Dr. W. S. Maxwell of Still Pond, Maryland, where Erwin F. Smith planned and carried out some of his most important peach yellows investigations. Pierce's demonstration of the fungicidal control of peach leaf curl in California added luster to the spreading fame of his other pathological achievements at Santa Ana and the whole of Southern California regions. Swingle commenced a large wheat rust experiment in Maryland. He and Smith, however, previously had been sent to Griffin, Georgia, where they discovered that, among other plant disease situations in the locality, Smith's inoculation experiments made the year before to examine peach rosette were astonishingly important and that culture study and further investigations of other problems in Florida required immediate attention. Smith's first culture medium was prepared, perhaps, as late as February 26, 1890—an agar medium, with beef broth—and was supplied by Veranus A. Moore of the Bureau of Animal Industry. So far as records of the division are concerned, this was, at least, among the first. Nevertheless, as early as December 6, 1888, Volney Morgan Spalding, in correspondence with Smith, wrote of potato culture work in progress at the university botanical laboratory.

A brief reference to the slow progress made in America in introducing widespread use of culture media in studying plant diseases is necessary at this point. As late as the year 1894, Louis Hermann Pammel, a pioneer American student of bacterial diseases of plants, complained that, while such diseases were being described at some experiment stations, inadequate attempts, in fact in instances no attempts at all, were being made to cultivate the causal organisms. The reasons were several, and some have been indicated. To quote another pioneer student of the subject, Harry Luman Russell, later dean of the college of agriculture of the University of Wisconsin, bacteriology then had not yet been established "as a field of scientific inquiry on a basis comparable with the older established sciences . . . chemistry, physics, and biology. . . . The preponderance of effort was in the application of the subject to the field of medicine or hygiene. . . . It was in large measure an appendix to a medical course, an 'anhang' as we used to call it in Koch's Laboratory in Germany."[14]

Russell in the spring of 1890 had studied at the university in Berlin under Robert Koch, and later, at L'Institut Pasteur in Paris. In 1891 he occupied the American table at the zoological station at Naples, studying the deep sea bacterial flora of the Mediterranean. In 1892 he spent part of a year studying the marine flora at the seaside laboratory at Woods Hole, Massachusetts, which was "the acknowledged center of biological research for the entire country." When President Harper began to build a new institution of advanced learning at the University of Chicago with Charles O. Whitman in charge of zoology and John Merle Coulter of botany, Russell was given a fellowship in bacteriology,

[14] "Getting started in Bacteriology," an unpublished mss. prepared by Dean-Emeritus Russell in 1942, copied in 1944, access to the materials of which has been afforded the author in 1947. Quotations in this and subsequent paragraphs are taken from this.

and gave one of the first lecture courses offered in this country in a distinctively "biological rather than a medical environment." The next year, 1894, Dean William A. Henry and President Adams of the University of Wisconsin recalled Dr. Russell to his alma mater to organize and conduct a new department of bacteriology in the college of agriculture of that institution. Bacteriology had been taught at the University of Wisconsin some years before by Dr. Edward Asahel Birge, zoologist; indeed, six years previously under him Russell had commenced his studies in bacteriology. Dr. Trelease had planned, as a part of his instruction in botany, to develop experimental research in bacteria causing plant diseases, and apparatus for the purpose had been ordered. But he had gone to St. Louis, and Russell, always interested from boyhood in plant life and the botanical rather than animal side of biology, had had to await his years as a student at Johns Hopkins University, before he could specialize in bacterial diseases of plants. There Russell obtained in 1892 the degree Doctor of Philosophy, the first such degree, it is believed, earned under the renowned Dr. William Henry Welch, since 1884 an appointed member of the original nucleus which constituted the beginnings of the later more celebrated medical school faculty and occupant at this university of the first chair of pathology in America established on a university basis.[15]

Twice Welch had studied abroad, and before 1884 he had served as professor of pathology, anatomy, and general pathology of the medical college of Bellevue Hospital in New York City. In 1889, at the opening of the great hospital at Baltimore and when William Osler became physician-in-chief, Welch was constituted pathologist-in-chief. Soon the laboratory method of instruction and experimental research in medicine at the two principal institutions created under the will of Johns Hopkins were leading the way, and inaugurating an epoch in medical science history on the North American continent.[16] While yet in Europe, Russell, realizing the benefit of an advanced degree obtained in America where he expected to live and work, had applied to Welch to study under him. Despite the little attention given plants by workers in bacteriology both in America and abroad, Welch immediately became interested in the thesis in plant bacteriology which Russell promulgated. Able and learned as a research investigator as well as doctor, Welch "readily saw," Russell has revealed, "the relationship which existed between healthy and diseased cells in the animal body. Much to [Russell's] gratification Welch instantly grasped the situation, saying he knew

[15] Harvey Cushing, *The Life of Sir William Osler*, i, chapter xiii, "The Johns Hopkins Hospital," pp. 311-315, at p. 313 (Oxford: Clarendon Press, 1925).
[16] S. and J. T. Flexner, *William Henry Welch and the Heroic Age of American Medicine*, 1941, The Viking Press.

nothing about the pathology of plants but saw no good reason why the same general basic principles would not obtain with plant life as obtained with animal life." He, therefore, approved Russell's proposal to present a thesis in the pathology of plants. Finding no greenhouse research facilities adequate and available at Johns Hopkins University, Russell was granted permission to use the facilities of the expanding laboratories of the United States Department of Agriculture at Washington. There, since at least the summer and autumn of the year 1889, Merton B. Waite, as a part of his study of the pear blight disease, and Erwin F. Smith, as a part of his investigations of the peach yellows disease, had been conducting some bacteriological research.

Russell made weekly trips from Baltimore to Washington and was delighted with the stimulating atmosphere of the Bureau of Animal Industry and the division and sections devoted to plant study. Secretary Rusk allowed him space in the greenhouses for his plants, and he became acquainted with the work of Galloway, Fairchild, Swingle, Waite, Smith, and others. His thesis subject being "Bacteria in their Relation to Vegetable Tissue," he began to bring together "for the first time, a compilation of all known bacterial diseases of plants. This included those diseases in which the canons of Koch[17] had been thoroughly satisfied; those in which specific organisms had been found, but the evidence was not wholly conclusive that Koch's canons had been rigidly enforced; and finally a list of plant diseases that were probably of bacterial origin but not definitely proven." In America, especially, this thesis supplied a lack, both in corroborative research and in the scarce literature in plant bacteriology.

Russell's doctoral examination took place in the spring of the year 1892. On February 28, 1893, while at the University of Chicago, he, recognizing Erwin Frink Smith's "wider experience" in these studies and "better access to this class of literature," asked Smith to look over proof of his list, solicited ideas and suggestions, and added: "I have deemed it wise to exclude from the actual list all diseases that have not been subjected to infection experiments by means of pure cultures." Only those diseases were listed where the probabilities of bacterial origin were strong and shown by inoculation of diseased tissue. The list was to present a nucleus around which more elaborate compilations could later be made.

In 1892 W. Migula in Europe had reviewed the subject of bacterial plant diseases. Not since DeBary's years, however, had the field been

[17] The postulates which Koch found necessary to establish a bacterial disease were: (1) to isolate the causal organism from diseased tissue (2) to cultivate this organism in pure cultures (3) to inoculate the pure culture into a healthy susceptible host (4) to produce the disease by artificial inoculation (5) to recover the identical organism from inoculated animal tissue.

critically surveyed. Smith pointed out that Russell's experiments had preceded by a year Julius Wiesner's researches published abroad,[18] and, more to the point, had "the merit of being properly performed, i.e. with sterile juices and pure cultures so that the conditions under which the experiments were made [could] be reproduced by other investigators." To illustrate, 1893 was the year when Pammel published in the *Botanical Gazette* what Smith described as "the first important paper"[19] on the black rot of crucifers, a disease which later Smith, Russell, and Harding, with Pammel's approval, restudied. Pammel, be it said also, in pursuance of his investigation, used gelatin culture with neutral or slightly alkaline media.

The story of how plant bacteriology became related to, and a part of, medical progress and industrial research is too voluminous to be attempted here. What must be remembered is that the epoch-making research triumphs of Pasteur, Koch, and other pathologists of lesser importance but great nevertheless owing to the discovery of new pathogenic organisms in disease, vastly expanded and advanced scientific research the world over, and study within the American plant and animal sciences was not the least to benefit. New economic values and potentialities were at once demonstrable. On going to the University of Wisconsin, Russell turned his attention to the comparatively new field of dairy bacteriology. He is authority for the belief that "So far as America was concerned there was practically only one scientist who had then turned his attention particularly to the study of milk and its relation to bacterial activity and [he] was Professor H. W. Conn of Wesleyan University, Connecticut." By 1896, Smith had gathered together sufficient research data, based on his own and others' studies, to outline, in a series of articles entitled, "The Bacterial Diseases of Plants" and published in the *American Naturalist*, the scientific procedure which Pammel believed should be, and was, followed almost as a pattern by the preponderant numbers of workers in the field, who increased with every year. The entire series was never completed, owing to the fact that Smith decided to begin work on his monumental three volume study, *Bacteria in Relation to Plant Diseases.* During the last half of the 1890's, the *Centralblatt für Bakteriologie, II*, was established and of this Smith became an associate editor for the first twenty-five volumes.

During the summer of 1893, from material found at Anacostia, District of Columbia, and later that year in the middle west in Michigan and Ohio, Smith had begun to investigate a bacterial disease of cucum-

18 "The Bacterial Diseases of Plants: A Critical Review of the Present State of our Knowledge," *The American Naturalist*, xxx (August, 1896), pp. 631-632.
19 *An Introduction to Bacterial Diseases of Plants* (W. B. Saunders Co., Philadelphia and London: 1920), p. 159, "Literature."

bers, muskmelons, and squash. In this research, Smith, himself the one who later admitted this, very much improved his technical proficiency. He sought to complete his proof according to the canons of Koch, which, tersely stated, required that the germ be cultivated outside the body, reproduced by inoculation, and found invariably present. From that time forward, he gave most of his time to studying bacterial diseases of plants though other investigations also required much of his time and energy. For example, from the far west, James W. Toumey, botanist and entomologist of the Arizona Agricultural Experiment Station and later dean of Yale Forest School, sent specimens known as "crown-root gall." A few inquiries and specimens from other sources arrived, and about 1892 Smith probably began his later thorough studies of this subject. More urgent situations presented themselves and he had to content himself with publishing a "Field Note" on "Stem and Root Tumors" in the *Journal of Mycology* of that year.

Diseases of cultivated crops of the southern states, most immediately, a watermelon wilt devastatingly prevalent and threatening the melon industry in several sections, required ingenuity of action, and so, after Smith had gone to Georgia and Florida and done some further work on peach yellows and cucurbit wilt in the north, he was sent to Charleston and Monetta, South Carolina, where during the summers of 1894 and 1895 much field investigation, supplementary to laboratory and greenhouse research in Washington, was pursued in melons, cotton, cowpeas, potatoes, tomatoes, and cabbage. The year before Smith had established the pathogenicity of an *Alternaria* disease of muskmelons which had done much damage. In pure culture he had isolated the fungus, during most of his work, not knowing that the disease was also being studied in Italy. Beginning in 1894, Smith realized while in the south that in his study of the wilt of melon and other crops he was finding soil parasites of the form genus Fusarium, more destructive perhaps than the Peronosporas. Not only did he modify the widely accepted supposition of the saprophytic nature of the Fusariums, but possibly of greater significance, he also developed the already referred to theory of fungous infestation of soils. Nor was this all.

In the spring of 1895, specimens of diseased tomato plants were sent to Smith at Washington by Franklin Sumner Earle, a former student of, and collaborator with, Burrill at the University of Illinois, and who at this time was studying Mississippi fungi with Director S. M. Tracy of that state's agricultural experiment station. These specimens arrived from Deer Park, Alabama, and points in Mississippi, and, while in South Carolina, Smith found in eggplants the same diseases from which the tomatoes were suffering—a new bacterial disease. Elaborate, cautious, and skillfully wrought researches, utilizing the technical proficiency in biochemical and biophysical research which placed Smith far in advance of other plant pathological investigators and among the leading research scientists of the world, established the two great lines of investigation with which Smith occupied himself the rest of his life—first, in the study of soil infections due to Fusariums, of which the watermelon wilt was an expression, and, second, the study of bacterial plant diseases, in the foregoing briefly described instances of which Smith isolated and differentiated the *Bacillus tracheiphilis*, cause of the wilt in cucumber, muskmelon, and squash, and *Bacillus solanacearum*, cause of the brown rot of tomato, potato, and eggplant.

Scarcely a research project of any man or woman of the federal pathological service could be described, without finding at some point or another the contributing direction or collaboration of Galloway and later Woods, the administrative officers of the division of vegetable physiology and pathology, as its work became known during the last years of the century.[20] Fairchild individually collaborated with Dr. Halsted in the study of, and treatment for, certain fungous diseases of sweet potato. There were many more division projects worthy of elaboration.

One, to which reference has already been made, should be recalled as in progress during the 1890's—the work of Waite furthering the studies of Burrill and Arthur in pear blight. Almost every worker, Waite included, investigated fungicidal treatments of diseases. In grape disease study alone, experimental areas in South Carolina, New Jersey, Missouri, Virginia, and elsewhere, were established. Waite continued through several years the research of the life history of the pear blight organism. How a research could originate in, but extend beyond, a strictly pathological investigation, was illustrated in his experiments made during the seasons of 1891 and 1892 at Chestnut Farm, Virginia, Washington, Brockport, Rochester, and Geneva, New York, with reference to "The Pollination of Pear Flowers," published more or less *in extenso* in 1894 as Bulletin 5 of the Division of vegetable pathology. Practical, as well as eminently scientific, conclusions emanated from this investigation. Waite was envied by every scientist of the division for his "good points," to quote a letter from Pierce to Smith of May 5, 1891, when he demonstrated that crab apples and pears may be "blighted through the flower without puncture, and that the other flowers on the same tree will be blighted without further inoculation—probably by transfer of germs by insects. [He had] captured insects and grown

---

[20] See an illuminating article by Albert F. Woods, "Work in Vegetable Physiology and Pathology," *Yearbook of the U.S. Department of Agriculture* for 1898, pp. 261-266, in which the division's work in the grain smuts and rusts, Smith's work in black rot of cabbage, and other important diseases, including its coordination with the work in plant breeding, is discussed.

germs from them. [He had] shown on a small scale that Bordeaux mixture [would] kill germs in inoculated flowers and also prevent the blighting of the same. Good strong points, and valuable in my estimation." This notable discovery, involving insect transmission of disease, accentuated an aroused interest in control methods, the same as discoveries of disease transmission by soil infection from fungi and transmission of diseases of plants and animals by a considerable list of entomological hosts— beetles, aphids, ticks, et cetera. As illustrations, Smith proved in 1895 that the bacterial cucurbit wilt was transmitted by *Diabrotica vittata*, the cucumber beetle, and in 1896, the bacterial brown potato rot by the Colorado potato beetle. Joseph Charles Arthur had suspected that insects communicated pear blight. But Waite proved the fact, by cultivating the "germ" or parasite from the mouth parts of bees during the years 1889-1891. Furthermore, Waite devised practical methods, in the light of the new knowledge, for orchard owners. Anything that would keep transmitting insects away from the flower buds would keep the trees from blight. Yet, some trees were found to require cross pollination, and bees performed this work of nature. It was but another step to elaborate in form the hypothesis that some trees are self fruitful and some self unfruitful, that is, require pollination in order to fruit. Waite analyzed the capabilities of varieties of orchard species either of themselves to set fruit or the extent to which pollination by outside agencies was necessary; further, what should be done to promote or make possible healthful and vigorous functioning. From this emerged Waite's principle of mixed plantings in horticulture. In instances, control methods by proper planting and protective devices were indicated. In others, extermination of disease-producing agency or agencies, by eradication of species or treatments by chemotherapeutical remedies.

Could the fungous spore or fungous infection at various stages of development be eliminated, often the trouble as well as cause was removed. How plant pathological science has kept pace with technological progress has been interestingly illustrated by the utilization of airplane equipment to collect long distance flights of fungous spores.[21]

North, west, south, and east, the work of the state experiment stations increased in effectiveness. To the northwest, in the early 1890's, Henry Luke Bolley in North Dakota was bringing science to large important agricultural regions. Bolley had begun pathological studies in plants while a student at Purdue University, collaborating in re-

[21] See E. C. Stakman, A. W. Henry, W. N. Christopher, and G. C. Curran, "Observations on the Spore Content of the Upper Air" (abstract), *Phytopathology*, XII, 1 (January, 1922), p. 44. This was a part of a rust epidemiology study made by the office of cereal investigations of the United States Department of Agriculture. Frederick Meyer and Charles A. Lindbergh are said also to have been leading figures in developing this work.

searches with his professor, Joseph Charles Arthur. In 1890 he joined the faculty of North Dakota Agricultural College where his noted prescriptive remedies against prevalent crop diseases, including corrosive sublimate against potato scab and later formaldehyde treatment against oat, flax, and wheat diseases, during the decade began to improve and augment the value of the state's and northwest's farm economy.[22] Called the "grand old man of flax," Bolley's "plot 30" of the state experiment station at Fargo is a landmark in the agriculture of that state. We will later refer to a number of wilt resistant flax varieties which he originated there by selection. Cross breeding for disease resistance, yield, oil content, and quality are said also to have been involved in this work traceable in origin to his first years in North Dakota, about which a number of experiment station bulletins have been issued, and in furtherance of which he was sent in 1903 by the college and the United States Department of Agriculture to Russia and other countries to study the origin of flax diseases and obtain new types of seeds and plants. Space does not permit a complete discussion of his accomplishments.[23] Surely Bolley was one of Arthur's most able students. Arthur himself, in the course of his illustrious career, which included the invention of apparatus for physiological investigation, a number of important researches in plant pathology, and an associate editorship of the *Botanical Gazette*, studied fungous diseases of plants and weed control, and in 1896 advocated, under the trade name. "formalin," the use of formaldehyde as a fungicide.[24]

To the southwest, at Kansas Agricultural College at Manhattan, William Ashbrook Kellerman and Walter T. Swingle, among other important researches in cereals, were investigating and publishing results (1888-1892) on treatments for smuts in oats, barley, and wheat. Since 1887 the famous hot water treatment of the Danish agriculturist Jensen had been known but its utilization in America under differing conditions and on various crops (as well as its mycological basis in differentiation of species and further chemical treatments devised—potassium sulphide, as an illustration) had to be studied. Kellerman, as professor of botany, became affiliated with Ohio State University, and Swingle went to the

[22] *North Dakotan,* XVI, 4 (April, 1941), pp. 1-2. For an early article written by Bolley on "Potato Scab," see *Science,* XX, no. 516 (December 23, 1892), p. 355.

[23] For a listing of Bolley's accomplishments, see *Who's Who in America,* XI (1920-1921), A. N. Marquis & Co., Chicago, p. 295. See also "Treatment of Smut in Wheat. Treatment of Potato Scab," Bulletin 19, North Dakota Agric. Experiment Station, April, 1895; also, "Flax Wilt and Flax Sick Soil," Bulletin 50, *idem,* December, 1901; "Flax Cropping," Bi-Monthly Bulletin, *idem,* III, 6 (July, 1941), pp. 9-12.

[24] Based on an unpublished memorandum prepared by Arthur, February 15, 1916, supplementing data furnished Iowa State College of members of the class of 1872, and made part of a further memorandum entitled "The Purdue Herbarium Basis of the Rust Project," all of which were furnished the author of this book by authorities of the Herbarium of Purdue University.

United States Department of Agriculture. Their work in Kansas, however, preceded and, in considerable part, laid important groundwork for the eminent career started at the same college, of Mark Alfred Carleton in the study of grain rusts and smuts.

Spraying, disinfecting, eradication, cultural methods, and the invention of mechanical appliances, as well as advocacy of and the introduction of quarantine and police measures, came into use as agencies to combat all sorts of crop diseases. Research, utilizing pure cultures, advanced—notably in the capable hands of George Francis Atkinson, in his Alabama studies of cotton diseases and his Cornell University biological research in diseases of vegetables, for instance, the oedema of tomato.[25] Progressive agricultural experimental research had been inaugurated in practically every state of the union where a station was found: in 1890, of 29 botanists employed at these stations, 16 replied that the study of fungous diseases of cultivated plants was regarded as of most immediate importance. Next in order were the study of grasses and forage plants, next, the subject of weeds, and, then, forests and forest-trees, and plants for barren lands.[26] By 1893, at least 32 stations were giving attention to botanical work, and, additional to systematic investigations of the native flora, fungous and bacterial diseases and their treatment were receiving most consideration.[27]

We shall refer again to the work of Peter Henry Rolfs at the Florida Agricultural Experiment Station at Lake City. At this point, however, mention should be made of his discovery of a sclerotium disease, a research disclosed at the Madison meeting of the American Association for the Advancement of Science in 1893, at which time, Rolfs, a former student of Pammel, revealed that the disease was found in at least sixteen different plants of five orders. Workers, including Smith while in South Carolina, studied this subject further. The latter distinguished his wilt disease of cotton, watermelon, and cowpea from the similar wilt described by Rolfs and from the cotton root rot of Texas.[28]

Vegetable and orchard crops were studied at experimental stations of the northeastern states. We will consider later in this book the work of Lewis Ralph Jones at the Vermont Agricultural Experiment Station. The research results of several workers at the Massachusetts station at

[25] George F. Atkinson, "Dropsical Diseases of Plants," *Science*, xxii, no. 567 (December 15, 1893), pp. 323-324. See also Herbert Hice Whetzel's *An Outline of the History of Phytopathology* (Philadelphia and London: W. B. Saunders Co., 1918), p. 104, note 3.

[26] *Botanical Gazette*, xv (1890), p. 279. See also an article by Byron D. Halsted, "What the Station Botanists Are Doing," *Botanical Gazette*, xvi (October, 1891), p. 288, in which the individual work of various botanists are described.

[27] *Botanical Gazette*, xviii (February, 1893), p. 81.

[28] Bulletin 17, Division of Vegetable Physiology and Pathology, U.S. Department of Agriculture (1899), p. 44.

Amherst were nationally famous, and the small world of plant pathology was taking note of the experimental investigations of the plant physiologist and pathologist J. E. Humphrey who later helped form the Society for Plant Morphology and Physiology. In 1892, among a number of specialties, he was studying black-knot of plum, a violet disease, diseases of potato, lettuce, and other crops, and publishing his graduate thesis submitted for the degree of Doctor of Science at Harvard University on the *Saprolegniaceae* of the United States. Roland Thaxter, appointed in 1888 as the Connecticut station's first employed botanist, utilized in his classic research of potato scab the most advanced technique known, describing both the disease and its causal organism. Making use of pure cultures, inoculation, and rigid experimental conditions, he showed that the disease was due "to the direct action of a very peculiar filamentous fungus of extremely small dimensions." Difficulty in settling whether this disease is of bacterial or fungous origin was not typical of all pathological research. But an efficient program of germicidal and other treatment, made possible after the causal organism was isolated, compensated for the years of study required. Onion smut was one of the first plant diseases studied at an American university. In the middle 1870's, when C. V. Riley in Missouri was writing on harmful insects and insecticides and Burrill in Illinois was seeing to it that a considerable number of microscope stands were in his laboratory, for work on fungi and pear blight, Farlow was studying onion smut, pursuant to research tenets he had learned under DeBary. The results were published in 1877. Thaxter continued this study and also the examination of gymnosporangia, already discussed. He published his findings on the smut of onions in the station's annual report for 1889; on the mildew of lima beans, and, among other matters, on parasitic fungi. Later, Thaxter, and William Codman Sturgis, another Harvard graduate who served as assistant in the Cryptogamic laboratory during 1888-1889 and who in 1891 became vegetable pathologist of the Connecticut station, showed that onion smut was principally a disease of the seedling stage and that transplantations may safely be made to fungous infested soil, once the plants have passed seedling growth. We have selected a few typical research projects at a few representative stations of the country. These must suffice to illustrate the research trends. Biologically trained botanists were not numerous. But they were studying and working in the field and laboratory.

These, and other studies, were of national interest. Moreover, there were projects aimed at developing potential regions. Plant introductions to make possible hardy fruits for the northwest plains had proven of value, not only in the Northwest and Canada but in northern New England near the Canadian boundary. One of Van Deman's first acts as

United States pomologist had been to request Dr. T. H. Hoskins to write an article on "Orcharding in New England,"[29] in which he outlined a history of hardy fruit introductions and their successful culture in the northern parts. The pioneering skill and valuable accomplishments of Peter M. Gideon of Minnesota were given both mention and tribute.

The great fruit-growing regions of the South and Southwest were also of economic concern. A semitropical and tropical horticulture, scientifically advanced, was needed. For a number of years disease complaints had been received by the division of pathology, which urged investigation of alarming citrous fruit diseases. Owners of large orange groves, and others, by letters and petitions, urged vigorously that control methods be sought. Secretary Rusk instructed Galloway to do something. Smith, who was studying peach rosette in Georgia, was joined in June by Swingle. They, after each completing work at Griffin, went on to Florida, where more new diseases were encountered. Although Smith stayed in Florida only until July 10, Swingle completed "the circuit of the more important orange-growing regions. Groves," reported Galloway, "were carefully examined and the orange growers interviewed at twenty-six towns in fourteen counties. The growers everywhere showed the greatest interest in the work, and every courtesy was extended to the special agents." Swingle remained two months, studied a variety of plant diseases, particularly those of citrous fruits, found reports of injury not exaggerated, and no substantial preventive measures being taken, due largely to the obscure nature of the maladies. Growers and organizations responded encouragingly to the possibility of a federally sponsored program to eliminate the most prevalent and destructive diseases. A capital of over one hundred million dollars was believed represented in their industry. Swingle obtained and returned with numerous signed petitions.

Because of lack of funds, no further action was taken until March, 1892, when Swingle again was directed to go to Florida to study orange blight during its most prevalent period. In July, when the division's appropriation was increased $5,000, the understanding was current that a sufficient sum would be made available to equip a laboratory. Swingle was recalled to Washington to map a plan for facilities and work. Eustis, in the heart of the orange region, was selected as the laboratory's site. Citizens of the county offered to erect the laboratory there and donate enough grounds for experimental plats. In various places in the state, division officials, who it was finally agreed would superintend construction of the buildings, were immediately given access to large and small groves to commence investigatory work.

Together with the Florida state experiment station at Lake City, an

[29] *Report of the Commissioner of Agriculture* for 1886, pp. 274-276.

excellent service became available within a few months, and diseases of many economic plants of the South were studied. The laboratory began to serve the farmers and orchard growers, similarly as Pierce and his gradually evolved laboratory at Santa Ana, California, began to serve the agricultural and horticultural communities of the Pacific coast. By 1894 Pierce was conducting his large scale experiment to control peach leaf curl by spraying, was studying various fungous diseases, and making new crosses of raisin grapes to improve and expand the industry, a "most fertile field and wholly unoccupied," he wrote. His pathological researches extended then as far north as the orchards of Oregon. Orange, fig, almond, grape, prune, and peach figured prominently in Pierce's disease research in southern California. The Santa Ana laboratory brought to the west coast the latest in research on pathology, up-to-date facilities, and a thorough, farsighted, and aggressive scholar intensely interested in advancing the science of combating diseases of plants throughout the world. Moreover, both at Eustis and at Santa Ana, the importance of bacteriological investigations was recognized.

Breeding plants for disease resistance also became a contribution of both laboratories. In June, 1892, Swingle found a grower who had made "many exceedingly valuable crosses" in citrus. Immediately he sensed new potentialities and, as a part of the morphological and physiological examinations incident to his study of orange blight, he took up a close inquiry into orange pollination and the agencies participating in the processes. Success crowned the work of the Eustis laboratory in its conquest of several diseases. By 1894, Galloway reported as to the work on citrus, "Sooty mold, a destructive disease of the orange and other citrous fruits, has been successfully treated. Scab of lemon, another very troublesome disease, has also been held in check by the application of fungicides. It is believed now that with the increased knowledge as to the cause of these diseases they may be held in check at comparatively small expense. The more obscure diseases of the orange such as blight, foot rot, and die back, have been further studied and much additional information has been obtained in regard to them."

Pierce was especially interested in the progress made with "foot rot." At this time, it had been discovered that as a method to prevent the blasting of grape flowers, a disease in California causing huge losses, cross pollination, grafting, and the application of stimulating fertilizers during the flowering period could be utilized to overcome what was described as "constitutional weakness of the vine." "Already," reported Galloway, "many seedlings of promise have been obtained and the grafting and fertilizer experiments inaugurated have also in a measure been successful." Hybridization as a method of conquering disease, therefore, was definitely under way among workers of the division of vegetable pathology during the first half of the century's last decade. Extensions of technique in this regard during the next years were to be even more important, as we will discover.

In 1892 Swingle had selected a young graduate student under Trelease at the Shaw School of Botany—Herbert John Webber—to work with him at Eustis. Webber had been a former student of Bessey, was interested in the fungi, and had been a compiler of a valuable catalogue on Nebraska's flora. On September 15, Webber received his official appointment, and after spending two or three weeks in Washington receiving instructions and getting together necessary apparatus, he and Swingle went to Eustis by way of Jacksonville and the St. Johns River to Sanford, "the early seat of American Citrus culture" and the home of one of the greatest practical orange growers in America. Impressed with the natural history and agricultural resources of Florida, they went at their task with delight. The possibilities of scientific development in the citrous industry were challenging. A building of three research rooms, a darkroom for photographic work, closets for storage, a library, and a shed equipped to furnish gas, desks, and tools for carpentry work, and implements and apparatus for field study, were in use by spring of the next year. Immediately, however, Swingle and Webber began histological investigations of orange leaves and conducting tissue in health and disease, the object being to study transpiration and the entire physiological structure of the orange tree and fruit. The problems presented were not easy of solution, as has been pointed out. In the process of obtaining information concerning abstruse situations, they became convinced that what was needed was science in the exact, pure sense. A knowledge of fungi and fungicides did not produce solutions in every instance. Since injudicious use often brought on disease, a knowledge of fertilizers, while often very important for certain purposes, was not always conclusive. To know the species taxonomically was necessary and fundamental but disease problems were not solved by such knowledge, except as species might be discovered suitable for breeding experiments for disease resistance. Both Webber and Swingle closely followed the literature from this country and abroad. The work of this laboratory, however, shared the experience of all laboratories interested in plant study. Practical results counted in obtaining financial appropriations. In a word, propaganda values could not be slighted, and reports required time to prepare. Furthermore, an evident need to educate a public, grossly ignorant of beneficial potentialities to be realized in plant science research, ambitiously conceived, compelled Swingle and Webber —Swingle, particularly—to devote a considerable portion of time to giving addresses and writing articles of a more or less popular nature.

One very important address, delivered at Pensacola, Florida, in 1893, treated advantages to be gained by the Florida agricultural economy from plant introductions. Although older students had introduced plants from foreign lands into Florida, in every sense, as an advocated program maintained and sponsored by a society dedicated to horticultural advancement and utilizing the resources of an experimental laboratory, this address, scientifically conceived, was pioneering. Swingle that year, in addition to seeking to isolate the cause of orange blight, in addition to conducting a "good number of cross pollination experiments" in oranges with a view to studying "the means by which it is accomplished in nature," in addition to collaborating with P. H. Rolfs of the Florida experiment station in entomological and pathological research, sought an appropriation to finance research in fertilizers and their relation to disease in plants, and, much more important, to advance what he described as an "acclimatizing scheme," which in essential points is what today is called plant introduction. Certainly no one may question the originality, the creative genius, the indefatigable industry, perseverance, and vision, of this scientist who today is an unquestioned authority on citrus and tropical horticulture and agriculture. In a letter of July 3, 1893, written at Eustis to Erwin F. Smith, Swingle urged that the *Journal of Mycology* be changed to "a Physiological and Pathological Journal. Even as it stands," he wrote, "we should get out some *scientific work on fungi* and non-parasitic diseases." Where possible, he aided Smith as the latter pursued his South Carolina investigations. Smith's elaborate, exact, and thorough presentation, based on research done again and again in the interest of certainty, of the brown rot of Solanaceae due to *Bacterium solanacearum* was received in 1896, to quote L. R. Jones of the department of botany at the University of Vermont, as "unrivalled as a thorough piece of work on bacterial disease of plants," and immediately attracted attention throughout the world. Another source of prestige, moreover, was soon to be found in the work of plant introduction.

On November 8, 1894, Galloway reported to Secretary of Agriculture J. Sterling Morton, "Recognizing the great importance of the cereal crops produced in this country and the immense losses resulting to them from the attacks of certain diseases, particularly rusts and smuts, an assistant was appointed early in the spring to take charge of investigations on this subject." On June 26, Galloway had commissioned M. A. Carleton to proceed to Kentucky, Tennessee, Missouri, Kansas, Nebraska, Illinois, Ohio, and west into Iowa, South Dakota, Minnesota, Wisconsin, and New York, to study "the life history of the rusts by observing their development over an extended range of country. Then," continued Galloway, "there is the study of varieties of cereals as to their disease-resisting powers, as well as the various effects upon them of different soils and climates, which can be begun satisfactorily only by visiting the regions themselves. It is also desired to procure soil samples for examination and alcoholic specimens of the plants for anatomical study." Carleton was a scholar, endowed with amazing resourcefulness and genius for the study of cereal crops. Soon his work paralleled in importance that of the federal laboratories at Santa Ana, California, and Eustis, Florida, and, indeed, also the expanding and flourishing laboratories at Washington. Collaborating with plant students at his alma mater, Kansas Agricultural College, and, among others, Bessey at the University of Nebraska, Carleton devised techniques, demonstrating the sharpest originality, in mycological and pathological research. Enlarging and concentrating his experimental examinations in wheat, he imported varieties from the Dominion Experimental Farm at Ottawa, Canada, and from Russia and Italy. On May 25, 1897, he informed Galloway: "Wheat, in general, is very good. Three or four of the Russian sorts are going to prove just the thing for this country, being extremely hardy and of good quality." Finding varieties rust resistant was of immense value to the central west. Discovering varieties, or breeding hybrids, resistant also to cold, became added as another scientific objective which influenced work not only in the maritime regions of the Pacific coast but also, as we shall show, in the subtropical climate of Florida. The agricultural explorer was soon to arrive in larger numbers on the agricultural scene in the United States. Within another year, Carleton, as one of several such explorers, commenced tours in Europe to find new, valuable, introducible cereals.

In 1898 Carleton visited the farms of R. and J. Garton, cereal breeders of northern England. There he was shown results which were "astonishing," he wrote to Woods, "beyond even the expectations we have had of such work. They practice the most intricate composite crossing," he stated, "and some of their results with naked oats &c may well revolutionize the cereal food industry." Although Carleton then regarded his "real specialty" to be the rust diseases, he resolved to "continue to have in mind the work of cross breeding cereals." Planning to that end, he urged that "a special station for cereal breeding and cereal diseases" be established in the United States. Because of insufficient appropriations, the Department of Agriculture found that it could do no more than offer to test the Gartons' new cereal breeds at the agricultural experiment stations. But Carleton's rapture over the new possibilities in cereal crop improvement enlivened his continued study in Russia.

Russia was known as the "second greatest cereal country of the world." Carleton, therefore, took lessons in the language, purchased at his own expense thirty or more volumes on foods, cereal products, agriculture, and plant geography, learned culture methods, and especially examined their foods. "There are dozens of things in that line," he told Woods in a letter of October 22, 1898, "that we know nothing of in America, or in any other country, especially cereal foods." And on November 10, he added:

. . . I am already finding new types (wild) which I shall bring back to use in my cross breeding work. There are at least two species of *Aegilops* here, though I have not yet obtained them. And I have now two wild species of *Avena*, not known in America. But I should expect next season to get dozens of excellent things, when I would be able to search, myself and thoroughly too. The investigation of the relations of these cereals and forages (wild and cultivated) to the climate, soil, diseases &c is of *extreme* importance. . . . It is highly important that while I am here I should take an entire summer for exploring the Kirghiz Steppes. I am satisfied there are some of the most invaluable things in that region for our desert districts. . . . I am becoming more and more enthusiastic all the time as to my work with the cereals, as I study this country, but I think I should first get the best things this country affords. I might work for years and produce a type of cereal no better than might be obtained by a little improvement of some species already existing over here in the steppes somewhere. It is highly important to obtain these at once to begin with. The trouble I think with all the cereal breeding heretofore done in America and Australia is that they did not broaden out enough, and take in enough different types into their combinations, as the Gartons have done.

Carleton's grain work in the United States during the first years of the century were to be developed along two main lines: first, a survey of wheat culture throughout the country, including the Pacific coast states and the semi-arid regions with and without irrigation; and, second, field experiments, including the introduction of foreign varieties and the making of crosses, adapted to the various wheat growing districts, to secure early varieties, rust-resistant or non-shattering sorts, better yielders, or hardier varieties. As early as June 30, 1900, it was reported that in Kansas alone, under Deane B. Swingle, more than 200 wheat crosses had been made. Moreover, there was good promise that, even in semi-arid regions without irrigation, average wheat crops were possible under suitable culture methods and variety selections. And, of course, most important of all, it had become "certain that the macaroni industry [would] become well established in this country and greatly add to its wealth." Wheat was but one crop, and included within its range were winter varieties. On July 31, 1901, Carleton, as cerealist of vegetable pathological and physiological investigations of the bureau, would transmit to Chief Galloway his paper, "Macaroni Wheats," to be published as Bulletin 3 of the new Bureau of Plant Industry. The work on a vast scale encompassing other grains was soon receiving generous support, both in appropriations and public endorsement, and the United States corps of agricultural explorers, in increasing numbers, went deeper and further into remote lands. Each year progress was greater.

Soon after the establishment of the Eustis, Florida, laboratory deep freezes destroyed Swingle and Webber's hybrids, some grown for disease resistance. This inspired them to enlarge their work to include cold-resistant strains. When Swingle decided to extend their work also further south to escape the cold, he went to Miami by stage. Indians came about his campfire. He surveyed a small tract of land—a "tropical garden," as it was first regarded—in a completely unpopulated area of what is now Miami. There and at Eustis were developed Swingle's celebrated originations—the tangelo, the citrange,[30] the limequat, and other new citrus fruits of lesser importance. Years, of course, went into the process of initiating, and completing the work of hybridization. Much time also was consumed in testing and marketing these products. And a number of workers collaborated in their production. But for the most part, the hybrids that proved valuable, were crosses made by Swingle. Some idea of the extent of Swingle's labors may be conveyed by his report to Smith on April 3, 1897, "I have just finished crossing the orange and pineapple. . . . Crossed nearly 600 flowers of the orange and over 700 of the pineapple. So far I have about 110 oranges 'set' and hope I will get about 75 to ripen." He was also planning to hybridize the European grape and the Florida Scuppernong.

During the year 1897 Swingle's zeal had been very much quickened by some very inspiring study in Europe, begun in October, 1895, and continued a year at Bonn and Naples. While there very definitely he had come under the influence of Eduard Strasburger. Cytological research was capturing great spheres of influence in Europe and America. The growing renown of the instruction and laboratory research of Wilhelm Pfeffer and Strasburger was soon to affect every corner and trend of investigation in the plant sciences. In 1897 Bessey, as one of the botanical editors of the *American Naturalist* (the other, in vegetable physiology and pathology, was Smith) happily observed that in Pringsheim's *Jahrbücher für wissenschaftliche Botanik* (edited by Pfeffer and Strasburger) cytological work, "remarkable for the richness of its contents," included American names. Among the early American botanists to study abroad, F. C. Newcombe and Volney Morgan Spalding, who studied under Detmer and Pfeffer at the University of Leipzig, were prominent. Another University of Michigan student, Douglas Houghton

[30] See an elaboration of this subject, "New Citrus Creations of the Department of Agriculture," by Webber and Swingle, *Yearbook of the United States Department of Agriculture* for 1904 (Washington: Government Printing Office, 1905), p. 221; also, "New Citrus and Pineapple Productions of the Department of Agriculture," by Webber, *Yearbook* for 1906, p. 329, and articles referred to therein.

Campbell, whose research in Archegoniata was to be ranked high among the most important botanical contributions of the decade, also studied in Europe during these years. Pierce, formerly an assistant in Goodale's laboratory and also a student of Strasburger, had taken work under Pfeffer at Leipzig, his table being next to Spalding's.

Swingle went to Europe to join Fairchild who had been studying abroad since 1893. On October 5 of that year Fairchild's resignation as first assistant of the division of vegetable pathology and associate editor of the *Journal of Mycology* had been accepted. Commissioned as a special agent of the United States Department of Agriculture to visit European countries to make a special study of plant diseases and other subjects connected with scientific agriculture, he had secured the privilege of occupying the American chair at Naples and, after some study under Brefeld, had become a member of the group about whom Bessey wrote in such laudatory fashion.

Fairchild who was acquainted with many plant scientists of world influence, in Munich, Berlin, Paris, and other centers of botanical scholarship on the continent, did much to overcome a prevailing skepticism, in some quarters, prejudice, toward the value of American experimental research. Cordial relations in all spheres of plant study existed between Americans and scholars of the British Isles. Few, if any, scholars of the continent questioned the enduring worth of American taxonomic productions. But recognition of the right of America to participate (and eventually in points lead) in the world movement toward experimental plant research had yet to be won and established on the basis of merit.

After his advanced studies in the laboratories of Europe, Fairchild journeyed around the world. While on the continent, pursuant to the directives of his special agency for the department, he reconnoitered, in the interest of valuable plant introductions, parts of Europe and islands of the Mediterranean. In 1895 he was invited to go to Java, and some time was spent visiting islands and continental regions of the Pacific and Far East. Bernhard Eduard Fernow, anxious to extend forestry to treeless and arid regions of western United States, arranged that his division should make use of the new knowledge acquired by Fairchild in Europe and other regions. After his return to America, Fairchild prepared a bulletin on "Systematic Plant Introduction." It was published in 1898. The division of pomology for more than a decade had sought and imported from remote regions new and valuable products, especially some from Egypt and North Africa. Webber, Swingle, Fairchild, Taylor, and others, conferred on new introducible varieties which could be added to grapes, dates, and other fruit finds which already had much more than recompensed for the costs of their importation. Plant introductions, inaugurated a few decades previously by William Saunders with a meager appropriation made to the seed division to obtain useful plants and seeds from foreign countries, leaped into prominence during the last years of the century. Fairchild, in his book, *The World Was My Garden*, has presented an interpretation of the events which led to the creation in 1897-1898 of the office of seed and plant introduction in the United States Department of Agriculture. Fairchild and Swingle took the lead in securing official recognition of the work, and Fairchild was the first man placed in charge of the office. While the Secretary of Agriculture and other officials, convinced of the value and need for world scale action, arranged the administrative matters of departmental organization, Fairchild and Swingle prepared lists of introducible plants. These two zealous and resourceful men, both scholars and explorers of experience, conceived of this work as an integral part of the progressive program of experimental research being expanded in every division and laboratory of the department. Both men believed, and Swingle wrote to Galloway on February 11, 1899 to this effect, that America would soon lead the world in plant breeding and plant introductions. American plant science research had arrived at another "new"—a new physiology, he believed, and would study the heredity and improvement of a valuable product such as corn as much as the ox-eye daisy. The role of nutrition in plant breeding and adaptation would be further investigated. Swingle's and Webber's paper, "Hybrids and Their Utilization in Plant Breeding," published in the *Yearbook* of 1897, had stimulated research and anticipated the later effective work of the laboratory of plant breeding.

Space limitations do not permit complete evaluations of the accomplishments and spheres of influence of each American student who studied abroad contemporaneously with Swingle and Fairchild. Each has attained a position of eminence. Robert A. Harper, formerly professor of botany and geology at Lake Forest University, was another Bonn student. He, as did Swingle also, deservedly earned an estimable reputation of being one of America's leading students of botanical literature as well as investigator of note, and has occupied chairs of botany at the University of Wisconsin and Columbia University. Before going to Bonn, Harper had demonstrated brilliantly in research, having found and shown the existence of sex in certain obscure lower plant orders. The phenomenon of sexuality in plants presented itself then as a subject vital not merely to evolutionary understanding, supplying missing structural and physiological links from the lower to higher plant forms, but, of more immediate practical significance, light was shed on the exceedingly complex and variable subjects of plant fertilization and nuclear history, including that of the micro-organisms. Another illustrious member of the Bonn group of American students was Winthrop J. V. Osterhout, later to teach at the University of California and to occupy Goodale's chair at Harvard University, at least, to follow next in order to teach plant physiology there. In the United States, he has been outstanding in his leadership of a type of plant research, which, related to the medical sciences, has made for enduring good and valuable scientific progress. The last of the group singled out for distinction by Bessey in 1897 was David Myers Mottier, a very able botanist and holder of the chair at the University of Indiana for many years.

Up to this time, plant introduction work had been organized principally within one investigation sphere—that which discovered a new plant in one geographical locality, and, by seed or seedling, naturalized it to a new climate or soil. Preeminently, the requirements were two: first, an explorer with at least a gardener's knowledge of many plant varieties, preferably one botanically trained, certainly one equipped with the unique capability of discovering and discerning plants new to the American or other world economies, and whether the probabilities favored its utilization; second, an experimental plat or greenhouse where the plant's ability to grow and thrive in the new area might be demonstrated. It has been shown that for many years investigators had been conducting physiological researches, aimed at ameliorating and enlarging the plant domain of given localities. Scattered fragments of genetical knowledge had been accumulated. A wealth of morphological and anatomical learning had been harvested. Problems of taxonomy and phylogeny, however, still dominated the research of most American laboratories. Considerable truth could be found to justify the contention that botanical scholars, even as late as the turn of the century, knew more about algae than economic crops. Plant breeding was still one of agriculture's adornments, even as hybridization was more an art than a science within the realm of horticulture. What, other than taxonomy, was to bring the indoor and outdoor laboratories of the plant sciences together? Ecology and genetics had not arisen to the stature of independent sciences. We have shown that pathological investigations, once work went beyond description and diagnosis, compelled students in arriving at solutions to summon every resource of knowledge available. Artificial and conventional distinctions were bound to give way to the more substantive. The old and the new was bound to be reworked in the light of new discoveries supplied by cytology and physiology. A new philosophy was in order, but who was to be the philosopher? The reshaping was going the length and breadth of the plant sciences.

Presently we will show the role which Bailey was to fill. But before doing so we must consider still further some important accomplishments of workers of the United States Department of Agriculture.

When Swingle made his first trip abroad and came so definitely under

the influence of European scholarship, Webber continued the work at
Eustis and Miami. Briefly considered, Swingle's career during these
years is divided into at least two periods: first, the period of investigating the pathology and crossbreeding of citrous fruits, 1891-1897, work
in which Webber collaborated. Their pioneer publication on citrous diseases laid the foundation in this country for subsequent pathological
study in these groups. The second period of Swingle's researches was as
an agricultural explorer during 1898-1899. At this time, Swingle left
in Florida a number of hybridizations in the field, and Webber grew
and tested the hybrids from seed, of itself a large task. It was during
these explorations that Swingle, despite warnings from even scientific
authorities that nothing could be accomplished by the introduction, was
among the first, if not the first,[31] to find and bring to the United States a
fig insect which rendered possible the culture of Smyrna type figs. Moreover, he shipped new standard varieties of date palms from Algeria into
California and Arizona. These accomplishments, together with his already mentioned Florida citrous hybrids, and certain valuable cotton introductions in the southwestern states were outstanding and helped to
bring about large scale crop physiological and breeding investigations
by the United States Department of Agriculture. In the furtherance of
these Swingle occupied positions of high responsibility.

As the century drew to a close, Webber was summoned to Washington to take charge of a laboratory which bears the closest analogy to
Smith's laboratory of plant pathology—the laboratory of plant breeding. Webber was an able cytologist and physiologist. From the beginning of his Florida experience, fecundation in plants had absorbed his
attention. Discovery of an entomogenous fungus parasitic upon the larvae
of the white fly and scale insects had been one of his and Swingle's
early triumphs. Most noted, however, was Webber's studies of fertilization in Zamia, an American cycad in which he had been interested since
his years at the University of Nebraska. In 1897 Webber startled Ameri-

---

[31] In 1898, after further European study under Pfeffer and Ostwald at Leipzig,
Swingle went into plant introduction work. Beginning intensive study in libraries
of France and other nations and pursuing further special investigations of citrous
varieties, Swingle followed up an already strong interest in fig and date culture and,
of course, a study of such native products as the olive. He went to Sicily, Italy, North
Africa, Greece, Asia Minor, and planned to go to India and Java. His belief in the
possibilities of tropical horticulture and its study was exceeded only by his urgent
advocacy of placing the crop introduction program on a scientific as well as practical
basis. Evidently, before Swingle, as a plant explorer of the government, brought the
Blastophaga to this country in 1899, the fig wasp had been introduced by private
sources, in California. The accomplishments of practical farmers and growers may be
withheld from public use, whereas that done by government workers becomes available
to every citizen. Bailey in his *Standard Cyclopedia of Horticulture*, 1915, page 1237,
said that George Roeding of Fresno, California, in 1896, and Swingle in 1899, "working
separately at different points of the problem," established the Algerian Blastophaga
for Californians, whereas, three decades previously, on the Gates farm near Modesto,
the fig wasp had become accidentally established.

can and British botanists at a meeting in Toronto of the British Association for the Advancement of Science. The force of his finding of motile spermatozoids, or antherozoids, in *Zamia integrifolia*, so astounded botanists, even his good and faithful teacher Bessey, that his proof had to be presented a second time. For, the disclosure was of great significance in evolutionary understanding, specifically in fundamentals pertaining to plant sequential development. Some incredulous scholars believed that the warm climate of Florida had affected Webber's mind. But the lecture was repeated, and America had produced a research which ranked in importance with the scholarship of Europe. Swingle's thesis, prepared under Strasburger, demonstrating the existence of centrosomes in plants was of no more consequence. Be it known, nevertheless, Swingle was in Eustis when Webber performed most of his research preparatory to writing his internationally recognized paper on Zamia and its fertilization. Webber had the benefit of Swingle's alert, vigorous intellect and often consulted with Swingle.

Other contributions of these and other men during the decade to plant science progress at Washington might be delineated. The presence of Albert Frederick Woods as assistant chief of the Division of Vegetable Physiology and Pathology—appointed since 1893 to the position formerly held by Fairchild—added excellent administrative ability as well as sound research talent at the main laboratories at Washington. Woods was a capable plant physiologist and pathologist, schooled under Bessey, and once a member of that brilliant constituency which comprised the historic "Sem. Bot." of the University of Nebraska when its botany seminar was founded and began its effective and creative studies of plants and plant life of the state. Establisher of the laboratory of plant physiology at the university and appointed professor of plant physiology and pathology immediately after his graduation in 1890, Woods came to Washington highly recommended. Chosen by Secretary of Agriculture Morton, his appointment was urged by Galloway as providing "a man of pleasing address, good executive ability, and thoroughly trained in our special field of work." Woods had shown unusual aptitude for pathological research while at the University of Nebraska by virtue of an exceedingly clever and resourceful study of tobacco mosaic. Woods closely approximated a complete explanation of this disease, now placed in the virus group. Furthermore, after his arrival at the United States Department of Agriculture, he pioneered, among a number of researches, in study of floricultural diseases, including, at least, one of bacterial origin, the causal organism of which Smith named *Bacterium woodsii*. Quite a story of researches is clustered about this and the study of tobacco mosaic and must be reserved for another book. Our story now must return to Bailey and his participation in these and other developmental expansions of the decade.

Bailey had initiated a program which was to make him the world's leading agricultural author and editor. His contributions toward developing a literature of the land and its products were profound. When he arrived at Cornell in 1888, although his interest was mostly in research, facilities to conduct experiments on a large scale were lacking. He built a "nice" forcing house "for $800, heat and all complete, and [having] heating capacity for one or two more of the same size." By 1890 this had become a "plant" which covered more than five thousand square feet with large work rooms, a photograph gallery, and of which about four thousand square feet were covered with glass. Seven glass houses were used for growing various plants—one for tomatoes, one for cucumbers and melons, one for "the cooler plants, such as lettuce, radishes, spinach, peas, tulips, verbenas, etc.," one for ornamental plants; one was considered "a model laboratory greenhouse"; one was a fruit house where it was expected to grow peaches, nectarines, grapes, and other fruits; and one was "a laboratory-house." These buildings using various kinds of glass and styles of construction were connected by other buildings, all of which were either steam or hot-water heated. A large station barn having storage cellars, grafting room, tool room, fertilizer storage room, stables, and other equipment, was available.

On October 15, 1890, Bailey outlined to Smith:

> . . . I have my plans of life work . . . firmly and fully set. . . . A large work which has floated as a phantom before my mind for years is now assuming shape and I hope to see it done in a couple years. It is a work, a philosophical work, upon the variation of plants under culture. I am getting a number of minor works off my hands to leave me freer for this. Rule-Book is done and Annals is launched. I have mss for a companion to [the] Rule-Book almost done and it will go to printer's hands in two or three weeks. Two other small books are well under way and I shall get them off within a year if all goes well. Then I have the most interesting and extensive series of experiments on plant variation ever planned in this country. These demand constant attention. Besides I am making a comprehensive study [and herbarium] of cultivated plants.

For many years, Bailey submitted his manuscripts to Smith for reading. Smith always responded with valuable criticism and suggestions for improvement. In no sense did he become a co-author, and, of course, as the research of the two men took different directions and each became an outstanding authority in a different field, their consultations grew fewer. Neither, however, lost interest and faith in the other's work. For instance, when Smith's *Bacteria in Relation to Plant Diseases* (volume 1) was published in 1905. Bailey congratulated Smith on his research and good judgment: "It seems to me that this is going to place the subject of the bacterial diseases of plants on a safe and rational foundation, and I am gratified to know that an American is to have the credit of it." On June 29, 1916, acknowledging the receipt of some prints of Smith's epoch-making plant-tumor studies, he stated:

I have followed your work in this field in a general way, and shall be interested to see how it comes out in the end. Certainly you are well qualified to do such nice pieces of work as this, and I am glad that you are able to do it. How far the roads have taken us since the days of Ionia and M[ichigan] A[gricultural] C[ollege]!

At Cornell University, by 1890, the horticultural experiment grounds amounted to fifteen acres. These contained orchard plantations—dwarf pear; apricot, plum and pear; huckleberry; apple; cherry; peach; nectarines, almond, mulberry, nuts, and other tree fruit; blackberry, raspberry, currant, gooseberry, strawberry; many wild fruits, including juneberry; a small but growing Prunicetum to grow native American plums; a Rubicetum, into which wild brambles were being collected. Of each there were many varieties. There were also, of course, the vegetable gardens to which Bailey had given his earliest attention. In his 1890 report Bailey insisted, "The variation of plants under culture is the perennial theme of investigation . . . keeping track of the kind and extent of variation in plants, and also for the purpose of answering any questions . . . studied with reference to the influence upon them of soil, culture, and climate, and especially with reference to the effects of crossing and hybridization." For example, experiments were being made to find to what extent color can be regulated by crossing and hybridization in coleus, mimulus, silene, phlox, tomatoes, and other plants. Influence of fertilizers on fruit trees to find effects of excesses of potash, phosphoric acid, nitrogen, and other elements, were studied both from the standpoints of profitable concentration and to learn something of controlling factors. The "moot point" of relative merits of budded, crown-grafted and root-grafted apple trees was being investigated. Forcing, grafting, germination, plant food and many "secondary" experiments were included. Most of them had to do with the orchard or garden although "a large experiment with hardy foreign and domestic roses" was in progress in 1890. Some systematic studies had also commenced, of horse-radish for propagation and improvement and of dwarf lima beans, then a new type of garden vegetable in contrast to the "pole Limas" which had been found an uncertain crop in parts of western New York. The consequence of all this work was that Bailey was performing two tasks using equipment assembled within three years: he was studying academically the principles of horticulture and contributing, practically, to New York plant growers valuable knowledge and information.

When Bailey had gone abroad in 1888 and studied carices, he returned with some remarkable photographs of specimens. In introducing photography, Bailey initiated a distinct innovation in American taxonomic procedure. Theretofore, the practice had been almost wholly that of reproducing specimens by drawings. The photographic procedure was continued at Cornell. In 1890 Bailey pointed out, with reference to systematic studies, "In all our work, photography is used freely as a means of preserving accurate records."

At Cornell University agricultural instruction on a college basis was organized when the federally aided experiment station was established. Roberts was then dean. Agriculture shared space with horticulture on the second floor at the north side of Morrill Hall, perhaps the most historic building of Cornell University's campus. It was built, it is said, in 1866, of native lime rock. In 1890 the university board voted $80,000 to erect a building for the use of the four divisions of the college of agriculture and the experiment station. However, chemistry was found to need a new building. So Morse Hall was built.

Horticulture remained in Morrill Hall, in the second floor rooms on the south side of the hall at the north end of the building. Botany, having charge of the general herbarium, care of the grounds, and the historic Sage Conservatory, was quartered in the south wing of Sage College. Botany had its own garden, hotbeds, nursery rows, laboratories, and general equipment. Both the flower conservatories and the museum herbarium were utilized in its experimentation. The most important experimental work, aside from its taxonomic studies of lower plant orders, was its work in plant diseases. Clover and hollyhock rusts were examined in a work that anticipated more exact pathological investigation. Some of America's most important early mycological work was done at Cornell. The entomological division work in certain insect families had the largest and most valuable collections known. The botanical department's possession of some of the most valuable collections of fungi material also added to the university's fame.

Bailey devoted the use of one of two horticultural offices in Morrill Hall to the maintenance of a garden herbarium. Containing pressed and mounted specimens of every variety of every species grown in the garden, the herbarium was growing large and a "most important feature." "Besides this," Bailey said, "collections are made at leading nurseries in various parts of the country and arrangements are being made by which cultivated plants of foreign countries are to be secured. In short, the scope of the garden herbarium is nothing less than an herbarium of the cultivated species and varieties of the world. This I consider an invaluable auxiliary to any complete and comprehensive study of the variation of cultivated plants. The division also owns a great number of charts and prints of various kinds. The library contains files of all the leading journals, both domestic and foreign, and a very large selection of the best horticultural writings. Most of the periodicals are also laid directly before the eyes of students by keeping them on file in the agricultural reading-room." Therein, more than five decades ago, began the accumulations, the nucleus, of the today world renowned Bailey Hortorium, an institution unique in the world and representative of a lifetime of labor.

Bailey's photographs, not only of herbarium specimens but also of famous European gardens and flowers, brought another result. He made the acquaintance of J. Horace McFarland of Harrisburg, Pennsylvania. Bailey early began a custom of going to horticultural meetings, in June of 1889 attending a meeting of horticulturists of various agricultural experiment stations at Columbus, Ohio, where assembled to discuss variety tests and naming of new varieties to be published by the Office of Experiment Stations were W. B. Alwood of the Virginia station; W. H. Bishop of the Maryland station; G. C. Butz of the Pennsylvania station; W. J. Green, J. Fremont Hickman, and W. R. Lazenby of the Ohio station; James Troop of the Indiana station; L. R. Taft of the Michigan station; and others including C. E. Thorne, remembered as a pioneering leader in plat experimentation, and Clarence M. Weed of the Ohio station. The work of experiment station bulletins was one branch of the work: the work of the popular magazines was another.

In 1887 the *Ladies' Floral Cabinet*, and in 1888 *The Gardeners' Monthly and Horticulturist* were merged in *The American Garden* and this, in turn, in 1891 united with *Popular Gardening and Fruit Growing* but kept its title *The American Garden*. Bailey had contributed to this magazine in 1887, when it was edited by Edgar H. Libby. In 1890, after the Rural Publishing Company became its publisher, Bailey himself became the editor. Years before, Bailey had told Bessey that he hoped that all horticultural books could be published by one house. A plan, to which Bailey agreed to lend services, was formed to effectuate this. In 1889 the Garden Publishing Company whose printing work was done by McFarland—also a lover of plants, interested in fruit and flower photography—had placed on the market Bailey's *The Horticulturist's Rule-Book*; a compendium of useful information for fruit-growers, truck gardeners, florists and others, completed to the close of that year. In the course of this book's printing, or, perhaps at an earlier horticultural meeting, Bailey and McFarland became acquainted and McFarland, much impressed by Bailey's photographs of European gardens and flowers, told others of the possessions of the zealous Cornell professor of horticulture. Since improved methods of photography were rapidly gaining ground and since all means of producing better and more reliable seed catalogues were commanding much interest, McFarland fell in readily with Bailey's expanded dreams of improved agricultural and horticultural education.

To make a stronger publishing unit, the Garden Publishing Company associated itself with the Rural Publishing Company, of long and honored standing in American agricultural circles. This company had been organized about the middle of the century in Rochester, New York, a point of yet great American horticultural interest. It had moved to New York City in the 1860's where, in a center of still greater advantage, Elbert S. Carman, one of the greatest early horticulturists, famous for his originations of new potatoes, grains, and flowers, and as a pomologist, whom Bailey knew and visited, became editor of its widely influential publication, the *Rural New-Yorker*. This publication for many years has been one of the nation's leading agricultural journals. After Carman, Herbert W. Collingwood, Bailey's fellow student at Michigan Agricultural College, became its next editor of outstanding rank. Late in the 1880's Carman, also the owner, negotiated a sale of his company and journal to a group, among whom were McFarland and Libby, and of which Lawson Valentine, a New York varnish manufacturer whose fortune had been made, was the principal support.

Valentine should be accorded an honorary place in the history of American horticulture. In 1876, desirous of creating an "American Rothamstead," he had founded at Houghton Farms, on 1,000 acres of land, at Cornwall, Orange County, New York, a private scientific and experiment station. It was a work for agriculture somewhat analogous to the work for forestry performed on the historic Girard estate in Pennsylvania where planting began about 1877. Valentine employed talented workers of no less ability than Manly Miles in agriculture, Samuel Parsons, Jr., in landscape gardening, and David Pearce Penhallow as botanist and chemist.

Another employee of forthcoming renown was Samuel Bowdlear Green. Born at Chelsea, Massachusetts, in 1859, Green was graduated twenty years later from Massachusetts Agricultural College of which institution Penhallow was also a graduate and where Penhallow assisted Dr. Goessmann with noted physiological investigations. Like Penhallow, Green went to foreign lands and there acquired an expanded view of plant science investigation. Returning to America, Green spent four years at Houghton Farms in charge of the horticultural department, arriving the year after Penhallow left to go to McGill University in Canada, where he achieved enviable prominence as paleobotanist and botanist. Penhallow's vision of foreign work was largely acquired in Japan, Green's in Europe. Penhallow had been also much influenced by Asa Gray at Harvard. Green studied under Parsons. In 1888 he became professor of horticulture and applied botany at the University of Minnesota; and in 1892 professor of horticulture and forestry.

Green in every sense was a western pioneer in educational phases of plant study. During his career he wrote books on forestry, vegetable gardening, and fruit growing. His work in forestry was particularly important in prairie tree planting and nursery practice. But this was by no means all.

Minnesota had led other states of the United States in organizing a state forestry association. State and federal work in the Minnesota forests awakened some of the first hopeful signs of realizing an "American forestry." In the late 1880's efforts were made by the national government to segregate on the Indian reservations agricultural from "pine lands." For the first time, it is said, the government adopted a policy of estimating and selling the land on the basis of amount and value of the pine stand. Minnesota's pine forests were world famous. One of the first vigorous voices raised in America on behalf of a "good system of forestry administration" in the United States was that of General C. C. Andrews of St. Paul. The University of Minnesota was quick to respond to the need of forestry instruction. By 1902 it had created a four year course leading to the degree of Bachelor of Agriculture in Forestry. Summer work was later begun in Itasca Park. Green's contribution was not confined to forestry but was made in all fields of agricultural investigation. He was so influential, it is said, that he could have been elected governor of Minnesota, had he wished the honor. Eventually he became the first dean of forestry at the university. Green was another close friend of Bailey's.

Reports from Houghton Farms during its more than a decade of existence had occupied a "high place in the current agricultural literature." Valentine and his associates bought the Rural Publishing Company and an ambitious project was outlined. *Rural New-Yorker*, the *American Garden*, and a book publishing department under Bailey were parts of the plan. Had not Valentine died, everything might have gone well. Financial difficulties ensued. The ventures, however, were intrinsically sound, as proved by *Rural New-Yorker's* quick recovery, by the facts that magazines of the standing of *American Garden* weathered periods of instability, and Bailey's book department under later management heralded the founding of a substantial American agricultural literature. Nevertheless, the company had to undergo a change of ownership, John J. Dillon becoming part owner in 1893 and sole owner in 1897.

Bailey's concept of a "Rural Library . . . a series of monthly issues of popular pamphlets on scientific and practical topics in agriculture and horticulture" was to prove imperishable. In fact, the concept would be enlarged as agriculture, both educationally and practically, expanded. Intended to be complete manuals of subjects treated, the series' authors and editors were to be "men and women whose broad knowledge of the specialties on which they [wrote was] undisputed." *Cross-Breeding and Hybridizing*, "The Philosophy of the Crossing of Plants, Considered with Reference to their Improvement under Cultivation," with bibliography, a lecture given before the Massachusetts State Board of Agriculture in Boston, December 1, 1891, was published as the first of the series. This small but highly significant booklet contained a concise evaluation of Bailey's experience in the subject:

Encourage in every way crosses within the limits of the variety and in connection with change of stock, expecting increase in vigor and productiveness; hybridize if you wish to experiment, but do it carefully, honestly, thoroughly, and do not expect too much! Extend Darwin's famous remark to read: Nature abhors both perpetual self-fertilization and hybridization.

The lecture, and its publication, met with instant favor everywhere.

In 1891, the Rural Publishing Company also published Bailey's *The Nursery-Book*, a complete guide to the multiplication and pollination of plants. David Fairchild has since characterized this as a "bible for propagating work," full of absorbing and useful information. Written in the light of the knowledge of that time and limited to horticultural areas then familiarly known, it supplied all persons interested in the growing and reproducing of plants by man's agency with a valuable manual. This, and the *Horticulturist's Rule-Book*, were made parts of a garden-craft series, comprising practical handbooks for horticulturists, which explained and illustrated in detail various important methods which experience had demonstrated to be most satisfactory. Manuals of practice, they would be revised and brought up to date from time to time and go through many editions. Other books made parts of this series were Bailey's *The Forcing-Book* (1897) and *The Pruning-Book* (1898), works on which he was at this time exerting himself in far flung efforts to gather together all latest and most effective methods and data and to form basic philosophies of these phases of horticultural endeavor. Also to be made a part of the series would be the historic and renowned book on *Plant Breeding*, which ran through several editions and of which "Cross-Breeding and Hybridizing" was the basic lecture.

During this period the Rural Publishing Company commenced publication of, perhaps, Bailey's most highly commendable project, the scholarly *Annals of Horticulture*. The first one was published in 1890 and concerned the work of the previous year. These volumes were continued for several years. Had they been continued (as Bailey intended), each year to the present, their worth would be of inestimable value.

Nevertheless, the service they performed toward the advancement of scientific horticulture was incalculable. In them Bailey assumed a leadership which placed him among the foremost horticultural editors.

As editor of *American Garden*, Bailey had been given a coveted chance to popularize horticulture. He made use of the opportunity, either imparting interesting information or discussing with his readers progressive advances made or prospects looking to the future.

Many of the important fundamental investigations were described at one time or another—the attack on destructive insects and fungi; top-grafting; training fruit trees; studies in root-grafting; protection to the originator of a variety; electro-horticulture including the four experiments, with naked light running all night, without natural light, with a protected light running all night, and with naked light running part of the night; forcing and crossing tomatoes; forcing English cucumbers; and in *American Garden* Bailey published "Notes from a Garden Herbarium," taxonomic studies of dewberries, blackberries and raspberries, cultivated chestnuts, Japanese flowering cherries, Soulard crab and its kin. Numerous other notes appeared, including articles on tuberous begonias, double roses, Say's rose, Cape Cod cranberries, Japanese walnut, the tree tomato, peach culture in Michigan, the bloomless apple. Bailey did not exclude articles of historical significance on literature and men of the science although he regarded horticulture's literature up to that time as "meagre." Most especially, he never missed an occasion to discuss horticulture as a new science. These were subjects of much interest to gardeners and farmers, and the public generally. Although Bailey's editorship lasted only from 1890 to 1892, inclusive, he accomplished great things. For himself he saw what popular journalistic work could do in aid of a science. For the welfare of all, he saw even more widely the great service to be performed by advancing American horticultural interests. The *Annals of Horticulture* were, therefore, addressed to the men of the science primarily and, incidentally, to the general public.

Aside from his book and bulletin writing, Bailey had the advantage of editing the "Cultural Department" of Charles Sprague Sargent's *Garden and Forest*. This publication was a beautifully prepared and increasingly prominent scientific journal of general interest to landscape gardeners, floriculturists, arboriculturists, and all persons interested in the cultivation and study of woody plants. It was issued from the Arnold Arboretum at Jamaica Plain near Boston, Massachusetts. Bailey had begun to contribute generously to this magazine in 1888. The following year his "Cultural Department" began issuing notes, answering inquiries, narrating new scientific developments of interest, in general, a work quite similar to that of an editor but more specifically limited.

By 1890 Bailey had three tasks superimposed on his teaching, book writing, and experiment station work: this, the editorship of *American Garden*, and preparation of the *Annals of Horticulture*.

From his Garden Home at Ithaca, on December 31, 1889, Bailey sent to the printer the first volume of the *Annals* of which the preface read:

A series of Annals of Horticulture of which the present volume is the initial, is projected for the purpose of preserving in convenient form a record and epitome of yearly progress in horticulture. Our horticultural interests are becoming so various and extensive and records of them are so widely scattered, that such compendiums are a necessity; and summaries of the most important discoveries and discussions must have a direct and immediate practical use, wholly aside from their values as history.

A leading feature of the series must necessarily be complete records of the introduction of horticultural plants; and the author desires that these volumes shall comprise the standard publication of new varieties. . . . To this end, all North American originators and introducers are solicited to make records of their novelties and introductions. . . .

Complete lists of all the varieties of fruits, kitchen garden vegetables and ornamentals now cultivated in North America, are needed. . . .

The present volume is in many directions fragmentary and incomplete in design. It is prepared under the pressure of many new enterprises.

Chapters discussed yields and prices; trees and shrubs for the cold north; new fruits of the south; tendencies in California horticulture; oriental fruits; recent tendencies in ornamental gardening and in ornamentals; plant diseases and insects; recent literature; the year's tools and conveniences; the horticulture of other lands; directories of the societies and the more prominent gardens, and the seedsmen and gardeners; directories of the national societies—American Pomological Society, Society of American Florists, American Association of Nurserymen, Association of American Cemetery Superintendents, Northwest Cider and Vinegar Makers Association were included, in addition to chapters expressly devoted to the objectives stated in the preface.

They showed definitely American horticulture to be a business. They established it as an independent industry, apart from and yet a partner with the other plant sciences. Most certainly it was associated with botany and agriculture. In some quarters it was linked to the developing subjects of agronomy, the study of soils, and meteorology, the science of climate and weather.

A catalogue of American kitchen garden vegetables "constituted the kernel of the book" for 1889. For the issue of the year 1890 Bailey planned "a complete annotated census of all native North American plants and their horticultural varieties" introduced into cultivation. But so difficult did the collection of data prove to be that it was not published until the 1891 volume and then as a "Census of Cultivated

Indigenous Plants. A Record of all the Species of Plants Native to North America, North of Mexico, which have been commercially introduced to cultivation."

Although Bailey confessed that his records for each year might not be thorough and complete, his data by this time indicated that 434 plants were introduced in 1889; in 1890, 575 plants; in 1891, 884 plants, of which 668 were ornamentals, 108 fruit-plants, and 108 vegetables. The disparity in numbers of species published for these years on different occasions was of itself proof of the active and disorganized state of the growing science.

Horticulture was making rapid progress in the South. Bailey estimated that, including the pecans, 185 native species and varieties unknown to cultivation or sparingly disseminated, had been marketed. Of these 24 were introduced as fruit-plants. Twelve, introduced as ornamentals, had edible fruits. The combined census and catalogue afforded an inventory of American horticultural resources. Bailey hoped later to inventory the fruits and ornamentals alone.

Bailey emphasized the desirability of developing the widest horticultural uses. In the *Annals* for 1889 he said:

Unhappily, there are comparatively few horticulturists who possess the delicacy of feeling necessary to the full enjoyment of the art, and there are perhaps fewer still who have the special knowledge necessary to the largest material success. There are few, even, who know the scope of horticulture. Pomology and floriculture are so widely separate in the minds of most cultivators that no affinities are seen between them. The horticulturist must possess both narrowness of application and breadth of view. He not only needs books, but he must have them. To read and to digest his thoughts must become a part of his business rather than wholly his pleasure.

Bailey continually delivered addresses before horticultural groups. In 1890 speaking before the Western New York Horticultural Society at its thirty-fifth meeting on "Forcing Vegetables under Glass," he concluded:

. . . There are six general essentials to successful forcing of plants: (1) Bottom heat (2) Abundance of light (3) Proximity of plants to glass (4) Fresh air. We must outgrow the notion that we ventilate simply to cool off the house. The primary object of ventilation is to give fresh air, and this should be secured without allowing drafts upon plants or changing the temperature of the house suddenly. (5) Humidity of atmosphere (6) Adaptation of methods to change of habits in plants. Plants rarely, if ever, maintain the same habit of growth when forced as they naturally possess out-of-doors. The struggle for light is the chief cause of change of habit. It is the adaptation of methods to this change in habit and rapidity of growth which largely determines the good gardener.

In Boston at the fifteenth annual meeting of the American Association of Nurserymen, Bailey furthered his challenging and effectual dealings with men of the trades. For some time he had exchanged materials and viewpoints with them. He was well aware, too, of how much the knowledge of practical gardeners had meant to Darwin in collating masses of observation of plant variation among domestic species. Gardeners and tradesmen had considerably aided the great Englishman in presenting in scientific form many results of years of work with vegetable materials. Darwin had extended and coordinated many of the results. Bailey envisioned the aid which education might mean practically to garden workers as well as toilers in the larger agricultural crops. The new sciences were largely intended for them. Agricultural experimentation was not conceived as a cloistered enterprise dedicated solely to the revelation of fundamental life processes, of the great principles and laws of evolutionary change and development.

At the thirty-sixth meeting of the Western New York Horticultural Society, Bailey read a paper on the subject, "Do Varieties Run Out?" This was one of a number of papers which showed the lasting, persistent influence of Gray on the young horticulturist who was doing in large measure for his chosen science what Gray had done in America for botany—integrated and coordinated its basic foundations. Bailey argued:

> The presumption is . . . as Dr. Gray long ago pointed out, that the older the variety, that is, the greater the number of its generations, the greater must be its chances of permanence, because it has become pronounced in its character and has proved its capability to persist. But I propose to limit the present discussion to the mere disappearance of varietal characteristics through which we lose sight of the variety, rather than to extend it to the philosophical question as to whether varieties, like individuals, become old and die, or wear out.
>
> My proposition and the proof of it are simply these: Running out is the disappearance of varietal characteristics through change; all plants vary or change; therefore varieties must tend to run out. . . . We can divide variation into general groups, seed-variation and bud-variation. . . .
>
> The conclusion of the whole matter is simply this: Varieties grown from seeds tend to vary or run out, while varieties grown from buds tend to remain permanent or nearly so, unless the parts which are propagated possess abnormal, or what we might call fictitious or unstable characters, in which case further variation or running out may be expected.

Two years later, before the same society, Bailey would discuss, "Are the Varieties of Orchard Fruits Running Out?" and would conclude:

> Varieties of orchard fruits, which are propagated by buds, very rarely run out, but they may disappear because they are ill-adapted to various conditions, because they are susceptible to disease, and because they are supplanted by better varieties, or those which more completely fill the present demands or fashions. The disappearances are, therefore, so many mile-stones to our progress.

On December 8, 1892, before the Illinois State Horticultural Society meeting at Champaign, Bailey discussed, "Why Do Promising Varieties Fail?" concluding:

. . . The blame for the introduction of unsuccessful varieties is not so much moral dishonesty as a misconception of the merits of the varieties and the nature of the demand which they are to meet; and the remedy of the evil is a better understanding of the points at issue, both by the introducer and the purchaser.

The points at issue were said to be:

New varieties are often not fixed or permanent in their characteristics, or do not show their full attributes at once.

New varieties are often not adapted to a wide range of conditions.

Varieties bear a variable and uncertain relationship to disease and insect attacks.

The standard of merit is constantly rising, and varieties which have been acceptable at one time may no longer find favor.

Bailey believed, and he said in an address, "Are American Varieties of Fruits Best Adapted to American Conditions?" before the American Horticultural Society at its Chicago meeting in 1892, that "American fruits constantly tend to diverge from the foreign type, which were their parents and they are, as a rule, better adapted to our environments than foreign varieties are. In less than a century," he argued, "we have departed widely from the imported varieties which gave us a start. At the expiration of another century we should stand upon a basis which is nearly, if not wholly, American." He regarded the Russian importations "as of immeasurable benefit to our horticulture" but he looked on them as means rather than ends. "The history of our horticulture," he observed, "everywhere emphasizes the probability of a secondary and more important outcome."

Annals of Horticulture for 1892 showed the olive becoming an important product in southwestern United States. Nut growing was developing in California. Fig culture was being agitated there.

California had had a wonderfully colorful history, horticulturally. A maritime area, it had both high and low elevations, both hot and cold lands, both wet and dry—extremes in each—besides a rich native growth. Its horticulture combined early Russian importations brought by Russians themselves and early Mexican influences brought by early Spanish and Mexican settlement: the marvelous ingenuity of the early mission padres and helpers who saved souls by feeding bodies. The padres had developed systems of irrigation. They knew winemaking. They grew beautiful gardens. They brought in citrus fruits, olives, grapes, figs, pomegranates, date palms for religious services. They tiled ditches, built dams, diversion dams, viaducts, and means of keeping

water clean. Although on the Pacific coast the first fruit trees were probably grown in Oregon, nevertheless, apples, olives, grapes, figs, pomegranates, quinces, cherries, plums, apricots, peaches, and pears, had
begun to thrive on what is now California soil. Because of widely
diversified conditions, California took an early aggressive stand for
scientific agricultural development. Developing its own land, it also
early interested itself in the progress made by growing fruits in arid
Utah with the aid of irrigation—for California had desert areas, too.

The great central western areas to the east, however, were slow in development. Large regions there were the last in the United States to be
geographically and scientifically explored. For decades their lands were
sparsely populated. Owing to difficult soil and climate problems, immense
barren areas went uninhabited and unfarmed. Fruit trees were not extensively grown. For decades only enough vegetables necessary for
livelihood were cultivated until, aided by land reclamation projects,
important plant industries, notably sugar beets, were made possible.

As a matter of fact, before the arrival of the Spanish, this was so
over nearly all western areas. There was little agriculture as we know
agriculture. The Indians had done very little toward the development,
even in the wild state, of grape fruit, lemons, oranges, and similar
luxurious horticultural products.

Into the Southwest these fruits were brought by seed from Florida,
along the old trail through Texas and New Mexico to Arizona and California. Padres and voyageurs brought them up from Mexico. Or, they
arrived by way of the Isthmus of Panama and north along the Pacific
coast to the historic chain of missions and settlements. Indians knew
grains and their growing. So did Mexicans. We learned much from
them. But a progressive agriculture throughout the Southwest and West
did not develop until the years of Spanish and American settlement.
Not until the advent of the colleges did it become scientific. Even then,
since the Pacific flora is unlike that of Asia, new plant introductions
from Japan and China went mostly to the Atlantic areas. Asa Gray had
studied this problem from the standpoint of plants of the wild. Bailey,
in the course of a few years, was to become interested in it too and to
write an illuminating article dealing with its horticultural phases. He
also made a comparative study of the horticulture of the Pacific coast
and the Atlantic states.

The *Annals* for 1892 announced that, while introductions were less
than in 1891, all together 716 varieties and species, of which 503 were
ornamentals, 122 vegetables, and 91 fruits, were first put in trade that
year. Potatoes, beans, and tomatoes each had a dozen or more. Grapes,
strawberries, and apples led in pomological products. The ornamentals
vastly dominated: chrysanthemums, 156; carnations, 40; roses, 36;

petunias, 26; and phlox, 17. For the first three, national societies had been organized.

At the first annual meeting of the American Carnation Society held at Buffalo, New York, Bailey spoke on "John Thorpe's Ideal Carnation," and traced, historically, breeding methods employed in carnation development. Explaining that of two methods to produce a four inch flower, he preferred to increase the length of the outer petals, rather than increase the mass of the flower. Better results would be obtained, "for by that means," he said, "we shall probably avoid some of the tendency towards bursting of the calyx, and we shall be likely to obtain a more shapely flower, and one which will not need Mr. Thorpe's pencil-stem for its support." In this, value of the study of origins and evolution of garden varieties was demonstrated. Large carnations of former years had disappeared. It was a flower of fashion and had risen and fallen in favor. Bailey seemed to feel no doubt that Thorpe's "bold prophecy that within eight years we shall be able to grow carnation flowers four inches in diameter, and to sell them for one dollar each," would be realized. He said:

Select that variety which most nearly approaches the standard, and by high cultivation and very close pruning force it into great size. . . . The four-inch flower can be produced, because it has already been recorded; whether the other characters of Mr. Thorpe's flower will appear will depend much upon the care which we give to forceful cultivation.

Before the society's second annual meeting at Pittsburgh in 1893, Bailey would elaborate "Some Types and Tendencies in the Carnation," and discuss among other matters differences and variation between American grown plants and European, including that grown in the wild state in the Mediterranean region, and the possibilities of further introductions. "It seems to me to be important," he stated, "that the whole field of carnation culture should be encouraged in America, rather than to confine our attention to a single type of the family. It should be remembered that the perpetual or bench carnations are of recent origin, and are therefore not yet perfect. . . . Good results in originating new varieties will come, as a rule, only from persistent effort extended over a series of years and founded upon a strong and uniform stock." That Bailey's discussions met with favor was shown by his speaking at the society's next meeting in 1894 at Indianapolis on "Border Carnations," the out-of-doors types which, in contrast to American grown winter or forcing types, had been grown for centuries in the gardens of Europe.

Floricultural interests in 1892 had shown "a steady increase in trade and popularity. The public appreciation of ornamental gardening and the artistic values of plants," wrote Bailey, "is now increasing. . . . The movement for national and state flowers, while not specifically floricultural, is still worthy of note." This movement, now four years old, had engaged discussions as to a national emblem and state choices. Among these, golden rod, mountain laurel, mayflower, water lily, magnolia, aster, and columbine had been "pressed for public favor." Minnesota had passed a resolution naming the moccasin flower. The Oregon state horticultural society favored the Oregon grape. All of the states were to have an official state flower; some to choose native plants of their wild regions, and some cultivated plants of more obvious decorative value. Nevertheless, at this time, those most favored were the rose, the winter carnation, and the chrysanthemum, in the last of which progress had been made by shipping flowers frozen in cylinders of ice from New Zealand to England.

In the Columbian Exposition held at Chicago in 1893, noteworthy exhibits of azaleas and rhododendrons impressed Bailey. In *Garden and Forest* he said: "There seems no reason why American nurserymen should not originate races which will be perfectly hardy and happy in our climate. . . ." Furthermore, in a paper styled "Horticultural Geography," read before the American Association of Nurserymen at the world's fair, he said:

I am greatly impressed with the influence which locality exerts upon the exhibits. It would seem as if the climate of any geographical region determines very largely the character of all the open air plants which grow there, both in modifying whatever varieties have been permanently introduced, and in preventing the establishment of other varieties which may succeed in contiguous areas. Both these influences of climate or locality are admirably shown in the apple exhibits which are now upon the shelves of the Horticultural Building, for while none of these exhibits show the entire apple flora of any state or natural area, they are, nevertheless, fairly representative, and are useful for comparison. . . .

The entire horticultural exhibition . . . greatly strengthens the conviction which has been growing upon me in recent years, that the study of the adaptation of varieties to geographical and local conditions is a most imperative demand in horticultural pursuits. I therefore look with much distrust upon the promiscuous distribution of varieties over great areas. . . . Climate and environment must eventually force the nurseries into nearly as narrow limits as the adaptability of the stock which they grow, although this contraction will follow some distance behind the determination or discovery of the limits of adaptability of the varieties themselves. The European nurseries have had this experience to an important extent.

Right here you may wish to cite me to the excellent displays of rhododendrons and azaleas upon these grounds as proof that nursery stock can be successfully grown far away from the geographical area in which it is to mature, for these plants, with unimportant exceptions, are grown in Europe. But I shall contend that the most important reason why these plants do not succeed well in America is because they are European-grown. It is always said that the American climate is not adapted to the rhododendron, but with all due respect to those much older than myself, I must still decline to believe the statement. One of the most important species of cultivated rhododendron is native to our Alleghany region, and evergreen ericaceous plants in variety are indigenous over much of our territory. . . . There is not the slightest reason to doubt that if American nurserymen were to originate varieties of rhododendrons, we should soon have sufficient adaptive kinds to meet our needs. Even the cultivation of the apple never became an unqualified success in the United States until we produced American varieties. All success in the cultivation of raspberries and strawberries and gooseberries was delayed until we had American species or varieties. . . . All the older men in this audience can remember when it was thought that the American climate would not allow of successful rose-growing out of doors, but now rose gardens are common, and there are more prizes for us among American novelties than among the European. I have the fullest confidence that there is not a more promising field for the faithful and patient American nurseryman than in the evolution of an American race of rhododendrons and azaleas.

In May of that year Bailey wrote, for *American Gardening*, "Evolution of the Petunia." He urged similarly more attention to this plant from flower lovers, since of late years its improvement had been neglected. When a few years later Rollins Adams Emerson, graduate of and professor in the University of Nebraska, would spend a summer at Ithaca, he would study color cross pollination of petunias with Bailey's endorsement. All plants interested Bailey, whether clover in the field or begonia of the hothouse or the gingko tree of antiquity. Speedily becoming the leading American college horticulturist, his predisposition was always toward progress. For example, carices, he thought, could be placed to ornamental uses. In 1892 in *Garden and Forest*, he said, "I have long thought that Sedges and Carices will some day be considered valuable ornamental plants, and I have begun their cultivation for that purpose. I have just seen an excellent example of their value in the unique botanical garden at the Michigan Agricultural College, where Mr. C. F. Wheeler, who is a most ardent lover of wild plants, and of Sedges in particular, has collected many of our native species." Sargent's great *Silva of North America*—especially volumes which included treatments of the rose, plum, cherry, apple, hawthorn, magnolia, and the forthcoming one on conifers—were commended as of "noble character." Numerous other examples could be cited pointing to Bailey's substantial interest in floriculture.

Bailey frowned on "wholesale growing of many ill-sorted varieties by any one nursery, and the indiscriminate dissemination of them over the country" as opposed to best experience and science. He said so, in a paper, "Reflective Impressions of the Nursery Business," read before the American Association of Nurserymen at Indianapolis in 1895. Teaching people that fruit trees differ in habits of growth as in kinds was necessary, he maintained:

Why may not a catalogue explain that a tree may be first-class and yet be crooked and gnarly? Why not place the emphasis upon health and vigor, and not upon mere shape and comeliness? And why may not a nurseryman give a list of those varieties which are comely growers, and another list of those which are wayward growers? . . . I cannot escape the conviction that the common staple or commercial varieties are not always the best for the fruit grower. If this is true, then the remedy is education for the grower, that he may select the varieties which are best for his purposes and conditions; but this education, it seems to me, should at least be fostered by the nurseryman, inasmuch as his ultimate success is determined by the success or profitableness of fruit-growing. . . .

Scientific knowledge of the best practices in dealing with insects and fungi, in improving quantity and quality of plant food, in selecting buds and cions to propagate nursery stock, in grafting, in the whole range of horticultural and agricultural practice, was necesary to supplant bounty for barrenness, health for ills, vigor for weakness. Furthermore, Bailey, in an address before the Western New York Horticultural Society in 1894, approved "the tendency to produce new varieties [as] the means by which cultivated plants are ever more and more improved and fitted into new conditions and uses; and novelties," he affirmed, "must pay if horticulture is to forever pay." But, answering "Are Novelties Worth Their Cost?" he pointed out that

. . . not all novelties pay. . . . They may not be good enough to pay. Novelties are introduced both hastily and indiscreetly. If the philosophy of the question . . . teaches us anything, it is:

First, that the older and more improved the type, the less are the chances of securing a worthy novelty; Second, that there is most use for novelties in those plants which are propagated by seed and by abnormally developed parts, because such plants usually quickly run out by variation; Third, that worthy novelties appear less frequently in old regions than in new ones, because of greater competition of established varieties there; and Fourth, that the merit of a variety lies in its adaptability to some particular use or demand. . . .

I believe that the time is now at hand when a man can establish a more lucrative nursery or plant business by giving his novelties careful and discriminating tests, and by telling what they are not good for as clearly as he tells what they are good for, as he can by possessing himself of the desire to introduce a certain number of novelties each year, and to paint them in such faultless colors that every thoughtful man knows that the descriptions are false.

Bailey remained active in botanical circles. At a meeting of the botanical club of the American Association for the Advancement of Science, in August of 1892, he proposed organization of a "permanent American Botanical Society." In response thereto a resolution was offered and adopted: "That a committee of nine members be appointed by the Chairman to consider the formation of an American Botanical Society after obtaining the views of the botanists of America on the proposition."[32] Bailey was named chairman, and members of his committee were Farlow, Emily Gregory, Halsted, James Fletcher, D. H. Campbell, Barnes, Scribner, Lester F. Ward, and W. P. Wilson. Having some correspondence with Farlow about nomenclatural matters and the preparation of horticultural articles for Johnson's *Cyclopedia*, Bailey wrote Farlow early in 1893. He said he had prepared a circular and asked Farlow's advice about circulating it to obtain a consensus of opinion before the Madison meeting of the botanical club of the Association. On June 26 he wrote Farlow again:

. . . Although I have not written you since . . . , I have not been wholly idle for the views of several botanists of eminence have been obtained touching the points at issue.

Eight of the committee express themselves either as opposed to the organization of such a society or as desiring some distinct qualification to membership; and every other botanist whose views I have obtained desires some restriction placed upon membership. The new Section G of A.A.A.S., which, it is expected, absorbs the Botanical Club, affords a general mass meeting of American botanists. A new society which allows every one to join would simply duplicate, in essential features, this Section G.

I fully sympathize with this feeling, but I cannot see how the committee can recommend any restriction in membership when it reports to an unrestricted body. That is, the Botanical Club or Section G, its successor, could hardly be asked to vote to exclude some of its own members from membership in a new body which it itself designs to organize. Nor would it be expedient to ask the Club to designate any committee with power to organize and to exclude some of the members who might vote to establish the committee. The truth is, an exclusive body cannot arise from a diffusive one. The proper method of organizing an American society, it occurs to me, is for some spontaneous nucleus of botanists to invite others to join them in such an organization. . . . What do you say to the proposition to report that the committee thinks it inadvisable to organize an American Botanical Society?

After the Madison Botanical Congress (as it was styled because of a certain international significance which it had) had met and a committee on organization had been named to choose fifteen others and constitute a charter membership of twenty-five of the society, Bailey wrote Farlow on October 12:

The report which I sent to Madison said that while nearly all members of the committee favored a botanical society, they felt that its method of origination was unfavorable because all members of the Botanical Club would be charter members, and there could be no restriction of membership. This adverse report was the means of presenting the problem to the Club and, under the leadership of Barnes, the Club itself removed the difficulty by the election and appointment of 25 botanists who shall have power to add to their number. With this scheme I am in hearty sympathy, and there is no reason so far as the action of the committee is concerned, why each

[32] *Bulletin of the Torrey Botanical Club*, XIX, 9, September 10, 1892, pp. 293 ff.

of us should not become active in the organization of the new society. My report was put in such shape that it would not prejudice our future action as individuals. So I hope you will act with us . . . I think the prospect good for a *pure science* society.

Bailey was one of the original charter members. Moreover he became one of a committee of five to organize the society which, at the next meeting of the American Association for the Advancement of Science, held at Brooklyn, founded The Botanical Society of America with Dr. Trelease as the first president. Bailey's hope of a *"pure science"* society was realized. Membership was limited to those qualified in research.

Bailey's heart at this time was closer to botany than agriculture. Botany was the science which would elaborate the patterns of *"pure science"* work in horticulture. An invitation to revise Gray's *Field, Forest and Garden Botany* had come to him and he had undertaken the task. First commending performance of a task which should have been done years before, Bailey had written Sereno Watson October 31, 1890:

I am glad that Field, Forest and Garden Botany is to be revised. You certainly cannot expect to insert all garden plants, else you will make a book larger and more difficult than the Manual. I should try to insert only the common garden plants and favorites. If you attempt anything more you at once destroy the plan and essential feature of the handy little volume. The florists would not help you much. Their names would only confuse you. In order to insert any worthy enumeration of them (florists' plants) would demand a study of the plants themselves and this could not be done. I should dislike to see the volume much extended in its plan. It should be brought down to date as the Manual has been, and I think that the authorities for the species should be added.

If I can be of any aid to you at any time, do not hesitate to call upon me. . . .

Robinson called on Bailey in 1892 to do the work and he accepted. On December 13, 1892, Bailey wrote Bessey in the course of preparing the revision:

I am greatly obliged to you for your suggestion concerning the revision of "Gray's Field, Forest and Garden Botany." It is an almost impossible task to make this book what it should be, from the fact that it includes everything, and yet is not expected to be complete. The publishers desire that the book shall not be increased in size, and as it is very weak in cultivated plants I fear that I shall not be able to increase it so much in wild plants as it needs. However, I appreciate the difficulty in the west and hope to be able partially to meet it. I have but very little acquaintance with the Flora of the west, and the only way in which I can get in the most important species is for you or some of your students to make me a list of those which should be inserted. . . .

The work was not completed until 1895. When it did appear, however, it showed conclusively the direction in which Bailey was going. To illustrate: let us first examine Gray's description of the rose family: "Exotic Garden Roses proper, from Europe and Asia. Merely the principal types: the greater part of the modern garden roses too much mixed by crossing and changed by variation to be subjects of botanical study." Bailey's description read: "Exotic Garden Roses proper; from Europe and Asia. Merely the principal types; the greater part of the garden roses much mixed by crossing and changed by variation." Bailey omitted the phrase "to be subjects of botanical study."

When Coulter studied Cactaceae, he complained that systematic work was made confusing by too much greenhouse synonymy and endless cultivation. Botanists shied away from cultivated plants. Many were indoor men who never became familiar with the garden. In the Harvard botanic garden during Gray's time, the native asters were wild plants that had been introduced there. Many had become cultivated plants, horticultural varieties derived from originals. Merely transfer from the wild state to a garden does not make a cultivated plant, necessarily. When the plant is cultivated by the horticulturist, however, and he takes it up and studies it and it begins to vary and horticultural forms arise, the branch of plant science known as horticulture begins its work. Bailey envisioned that botanists and horticulturists should join in this common task, especially when studying the plants in their biologic and physical phases. Botanists listened but did not heed his plea. Bailey, as a consequence, went forward with his work.

CHAPTER VI

EXTENSION WORK. FORESTRY. NATURE STUDY. RURAL SCIENCE SERIES

IN November, 1889, at a convention of the Association of American Agricultural Colleges and Experiment Stations, a resolution, which requested the United States Department of Agriculture to aid in collating and publishing the results of soils investigation at several state experiment stations, was enacted. Director W. O. Atwater of the Office of Experiment Stations included, therefore, in his report for the year 1890 a chapter which indicated two specially recommended lines of inquiry to be pursued in the future at all stations: (1) investigations of feeding stuffs and foods, and (2) soils investigations. With respect to the former, reforms in research in analytical, organic, physical and physiological chemistry were advocated. With regard to soils research, an eastern model, the work being performed at the South Carolina station under Director Milton Whitney, and a western model, the work under Director Hilgard in California, were designated. Experimental laboratory study of soils of various station farms—including examinations of geological formations and supplemental field observations, particularly in relation to the demands of agriculture and crop improvement—was outlined, and cooperative arrangements between the state and federal agencies were urged.

We will have occasion to refer later in this book to agronomic research conducted under Hilgard in California. In South Carolina, Whitney, the report disclosed, investigated soil physical properties—moisture, temperature, particles, and meteorology—in their relation to Sea Island and Upland cotton production. On the three experimental farms of the South Carolina station, R. H. Loughbridge specialized in mechanical and chemical analyses of Sea Island cotton and rice land soils. The work progressed with promising results and, by January 13, 1892, Whitney, in charge of a division of soil investigation at the Maryland Agricultural Experiment Station, was encouraged sufficiently to agree to help Erwin F. Smith solve the problem of "peach yellows." At this time Whitney was also a special agent of the United States Department of Agriculture and his work made use of certain laboratory facilities of Johns Hopkins University at Baltimore, Maryland. Whitney was a progressive and energetic scientist. After the United States Bureau of Soils was created, he served many years as its chief. Whitney's belief that a solution to the "peach yellows" problem might be found either wholly or in part through soils research was based on his previous study of cotton production and soil conditions. Rather than seek to find an answer in any lack of plant food, in ordinary fertilizing materials, he suggested that if the cause was a nutritional disturbance, often the appropriate corrective remedy lay in such elemental factors as water supply, arrangement of the soil grains, top-and-under drainage, light, and meteorological conditions. Whitney did not neglect the importance of studying chemical needs—acid phosphate, lime, organic matter, et cetera. He did, however, stress the value of understanding thoroughly the physical environment of the plant in growth, and he and Hilgard in these pioneering years contributed enduringly to the development of an exact science of soil physics and soil chemistry. Whitney must have had something to do with accentuating Smith's interest in soils study, because, on March 26, 1892, Smith chose as the topic of his address before the Botanical Club of Washington, "Relations of the Soil to Plant Nutrition."

During these years, the results of other noteworthy investigations of the United States Department of Agriculture were presented. The department's 1891 report contained a summary of conclusions arrived at by Richard J. Hinton, special agent, charged with investigating artesian and underflow waters between the 97th degree longitude and the Rocky Mountain foothills and, also, furthering the inquiry into irrigation matters inaugurated in 1885 and then entrusted to the Department of Agriculture. The special subject studied recently had been the best methods of cultivating the soil by means of irrigation. Another valuable report, published in 1891, was Charles Richards Dodge's special agent's examinations of Sisal hemp culture in Florida and flax culture in the northwest, in which the author discussed the interrelationships of soil, climate, and culture.

While these types of researches were not new, great profit was derived from them, sometimes for no other reason than uncovering another source of fruitful inquiry. Crops were being studied, both qualitatively, geographically and in terms of their present and potential economic value, and, at times, examinations produced much information which furthered knowledge in matters of fundamental biology. The years of biological surveys were not past. The more facts that were revealed concerning the nation's natural and productive resources, the more scholars were challenged to organize the new knowledge in the light of an informed and fundamental science. Taxonomists seldom, if ever, were lacking in materials for their work. The indoor laboratory physiologist, too, could choose between a wide variety of problems. Bailey at times was neither taxonomist nor physiologist, although more often than not he was both. Always, however, as he studied and wrote, whether of products of the greenhouse, garden, or orchard, an insatiable desire to understand and make known the biology of living forms permeated his work.

For many years Bailey had been interested in studying seeds to find influences of varying conditions upon germination. For example, the influence of different quantities of water on the rapidity of sprouting in various plants, the hastening of germination by soaking in lime water, and influences on germination generally exercised by various chemical agents, had received his attention.

Through these, and numerous experiments in ameliorating plants, he had become interested in correlating the results of his investigations. So, for an address in 1892 before the Rochester, New York, meeting of the biological section of the American Association for the Advancement of Science—at which time Section G, devoted to botany, was organized—he chose as his subject, "The Supposed Correlations of Quality in Fruits," a subject, concerning which the experimental laboratory today has supplied much more exact knowledge, but it served the purpose of stimulating further research. As a basis for his study he chose a fruit catalogue of the Michigan Horticultural Society prepared almost wholly by T. T. Lyon. Bailey selected seven characters commonly correlated with quality: three belonging to the fruit itself—decrease in size, seed production, and high color loss in the fruit; four belonging to the plant as a whole—tenderness, lack of vigor, short life, unproductiveness of the tree. The study was significant for its anticipation of qualitative investigations of the future, and for its effort to get at fundamental principles. To illustrate, Bailey said: "Seed production appears to me to be subject to the same laws of variation as other attributes of plants, and it appears independently of other characters, in the same manner as size and color." In other words, he regarded the correlations as supposititious and concluded that

quality and other characters of cultivated fruits appear independently of each other; that there is no true correlation between these characters. There is a general increase in all characters as amelioration progresses— at least in all characters which are particularly sought by horticulturists; and this fact must ever remain the chief inspiration to man in his efforts to ameliorate plants.

In the analysis of elements and the control and regulation of those elements in amounts and concentration modern work of today emanates from exact laboratory experiments which employ methods and techniques generally unknown in those years even in botanical circles.

The horticultural laboratory was to contribute profoundly to physiological investigation. Confessedly it was largely to use botanically devised techniques. One does not have to search far for illustrations. Scarcely a page of a plant science journal can be turned today without encountering in one phase or another physiological examinations. Even pathological diagnoses must utilize physiological research. Modern analyses seeking to change behavior or induce an indicated performance on the part of the plant owe their origins in large part to physiological study. Bailey, in this study, was inquiring, philosophically, into the largest of all problems of that time—the improving and amelioration of plants. How else could quantitative data have been organized? There was then little modern research as we know it today. Philosophy had to precede exact quantitative analysis. Today the philosopher may have to follow the research man. In those years the philosopher had to precede and follow. For research instrumentalities were still mainly in the field.

In 1893 Bailey returned to his native state to discuss philosophically "Sex in Fruits" before the horticultural society. Michigan had been an early home of the warfare against insects and fungi. There Cook had used London purple and bisulphide of carbon, there Paris green had been introduced in use, there bordeaux mixture had found its way, there, as in New York, combinations of these had been studied to find the most effective sprays. There Kedzie in the 1870's had begun a study of the peach yellows, and other great work had had origins there. Science in the orchards of states such as Michigan and Illinois already was transforming their economies from a once pioneering status to great wealth-producing areas. Bailey spoke of recent discoveries, saying:

Since the demonstration of the value of sprays for exterminating the insect and fungous enemies of fruits, the most important advance in American pomology is the discovery that some varieties of fruits are unable to fertilize themselves. Much of the failure of apples and pears and native plums to set fruit, even when bloom is abundant, is unquestionably due to too continuous or extensive planting of individual varieties; and it is safe to expect that other fruits are also jeopardized by unmixed planting. This knowledge, as soon as it becomes more extensive and exact, is sure to modify greatly the planting of orchards.

Bailey referred to the remarkable discoveries of Merton B. Waite, already alluded to, and he proposed on this occasion to suggest a philosophical side of the problem. "Why are varieties infertile with themselves? What relation does such infertility bear to the evolution of varieties? Is it likely to increase or diminish in future varieties?" he asked, and answered:

A broad epitome of the whole problem seems to run something like this: There is a general tendency in nature toward a separation of the sexes, or unisexuality, and this tendency is probably hastened among plants by high cultivation. The first signs of separation—and beyond which most plants may never go—are differences in the time of maturity of the two sex-elements and the failure of pollen to impregnate its associated pistils. Subsequent steps are the failure of many normal flowers to set fruit, and diminution of the pollen supply. The extensive multiplication or division of impotent or self-sterile individuals, and the setting of the resulting plants in large blocks, have given us unfruitful orchards. If increasing amelioration tends toward a sexual unbalance, it must follow that unfruitful orchards are likely to increase unless intelligent mixed planting is brought to rescue.

Bailey envisioned intelligent experimentation and increased study as the means to achieve accomplishments that would result in greater harvests of improved quality. In this, he was indisputably right. Education would prove to be the central hope of the farmer. False directions might be taken as, for example, "the potomato"—grafts of tomato on potato and potato on tomato—of interest to physiologists but with no discernible consequences of economic importance. Progress was not to be realized through physiological novelties but through understanding of physical and physiological evolution by exact and thorough experimentation, and by an equally important accompaniment of truthful evaluation of just how much had been accomplished. Interpreters were needed as well as men of research. For the next decade Bailey would dedicate his strong intellectual energies to the often unwelcome and hostilely met task of making known new implications of evolutionary understanding. Two facilities would have to be leagued to accomplish this: an intelligible literature and college extension work, a teaching of rural and city folk, old and young, who could not attend the university, either for the recently established short winter term or for the complete horticultural and plant science study provided.

Already he knew that to realize completely the great agricultural vision, increased equipment would have to extend the campus and farm boundaries of all universities giving agricultural instruction. To build edifices worthy of the study of America's basic industry, he also knew, required public endorsement. People must see more in land than crops and timber. People must learn to know these as things of creation.

Agricultural degrees had then comparatively little standing, academically. The "ag" student was looked down on by the arts and science student, much as the urban man regarded the farmer—a man, strong of body, but of inferior intellectual attainments. Sound bodies made for sound minds. But what if facilities to educate these bodies and minds were inadequate? At Cornell, when Bailey had arrived, but two graduate students were registered. Annually, until 1887, the entire register of agricultural students had not exceeded fifty persons. During Bailey's first teaching year, interest in horticulture, including graduate study, increased. But even with the winter course the school year 1892-1893 numbered no more than one hundred and three students.

Cornell University was situated in a setting of great natural beauty. Picturesque, smooth, rolling hills surrounded placid Cayuga Lake. There boats of commerce still plied their side-wheels through its quiet, blue waters to docks of business concerns and settlements. On every side, among the high, forested hills, deep chasms had been carved by rushing streams which hummed and sang their bright and somber chants. The quiet folk who resided there loved the harmony and peace that generally prevailed. Agassiz regarded the region as unsurpassed for richness of natural history materials. To him its beautiful valley had proved a superb source of inspiration and study.

Why shouldn't Cornell University become a great center of natural history learning? Why shouldn't it become the great agricultural center of eastern United States, leading America not only in horticulture but also in all plant science study? Ezra Cornell had given his farm, his money, and his energies to create a great university in New York state. He had endured calumny to win a decades-long struggle to found a university which combined agriculture, mechanic arts, science, and the classics in its curricula. Once when in England, he had visited Rothamstead, and had been greatly impressed by a new order of agriculture he saw developing. Returning to America, he used his strength and executive ability toward promoting a great agricultural program for New York state. From the very beginning agriculture figured as a basis in the formulation of plans for a university.

A long, complicated, heated struggle ensued, but Cornell and his associates won.

The university's first president was Andrew Dixon White. White had persuaded Cornell that the new institution should be nonsectarian. Together they joined heart and mind and at length there was put into action the plan to combine the entire New York land grant resources of the Morrill Act of 1862—some 990,000 acres—and the munificent gift of Cornell. The latter's benefactions totaled about $500,000. His 207 acre farm was given as a site. Today the campus and farm ground still consists in the main of Cornell's donation but there have been additions. By 1914, the campus space alone was estimated at more than 350 acres. We shall see later that numerous additions to the farm area were made, and that the greater part of the available land of the old farm became the student commons.

In 1868, on a high hill overlooking Cayuga Lake, the new university, composed principally of Morrill Hall, had inaugurated its career. Before Ezra Cornell died, his gift amounted "to about $750,000." He had planned to give a million dollars more. He believed confidently that someday 5,000 students would be enrolled at the university. But he never lived to see his dream attain more than partial reality. To bring a railroad near the university he invested heavily in the Lehigh Valley and other railroads. A "Black Friday" panic broke him and he died from overwork in efforts to save his investments.[1]

It had not proved difficult to start the mechanical arts work. It had not proved difficult either to get civil engineering or the classical and scientific courses under way. Famous lecturers were invited, among them, Agassiz, Lowell, Bayard Taylor, and George William Curtis. Lectures in agriculture were given by John Stanton Gould. But not until Roberts arrived was the *land* utilized for anything like progressive farming. Roberts had taken a wholehearted interest in the agricultural "college." His work for the department was like that of a strong horse at a plow in unfurrowed land. Several predecessors had left the farm work in deplorable state. He had found "100 acres of arable land" in contrast to an 800-acre farm he had had at Iowa Agricultural College, 12 "miserable" cows instead of 100 cattle of four breeds, a "half-dozen pupils" in place of 50 to 75 students. But he manfully assumed his difficult labors. One of the ablest men in Cornell University history aided and inspired him—Dr. James Law, head of the veterinary department, the "horse doctor" Ezra Cornell had directed President White to bring back with him from Europe when the latter had gone abroad to study agricultural, mechanical and civil engineering, and veterinary colleges.

Roberts had been shocked to find a certain theological "violence of feeling" circulating in New York state about Cornell University. One journal called it "a school where hayseeds and greasy mechanics were taught to hoe potatoes, pitch manure and be dry nurses to steam engines." Another coined the epithet of a "Godless, freshwater college planted in Ezra Cornell's potato patch." The year before Roberts' arrival in 1874, agriculture under Henry H. McCandless of the Royal Agricultural College, Glasnevin, Ireland, had graduated its first class, one student. In 1874 two students completed the four year course. Nevertheless, since brain power and emotional maturity are the real cornerstones of an educational institution, only a few men of the caliber of Caldwell, Comstock, Law and Roberts, were needed to transform the complicated and disjointed small department into a college with an accredited experiment station of potential national significance. Under Roberts, the wisest farmer Bailey had known, this had been accomplished.[1]

In 1894 Bailey was still more stimulated by possibilities in horticulture than agriculture. After all, he was the professor of horticulture. That was the work expected of him and in that art and science research projects were unlimited. Roberts, however, was growing elderly and more and more relying on Bailey. In 1892 Bailey had undergone a

---

[1] The foregoing material is based largely on material of an "Historical Number," *Cornell Countryman*, XII, 3 (December, 1914), pp. 177-226.

serious illness remedied by an operation performed by Dr. Robert T. Morris. Bailey had two able helpers. E. G. Lodeman was an instructor in horticulture who had performed nationally recognized experiments in disease control, studying therewith comparative and mixed values of various sprays. L. C. Corbett was an assistant in the experiment station and an able greenhouse man.

In 1891 Bailey had an opportunity to go to Brazil for a fabulously wealthy gentleman to study and survey that country's agricultural future. W. A. Taylor had met Roberts at an American Association for the Advancement of Science meeting. Asked where Bailey was, Roberts replied, "Dallying with the tempter." The rich man wanted someone of proven research ability who could write books and Bailey seemed to be the man.[2] But he did not go because Mrs. Bailey did not wish to. To permit her husband to give his undivided attention to his work, she had relieved him of almost every household task of ordinary character. The tropics did not appeal to her either for herself or their daughters. That settled it since he fully considered her wishes in every action of his life. His imagination, nevertheless enkindled, kept steadfast. There was a world view in horticulture.

Extension work had really originated in a kind of county agent work, an observational and coordinated survey in the interest of agricultural advancement conducted by agents of agricultural and horticultural societies to familiarize local and government sources with needs and problems. For years, of course, the agricultural department at Washington had pursued a method of sending out investigational agents. In most of the states, for example, Nebraska, men such as Frederic William Taylor, holding official positions in the state horticultural society, had accompanied Bessey on expeditions incident to his survey as state botanist of the state flora. He had also gone alone or with others on farmers' institute work, to supply speakers, answer inquiries, and confer with men on the land concerning problems of agriculture, horticulture, live stock, all matters pertaining to rural development. In the instance of Taylor, two or three years of this had preceded his acceptance of the chair of horticulture for which Bessey chose him. When Bessey had gone from Iowa to Nebraska to serve as professor of botany and dean of the Industrial College, the understanding had been that he "was to be the Professor of Botany, and that as such [he] was to *prepare the way* for horticulture." Almost eight years were consumed before the preparatory work was sufficiently advanced to warrant the separation of botany and horticulture. From botany and horticulture, furthermore, forestry work was segregated.

[2] Told the author by Dr. Taylor.

Before this time, however, even the investigational agent's work had been generally adopted in various states. Indeed, as early as 1881, when he was a senior and also editor of *The College Speculum* at Michigan Agricultural, Bailey had urged each Michigan county to have within its limits "one business-like graduate of some scientific institution, and he a farmer" to supply leadership for vigorous application of the principles of scientific agriculture.

A kind of extension work had also been performed by Dean Roberts, when, coming from Iowa to Cornell University, he had found it necessary to go about the state of New York to acquaint himself with most effective methods of practical farming, in other words, to learn eastern agricultural conditions as distinguished from middle western.

Where remedies or cures for prevalent plant diseases were not known, statistical surveys of conditions of plant growth and spread of the disease were resorted to; in instances, experimental tracts were established to examine the chemical and physical soil conditions, the effects of fertilizers and other plant foods, the effects of climate, moisture and winds, in short, all environic factors; and sometimes factual data assembled provided persuasive arguments for states to enact regulatory legislation, two illustrations being the efforts to solve the problems of the "black knot" and "peach yellows." Since 1886, Bailey had helped Smith, whenever possible, with his peach yellows investigations. In the January, 1891, issue of *American Garden*, Bailey prepared and published an article, "Peaches and Yellows in the Chesapeake Country," in which he described Smith's work on the subject extending, as it did, from Michigan to southern New Jersey, Delaware, and eastern Maryland, and even his peach studies in Kansas and Georgia. He pointed out that Smith had 100 field experiments in orchards of Delaware and Maryland. Indeed, had Bailey stayed at Michigan Agricultural College, he would have taken 150 yellows trees for planting and study on a sand land farm tract north of the college, for which he was negotiating. Going to Cornell University, however, and finding the peach yellows problem there also, at Smith's invitation, Bailey journeyed to the Chesapeake peninsula and examined Smith's work. So convinced was he that Smith was conducting an investigation truly great in its scope that Bailey wrote not only the article referred to in *American Garden* but also as university extension work developed at Cornell University he prepared bulletin 75 on the subject's pertinency in New York, which bulletin was published by the agricultural experiment station. On December 10, 1890, two months after his visit to Maryland, he forwarded to Smith a copy of his article which was climaxed by the facts that Michigan, New York, Virginia, and Delaware, had "definite yellows laws." Value of eradication of the tree as soon as the disease was discovered, and this enforced by law, was being demonstrated in Michigan where the disease was believed to be on the decline.

The previous August, Bailey had published his very important "Report upon the Condition of Fruit-Growing in Western New York," the result of an inspection in July of orchards in Niagara, Orleans, Monroe, Ontario, and Cayuga counties. During this catastrophic year thousands of acres of apple orchards appeared to be dying. Quince orchards in many places were scorched. Pear foliage was specked. Peaches dropped leaves and fruit early in the season. There were sections where the blackberries and raspberries were dried up and their bushes looked unhealthy. Rot and mildew were present in vineyards. These diseased conditions Bailey pointed out could be checked by "timely and persistent use of Bordeaux mixture." He urged systematic studies of diseases such as raspberry anthracnose. He recommended fungicidal treatments. His final conclusion had been:

. . . we urge upon fruit growers the importance of considering the advisability of endeavoring to secure a state law looking toward the control of contagious diseases. New Jersey has lately made such a law. Some officer should be empowered to look after these interests when occasion requires.

In 1893, largely in accordance with Bailey's recommendations, New York state enacted a yellows and black-knot prevention law.

The wholesale failure of one of the most extensive fruit-growing districts of the nation, certainly a most important apple-growing region in the United States, had aroused Bailey to investigate causes and remedies. In an area which by 1894 had 9,000 acres devoted to commercial peach orchards, a need to introduce more systematic and scientific methods to cope with the problems was clear. By 1896 Cornell authorities had traveled "no less than 25,000 miles in western New York" investigating "hundreds, if not thousands, of plantations." A prevalent notion that the apricot tree was too tender to withstand the winters of western New York had to be overcome. The apricot, he knew, could be grown as easily as plums and peaches. As late as 1894, it was not generally known that a healthy plantation of many hundreds of apricot trees had thrived. Today efforts are directed toward making the apricot more productive in western New York and other northern states. Bailey conceived a whole philosophy of the orchard, which, embodied all phases of action, products, covers, cultivation, mulches, and extended even to the subject of weediness. He quoted Virgil:

The father of humankind himself ordains
The husbandman should tread no path of flowers,
But waken the sleeping land by sleepless pains.—
So pricketh he these indolent hearts of ours,

Lest his realms be in hopeless torpor held.
... And all these he did,
That man himself, by pondering, might divine
All mysteries, and, in due time, conceive
The varying arts whereby we have leave to live.

To know what, when, where, and how to plant as well as when, where, and how to care for what was properly planted were necessary prerequisites of good orchard cultivation, and good farming. Bailey said:

The gist of it all is that orchards should be cultivated and fed. Cultivation should begin early and be continued often. It may be stopped in August if the grower thinks best, and then, if the land needs it, a green crop may be sown for turning under the next spring.

What was so of fruits was similarly true of many vegetables. Bailey had begun early to explain what added vegetables and small fruits could be grown in these regions of large American horticultural significance. The cultivation of egg plants, for example, had received little attention from either gardeners or students. Pepino; Spanish salsify; vetch as an orchard plant; winter cauliflowers, beans, muskmelons, and, also, winter tomatoes which he had studied for years; chorogi; *Stachys floridana*, a tuber sent by Smith from Florida; docks and sorrels; recently introduced Chinese and Japanese vegetables including so-called cabbages and mustards; and many others worthy of increased or commenced cultivation, received industrious consideration. Concerning these he wrote experiment station bulletins. Never did Bailey indulge in injudicious praise of novelties or new types of fruits or vegetables. His criticisms were always soundly based, as shown by his criticism of the use of the apricot plum, the Crandall currant, the wineberry, and dwarf juneberry.

With so much out-of-door and field work to be done along with the station experiments, Bailey was unable to give as much attention to taxonomic studies as he wished. Nevertheless, in 1892, there appeared his bulletin of "The Cultivated Native Plums and Cherries." In the years following were published studies of native dwarf cherries, mulberries, blackberries, evaporated raspberries, and in the consideration of plums were included the Japanese varieties given circulation largely by Luther Burbank of Santa Rosa, California. In a bulletin in 1891 Bailey gave attention to the cultivated dewberries in which "no systematic attempt [had] been made to determine their peculiarities and values." The same was true of the plums of which he said, "Over 150 varieties have been named and more or less disseminated, and [these] pages record 140. There has been no attempt, so far as I know, to make a comprehensive study of these fruits, and, as a consequence, our knowledge of them is vague and confused. In fact, the native plums constitute probably the hardest knot in American pomology. The botanical status of the native plums is equally unsatisfactory, and the group is one of the most inextricably confused of any one of equal extent in our whole flora." Later, when Bailey again considered the cherries, his account was more or less confined to cherry growing in western New York, no longer "scattered settings along lanes and roadsides, and about farm buildings." By 1895, although sweet cherries were "scarcely planted" in orchard blocks in western New York, sour cherry planting had increased "to an important extent" about Geneva and other localities. In fact, cherry orchards enjoyed "a new interest" from a rising canning factory demand. Still, Bailey said, "The literature of the whole subject of cherry growing is so meagre and so unsatisfactory, that I have taken much pains to ascertain the best methods and varieties for western New York." Another subject Bailey continued to study was strawberry varieties and remedies for their leaf-rust.

Illustrations of other interests which absorbed Bailey are numerous. They were as many as there were crops and as extensive as the world areas where they were grown. One other, however, is deserving of special mention—grapes. In this product, the literature was more up-to-date and better systematized, thanks to the splendid work done by T. V. Munson of Denison, Texas, a most remarkable originator of new varieties, owner of one of the South's most famous vineyards and of a well-known nursery. Once employed as a special agent of the federal pomological division Munson had been an explorer in viticulture over the West to California. He was the author of the classic work *The Native Grapes of the United States,* and assembler of an herbarium which threatened the supremacy of all others including the Engelmann herbarium at St. Louis. Concerning an exhibit at the Columbian Exposition in 1893 Bailey had written: "The most exact and scientific pomological exhibit in the Horticultural Building is a collection of grapes shown by T. V. Munson. . . . No other single individual is making a stronger impression upon American horticulture." Grapes, as well as apples, had interested Bailey from the beginning of his career. In 1893, his book, *American Grape Training. An Account of the Leading Forms Now in Use of Training the American Grapes,* was published by the Rural Publishing Company.

The year before in September Bailey had made some "remarks" on "Evolution of American Grapes," at a farmer's institute held at Forestville, Chautauqua county, New York. That, together with his *American Grape Training,* interested vineyard owners there. In 1893 a county group asked the Cornell experiment station to undertake viticultural experiments for them. Because of lack of funds the request had to be refused. Influential persons rallied forces, however, went to Assemblyman

S. F. Nixon of that county, and he, early in 1894, procured from the legislature an appropriation of $16,000, one-half of which was to be used by the station in horticultural study in the state's fifth judicial department, an area of sixteen counties in western New York.[3] "This is the only instance, as far as I know," wrote Bailey, "of a movement for experiment station work which has been initiated and pushed to a final passage wholly by a farming community."

The passage of the Nixon bill of 1894 laid the foundations for large scale horticultural extension work. The work was to be more than inspection and survey although these, as techniques, would be a part of it. It was to be more than a definite program of exploring horticultural resources although this would also be involved, including research in diseases and remedies and in methods to improve varieties. Indeed, Lodeman, in whom immediate charge of the work was first placed, went to Europe and observed the Rhine, French, and Italian vineyards. In his absence, Mark Vernon Slingerland, assistant entomologist of the station, took over the entomological inquiries and Michael Barker was brought from the Harvard botanic gardens. G. Harold Powell took charge of the pomological research. Of course, from the very beginning, Bailey was named the "horticultural expert" in charge of extension work. This term was employed in the Nixon bill's provisions and, as such, he directed and conducted the investigations. Under his guidance, the work, to arrive at standardized methods, had to pioneer its way to find how best results could be obtained. Nevertheless, with the years, the distinctive development of the past decade—"the extension of university teaching to the people"—crowned the efforts of the Cornell station workers. Extension work, first, in horticulture, and later, in the whole of agriculture, became a well rounded program for widespread improvement of agricultural interests—a model for the nation—a reality which Bailey had long visualized.

Funds were immediately available to complete and publish the labors commenced before 1894. Funds were also assured to initiate new enterprises: further surveys of resources; more exact analyses of weather conditions and soil factors, such as texture, moisture, and depletion causes. These studies included not merely fertilizer and crop relations but even geologic history of important horticultural areas such as the Chautauqua county grape region. Physiological and pathological inquiries were encouraged. Investigation now imposed the obligations of studying more business industries. These were not confined to cattle, pigs, and poultry but included all promising new plant industries such

[3] New York state later adopted a new constitution. The judicial districts were reorganized.

as sugar beets, concerning which cooperative tests with the United States Department of Agriculture were commenced.

In 1893 the New York legislature, on strong recommendation of the governor, had appropriated $50,000 for dairy husbandry and other agricultural pursuits. The governor had said:

I desire to call the attention of the Legislature to the advantages offered by the State Land Grant College, Cornell University, for carrying on the scientific work of agricultural promotion which is now divided among several agencies, and which should be concentrated under the direction of such a bureau as I have recommended. I think it will be conceded that more effective scientific work of this nature can be done in connection with a great educational institution, and the grouping of these now scattered departments of agricultural effort at one place and under one general supervision will also be a considerable saving of expense in maintenance. Cornell University furnishes an excellent nucleus for carrying on this State work. . . . The State Meteorological Bureau is already located there. There is also an agricultural experiment station already established and doing effective work. Moreover the institution has established practical courses of instruction in agriculture, botany, horticulture, dairy husbandry, animal industry, poultry keeping, and veterinary science. It offers free of charge and without examination, to all persons who are 16 years of age, competent instruction in these subjects for one or more terms. . . . It is entirely . . . with a view to State advantage that I would urge the concentration at Cornell University of the various agencies for promoting scientific agriculture. . . . The proper diffusion of knowledge with reference to the preservation of our forests is of vital interest to the future welfare of the State and could be obtained through such an agency. The same is true of the spread of veterinary science. Public attention has only lately been called to the vast importance of this subject—not merely as it affects the value of our live stock, but because of its intimate relation to the question of public health. Modern science has demonstrated that a large proportion of human diseases is directly traceable to diseases of animals, conveyed through milk, meats, eggs, and other animal food. Thousands of milch cows in this State, suffering from tuberculosis, are furnishing milk to families and thereby endangering human lives by the transmission of this dread disease. . . . The time is ripe for the adoption of some comprehensive, systematic, and intelligent policy which shall assure the best results at the least expenditure. . . .

At this time, study of all the subjects mentioned by Governor Flower was in progress at Cornell. Within a month after the governor's address, Bailey lectured before the Agricultural Association of Cornell at Franklin Hall on "Agricultural Education and Its Place in the University Curriculum." Tracing historically all education in America he emphasized the "technical revolution" begun with the establishment of a chair of chemistry at Harvard in 1783. He traced briefly the development of modern scientific agricultural education and considered the subject of governmental aid, both state and federal. Bailey urged:

The laboratory is the indisputable and vital part of its curriculum. And the indispensable and vital part of agricultural teaching is—agriculture. . . . It is not lectures alone, not laboratory work alone, not experiments alone—but agriculture! But we cannot teach agriculture until we break away from the common traditions of teaching. All the late developments of educational methods have tended uniformly in one direction—towards popularizing academic work, towards bringing it before the people that its influence may be felt by all men. This is university extension. The college and university are philanthropic institutions. Their mission is to inspire all men to better things as individuals and as citizens. The schools are the greatest charities of the time . . . I am more and more impressed with the importance of encouraging those students who have neither the time nor the money to take the full courses. They are among our best and most earnest students. They are sons and daughters of the university . . . I should like to see the principle officially recognized that the office of universities is primarily a mission to the people, and that mere graduation of students is an incidental or secondary feature. . . . For the teaching of agriculture, then, we must make a new species of curriculum, and some of the instruction must be given away from the university, where special needs or special equipments exist. This instruction, for best results, should be given partly in class-work, partly in actual laboratory practice upon a sufficient scale to demonstrate the value of the methods as farm operations, and partly upon farms and in gardens in various parts of the State. Instruction by the teachers and instructors in charge, must be liberally supplemented by lectures upon special topics from men who have made signal success in those directions.

These prophetic utterances were made more than a year before the passage of the Nixon bill, before the initial request for experimental work in Chautauqua county, and they described, almost with exactness, the programs of university extension work adopted in New York and throughout the United States generally. Small wonder that men in authority at Cornell saw in this tall, lanky, and alert young product of Michigan fields and forest an aggressive, forward looking, practical leader of future American agriculture.

"This broad agricultural teaching," continued the young professor who theretofore had been regarded foremost as a horticulturist, "demands many departments of instruction, both scientific and economic, but there are five main lines which must be fully endowed, at least in New York. . . . General Agriculture, which includes all the broader principles of rural economy and the general management of all the natural forces which concern the farmer, Dairy Husbandry, Horticulture, Veterinary Science, Forestry; and a very prominent sub-division of General Agriculture must be one devoted to Roads. . . . The greatest need in specific laboratory equipment is the establishment of a department of Dairy Husbandry upon such a basis that it can give instruction adequate to the great demands of the state. . . . Upon the farms alone of New York State, 10,000,000 pounds of cheese, 120,000,000 pounds of butter are produced annually, and 300,000,000 gallons of milk are sold to butter and cheese factories. Much of the product is inferior and unprofitable. For the establishment of this department, the first gift should not be less than $50,000." Precisely this sum was given by the legislature on the governor's recommendation that year for the Dairy Husbandry building. Bailey said further:

Horticulture comes next in importance in New York State. All the great interests of fruits and vegetables and ornamental gardening, with the wealth of botanical science connected therewith, should find adequate representation here. The fruit interests of New York are greater than those of any other state, save only those of California. The cultivation of the finer plant products is yearly becoming more attractive and profitable to those who understand it, and it is the chief encouragement to small holdings of land. One division of horticulture has been entirely overlooked in educational institutions. This is Floriculture, which is probably expanding more rapidly as a business than any other agricultural occupation. Two years ago, nearly 20,000 people were engaged in commercial floriculture chiefly under glass, and the value of the product was over $26,000,000. It is an industry to which women are specially adapted, and about 2,000 women were engaged in it in the census year. Moreover, the amateur interest in flowers and ornamental gardening is enormous, probably even exceeding that of fruits in the eastern states. Yet there is no school in North America to which the florists can turn for professional instruction. The Society of American Florists, which is the strongest agricultural organization in America, has repeatedly urged the importance of floricultural education. There is probably no class of our population of equal extent which is entirely without the means of higher education. Here is an unexampled opportunity to make a signal departure in educational institutions. Shall Cornell first enter the field?

The answer to Bailey's mind was, yes.

In 1894, in a bulletin on "The Cultivated Poplars" the following year after his address, he observed:

There has been little attempt in experiment station literature to discuss matters of ornamental gardening. The so-called practical problems connected directly with bread-winning have necessarily and properly absorbed the energies of investigators. But the ornamentation of rural and suburban homes is quite as much within the province of experiment station work; and it should also be remembered that the growing of plants is itself an industry which enlists a vast amount of capital, and this nursery business has received little direct and explicit aid from experiment station publications. The present essay is undertaken for the double purpose of explaining certain fundamental principles in landscape gardening—a subject to which the poplars readily lend themselves—and of unraveling a web of difficulties respecting the species and varieties of poplars, into which the nursery catalogues seem to have fallen. An investigation of the botanical and horticultural features of the poplars has been assiduously prosecuted for upwards of two years, and the writer has had the free use of variety nurseries and plantations in Western New York and the aid of botanists in many parts of the country. . . .

Surprising as it may have been to many, this article received plaudits from quarters, far and wide. In 1895, Bailey followed it with a study of "The China Asters," saying:

Last year this station published a bulletin upon the Cultivated Poplars, with some homeopathic remarks respecting the planting of grounds. It was a departure in our work, although it is clearly within the purview of the federal law that matters of ornamental gardening may receive attention from the experiment stations. A full edition of the bulletin was published, but it was very soon exhausted by the demands of correspondents, whilst the surplus of other bulletins touching upon matters of more immediate economic importance, still remained upon our shelves. The people are evidently interested in matters of taste.

Every rural home is touched by any message which is designed to add to the cheer and contentment of life, and with this conviction I have prepared the following paper. I have ventured to describe an allopathic treatment for the dejected conventional flower-bed of farmers' yards. The outlook of the paper is not wholly upon the sentimental side, however, although I have endeavored to treat the subject from the point of view of the amateur or flower-lover. . . .

"Recent Chrysanthemums," prepared by Michael Barker, followed. Each year varieties for that year were made the subjects of bulletins. But enthusiasm for floricultural studies in experiment stations did not meet hearty approval everywhere. Bailey told in 1896 in a study of "Sweet Peas" how opposition had to be overcome:

A good friend once wrote us that it might be well enough to make a bulletin on chrysanthemums for florists, but that what the people really want is a bulletin on cabbages. We replied that if we make a bulletin on cabbages, the florist will write that such literature may be allowable, but that the people want a bulletin on sweet peas. And the florist may add, with much force, that whilst there are bulletins enough on cabbages, there are none whatever on sweet peas. . . .

Funds from the Nixon bill made these studies possible. These and past years of effort laid the basis for what is believed the first four-year course in floriculture offered by any American college.

Another innovation of great worth was forestry. In Bailey's agricultural education address of 1893 to Cornell's agricultural association, he had said:

Forestry has not yet received adequate attention in the educational institutions of America. The forest is not only a stupendous crop which furnishes fuel and lumber and material for a thousand trades, but it is a cover which conserves the moisture, equalizes the distribution of water and protects the arable land. A large part of the country must always find its most profitable use in the growth of the forest cover, but the common intelligence upon the subject is so low that even wise legislation upon forestry matters is jeopardized. We shall soon find, to our sorrow, that forestal instruction should have been given long ago. In the meantime, I hope that Cornell may take a new and advanced position in regard to it, and that the State will open its forest reservations as laboratories to students.

And, at length, Bailey concluded:

Agricultural instruction . . . must proceed upon the eternal law that education must adapt itself to its specific ends. It must be freed from the conventionalisms of mere educational traditions, and relieved from all narrow estimates of its scope and value. It cannot be measured by the common pedagogic methods. It must be cast in a mould of unique pattern. The education of the great agricultural masses is bound to come. These people, the most numerous in our community, are the last to receive adequate instruction in their own occupations. Agricultural education is therefore the coming education. It is the only great field yet unexplored. It is also the most difficult of exploration. The State must foster it. Some institution must come to the fore, free from bigotry and convention and inspired with patriotic hope, to lead the rising armies on to victory. Let that institution be Cornell!

In July, 1898, five years later, Bernhard E. Fernow resigned his position as chief of the Division of Forestry of the United States Department of Agriculture to organize "the first professional forest school, the New York State College of Forestry,"[4] and Gifford Pinchot took over the division. Fernow was a great forester and a great leader and had laid firm foundations for a future American forestry. Bailey realized what he had sought to do, and knew he would do capably in an educational institution. Bailey recommended Fernow for the position. Indeed, by 1893, the year of Bailey's agricultural address, the American forestry movement, through the American Forestry Association of which Fernow was the indisputable leader, had convinced many leaders of American opinion that forestry practice and principles should be introduced on an aggressive scale to conserve the nation's vast timber heritage and preserve what natural resources the forest might safeguard.

By 1893, under Fernow's administration as chief of the United States forestry division, more than seventeen million acres of western timber land had been reserved from entry or sale by President Benjamin Harrison.[5] Forestry in the United States, before Fernow's rise to prominence, had been principally an educational program concerned with tree planting as distinguished from forest planting, with cultivating

[4] Bernhard E. Fernow, *A Brief History of Forestry*, University Press, Toronto and *Forestry Quarterly*, Cambridge, Mass., 1911, p. 487.
[5] During this year Grover Cleveland became president and at least one reservation of this acreage was due to his action.

various tree species in different regions, and, of course, from its inception the cause had fought to preserve the forests from wholesale devastation. Americans, notably Dr. John A. Warder and General C. C. Andrews, had gone to Europe and reported on forestry methods there. Their writings, however, had not awakened a wide response and it was only when Fernow came forward with an insistence that forests could and should be lumbered but, when lumbered, intelligent provision should be made to replace those harvested timber species valuable to American economic life, that a real response was shown. Years had been required to develop an awareness that forests should be, not only for the present, but also for future, generations. In 1891, in securing passage of the law which enabled the President to reserve timber lands—and section 24, the provision, might have been construed as an authority also to manage the lands according to forestry principles—Fernow and Secretary of the Interior John W. Noble had won a tremendous battle. With the President supporting the cause by reserving so much land by 1893, the cause of forestry loomed bright.

Consequently, during 1893, Fernow, with renewed courage, was urging the government to place the lands under management, to institute working plans (drawn with due regard to fellings by the axe for profit) to further the reproduction and development of young growth under proper conditions of soil, temperature, moisture, light and shade, and other physical conditions, the whole planned according to needs and conditions. But alas! Secretaries of the Interior under whose jurisdiction the lands were placed narrowly construed their authority under the enabling act. To secure forest management in the reserves, it became necessary to pass an "administration bill." The wheels of Congressional action moved slowly. Although within two years victory again seemed practically assured, compliance with a technical formality caused the bill passed by both Senate and House to go over from one session to another, and the entire procedure to be done over because one of the law's sponsors was not reelected by his constituency.

Nevertheless, despite this reverse, victory did come in 1897. During Fernow's administration as chief of the forestry division—on Washington's birthday, February 22—President Cleveland, although he knew a storm of protest would break loose, lent his signature to the cause of forestry by courageously proclaiming thirteen additional reservations comprising an added area of about twenty-one million acres. The combined area of the western reservations, exclusive of the national parks, was estimated at about thirty-nine million acres.[6]

After the federal reservation policy had been firmly established, after

[6] *Garden and Forest*, February 24, 1897, p. 80. See also *Forestry and Irrigation*, VIII, 5, p. 191.

the states had been well started in similar policies with their forests, Fernow realized there now was a need of trained foresters, of adequate forestry schools, specially and in the colleges of agriculture. Fernow's educational program had set the minds of agriculturists to thinking. In 1893, when forestry was really being made a promising reality on the American continent, Bailey had argued that the schools should awake to the need of adequate professional forestry teaching. By 1898 Fernow had earned the reputation of being, as President Jacob Gould Schurman of Cornell University described him, "far the best man in the United States" for the position as Director of the New York State College of Forestry at Cornell. A New York court in an opinion later characterized Fernow as "the foremost forestry expert in the land." On June 30, 1898, approximately the date when Fernow resigned his position at Washington and went to Cornell, the reserved federal forest area was estimated at more than forty million acres.[7]

Nor was this Fernow's only triumph. In 1890, Fernow had met with Filibert Roth, another German born forester, one schooled in botany under Volney Morgan Spalding at the University of Michigan. Roth was a strong man of brilliant mind. A product of a school of experience as buffalo hunter, cowpuncher, sheep raiser, and lumberman, he had become an advanced student of botany, zoology, and geology, had been a teacher in country schools, and since childhood had taken an avid interest in forestry. When a lad Roth had studied forestry "operations as they [were] carried on in the German forests in the same manner that a farmer boy becomes acquainted with the ordinary operations of farming by plowing, sowing, harvesting. . . ." He saw forest nurseries. He watched people plant forests. Coming to America, he acquired a thorough knowledge of lumbering, domestic animal grazing, and other knowledge useful to a future career in forestry. In 1888, after years as a science student at Michigan where he served as museum curator and made a valuable collection of wood specimens, Roth became "engaged in investigating into the technical principles of timber, and took up in earnest the study of forestry by reading."

According to Roth, Fernow and he met in 1890 at Indianapolis where they "cooked up [their] first plans in Timber physics." Fernow selected Roth for the timber physics work largely on Spalding's recommendation, the last named being one of a few eminent botanists who had aided Fernow to secure phenological data over the nation and lay first plans to apply scientific forestry principles to the work of the division. In 1887

---

[7] *Forest Leaves*, VII, 6, December 1899, p. 91; estimates as to this year vary between more than forty-three million acres, and thirty-eight million acres of the public timber lands. The last named figure is Fernow's estimate as given in *Forestry Investigations of the United States Department of Agriculture* 1877-1898, Washington, Government Printing Office, p. 26, 1899, by Fernow.

Fernow had visualized, written on, and in part initiated this work with the aid of competent engineers. The work of examining the physiological and physical properties of certain economically valuable tree species, in the laboratory and the forest, began. Fernow immediately sought also to interest in the work manufacturers who used wood and wood products. Therefore, what investigations were made by Roth during the first years were under Fernow's direction. Indeed, in 1890-1891, when Roth made his first notable tests to determine the strength and durability of timbers, he, with the aid of Mrs. Roth, performed them with crude apparatus in the basement of his home in Ann Arbor. By 1893 Fernow had brought him to Washington as "Special Agent and Expert in Timber Physics." At that time Roth regarded Fernow as "the best trained and best informed man in forestry matters in the United States." The writing of a biography of Fernow is being prepared by the author of this book. Hence, at present it is necessary to say no more than that by 1892 and 1893 timber physics investigation at the United States Department of Agriculture had received special recognition in Europe. From this work, which from its early years made use of a branch laboratory at Washington University, St. Louis, Missouri, developed the expansive programs in wood technology and forest products that have made American forestry singularly famous throughout the world. Bailey was always alert to all industrial expansions in plant science study. Fernow's and Roth's work in timber physics must have impressed him as one of the reasons why forestry teaching and research would be imperatives in American college curricula.

So necessary and valuable was this work to prove that, when it was abandoned by the Department for a few years largely because Roth went to Cornell to aid Fernow in developing The New York State College of Forestry,[8] manufacturers requested the reestablishment of a great wood testing laboratory. Branch laboratories were established at a number of institutions, when the work was revived as germane to forestry. In Washington, at Yale, at the University of California, at the University of Washington, and elsewhere, investigations revealed valuable knowledge concerning the structural and mechanical properties of timber species of various regions. Especially important was the laboratory established at Purdue University under Dr. W. K. Hatt, a man whom Fernow regarded as an able engineer but not a great scholar of the biology of plant life. Later, under the efficient administrations as chief forester of Pinchot and Henry S. Graves, the work of the laboratories

---

[8] Events relating to timber physics research during the years 1896-1898 will be more fully discussed in a forthcoming biography of Fernow by the author. The gradual discontinuance of this world famous type of timber investigation began with a policy change within the Department of Agriculture in 1896. All immediate efforts to reestablish the work ended in the year 1898.

was unified by a central office at Washington and eventually culminated in the construction of the world famous Forest Products laboratory at Madison, Wisconsin. Forestry became a great indoor, as well as outdoor, research field. This development was definitely foreshadowed as early as 1893.

New York state by 1892 had set aside nearly a million acres in the Adirondack and Catskill mountains as a forest preserve. A movement to extend the preserve over a larger area—3,000,000 acres, more or less—was well under way. This was envisioned by Bailey in his 1893 address on agricultural education as supplying a huge laboratory for forestal experimentation and research. For, as a matter of fact, the Adirondack League, a New York organization, had been among the first, if not the first, in America to map out a program of forest management. In Fernow's report dated November 15, 1890, he commended the organization "on the laudable intention of practically applying for the first time in the United States forestry principles to the management of its woodlands. . . ."

Bailey, however, was primarily interested in the significance of forestry work to agriculture. These phases emphasized plant growth in the woodlot and forest, and the variable subject of forest influences on streamflow, climate, and soils.

Bailey noted in his address that the forest "is a cover which conserves the moisture, equalizes the distribution of water and protects the arable land. A large part of the country must always find its most profitable use in the growth of the forest cover. . . ."

Over the nation, to control streamflow and protect the soil for forest growing and agricultural crop production, the federal and state forest reserves were being located at the headwaters or along the nation's most important rivers. Ecological and forestry research would seek to settle many vexing questions as to what factors were most necessary to healthful and abundant plant growth in forest and field. Water and light and their multifarious relations and conditions presented a multitude of problems for experimental research. No one knew all the answers to all the problems. But every one knew that water and light were requisites. Therefore, water conservation, including water storage, flood prevention, and the preservation of favorable moisture and undergrowth conditions, had become as vital as forest conservation. Soil conservation—saving the fertile top soil from erosion and run-off by water—was also imperative, since soils, the chemical and physical elements, determined in many instances not only what lands were best fitted to forest or agricultural growth but also what lands could be improved by irrigation, drainage, or other methods of reclamation or use.

Irrigation presented itself at first principally as a problem of the West. Like forestry, irrigation on a national scale did not become a settled government policy until years had been spent educating the public to its need. "Save the forests and store the floods" as a slogan gradually became "Save the forests, store the floods, reclaim the deserts, and make homes on the land." Gradually irrigation projects on an elaborate scale invaded the eastern and southern states. In the north Atlantic states, for example, it was officially found in 1906 "that for market gardens and meadows, irrigation [had] proven profitable," although its application in raising general farm crops had not been wide.

Fernow likened irrigation "to the discovery of a new continent, not by a lucky adventure, but by knowledge, skill, science, and art." Irrigation, like forestry, came forward as a national enterprise in the last decades of the nineteenth century. Probably, as much as anyone, Major John Wesley Powell, returning from his early famous explorations in the West, stressed the possibilities of intensive agriculture in the arid regions. Other far-sighted men of vision and engineering skill, such as Frederick Haynes Newell, by their work on the federal irrigation surveys and the proof of irrigation's worth and advantages, argued strongly that irrigation was not a work for private initiative alone but that it was necessary for the government also to take hold and reclaim arid lands for settlement. The formation of a National Irrigation Congress and National Reclamation Association brought this advocacy to wide popular and scientific notice. Botanists and horticulturists supported the work as it developed. In the early 1870's Sereno Watson, in his scholarly *Botany of the 40th Parallel*, studied the arid region's plant life and speculated on the possibilities of increasing the quantity and improving the quality of the region's plant growth by the aid of irrigation. He was one among a number. Not until 1902 did the vision of a national reclamation service become a reality. In that year Congress enacted the renowned National Reclamation Act. But in the early 1890's, the years when Bailey made such an effective impression by his address on the future of scholarly agriculture, irrigation and drainage problems were being freely discussed along with the problems of developing a national forest administration.

Tree planting of the arid and prairie regions had also been primarily western problems. Indeed, Fernow believed that the tree planting movement had done much to cloud eastern minds as to the real forestry problems of the East. Progress nevertheless from one decade to another demonstrated the essential fundamental unity of all scholarly agricultural work. To easterners and westerners alike, to the entire people as a nation, all of these matters were being brought together under the great inclusive title of conservation of natural resources. Conservation was shown as a plain need for the future of both urban and country life. The conservation movement, as it has been known, did not crystallize until after 1907 when at the suggestion of the Inland Waterways Commission, President Theodore Roosevelt called a conference of state governors to meet at the White House. From the movement's beginnings in the last three decades of the nineteenth century, its subject matter embraced those resources which are exhaustible, such as minerals, coal, oil, ores, gas, and the like, and those resources, such as the forest, which are replaceable by the combined efforts of man and nature, or by nature alone. Possibly the first formal action toward conserving a natural resource took place in America in the mining industry as early as 1871. If so, the whole of the forestry movement from its earliest formal inception in 1875—when Dr. John Axton Warder, an Ohio horticulturist and agriculturist, organized the short-lived American Forestry Association at Chicago—has been an effort to conserve another natural resource.

Fernow, to the best of this author's knowledge, was the first professionally trained forester in America. He became a naturalized citizen sometime before he became chief of the forestry division, having declared his intention so to become on December 14, 1877. Immediately on being selected to lead forestry development in the United States, Fernow outlined a magnificent program of forestal scientific research which emphasized study of forest conditions, forest crops, and the revenue therefrom. Only lack of finances retarded the program's being fully inaugurated. In essence, however, his every plan looked toward the conservation of a great natural heritage.

Surprising as it may be to some today, Fernow arrived in America imbued with the belief that natural regeneration was the favored method to secure forest reproduction. For many years he adhered to the theory that, in the forest, nature unaided should perform its work of forest reproduction. In fact, for almost three decades, 1876-1902, he held this view. And even when somewhat influenced by Thomas Meehan, of American horticultural fame, he modified his views to hold that man should intelligently aid nature by clear cutting and replanting forest areas, he still clung to the belief that special conditions and needs of the forest region should control in deciding which of at least thirty silvicultural systems should be applied. During the first years of experimental work at the Cornell forest tract in the Adirondacks, a project authorized and supported by the state as demonstration work of the New York State College of Forestry, Fernow applied the natural regeneration and selection system of forest management. The selection method was not applied to areas where logging and cutting operations were performed. The entire story of the work at Axton, where the demonstration forest was located, is quite complicated and will be considered more extensively in another book. It must be pointed out, however, that Fernow, to comply with statutory directions, became convinced that a clear cutting and re-planting policy was necessary. Fernow was trying to solve the problem of hardwood utilization in the Adirondack forests. Nevertheless, he made clear in pronouncement after pronouncement that the change was made partly for educational reasons and partly because he was con-vinced that a more extensive use of the latter silvicultural system was the only method by which the college forest could "harvest and reproduce woodcrops and earn a revenue therefrom" as required by the law.

At the turn of the century other foresters devised forestry working plans for other Adirondack tracts and adhered to the selection system. No criticism of their work is here intended. While in a sense their work was also educational, it was not educational in the formal sense the Cornell experimental tract work was. The economic conditions were distinguishable. Some years later, highly aggravated by Adirondack home owners who wished the huge Adirondack state forest preserve maintained as a recreation center, a fish and game preserve or kind of state park, a controversy ensued which challenged the soundness of Fernow's policy of logging hardwoods to increase softwoods. Bailey, with speaker Nixon and one or two other influential members of the New York legislature, visited the Cornell forest and sustained Fernow's work as proceeding in the right direction. Moreover, since that time foresters of highest merit, students of Adirondack forest problems, have said Fernow was wise in his choice of silvicultural method.

There are many other reasons why Bailey realized that forestry ed-ucation on a large scale would find its way into colleges. By 1893 Fernow had presented to the American public the problems of the relation of forests to streamflow, climate, and soils. He did not indulge in rash extravagance but concentrated his educational program on the need of study, of research, of experiment to determine, if possible, with scien-tific precision the extent and bounds of the forest's influences. By voice, by pen, and by action, he had sought to arouse the American people to the importance of the work he had taken up in 1886 in the garret room of the small red brick mansard-roofed building of the agricultural de-partment in Washington. Forest seed distribution; the organization of a volunteer service for phenological observations; the enlistment of the railroads' interest to discover whether metal ties could be substituted for wood ties, an interest in wood preservatives, in tree planting for future needs; these subjects, among others, occupied his attention. The preparation of statistical forest data had mainly occupied his predeces-sors, Franklin B. Hough and Nathaniel H. Egleston. Fernow carried this work forward but centered his attention on informing and warning the American people of the scarcity of timber supplies, of the impending dearth of such valuable species as the pines, spruce, all the conifers as well as hardwoods. Honest and straightforward, Fernow never claimed statistical accuracy. That was impossible in those years of pioneering. Always, however, he presented his arguments to convince a public hitherto smugly confident that the forest supplies were inexhaustible.

Forests, he said, were not to be regarded as mines since forest growth could be restored. A few moments could chop down a tree. Sixty to one hundred years were required to replace it. Capital, therefore, could not realize a profit from forest planting, except when done on an enormous scale. The duty of fostering forestry as a science as well as an art devolved on governments since governments were self-perpetuating entities and could afford and would profit by making forestry a state policy. Very well, said some, confine the work to the state governments. The federal government by law holds land only for disposal, not for competitive profit, certainly not for revenue realized from one generation to another. Moreover, when Fernow urged research cooperation between federal government agencies and state experiment stations, a charge of unwarranted paternalism confronted him. But Fernow and his co-workers emerged victorious. With astonishing precision Fernow evaluated the American forestal problem in its relation to agriculture, and agriculture in those years was basically the problem of the various states. Forestry presented itself alongside agriculture. For, lands unfit for agriculture could be utilized for forests. By 1893, in many of the states real progress had been made in state forestry, especially in New York and Pennsylvania, in Minnesota and the lake states, in the South, on the western prairies, and from Colorado westward to California. Beginning about 1876, state forestry organization, with gathering momentum, had begun to spread from Minnesota and Colorado to the east, south, and west, to Canada, and with time would encompass even Alaska and Mexico. The trials and tribulations were many. Progress would be made. Then retrogression would set in.

But, by and large, there was a steady development. Fernow participated in most of it, especially the amazing progress in New York and Pennsylvania, credit for which as to the latter state was preeminently due to Joseph Trimble Rothrock, a botanist of exceptional ability and vision.

The need for forestry education was clear. The real question was, where could this education be received? Should an aspiring forestry student go to Europe to study? Or should an institution, which might be a credit to American forestry, be established here? It seems incredible that as late as 1890 it was necessary to say that the first American forestry student had begun his studies in Europe—Gifford Pinchot at the Forest Academy of Nancy, France. Six years earlier when Fernow hung out a shingle as a consulting forester, he had received no clients. Although Fernow aided in various movements to establish a school of forestry in the United States, until adoption of a forest reservation policy by the federal government and the establishment of state reservations, he believed the action premature. But the years 1891-1897 changed the forestry scene in America. So swiftly were events to follow that in spite of the organization of a number of schools and departments of forestry the supply of students could not keep up with the demands. On March 21, 1896, Fernow expressed himself as being "on the point of leaving [the forestry division] because the office [had become] too burdensome." When, therefore, the New York state forestry movement crystallized in an advocacy supported by the governor, the superintendent of forests, and others of prominence, to establish a state college of forestry at Cornell University, Fernow applied for the position as director, and was appointed.

Whatever promoted agricultural education always aroused Bailey's support. In policies of administration, however, he sometimes took an individual stand, and the organization of the New York State College of Forestry proved such an instance. Bailey believed the error was not in Fernow's selection but in forming a separate college for forestry pursuant to a policy inaugurated in 1894 when a separate college for veterinary science was founded at Cornell. Bailey regarded forestry as primarily agricultural and, because of its significance botanically and horticulturally, a vast unexplored region for agricultural experimentation.

It is difficult to say when the first forestry experiment station was established in America. There were several instances of stations styled at one time or another forest experiment stations. In the state forest history of Ohio, Kansas, and California may be found examples. The Yale forest school work on the Pinchot estate at Milford, Pennsylvania, was sometimes referred to as an experiment station. Dr. C. A. Schenck's school of forestry, commenced at Biltmore, North Carolina, on the Vanderbilt estate the same year the New York State College of Forestry was organized, conducted work essentially experimental. Incidentally it may be pointed out that although prior to 1892 forest work in Minnesota and New York resembled real forest management, the classic illustration of forest systematic management in American forestry history was initiated on that estate in January of that year by Gifford Pinchot. His biographical memoirs have been published, and the story of another great American forester is told. Pinchot enlarged the estate's planting work and applied principles of management while forester there. The Cornell forest tract was at times regarded as an experiment station. Work on the Girard estate in Pennsylvania was also important. None of these instances, however, it is submitted, are viewed today as having been forestry experiment stations in the modern sense. Forestry sometimes was a phase of work at state agricultural stations. While earlier at Mays Landing the New Jersey station conducted a series of forestry tests, it is believed that not until 1901 did a state station—the Connecticut agricultural experiment station—have a forestry department. At that time Walter Mulford, America's first state forester, inaugurated an aggressive program of professional forestry with especial attention to farms.

On September 10, 1908, soon after the United States Forest Service had promulgated a plan to establish six forest districts with a district forester in charge, Raphael Zon wrote telling Fernow he proposed to go (and did go) to Europe to study work of the forest experiment stations there. The previous May Zon had written Fernow of another plan he had submitted to Chief Forester Pinchot to organize stations in connection with the national forests. By July the plan with slight changes was approved and that summer a site was selected on the Coconino National Forest in Arizona. On January 1, 1909, the station was officially established and by that time quarters had been selected for a station on the Pike Forest, Colorado—the site of the Alpine Laboratory located near the timber line on Pike's Peak, where Frederic Edward Clements had conducted ecological researches for a number of years. The contribution of botany, particularly ecological research, to forestry may be definitely seen in the work of these and other stations which were soon organized. Fernow was among the first to see in ecology a path toward the realization of a scientific forestry. In his *Forestry Quarterly*, a journal first conceived as a publication of the New York State College of Forestry, Fernow gave published works of the early leading ecologists, Frederic Edward Clements, Edgar Nelson Transeau, Henry Chandler Cowles, and others, important space in reviews, and himself wrote on the subject as early as 1903 pointing out how ecology could direct practice in solving numerous silvicultural problems. Forestry, under leadership of some of the greatest foresters America has known —Gifford Pinchot, Henry S. Graves, W. B. Greeley, Raphael Zon, R. T. Fisher, James W. Toumey, Clifton D. Howe, Samuel J. Record, H. H. Chapman, Harry Nichols Whitford, Ralph Sheldon Hosmer, Samuel Trask Dana, Samuel Newton Spring, Clyde Leavitt, and many others— attained the stature of an independent business and science. Its agricultural significance, however, has not diminished, and this side Bailey stressed. As late as 1910 he wrote Walter Mulford discussing proposed forestry teaching at Cornell: "I want to teach the farm forest situation in the State as a part of our regular work. I want at the same time to train professional foresters."

Until organization of the New York State College of Forestry, there were no American forestry schools. Bailey believed in a forestry department within a great agricultural school. After 1903 there were examples of both in addition to forestry departments at state universities. As early as 1880 General Andrews had sought a Congressional land grant to establish a national school of forestry at St. Paul, Minnesota. In California, at Tulare, a school of forestry had been considered in 1886 by a group from the University of Southern California, but evidently this amounted to nothing more than a plan. At one time, a chair of forestry for West Point Military Academy was urged. At another time a national school of forestry to be placed at Washington was advocated before Congress. A postgraduate school of forestry in the United States Department of Agriculture was advanced. Fernow's interest, however, seemed mainly to center in what to teach rather than where to teach. His series of forestry lectures in different parts of the United States are the foundation of forestry education as it is known today. Indeed, a course of lectures delivered in 1903 at the School of Mining, Kingston, Ontario, in a sense formally introduced him to Canadian education circles. He had delivered a conference address there previously in 1901. In 1902 he spoke at Guelph at a meeting of the Ontario Agricultural and Experimental Union. But the 1903 lectures were regarded "the first course on forestry given in Canada [and] as a historical event of great significance." Analyzing the forestry problem, Fernow nearly always put in the foreground the fundamental imperatives, the differentiation and care of agricultural and forestal lands. The woodlot and farm forest problems united, yet distinguished, agriculture and forestry. Bailey appreciated the common interests of forestry and agriculture. Both produced crops from the basic resource, the land.

Whatever helped the farmer Bailey made his concern. In the school year 1892-1893 there had commenced at Cornell what President Schurman described as "a sort of Winter School of Agriculture, a species of University Extension (though conducted at the University) for the special benefit of those who are engaged or who expect to engage in farming. The new departure was very favorably received, and, though the notice was necessarily short, 48 persons were enrolled in the course." Cornell had at this time 13 postgraduate students in agriculture, 22 four-year course students, 23 two-year course students, and the balance of a total of 106 students were in the short course. Bailey, contrasting this number with that of other American agricultural colleges, commented:

This is probably as large an attendance as can be legitimately ascribed to agriculture in any other institution. It must be remembered that the independent agricultural colleges give a general rather than a specific training, their curriculum covering essentially the same range of subjects which is comprised in the whole natural science and technological courses of Cornell University, with the addition, in many cases, of some of the languages and humanistic studies. Not more than forty or sixty per cent. of their graduates are expected to follow agricultural pursuits, while 106 of the 106 students whom I have here recorded will pursue such occupations! If the rosters of the separate agricultural colleges are to be compared with our own, then we must claim our right and insist that we now have 900 students; and even this does not give us a proper comparison so far as range of studies goes. I must not be understood as disparaging the work of the agricultural colleges. Far from it! But I wish to emphasize the truth— which is so often gainsaid—that the Cornell College of Agriculture has been and is now eminently successful. And these figures disprove the old fable that agriculture cannot be taught at a university!

Winter course instruction apparently originated at the University of Wisconsin. Earlier efforts toward popular and abbreviated courses had found expression in the Ohio Agricultural College, established at Oberlin in 1854; at Ohio State University, the next Ohio college to give agricultural instruction, in the years 1877-1878 and 1879-1880; and in 1866 Yale offered a "shorter course in agriculture." No one of these had lasted and, in 1906, when Bailey studied the matter, he concluded, "The short course in agriculture at the University of Wisconsin opened the first of January, 1886, and continued 12 weeks with an attendance of 19 pupils. This is without doubt the oldest short course which has continued growing in attendance." Cornell did, in 1894, what Wisconsin had done four years before—added a dairy course—and in 1905-1906 added a poultry course that year voting also to organize a horticultural course for the following winter. Steadily the attendance grew, and before a decade had passed, in 1902, the enrollment with 96 students had doubled, and by 1904, almost tripled. Bailey envisioned the great aid which winter instruction would be to farmers, and observed: "The agricultural community is becoming alert to the need of better education."

Ever since Bailey's address, "Agricultural Education and Its Place in the University Curriculum," in 1893, he had been forwarding this theme in New York state. He spoke urgently:

The primary education in the district schools is unsatisfactory. The agricultural press and the farmers' institutes have agitated every intellectual reform and have inspired new hope everywhere. The college-bred men who have gone back to the farm here and there have been so many missionaries; and of late, the experiment stations have inaugurated a new epoch. There is no class of our population which is now rising so rapidly and safely as the farming communities. This I say in full knowledge of the boldness of the generalization. No one can attend the farmers' meetings long without becoming deeply convinced of this fact and gaining new hope for the safety of his country. The farmers want education, but they want a kind which shall be adapted to their needs and means. There is no disguising the fact that educators, even when admitting the need of supplying agricultural education, seldom have any real or vital sympathy with the conditions which they discuss. The effort all along has been to force the farmer into the accepted university or academic methods. He has refused to accept them, and has spurned the artificialisms of university life. Now, I hope, the university will be taken to the farmer, will be adapted to his needs and the genius of the time. The small attendance of farmers' sons upon the agricultural courses is quite as much the fault of the universities as the fault of the farmer!

This did not mean that university students were not from the farms. "Perhaps a third of the students in this University to-day," observed Bailey, "are from farms. The difficulty is that they do not take the specific agricultural courses" due to "the failure of the institutions to clearly apprehend the problems at issue, and the depressed condition into which agriculture has been thrown by a complicated chain of circumstances, the chief of which, in my mind, is the unjust discrimination in the artificial laws of trade. Nothing will so stimulate agricultural education as the establishment of a commercial equality. The prospect of a commensurate reward for his investment and labor very largely determines the young man's choice of vocations. . . . Agriculture will thrive in any institution which will give it the proper soil, so soon as the heavens are cleared of smoke and it has a chance to grow!"

Farmers' institutes, "more than any single movement, [had] been the means of reforming the farm methods and of lending new aspirations to rural life. . . . In every state, the land-grant college or university [had] connected itself, either directly or indirectly, with the institute movement, and in many of them the institutes [were] creatures of the colleges. The movement is decidedly an educational one," continued Bailey, and added his belief that it was "most effective for ultimate good of any form of the modern impulse which in more specific forms is known as University Extension. In this work Cornell University has taken a prominent part." And he pleaded that Cornell University, because of its geographical position and its scientific equipment should "become the agricultural center of the State."

When the Dairy Building was constructed on Cornell University's campus, a symbol of more than the science of cows and feeding, milk and butter manufacture, and other accouterments of the dairy industry, was created. Representing a state policy, an intention was subscribed to bring together at one institution of learning the forces of agricultural education in New York. Within the next half decade after Bailey's address, furthermore, a strengthening instructional network—parts of the agricultural domain and composed of dairy husbandry, horticulture, vet-

erinary science, and forestry—each in turn, underwent profitable enlargements of facilities by campus buildings and university extension
work.

Another movement—nature study—enjoyed an accompanying, though
distinguishable, development. Nature study was needed more by urban
youths than those of the rural communities. It could be said that this
movement emerged from the city and became integrated with programs
of agricultural extension. Its strong, formal growth, during these years,
however, was in rural life. Nature study, as a formal phase of academic
study, certainly originated in America no later than with Jean Louis
Rudolphe Agassiz. We are discussing the movement which, with a
definitely outlined program advanced by a state supported school, arose
in New York as a substantial part of the still greater program conceived to better the agricultural condition, its life and its industry.
Nature study, thus evolved, built on and extended the rich heritage from
Agassiz.

By 1896 horticultural and agricultural extension work was well under
way. Bailey had consulted fruit growers at Batavia; 300 to 400 orchard
persons at South Bethany; 500 to 600 persons at a potato-spraying contest at Stafford; 1,500 to 2,000 persons at Nelson Bogue. He had addressed a western New York farmers' audience of twice that number.
Schools of horticulture had commenced in 1894 at Fredonia in Cha-
tauqua county, and in 1895 at Youngstown in Niagara county, at James-
town and Lockport. Bailey, Caldwell, Roberts, W. W. Rowlee, assistant
professor of botany, Lodeman, Slingerland, R. S. Tarr, professor of
geology and physiography, E. J. Durand, professor of plant nutrition,
and others, had constituted a faculty who had given practical and advanced theoretical instruction. He and his co-workers were thrilled by
the eager and interested response and how much could be taught men
and women who lived *on the land*. Now the work would go forward both
at the university and in various parts of the state. In 1896 Bailey made
his second report on horticultural extention work. During September
of that year twenty-four separate schools were functioning in various
parts of New York.

Benjamin Minge Duggar, an Alabaman by birth, holder of several
degrees from the agricultural and mechanical colleges of Mississippi
and Alabama and from Harvard University, was added to the faculty.
At Alabama Polytechnic Institute at Auburn, Duggar had been privileged
to study under George Francis Atkinson, Cornell University's professor
of botany in the college of arts and sciences, who, as already has been
pointed out, prior to October, 1892, as a biologist in charge of plant
pathological research, had initiated in Alabama and the south early
fundamental studies of cotton diseases. Atkinson had sprung into im-

mediate prominence as a leader, a mycologist of note, and, becoming cryptogamic botanist of the Cornell University station, had engaged, as he wrote in *Science* in December of that year, in studies of winter blight of tomatoes, a new tomato disease, a Botrytis disease of beans, carnation diseases, a new anthracnose of Ligustrum, and "damping off" fungi. While his student, Duggar had shown evident ability, and so, after Duggar had spent some years, first, in research at an Alabama experiment station, second, in study under Farlow, and, third, in the laboratory of Forbes's natural history survey of Illinois, he was invited to matriculate at Cornell University to obtain his doctorate under Atkinson. Duggar was made an assistant in the department, soon an instructor, and later an assistant professor in botany with reference to plant physiology. We will again consider his work in this book.

L. A. Clinton, assistant agriculturist, and G. W. Cavanaugh, assistant chemist, were also added. Most notable as far as nature study was concerned, however, were the additions of George T. Powell and Mrs. John Henry Comstock.

In October, a series of meetings was held in the fourth judicial department of the state. These, as Bailey explained, "were under the immediate supervision of Mr. George T. Powell, who was assisted throughout the month by Mr. John W. Spencer, of Westfield. These meetings were of the type which had been so successfully inaugurated in Westchester County a year before under the auspices of the Committee for the Promotion of Agriculture, a work which had been carried to its practical demonstration by Mr. Powell." Especially of consequence was the addition of Anna Botsford Comstock (Mrs. John Henry Comstock) for, in her instruction, was added the teaching of children—a realization of a long cherished fancy of a Michigan lad who had strolled the lake beaches at South Haven, picked his way through bramble thickets to the high hills, explored caves and swamps, and with an alert and lively imagination created natural history museums from ponds and fields. Nature study for American schools was one of the great contributions of Cornell extension and college work.

Writing of horticultural extension work, Bailey said:

The animus of the entire enterprise has been to attempt to inquire into the agricultural status, to discover the causes of the rural depression, and to suggest means for improving the farmer's position. This attempt has been specifically directed to a single great branch of rural industry, horticulture, in pursuance of the provisions of the law; but what is true of the horticultural communities is essentially true of other agricultural regions, and, moreover, these two types of agricultural industry cannot be separated by any arbitrary lines. The work, therefore, has practically resulted in a broad study of rural economics.

In 1895, to relieve a vexing problem of city congestion, the Association for Improving the Condition of the Poor found it necessary to inquire into the cause of the agricultural depression then prevalent. A committee was appointed and on its recommendation a conference was held and another agricultural committee resulted, with George T. Powell "director of what might be called agricultural extension." This committee reported, "One of the great and underlying causes for the discouragement that exists with farmers is the fact that, as a class, they have no special training or education for their business. One generation follows another, working from the basis of experience mainly."

In February and March agricultural schools had been organized in Westchester County and lecture courses in nature study in district and high schools illustrated what potentialities were in the work. Teachers were shown how they could introduce nature lessons, "not as regular studies from text-books, but rather as incidental work, in occasional periods; twice a week at first." Principles of germination in seeds, the renovating power of clover to the soil, insect injuries, insecticides, self and cross fertilization, pollination, and other matters—taught by chart and object lessons—were explained. The children were "greatly interested" in Slingerland's mounted specimens of insects and models of caterpillars and beetles. Their "greatest delight," however, was in Mrs. Comstock's talks on "Flowers and Their Insect Friends," illustrated by beautifully colored models. Half a dozen strawberry plants were promised any child who would plant them, care for, study, and write essays about them and what he had learned. Grammar school children of New York city and Brooklyn wrote and applied for plants to place in window boxes and on roofs, and nearly 2,000 plants were sent to children. The committee reported:

After the work done in the schools of Westchester County, in response to a large demand from the farmers in many parts of the State, to bring to their section the advantages which they felt they would receive from this kind of instruction, appointments were made in some western New York and other counties, where farmers came together for a day in a town and received two lectures in each place.

The present condition of their dairy and other work was well understood and carefully considered. The needs of the times were discussed. . . . These meetings, though held at a time when farmers were exceedingly busy with their farm work, were well attended. . . .

For the months of September and October an extended series of Horticultural Schools was held in the State. These schools were held under the auspices of the Nixon, or Experiment Station Bill, which appropriated funds for the dissemination of horticultural knowledge in the Fourth Judicial Department of the State. The work was in charge of Cornell University (Ithaca), and the instruction was given chiefly by teachers in that institution, under the immediate supervision of Prof. L. H. Bailey.

Investigation indicated a strong tendency among farmers and their families to leave their farms and go to the cities.

Following passage of the Nixon bill, Bailey and Mrs. Comstock in 1894 had toured the state with horse and buggy. They visited rural area schools to see what was most needed toward rural improvement. As a result of this and an independent study conducted by Mrs. Comstock for the Committee for the Promotion of Agriculture in New York State it was planned that there should "be fitted at Cornell University (this being the only institution of our State where scientific and practical agriculture and horticulture are taught) four teachers, as soon as possible. Two of these shall be sent to the Normal Schools, and two of them to those training schools that desire to undertake the work. These teachers shall prepare a certain number of lectures and practical exercises to be given in each school. These teachers," it was planned, "are to prepare their lectures and practical experiments with the direct aid and under careful inspection of the professors of agriculture, horticulture, botany, entomology, chemistry and geology, at Cornell University. The lectures are to deal with the elements of the sciences in a simple and interesting manner, while the practical exercises shall be illustrative of the lectures, and shall be simple enough so that any teacher can introduce them into any school with little expense. The object of both lectures and practical exercises is to lead the child on to knowledge by his own actual observation." Mrs. Comstock in course of preparing her report wrote principals of all the state normal schools. Except one who objected solely on the grounds of the depressed condition of agriculture, all received the proposition kindly.

Simon H. Gage, president of the Teachers' Science Association of New York State and professor of zoology at Cornell, heartily commended the committee's efforts toward introducing nature study "into even the lowest schools of the State." Consequently, Bailey and Mrs. Comstock went about enlisting aid: "Uncle John" Spencer, an idol of children, who could both speak and write for them; Alice McCloskey, later to edit the Rural School leaflets; and Mary Rogers Miller, a former botany student of L. H. Pammel at Iowa Agricultural, who went to Cornell in 1893 to study German under Professor Marx. Becoming acquainted with Dr. and Mrs. Comstock through Dr. Roberts with whom she lived, she was interested in nature study work and, after her graduation in 1896, gave her full time to it. Mary Farrand Rogers was married in 1899 to Wilhelm Tyler Miller, Bailey's able associate in preparation of the renowned *Cyclopedia of American Horticulture*. She became a lecturer in nature study extension and represented Cornell in a teaching capacity in state teachers' institutes and the summer state schools for teachers at Chautauqua and Thousand Islands. In 1899 and 1900 Mrs.

Miller served as an instructor in large summer schools held in nature study at Ithaca. In 1899 she also started the Home Nature Study Course leaflets. Others who participated in the work in noteworthy capacities were Ada E. Georgia, whom Spencer brought to Ithaca to aid him in answering the multitude of inquiries that flooded the work headquarters from junior naturalists; Julia Ellen Rogers, sister of Mary Farrand Rogers, who studied at Cornell to obtain an advanced degree and in course of her stay taught. Later she wrote two books of national prominence *The Tree Book* and *The Shell Book*. Too much recognition cannot be accorded Anna Botsford Comstock for the contribution she made to nature study—some years later she was voted one of the twelve greatest living women—indeed, her *Handbook of Nature-Study*, an 880-page volume of leaflets written by her during seven years. Bailey regarded "both a source book and a storehouse, readable, attractive, and embellished throughout with apt philosophy and quotation."

The Cornell nature study movement, being a movement for teachers of children, naturally utilized the services of women with much effectiveness. Nevertheless, aside from Mrs. Comstock, the leadership consisted of men. "Uncle John" Spencer, as much as anyone, had been responsible for the work's initiation and growth. For years he had nurtured an idea of interesting the children of New York state in farm life. Similarly, George T. Powell, a Quaker and director of farmers' institutes, had pondered ways and means of reenlisting farm interest as a means of solving the widespread agricultural depression of 1891-1893. He favored promulgation of a back-to-the-farm movement, a concept different from the concept of country-life-improvement stimulated in later years. The urgent need at this time was repopulation of the land from the cities. For this both men fought, being horticulturists. And Spencer, especially, saw the value of nature study. Often he would go to Ithaca and dine at the home of Dean Roberts, and tell him of his hopes for child instruction on the farm. When Roberts placed Bailey in charge of horticultural extension work, Spencer, of course, told Bailey of his ideas for nature study work. In Bailey was soon found the man to lead the movement. Not only had he long had similar ideas for child teaching but also he sensed the improvement such work would have on the rural schools. In 1897, Bailey was placed in charge of the whole enterprise.

Bailey made a strong leader because of the strength of his belief in the work. It is true that his leadership in part depended on Spencer and Powell. Spencer, as chairman of the Chautauqua horticultural society, had been more or less responsible for passage in 1894 of the Nixon bill, being a friend of Nixon and a firm believer in values to be derived from horticultural extension work. Two years later, in 1896, when the farmer's financial plight became more acute, Nixon, as chairman of the

Ways and Means Committee of the New York Assembly, favored grant-ing immediate money relief to the farmers. At this time, however, Powell stepped to the foreground. Convincing the Committee for the Promotion of Agriculture to secure state financing of an educational pro-gram based on the Westchester county and Cornell horticultural exten-sion plan he went to Nixon and persuaded him that future farmers, as well as those of the present, would benefit more from a university exten-sion program. When Abram Hewitt, chairman of the Committee, asked, "Who is fitted to administer such a fund?" Powell answered unhesi-tatingly, "We have an excellent Agricultural College at Cornell, and it must carry on this work."

Nature study, therefore, was not incidental but at the very founda-tion of educational extension work, although for years it was regarded as an experiment in education. It went through two distinct phases of development: the phase of the formulation of concepts and organization of the work, and the phase of developing a pamphlet literature to aid teachers and the organization of Junior Naturalist clubs which attained with the years a membership of more than 30,000 youths. In a Teach-er's Leaflet on June 1, 1897, Bailey defined "What is Nature-Study":

It is seeing the things which one looks at, and the drawing of proper conclusions from what one sees. Nature-study is not the study of a science, as of botany, entomology, geology, and the like. That is, it takes the things at hand and endeavors to understand them, without reference to the systematic order or relationships of the objects. It is wholly informal and unsystematic, the same as the objects are which one sees. It is entirely divorced from definitions, or from explanations in books. It is therefore extremely natural. It simply trains the eye and the mind to see and to comprehend the common things of life; and the result is not directly the acquirement of science but the establishment of a living sympathy with everything that is. . . .

Now, why is the College of Agriculture of Cornell University interesting itself in this work? It is trying to help the farmer, and it begins with the most teachable point,—the child. The district school cannot teach agriculture any more than it can teach law or engineering or any other profession or trade, but it can interest the child in nature and in rural problems and thereby fasten its sympathies to the country. The child will teach the parent. The coming generation will see the result. In the interest of humanity and country, we ask for help.

Children's education, a cornerstone in Cornell University extension work, expanded as a stronghold of the structure. The education of the adult grew with unprecedented spontaneity and was gradually extended to include both the male and female rural population. Each year for four years, from 1894 to 1897, the New York legislature had enlarged the scope and amount of its appropriations. The work included not only scientific investigation at the home experiment station at Cornell. It furthered devices to secure farmer cooperation by institutes. It sought to extend thrifty and sound agricultural and home economics teaching to widely separated and remote farm areas. The work produced sound methods whereby children shared fundamentally in a progressive agricultural pedagogy. The rural family and all rural institutions—schools, church, institutes, and granges—had a share also.

The results, moreover, were infectious and immediate. As early as 1894, Bailey reported in *Garden and Forest*, "Already the tide of a better agriculture has set in strongly." The following year, he added, ". . . It is gratifying to know that the rural population is at last ready to accept the teachings of investigators quickly and fully." Eastward and westward, fruit culture was spreading. On a gigantic scale, orchards were being plowed up and put in clean culture. Spraying was now practiced in almost every community and this, combined with remedial and control methods found in station and field investigations, was eliminating or reducing the spread of many harmful diseases and pests. More intelligent uses of fertilizers were being found to advantage. Special industries, including development of the evaporating industry in apples, peaches, pears, quinces, plums, cherries, currants, potatoes, peas, corn, and pumpkins, were on the increase. Marketing conditions were being improved. Under the law now, horticultural and agricultural work sustained relations with a state commissioner of agriculture. Joint investigations with the United States Department of Agriculture continued. Still, Bailey saw more, much more, to be done. "Books are full of good advice in regard to planting, pruning, grafting, varieties, and the like," he commented in 1895 in *Garden and Forest*, "but where is the book which instructs the orchardist in detail how to till and fertilize his soil?" Bailey refused to recommend extensive irrigation but he stood out as a stanch advocate for studying methods to conserve moisture and apply water artificially to lands not shown specifically to need large scale irrigation.

In 1893 at the International Meteorological Congress held at Chicago as part of the Columbian Exposition, he had reported on "Some interrelations of climatology and horticulture,"[9] saying:

The burden of my plea is twofold: First, while not discouraging the instrumental or conventional study of climate, I would encourage its study in terms of plant life. Second, it is essential that the synchronisms of local climate and the phenomena of plants be given the closest attention. . . .

He reminded his audience that prognostication, valuable to the mariner and general farmer, serves the horticulturist also, but not as valuably as some other factors. A knowledge of zones and life areas of various cul-

[9] Washington, D.C., Weather Bureau, 1894, pp. 431-435.

tivated plants was the horticulturist's need. Cultivated plants brought from other climates were like registers of meteorological peculiarities of given regions. The tremendous study of plant variations in relation to climates, soils, rainfall, and conditions bound up with growth and development were the great interrelations needing studious attention. In their study was involved the whole of evolutionary controversy. Particularly was included the gigantic question of the survival or inheritance of acquired characteristics impressed by agencies of the environment and the inner mechanism of the plant itself. A practical grower's interest more and more was taking over a scholar's interest in Bailey's mind. Bailey saw the explanation of the "physiological species," as distinguished from the more or less permanent and unchanging varieties of plants, to be the most important consideration confronting horticulturists, taxonomically and experimentally. The great needs were trained students and systematic data.

In 1896, in an article published in *Monthly Weather Review* entitled, "Instructions for Taking Phenological Observations," Bailey differentiated between two types of observation:

> . . . Those which record simply the external features of the passing life of plants and animals, and those which attempt to discover or construct some vital connection between life events and climatal environment. The one is concerned chiefly with mere observations, the other with experiment and the philosophy of life courses. While the recording of life-dates may serve either purpose, it must be left to the trained scientist to make the comparisons in the deeper studies of the mutual relationships of climate and periodical phenomena. . . .[10]

Bailey urged that investigations be conducted and restricted to a definite line of inquiry. More than the plant's natural history, climatic factors were to be closely examined in their relations to the general oncoming and fitful or variable features of spring, to the epoch of full activity of the advancing season, to the active physiological epoch, the maturation season, the oncoming of the decline of fall, and to the approach and features of winter. Bailey possessed an enormous capacity for stating research questions. Usually these stemmed from the practical necessities of a situation and graduated, where possible and desirable, into the higher objective reaches of pure science. One of the greatest influences which he exercised over his students was in this. The plant stood foremost as the research instrument. The reactions and responses of plants to varying conditions elaborated the pattern of investigation. Bailey did not depend on books primarily, although no one more than he recognized the importance of an up-to-date literature. His own investigations

[10] Pages 328 ff.

traced origins of cultivated species through not only the epochs of man on the earth but perused the great epochs of preglacial times.

In a famous address before the Philosophical Club of Cornell University, "The Survival of the Unlike," given April 20, 1896, he observed:

A virile plant is introduced into a country in which the same or similar plants are unknown, and immediately it finds its opportunity and becomes a weed, by which we mean it spreads and thrives everywhere. Darwin and Gray long ago elucidated this fact. The trilobites, spirifers, conifers, ginkgos, were weed-types of their time, the same as the composites are to-day. They were stronger than their contemporaries, the same as our own weeds are stronger than the cultivated plants with which they grow. After a time, the new types outran their opportunity, the remorseless struggle for existence tightened in upon them, the intermediate unlikenesses had been blotted out, and finally only one or two types remained, struggling on through the ages, but doomed to perish with the continuing changes of the earth. They became specialized and inelastic; and the highly specialized is necessarily doomed to extinction. Such remnants of a vanquished host remain to us in the equisetums and tree-ferns, in our single liriodendron, the single ginkgo and sassafras, and the depleted ranks of the conifers.

My attention was first called to this line of thought by contemplating upon the fact that cultivated plants differ widely in variability, and I was struck by the fact that many of our most inextricably variable groups— as the cucurbits, maize, citrus, and the great tribes of composites—are still unknown in a fossil state, presumably because of their recent origin. Many other variable genera, to be sure, are well represented in fossil species, as roses (although these are as late as the Eocene), pyrus, prunus, and musa; but absolute age is not so significant as the comparative age of the type, for types which originated very far back may be yet in the comparative youth of their development. . . . The most flexible types of cultivated plants are such as have probably not yet passed their zenith, as the cucurbits, composites, begonias, and the like. The varieties of cereals, which are old types, are so much alike that expert knowledge is needed to distinguish them. . . .

At this same time, Bailey announced a lack of sympathy with teleological explanations, current in American literature since the forceful writings of Gray and his period. "I have no sympathy," said Bailey, "with the too prevalent idea that all the attributes of plants are direct adaptations, or that they are developed as mere protections from environment and associates." Explaining the development of prickles, thorns, hairs, poisonous secretions, and water storage facilities, as protective devices of plants against common enemies did not satisfy Bailey's scientific sense for the simple reason that he refused to read into organic nature a concept of proximate design, not substantiated by exact experimental proof. "These particular attributes of plants are specialized features," said Bailey, "and it is always unsafe to generalize upon specializations. Each and every specialized feature must be investigated for itself." In this, Bailey stood somewhat in advance of his time for, more and more, research during the first decade of the next century would confirm the truth of this observation, especially as stages of plant growth and development would be studied under controlled conditions in plant science laboratories.

Bailey's position in American science was unique. His standing as a botanist was in a role of leadership. His growing importance in the vast developing fields of scientific agriculture was attaining national prominence. His leadership in matters such as rural child education was of itself sufficient to place him in the foreground. Over and above, however, loomed his unrivaled position in American horticulture. When the botanical club of the American Association for the Advancement of Science adopted at Rochester, New York, a code of nomenclature, Bailey endorsed the code for botanical writings, although for horticultural works he would have to continue the use of the "familiar system." "One generation cannot legislate for the next," he wrote *Erythea*, "particularly in matters of the usage of language, and I expect," he said, "that the time is not very far distant when the old herbalists will have their day and the Linnean standpoint will be upset. But I hope that, so long as we are in the muddle, the new rules may be adopted on all sides as a soporific for the present generation—if haply they wear that long."[11] In horticultural writings, moreover, for some years Bailey had taken the position that a determination, once properly made, should be forever fixed, subject, of course, to necessary changes induced by new knowledge or change of circumstances with regard to the plant. Revised opinions in the interest of truth were always allowable. Notably in Japanese plums and other newly introduced varieties he exercised the right of revision. Horticultural taxonomy followed as closely as possible the experiential and observational system of the older botanists, particularly those systematic laws found apt by Torrey, Gray, Engelmann, and other of the older botanists on whose experience the carefully constructed edifice of botanical taxonomy had been raised. But in many points horticultural species differed from those recognized by botany as worthy of classification. Distinguishing between those species having desirable market qualities and susceptible of being organized as aggregates and those which were mere varieties based on minor differences and attributes required in a multitude of instances real scholarship. For example, in a bulletin on tomatoes issued by Bailey about 1889, of 200 varieties tested, only six of the entire list combined desirable market qualities. Bailey then observed that good varieties seemed to run out in about ten years.[12] This was not so of the wild plants, those which had

[11] *Erythea*, II, 1894, p. 10.   [12] *Garden and Forest*, II (1889), p. 576.

survived the great struggle for existence. With the passing of years, as increased study refined knowledge of plant characteristics, differentiations as to genera and species would more and more treat plants as segregates. But cultivated plants originated in numerous ways, by asexual as well as sexual means.

In 1894, Bailey discussed the subject of "The Natural History of Synonyms" before the American Association of Nurserymen at Niagara Falls, New York. There are two opposing views, he stated, as to what constitutes a variety: one, that a variety is determined by its origin, and the other, that a variety is determined by its tangible attributes. "We have now found," said Bailey, "that no two plants are alike, no matter how they have originated; but it is only when the differences are great enough to create some new value in the plants that we regard them as new or distinct varieties." Synonyms arise by bringing together like plants of distinct origin, by divergences or modifications of plants of like origin, and by renaming. Bailey commended a procedure which sought first, to "describe a variable or cosmopolitan variety as a type, and then . . . treat the synonyms with reference to their history—placing in one category all those sub-types which have probably sprung independently from seed, in another all those strains which have been developed in certain localities by selection or the effect of environment, and in a third list all those duplicate names which have been given outright to the very same type." The more synonyms a plant has, the more likelihood there is that the plant will thrive "over a wide range of country and in many diverse conditions; and, in like manner," he argued, "varieties which belong to well-marked tribes or families usually have the strongest or most virile characters." The subject of synonyms, therefore, was of immense significance to the nurseryman, reflecting on "the adaptability of varieties to particular conditions and uses."

The important consideration to Bailey was not the origination of new forms by experimentation but rather the modifications under different conditions, and the persistence of these modifications from generation to generation. A variety might be re-originated from seed and the re-origination might produce strains or subvarieties having unique values for certain purposes. In a paper, "Experimental Evolution Amongst Plants," read before the Massachusetts Horticultural Society at Boston, February 23, 1895, he urged, "Consider that we cannot certainly identify the original species of the apple, peach, plum, cherry, orange, lemon, wine grape, sweet potato, Indian corn, melon, bean, pumpkin, wheat, chrysanthemum, and nearly or quite a hundred other common cultivated plants. It is immaterial whether they are called species or varieties. They are new forms. Some of them are so distinct that they have been made the types of genera. Here," he said, "is the experiment to prove that evolution is true, worked out upon a scale and with a definiteness of detail which the boldest experimenter could not hope to attain, were he to live a thousand years. The horticulturist is one of the very few men whose distinct business and profession is evolution. He, of all other men, has the experimental proof that species come and go." Bailey continued: "It is the fact that, in America at least, the whole body of garden forms is rapidly progressing, or departing from the original type."

Using the tomato as illustration, he observed, "For nearly a century, the tomato has been steadily moving forward . . . with all its botanical characters profoundly modified. . . ." The origin of the Upright tomato, for example, was so well known that the year of its origination and the man who sowed the seed were recorded. Yet the most remarkable feature of tomato varieties was their evolution, not their origins, although, combined with a knowledge of origins, inquiries of experimental evolution were in large part answered. "Similar observations respecting the evolution of forms of specific importance," said Bailey, "could be made for most species of plants which have been widely cultivated for a considerable length of time." In maize, botanists found a single species, yet as prominent an author as Edward Lewis Sturtevant recognized seven "agricultural species." In beans, Linnaeus made two species. Botanists since, finding by experiment and experience that these groups, the pole beans and the bush beans, were interchangeable forms of one type, had regarded the garden bean as a single species. Yet, Bailey noted, "within the last few years three well-marked types of true bush beans have sprung independently from the old types of Lima." Soy beans, an introduction of the past decade from China and Japan and "now coming into popular cultivation in the south," afforded another "most striking example of the evolution of a new species, and one, moreover, which is accepted by careful botanists." He epitomized:

The proofs of the evolution of species, drawn from the accepted practice of the best botanists themselves, could be indefinitely extended. We need only recall the botanical confusion in which most cultivated plants now lie, to find abundant proof of the evolution of hundreds of types so distinct that the best botanists have considered them to be species; but other botanists, basing their estimate of species upon origins, have reduced them or re-included them into the form or type first described. Consider the number of species which have been made in the genus Citrus, comprising the various oranges, lemons, limes and the like. Recall the roses. The Moss rose and others would be regarded as distinct species by any botanist if they were found wild, and if they held their characters as tenaciously as they do under cultivation. In fact, the Moss rose was long regarded as a good species, and it was only when its origin began to be understood that this opinion was given up. The earlier botanists, who were less critical about origins than the present botanists are, made species largely upon apparent features of plants, although their fundamental conception of a species was one which was created, as we find it, in the beginning. Yet, strangely enough, we at the present day, who profess to regard species as nothing more than loose and conventional aggregations of similar individuals, and which we conceive to have sprung from a common ancestor at some more or less late epoch in the world's history, make our species upon premises which we deny, by giving greater weight to obscurity of origin than we do to similarity of individuals!

The fact is that the practice of systematic or descriptive botany is at variance with the teachings of evolution. . . .

Or, stated in another way, Bailey maintained that "botanists still hold to the Linnaean idea of species whilst they profess the Darwinian idea."

When Bailey had undertaken revision of Gray's *Field, Forest and Garden Botany*, he had told Robinson that the book's "greatest defect is its poor characterizations of cultivated plants, resulting from Dr. Gray's imperfect knowledge of them. These characterizations are very bookish, a fact which Dr. Gray knew as well as anyone." As evolutionary knowledge widened, the species concept came more and more into discussion. Bailey, addressing the Botanical Society of America in August, 1896, on "The Philosophy of Species-Making,"[13] insisted:

Evolution, as a method, is either true or it is not true. It cannot be half true. If evolution is true, then the forms of life are not the units or entities in the organic creation; they are the disjoined remaining results of the world-long process of elimination, the incidental outcomes of a vicarious history. . . .

. . . As I now conceive of it, I should define a species as follows: *The unit in classification, designating an assemblage of organisms which, in the judgment of any writer, is so marked and so homogeneous that it can be conveniently spoken of as one thing. . . .*

The claims of the "physiological species" to taxonomic recognition were being advanced. The study of cultivated plants, of plant variations under culture, had not been claimed wholeheartedly by botanical science. Agriculture, in a restricted sense, had taken to itself the study of soils, fertilizers, and domestic animals.

Horticulture, therefore, was confronted more than ever before with the task of systematizing the abundant knowledge issuing from experimentation in schools and experiment stations. In an address on "Van Mons and Knight, and the Production of Varieties," delivered before the Pennsylvania Horticultural Society at Philadelphia on March 17, 1896, Bailey concluded:

I am constantly reminded that horticulturists do not apprehend the fundamental principles of the origination of new varieties simply because they refuse to look at the problem broadly, in the light of evolution, and

[13] *Botanical Gazette*, XXII, July-December, 1896, pp. 454-462.

persist in asking for some short-cut or so-called practical method which they can apply in the garden without testing its probable fitness by comparing it with the means which are operative in the uplifting of the vegetable world. Horticulture has always suffered by being cut off from the studies of scientific men, so that it has grown too much into a mere art, which is not conceived to rest upon the very same fundamental laws, so far as plant-breeding is concerned, as have been and are the slow but mighty forces which have been operating throughout the ages.

To Bailey and a few other students fell the task of leadership—to point the way for a "new horticulture," which, cognizant of obligations to maintain its traditional artistic and business spheres, had now the superimposed duty of adjusting and coordinating a new body of scientific knowledge. It was not unlike a new beginning in plant study. Basic knowledge and material had to be organized in the light of a new knowledge—with taxonomy as the fundamental it had always been, and doubtless always will be. Thereto was added also the duty of forming an adequate philosophy by which in the large the work might proceed.

Pomology and vegetable crops were not the only branches which shared the new science's development. The growing of winter vegetables increased in importance in northern greenhouses. Floriculture developed rapidly, despite a popular prejudice on the part of florists of the trade against the work of professors—an understandable prejudice predicated in their natural desire to protect their short-term markets and annual turnover. Bailey became an early member of the Society of American Florists and, attending a meeting at Boston, on one occasion was invited to speak. Years, nevertheless, were required to overcome prejudices held by many greenhouse men. Their opposition was produced by interferences—some imaginary and some real—with long maintained practices which science exposed as unsound or impractical. The attitude of the Horticultural Division of the Cornell Experiment Station was contained in its Bulletin 91 :

We refuse to test varieties simply because they are new. Our basis of study is the monograph—the investigation of a particular subject, rather than the indiscriminate growing of things which chance to be put upon the market in a given year, and which have no relationship to each other aside from a coincidence in date. When we take up a certain group of plants for study, we endeavor to secure every variety of it, old or new. These varieties are studied not only in the field, but botanical specimens are invariably made of every one, so that the experimenter has specimens before him for leisurely study when the hurry of field work and the excitement of bug-catching are done. We are always glad to receive the seed novelties of any year, but we do not agree to report upon them or even to grow them. If we were to attempt to grow them all, we should simply be making a museum of curiosities, and we should have no time left for investigation and experiment. . . .

Monographs, incorporating the history, culture, classification, and description of varieties, were the objectives of experimental and taxonomic study. Bailey had always taken substantial interest in any subjects that made for rural adornment and his study, "Suggestions for the Planting of Shrubbery," he conceived in 1896 as making "for the betterment of home grounds in rural communities." In his report for 1897, he reported, "In floriculture the work is confined to studies of cannas, dahlias, and to the vexed problems concerned in the forcing of Bermuda lilies for Easter, and to chrysanthemums." But it was as to the continuing account of sweet peas that the issue of the propriety of an experiment station to study a subject such as flowers was squarely put. Bailey answered the station's critics manfully:

The enclosed report is submitted for publication under the provisions of the Experiment Station Extension bill, and it is a complement to Bulletin III, issued a year ago this month. This Bulletin III was the first experiment station report upon sweet peas. It called forth some harsh criticisms, which were very largely due, I think, to a misconception of the problem at which we were working. Our motives in its preparation were two: to popularize the sweet pea, and to give an account of the varieties which were actually sold by the dealers last year. Our estimates of varieties were often very unlike the estimates which are currently made of them; and it was charged that many of our varieties must have been very untrue to type or else grown from very poor seed. If this charge was true, it only shows that poor seed was in the market and it is evidence enough that the test was needed. In other words, our effort was to determine the exact merits of the sweet peas commonly offered for sale, not to grow the strains of fanciers and plant breeders. . . . Having grown the sweet peas of the retail seedsmen last year, we have this year turned our attention to the types and strains of the experts and breeders. . . .

As Dean Roberts explained in a bulletin on chrysanthemums, the object had been to help florists and flower lovers everywhere. When in 1897 Wilhelm Miller prepared "A Talk about Dahlias," Bailey wrote an introduction, saying:

Although Mr. Miller may not agree, I do not consider the dahlia to be the chief merit of this bulletin. The best thing in it is the personal point of view. Flower-loving is sentiment and emotion, kindled with imagination. It depends vastly more upon the person than it does upon the flower. . . . I am convinced that the farmers need education in flowers and other incidental things quite as much as they do in wheat or potatoes, for it is the lack of cheer and color and interest about the home which is largely responsible for the dissatisfaction of the young people with the country. . . . Aside from our desire to extend flower-loving and nature-study to the country, we are under obligations to the flower-trade, which is a most valued constituent and supporter of the experiment stations. I may say that members of the trade may obtain a sketch of the varieties we grew last year by writing us for it.

A curious incident of our dahlia studies occurred in connection with the American Institute Fair in New York, at which we made an exhibit of over 200 varieties. A florists' paper said that "the only commendable feature of this stand was the great number of kinds staged." Another horticultural journal said that it was "a very extensive collection of dahlias, but the blooms were not of exhibition quality." We had not supposed that such a misconception of the office of an experiment station exists amongst the makers of public opinion. Surely it is no part of the business of a station to grow plants for mere exhibition. The growers themselves can do that, and they can usually do it much better than the experiment station can. . . . If the varieties were not satisfactory, it is easy to see where the fault lies; and there is therefore all the more need for an experiment to show the actual status of the business. We have found, as a result of considerable experimentation in various lines of floriculture, that we do not often get the best stock which the dealers have. We often receive the tag-ends. If the dealers are willing that the varieties should be judged by such plants, we have no reason to object. It is, of course, perfectly natural and proper that the originator of new varieties, or the exhibition grower, should retain the best strains for his own use, and for this reason the experiment station can never hope to equal the specialists in the quality of plants, even if such were its legitimate ambition. . . .

The officers of the Institute evidently caught the spirit of the exhibition, for, unknown to us, they awarded the Experiment Station a bronze medal and a diploma for " a display of 212 varieties of typical dahlias."

Two years before, in the autumn of 1895, the first annual meeting of the American Dahlia Society had been held. This group, gathered together to popularize the flower and collect and compare information concerning it, had succeeded notably in arousing an interest which rivaled the chrysanthemum's popularity. More than another decade would pass before a national sweet pea society would be formed. And when established, the society would place a trial ground at Cornell University. The insistence on high trade standards and quality of production built public confidence in the station and university. Although some hostility and antagonism were met, in time the general influence of improved scientific methods brought about in the trades a tremendous support of the work in floriculture. As graduate study in the subject grew, excellent theses of students included a wide variety of subjects such as the garden verbena, the genus Tulipa, bottom heat, effect of fertilizers on the colors of flowers. Special studies investigated greenhouse heating, winter forcing of plants, and a host of kindred researches. With the years, notable monographic studies of the peony in collaboration with a national society, and of the gladiolus, also maintained in conjunction with an American society devoted to the flower's study, would stress horticultural evolution and improvement, as well as systematically test, describe and classify all known forms and varieties. Iris, perennial phlox, climbing rose, other hardy perennials, in fact, every large genus of garden flowering plant possible, would become subjects of study and investigation. For study of the climbing roses, the American Rose Society would place a test garden at Cornell. So large and important would floricultural work become that during the school year 1912-1913 floriculture and vegetable-gardening would be "separated as coordinate departments." Floriculture was organized as a department in 1913-1914 under E. A. White. Vegetable-gardening was organized the same year under Paul Work. In 1910 had begun the division of Bailey's historic department of horticulture by organization under C. S. Wilson of a separate department of pomology. Bailey's zeal had initiated the work of each division. Floriculture, however, had been one of his great dreams. Truly, Bailey's vision in this branch of horticultural science[14] was brought to a noble and beautiful consummation at Cornell.

Pomology for a while suffered something of a setback on the campus at Ithaca. With the university's growth, invasions into the gardens and orchard grounds were made necessary. During the season of 1895, the entire cherry orchard, all of the vineyard, a large part of the native plum collection, and a sizable lot of seedling currants and other plants were destroyed to make way for the construction of a veterinary building. Grading work, the changing of the terrain, and college improvements required the moving of the famous experimental orchard containing one of the rarest collections of fruit species in America. "The work of several years was irrevocably lost. . . . Our area is now so small," wrote Bailey, "that we can not expect to plan much new experimentation therein in fruit-culture; and it is now so completely occupied by permanent planting that experiments in vegetable gardening must henceforth be very limited and must eventually cease." Nevertheless, those who believe in their work find a way. Observations in pruning, tillage, fertilizings, cover cropping, and other matters continued. By 1901 Bailey was able to report, "The land of the Horticultural Division is largely taken up with the orchards, which are now coming into full bearing."[15] Indeed, as early as the horticulturist's report for 1897, it had been said:

Among the tree fruits, progress has been made in the permanent orchards which were devoted to carefully planned and far reaching fertilizer experiments. Some new varieties of Japanese plums are fruiting for the first time. . . . A new vineyard has been set and important accessions made.

[14] See an interesting article on this subject by A. C. Beal, "Investigations in Floriculture," *Cornell Countryman*, xi, 5, February, 1914, p. 165; also "Development of the Department of Floriculture at Cornell University," by E. A. White, *ibid.*, xi, 5, p. 159.
[15] See also an article by H. B. Knapp, after pomology had been organized as a separate department, "Plans of the Department of Pomology," *Cornell Countryman*, xi, 5, February, 1914, pp. 157-158.

The work in small fruit culture has consisted largely of local fertilizer experiments in six strawberry fields of Oswego county, the results of which are very gratifying and of great interest. Two beds of strawberries have been set, one of new varieties, and one to continue the indoor work. In vegetable gardening we are in the midst of our second year of investigation with celeriac and Brussels sprouts. An acre of celery has also been planted on the onion meadows of Orange county in an attempt to introduce the culture of this crop within easy shipping distance of the large eastern markets. . . . The indoor work now looks toward a long series of cultural experiments in the forcing of fruits; collections of apricots, peaches, and cherries are ready, and as soon as the proper facilities are at hand the growing of grapes from a commercial standpoint is to be undertaken. One of the smaller greenhouses has been remodelled for a strawberry forcing house to follow up the successful work of last winter.

In 1898 experimental studies spread to other counties. Research in mushroom growing and G. N. Lauman's comprehensive study of the garden pea were outstanding. "Various treatments and studies in the experimental orchards, especially those concerned with tillage and fertilizing," wrote Bailey in 1899, "are our staple subjects of inquiry." Orchard pollination and self-sterility problems were included. In vegetable-gardening matters of geography and outdoor growing were considered. However, in this branch of work a new circumstance had arisen. The growing of short-time vegetable crops in Florida and the Southwest, and the improvement of transportation, refrigeration, and storage facilities, had commenced seriously to affect the northern greenhouse industry of winter-grown vegetables. It is said that, about 1899-1900, the growing of winter vegetables in the North on a commercial basis practically went out of existence. But floriculture benefited. Floricultural investigations took over much of the vacated greenhouse space to study ornamental gardening. Investigations of rare beauty and interest were elaborately developed in geraniums, tulips, and other flowers.

Due to political and economic considerations, the southern states for many years were slow to develop agriculturally. Before 1888, some states maintained services, substantially similar to work later more effectively done by federally aided state stations, as, for example, in the analyses of fertilizers. Fees collected for such service usually went to promote programs to better farm and plantation conditions. The universities after the Civil War had seen the necessity for modernized engineering. But, in agriculture, engineering was little used and work was largely confined to studies of cattle and crops. Methods employed were decidedly more practical than scientific. The South, like all regions, had born naturalists but places for exact plant science study were few. Whether a crop would thrive in a certain soil with a certain fertilizer or plant feeding was regarded as crucial. For many years technical studies refined the methods at first rather crudely applied. Development of dairies and creameries were given attention, notably in Mississippi at Stark-ville. In a word, however, the programs were more agricultural than horticultural. Forestry for many years received scant attention. At Ala-bama Polytechnic, the important botanical work of such leaders as George Francis Atkinson, Lucien M. Underwood, and F. S. Earle had significant beginnings, especially in the study of cotton diseases. The North Carolina Agricultural Experiment Station led in establishing a well equipped and adequately financed laboratory. Nevertheless, the splendid pathological work which emerged finally over the entire South originated with little more than mycological beginnings. Plant breeding among southern staple crops—cotton, corn, sugar cane, and the like—did not receive thorough and widespread attention for decades notwith-standing establishment of state and private experiment stations. Breed-ing for quantity and quality yields was given some attention. But what induced northern growers such as Cyrus G. Pringle of Charlotte, Ver-mont, to begin cross fertilizing wheat for hardiness as early as 1870 did not exist in the South. Between 1869-1879 Pringle did noteworthy plant breeding work in cereals, garden vegetables, and fruits. The ene-mies of the South, however, seemed not so much climate as diseases. Agricultural chemistry, soil study, entomological study of insects and pests, study of root rots and rusts, anticipations of true agronomic and breeding investigations, and many other phases of eminently practical work, dominated the agricultural scene of southern scholarly study for many years. The leadership was able but the problems were enormous. And inadequate financing retarded progressive action.

Florida, of course, was an exception, not primarily because of its sta-tion work, but more because of its subtropical and tropical location. Each state had its own agricultural problems. While at Alabama Polytechnic studies were enlarged to examine special crops, particularly cotton, Florida found itself confronted, along with plant diseases, by a still more unique situation, namely, the devastation of its citrus industry by all too frequent freezes. With the placement of a federal subtropical station at Eustis in 1892, the state station (first located at Eau Gallie, transferred by successive legislatures to Ocala and Lake City, and finally perma-nently joined to the university at Gainesville) had a helpful ally in scien-tific work. Pathological and breeding work in both federal and state in-stitutions advanced. With the opening up of the state by waterways and railroads, the citrus industry expanded from northern to southern Flor-ida and finally included the entire state area, carrying with it the re-markable extension of the already mentioned program of short-time winter growing of vegetables. So elaborate did the program become, there developed special areas for crop growing, such as celery, potatoes, tomatoes, and beans. Cocoanut growing had been introduced in extreme southern parts and this, together with other introductions such as bamboo and mangoes, added to a soon well defined horticulture including a naturally endowed floriculture unsurpassed by any state except possibly California. Florida, therefore, was well supplied with scientific advancements.

But what of other southern states with vast stretches of undeveloped and poverty stricken lands? What of the vast untilled and unplanted western regions of the United States? What of the entire nation's agricultural status? Governments alone could not cope with the profound tasks of growth and reconstruction. It was necessary for individual state colleges and stations to give aid and progress was impossible without more trained leadership. Trained leadership called for enlarged and more modernly equipped collegiate institutions. And underlying it all was a serious need for an adequate and modern literature. Literature on such basic subjects as plant physiology and plant pathology, in fact, in all the branches of plant science work was deplorably lacking. Indeed, it was amazingly scanty in nearly all the subjects of American agriculture. Systematic works were available. But of literature that incorporated the results of other modern scientific investigation there was little, especially in horticulture. Florida had advanced rapidly with the rise of scientific aid. So had Arizona, California, Wisconsin, Ohio, New York, the New England states, and other states where agricultural colleges wielded an influence. Bailey saw that a rural science literature would extend progressive advancements to all the states of the Union, to Canada, in fact, to all world regions where the agriculture of a particular area needed scientific study. In this noiseless revolution which eventually did take place Liberty Hyde Bailey played the important role of becoming one of the world's great agricultural authors and editors.

On August 1, 1896, in a bulletin entitled, "The Texture of the Soil," Bailey announced:

This bulletin and its successor [The Moisture of the Soil] are designed to inaugurate a new type of experiment station publication. They are written for the purpose of giving their readers a few simple and primary lessons in some of the most fundamental subjects connected with the cropping of the land. It is hoped that they do not contain a single new fact. It is their sole ambition to teach, not to discover or to record. The writers hope that they may be used as texts in horticultural societies, granges, and farmers' clubs. It is wished that they may inspire some persons to read further into the subjects, and especially that they may suggest the reading of King's book upon "The Soil," from which the bulletins themselves have heavily drawn. . . .

Franklin Hiram King, professor of agricultural physics at the University of Wisconsin, the first American chair of this subject, was one of five great leaders, whom Cyril G. Hopkins of the University of Illinois

The Lazy Club, 1896

Back row: Blair, Powell, Kains, Paddock, Lodeman. Middle row: Keating, Irish, Bailey, Munson. Bottom row: Miller, Wyman, Walker.

characterized as founders of American agricultural chemistry. Stephen Moulton Babcock, Eugene Woldemar Hilgard, Samuel William Johnson, and Robert C. Kedzie, shared the honors. But King was the man whom Bailey selected to write the first of the classic Rural Science Series, which Bailey edited. In his Editor's Preface to *The Soil* by King, Bailey stated the purpose of the series:

The rural industries have taken on a new and quickened life in consequence of the recent teachings and applications of science. Agriculture is no longer a mere empiricism, not a congeries of detached experiences, but it rests upon an irrevocable foundation of laws. These fundamental laws or principles are numerous and often abstruse, and they are interwoven into a most complex fabric; but we are now able to understand their general purport, and we can often trace precisely the course of certain minor principles in problems which, a few years ago, seemed to be hopelessly obscure, and which, perhaps, were considered to lie outside the sphere of investigation. Agriculture has developed into a system of clear and correct thinking; and inasmuch as every man's habit of thought is determined greatly by the accuracy of his knowledge, it follows that the successful prosecution of rural pursuits is largely a subjective matter. It is therefore fundamentally important that every rural occupation should be contemplated from the point of view of its underlying reasons. It should be approached in a philosophic spirit. There was an attempt in the older agricultural literature to discuss rural matters fundamentally; but the knowledge at the time was insufficient, and such writings fell into disrepute as being unpractical and theoretical. The revolt from this type of writing has given us the present rural literature, which deals mostly with the object, and which is too often wooden in its style. The time must certainly be at hand when the new teaching of agriculture can be put into books.

For many years the writer has conceived of an authoritative series of readable monographs, which shall treat every rural problem in the light of the undying principles and concepts upon which it rests. It is fit that such a series should be introduced by a discussion of the soil, from which everything ultimately derives its being. This initial volume is also an admirable illustration of the method of science, for the soil is no longer conceived to be an inert mixture, presenting only chemical and simple physical problems, but it is a scene of life, and its physical attributes are so complex that no amount of mere empirical or objective treatment can ever elucidate them. If the venture should prove that the opening century is ready for the unrestrained application of science to rural life, then it is hoped that the Rural Science Series, under the present direction or another's, may ultimately cover the whole field of agriculture.

Another volume of the series which was chosen was *The Fertility of the Land* by Isaac Phillips Roberts, a book really put together by Bailey from writings by Roberts, and introductory to which Bailey said:

. . . I confess that I have looked with some apprehension upon the rapid diffusion of experimental science of recent years, for there is danger that this knowledge may overshadow the importance of accustomed farm-practice, and lead the farmer to demand specific rules for each perplexity and to depend upon the Experiment Station and the teacher for his farming. The most important mission of the Experiment Station, at the present time, is to lead the farmer to understand more fully the underlying reasons for the common things which he does. . . . There are those who look for the time when agriculture shall be reduced to a rigid science, which shall be governed by a well-defined series of rules and precepts. But that time will never come! Happily, there is one vocation in which men engage which can never be bounded by methods or precedents, one occupation which is as elastic and untrammeled and unconventional as the blowing of the wind, the falling of the rain, and the singing of the birds! The fact is that there is no science of agriculture. The occupation is a business and an art founded upon the inter-play of many sciences, of which chemistry, botany, physiology, physics and climatology are chief; and these and all the business methods are coördinated by good judgment and skillful management. . . . There is danger that in the bewilderment of the multitude of new facts, we forget fundamental reasons and the importance of understanding the common things. The farmer should be a philosopher. . . .

Bailey himself wrote books of the highest value to horticulture and agriculture. During the decade of the 1890's, books issued from his pen that integrated American horticultural practice and remained standard works of the science for many years. Macmillan Company became his publisher and many new editions of older books as well as new books appeared. Some of the latter became issues of the Rural Science Series. In 1897 appeared *The Principles of Fruit-Growing* of which *Garden and Forest* said in a review:

Professor Bailey has been preparing a monograph on the Apple, and in the course of his work it became clear that many of the essentials of the science and art of pomology could be grouped together so as to be applicable to all kinds of fruits, and this volume is the result. Its range and purpose, therefore, is precisely defined by its title. It is a discussion of the principles which underlie the successful production of all kinds of orchard fruits and, indeed, most of the small fruits. . . . This book is an attempt, not only to establish the laws which must be followed if the best fruit is to be grown at paying prices, but it explains the limitations of climate and of location, which make fruit-growing a hopeful industry in one region and a doubtful one in another. The study of the geography of a fruit farm with reference to markets, to threatened frosts and the conditions which make them dangerous, to winds and air currents, to atmospheric drainage and other physical conditions, is full and, of course, instructive. Equally important is the chapter on the evolution of tillage, in which such subjects as the texture of the soil—that is, its physical condition, as distinct from the amount of plant-food it contains—are treated, together with all the operations necessary for the conservation of moisture, even down to the minutiae of detail. Of course, all the elementary facts . . . necessary for a fruit grower to know in relation to diseases and insects are clearly set forth, and we are glad to see that a most interesting bulletin of the Cornell Experiment Station on the general subject of spraying is largely incorporated into this chapter. Points of practice, like the laying out of grounds, the selection and setting of trees, choice of varieties, the proper methods of fertilization, with the latest methods of harvesting and marketing, are given with clearness and precision. Altogether, this is one of the best numbers of the admirable Rural Science Series, of which Professor Bailey is the general editor. Books like this go far to remove the reproach that there are no available manuals for the farm and garden in America which are at once practical in their directions and thoroughly scientific in their methods.

The Rural Science Series was not confined to plants. Although the second volume was E. G. Lodeman's *The Spraying of Plants*, books on milk, bush fruits, fertilizers, irrigation and drainage, animal feeding, and farm poultry followed as members of the series. Reviewing Lodeman's book, the *Botanical Gazette* noted America's leadership in the study of plant diseases and commented, "Nothing more remarkable has taken place in the history of botany than the development of methods for the protection of cultivated plants against the attacks of fungi and insects, especially by spraying, and the consequent encouragement given to the study of the life history of fungi." Naturally, therefore, Bailey as editor stressed the scientific aspects of plant study. He arranged for a volume on plant pathology by Beverly T. Galloway and one on plant physiology by Joseph Charles Arthur. William H. Brewer of Yale University was selected to write on animal breeding and N. S. Mayo on animal care. Better breeding and better care were visualized as the great potentials for a progressively advancing agriculture. How the new knowledge was to spread and attain practical application was explained by Bailey in a letter to Arthur September 17, 1897:

I arrived to-day from a summer in Europe and am now trying to get the strands of work in hand again. I am wondering how you are getting on with the book. . . . I suppose that the demand for a book upon the physiology of plants will be comparatively small among the general class of readers whom we desire to reach. I am preparing a botany which is designed to be used as a teacher's help in the secondary schools, working it out along the lines of our teachers' leaflets. It is, of course, to aim at nothing more than to teach powers of observation. It will call for a book upon simple experiments in plant physiology, and I am wondering if we cannot add that feature to your book. I should like to have your book contain two somewhat distinct features, first, and primarily, to be a reading book upon the physiology of plants, so written that a man of average education can read it with interest. In other words, I should hope that it might be something like a narrative of what a plant does. In the second place, I should hope that it might suggest a lot of minor and simple experiments by means of which a student, a farmer's club or a horticultural society might demonstrate some of the simpler and more obvious points of plant physiology. . . .

He suggested that about 100 simple experiments on different phases of physiology be included in the book.

With unexampled success Cornell University had developed its Farmers' Reading-Course. Voluntarily and at first without remuneration "Uncle John" Spencer had come, in 1896, to Ithaca to help in nature study work and been placed in charge of the Reading-Course. Through correspondence he had begun disseminating scientific agricultural facts, his courses reaching thousands of practical farmers. Without doubt, the work greatly promoted the effectiveness of the university's practical relations with the New York state farmers. Dean Roberts sent Spencer into the rural schools to study needs and, in teaching teachers and students, he "saw clearly that the first step in this great work was to help the teachers through simply written leaflets. I remember very well," wrote Mrs. Comstock, "being present at the conference, consisting of Mr. George T. Powell, Mr. Spencer, and myself, when this matter was first talked over. Mr. Spencer said that the Cornell professors should write these leaflets, and I, knowing well that these men were already overworked, told him that I thought it would be impossible. But nothing was impossible to him, and he did well in choosing the first contributor, for he went directly to Professor Bailey. The result was that masterly leaflet, 'How a Squash Plant Gets Out of the Seed,' and the next leaflet writer was Professor Cavanaugh, who produced a delightful article on 'How a Candle Burns.' Other leaflets followed, and soon Mr. Spencer had something to work with in his endeavor to interest and instruct the teachers who were so ignorant of everything pertaining to agriculture and nature."

In June, 1899, when the college issued its first "Cornell Nature-Study Bulletin," an organized effort was made to attract and enlist the child's interest directly. This was an added feature to the already established indirect method of reaching children through teachers and the *Teacher's Leaflets*. Bailey observed:

December, 1896, was the first issue of the nature-study leaflets. Thirteen leaflets have now appeared. Voluntary requests for these publications have now increased our mailing list to 25,000 live names. Most of these names are of teachers in New York. In the State of New York there are 29,000 teachers.

Our entire movement in nature-study is for the benefit of the children. We are now making an effort to reach them directly, as well as through the teacher, the parent, the garden and the flower-show. We have long had correspondence with many children. Many thousands have applied to us for information on the making of gardens and on various matters connected with the common phenomena of nature; but we are now inaugurating a definite effort at the organization of nature-clubs amongst the children of the State.

The correspondence arising from this educational work has come to be large. At present it averages over 1,200 letters a week. In a twelve-month as many as 80,000 circular letters of instruction have been sent. . . . For these reasons we have adopted a new form of publication. This Bulletin will be issued four times a year, and perhaps more frequently. . . .The animus of the endeavor is to cause the child to love nature and thereby to be content with country life. . . .

By 1900 editions of 25,000 copies of the "Nature-Study Quarterlies" or *Teacher's Leaflets* as they were also known, were being circulated. In the Farmers' Reading-Course, "in round numbers," 20,000 were registered. 35,000 school children in Junior Naturalist Clubs and 30,000 teachers were reported receiving leaflets, including *Junior-Naturalist Monthlies*. When in 1899 Miss Rogers inaugurated the Home Nature-Study Course, lesson I on germination of seeds went to 500 teachers. Combined with the cooperative experimentation of the Cornell station and work of the Bureau of Nature-Study and Reading-Course of which Bailey was chief and Spencer deputy chief, the college's state agricultural extension work was growing prodigiously. Today the Junior Naturalist Clubs have a counterpart in the nationally known 4-H Clubs, in which in 1941 New York state alone had 32,000 members.

When in 1908 the American Nature Study Society was organized, Bailey was named its first president—an honor issuing from his participation in this great work.

The nature study movement was revolutionary in that, in a sense, it anticipated the teaching of agriculture in the lower schools. With a scientific but not technical approach, its tendency was toward breaking up exclusiveness in education. So much of a departure from standard methods naturally met opposition. But its effectiveness demonstrated its worth. It had won after quite a struggle.

No experimental period was ever found necessary for the Farmers' Reading-Courses. Their worth and effectiveness were demonstrated from the beginning. In 1899, published as Bulletin 72 of the Office of Experiment Stations of the United States Department of Agriculture, Bailey wrote an historical treatise on such courses for adults. He summarized:

Two distinct ideas are represented. . . . The older or Chatauqua-Pennsylvania idea is that of a definite, prescribed, self-limited, technical correspondence curriculum, the completion of which is signalized by a certificate or diploma. The other, or Cornell idea, is that of a flexible, non-limited, untechnical reading course in which there is no system of counts, and which does not lead to certificatory honors. The former is intensive: it is adapted to the few. The latter is elementary: it is adapted to the many. Each is incomplete.
The ideal reading-course system is that which joins the two ideas. . . . The complete reading course is both a missionary and a school master.

In 1900, published as Bulletin 79 by the government, Bailey also wrote on "Farmers' Institutes: History and Status in the United States and Canada."

In Bailey's *The Principles of Agriculture* A Text-Book for Schools and Rural Societies, he expressed a credo: "Agriculture . . . stands upon business, but science is the staff. Business cannot be taught in a book like this; but some of the laws of science as applied to farm-management can be taught, and it is convenient to speak of these laws as the principles of agriculture." Spencer, L. A. Clinton, Cavanaugh, B. M. Duggar, Roberts, Law, and Wing, wrote chapters dealing with special subjects. Except for the chapter on plant physiology by Duggar, Bailey wrote most of the material relating to plants. "It is commonly assumed," said Bailey, "that fertilizing the land is the one most fundamental thing in agriculture, but this is not so; for if but one thing about farming practices were to be explained, that thing should be the tilling of the land." Similarly, he said, "It is customary to consider agricultural chemistry as the fundamental science of agriculture. . . . But agriculture has no single fundamental science. . . . In particular, we must outgrow the idea that by analyzing soil and plant we can determine what the one will produce and what the other needs. . . . The soil is the laboratory in which the chemical activities take place, but conditions of weather are ever modifying these activities; and it is not always that the soil and the plant are in condition to work together. . . . But if there is no science of agriculture as distinct from other sciences, the prosecution of agriculture must be scientific; and the fact that it is a mosaic makes it all the more difficult to follow, and enforces the importance of executive judgment and farm-practice over mere scientific knowledge." In other words, what agriculture sought was the production of agricultural wealth and the understanding of "those principles and facts which are common to all agriculture, or which may be considered to be fundamental. . . . We shall seek to ask why before we ask how. Principles apply everywhere, but facts and rules may apply only where they originate." He distinguished his point of view from those "teachers who would have us believe that [agriculture] is chiefly the overcoming of mere obstacles, as insects, unpropitious weather, and the like." He, therefore, declined to discuss the incidentals, as he termed subjects such as the kinds of weeds, the brands of fertilizers, the breeds of animals, and the varieties of flowers. He stressed the three great fields which make agricultural wealth—the soil, the plant, and the animal.

Bailey's point of view was practical. These were developmental years of agricultural instruction in all quarters of the nation. In 1888, thirty-nine states of the Union had agricultural colleges or university departments of agriculture. By the end of the century, North Dakota, Idaho,

Montana, Utah, Washington, and Wyoming were admitted as states. Oklahoma would follow in 1907, and Arizona and New Mexico in 1912. In a few instances, agricultural colleges were founded before the state's admittance. By the end of the twentieth century's first decade, one college, and in some states several colleges, which devoted large portions of their energies toward advancing their state's agriculture, were to be found in every state. Nevertheless, the existence of such colleges was no guarantee as to their effectiveness. Academic points of view had not transformed the practical man's viewpoint everywhere. Fear of paternalism on the part of the federal government, the jealous regard for states' rights, the wide differences in economic and geographical necessities of each state unit, and a host of other factors, served to retard development of a national agriculture. Most certainly, the development of a universal scheme of agricultural education, based on objective principles of science, was impeded. What other than a practical outlook could an educator like Bailey have taken? He saw an era of propaganda foreshadowing realization of an ideal system. An unwavering belief in the need of agricultural betterment had to precede formulation of concepts and schemes. Exact science could not supply all the instrumentalities for improved agriculture. The farmer was an isolated citizen contending with problems unlike that of the urbanite. The telephone, the automobile, good roads, modern railways, the interurban, the motor bus, the telegraph, were not available in all rural areas. These were distinct luxuries if had at all. The radio and the motion picture were totally unknown. There was only the school, the church, the grange, and the institutes with fairs and community events. There were many regions that had not even these, or were so far distant that only on rare occasions could they be enjoyed. Obviously, there was a great need of missionary work in American agriculture. The whole subject, the whole outline of the new work, had to be presented to the people. Agriculture had to be put in pedagogical form. In these years there was still little modern agricultural pedagogy. "Go ye into the entire world and preach a gospel of the land and its possibilities" was an imperative that would send educated men to Brazil, to China, to many agriculturally undeveloped world regions. But no closely woven and highly refined fabric of technical and scientific methodology would be required for many years. Yet agricultural frontiers were not infrequent even in the United States. Bailey knew what was needed—statistical studies and scientific solutions of the immense problems confronting them. But, first, the adult and the child must be educated in science.

To this end there appeared in 1895 Bailey's revision of Gray's *Field, Forest and Garden Botany*; in years following, new editions of his Garden-Craft Series; in 1898, *Lessons with Plants* and an abridgment or

First Lessons with Plants; in 1898 *Botany*: "An Elementary Text for Schools," about which Bailey wrote Bessey on December 31, 1900:

If you have looked over my new Botany and have found things which ought to be changed, it would be a great satisfaction to me if you could give me the points as we are obliged soon to reprint the book. As I think I wrote you before, I do not look on this book as competing with other books, but merely as an effort to open the way for the more critical study of plants. It is the outgrowth of our nature study movement.

In 1898 also appeared, aided in authorship by L. R. Taft, F. A. Waugh, and Ernest Walker, Bailey's *Garden-making*: suggestions for the utilizing of home grounds, another of the Garden-Craft Series. Probably, however, the two most noted books which Bailey produced during this period were *The Survival of the Unlike*, A Collection of Evolution Essays Suggested by the Study of Domestic Plants, which appeared in 1897, and *Sketch of the Evolution of Our Native Fruits*, appearing in 1898. His *The Principles of Vegetable-Gardening*, published in 1901, contained discussions of the ideals of olericulture, of its American geography particularly with reference to the South and Middle West, and on the whole extent of the subject in the United States. Chapters on greenhouse growing, on the soil and its treatment, on tools, on seeds and seedage, on management and marketing, and on the specific crops would make the book another authoritative member of the Rural Science Series.

Bailey studied systematically all cultivated vegetables as he grew them in his garden. For example, as to the cultivated Brassicas, he said in 1897:

. . . I am acquainted with no group in which many of the difficulties of classification vanish more quickly upon a study of the growing plants than in these Brassicas. . . . The Chinese Cabbages, which are now coming into cultivation, possess unusual interest to both the horticulturist and botanist. . . .

So influential were Bailey's books and studies that the trustees of the Veitch Memorial Fund selected him that year as the recipient of their medal "in recognition of the value of his lectures and writings as a help," *Garden and Forest* said, "in placing the cultivation of plants on a scientific basis, and his efforts to promote the extension of horticultural education, and his efforts to improve economic plants."

Nor did Bailey confine his teaching to books and his classes. In 1896, at "Garden Home," the Bailey family's first Ithaca home, on the campus, he organized in January the world famous Horticultural Lazy Club of Cornell University. On November 19, the club met in their new club house, a small room off the forcing house with a large table in the center of the room, a book case at one end, and with chairs informally arranged.

One of the contributions made by the club was the compilation of rules of nomenclature known as the Lazy Club code. All of the "original eleven" have attained prominence and have perpetuated the ideals of its leader. Joseph Cullen Blair, M. G. Kains, Wendell Paddock, W. N. Munson, G. Harold Powell, H. C. Irish, Ernest Walker, Lodeman, Miller, Wyman, and Keating, a forceful group of students, were its original members.

CHAPTER VII

EVOLUTION. PLANT BREEDING. DEAN
OF THE NEW YORK STATE COLLEGE OF AGRICULTURE
AND DIRECTOR OF THE CORNELL
EXPERIMENT STATION

BAILEY's most effective horticultural teaching was in "the courses of evolution of cultivated plants, pomology, and in the botany of cultivated plants. During many years," Dr. G. N. Lauman has related, "the glory of the instruction in the horticultural department was centered in the course in evolution. In its day it was the most effective presentation of evolution given in Cornell University and attracted students from all colleges. By gradual and easy steps the student was led from the simple facts of variation to the most profound problems of evolution. Between a Socratic method of his own and a wealth of illustration especially physical, wherever possible, the student finished the course with a point of view, not necessarily that of the instructor, giving him a grasp of the conditions in the biological world as few students outside of this course attained. . . . The course in pomology was based on Professor Bailey's text book, but the skill with which the principles were instilled into the student was not a text book foundation, and the delights of the walks and talks in the orchards, gardens and laboratories and the excursions to other regions which came as a part of the laboratory work will never be forgotten by those who had the good fortune to be members of these classes. To the advanced and graduate student the course in the botany of cultivated plants was a rare treat. Not only did he get the theory and practice of systematic botany as applied to the cultivated plants but here in the intimacy of a small group the restraint of the class room was absent and the sketches of such men as Asa Gray or Edward Drinker Cope, the narratives of his own finds or the expounding of some philosophical conception in the field of biology made these hours unforgettable."[1]

In the summer of 1895 Bailey gave two addresses on plant variation and the origination of domestic varieties. These were delivered under the auspices of the American Society for the Extension of University Teaching, meeting at the University of Pennsylvania. Before a class in biology, he expounded on "The Fact and Philosophy of Variation," considering, first, seed individuals as distinguished from bud individuals and, second, causes of plant differences, to wit, inherent organic plasticity without any immediate inciting cause; *sexual* reproduction as a rejuvenative, reinvigorating factor making for modification of offspring;

[1] *Cornell Countryman*, II, 3 (December 1913), pp. 74-75.

and those variations arising from *asexual* reproduction by cell division and vegetative multiplication. He also considered the factors of the influence of physical environment—climate, food supply, effects of seed transfers in planting, multiplication of bud variations or sports, and the like. Bailey regarded the struggle for existence as itself a cause of plant differences. He denied that organic matter was originally endowed with the power to reproduce all of its corporeal attributes, maintaining that organic creation began with no definite tendencies. Tendencies, including the hereditary mechanism with *a* sum of environmental modifications, he argued, were developed as matters of necessity. He distinguished the developed propagation tendency in plants from the acquired characters of heredity and accumulation of vital energy. He addressed the American Philosophical Society May 1, 1896, on "The Factors of Organic Evolution from a Botanical Standpoint," saying:

I look upon heredity as an acquired character, the same as form, or color, or sensation is, and not as an original endowment of matter. The hereditary power did not originate until for some reason it was necessary for a given character to reproduce itself, and the longer any form or character was perpetuated the stronger became the hereditary power.

Unlikenesses, therefore, arise, and unlikenesses survive, ancestrally, and as physiological responses to stimuli. Rather than like begets like, similar produces similar. The marvel to Bailey was that nature exhibited so much rigidity of form. In an appendix article, "How Did the Varieties of Fruits Originate?" a part of *The Principles of Fruit-Growing*, he pointed to the inheritance of "certain type or family characteristics" observable. "Apples give rise to apples," he wrote, "and sometimes there is a closer reproduction of the parents in tribes like the Fameuse apples and the Crawford peaches; but there is seldom or never an exact duplication. . . . In other words, rigidity of generation may be the thing to be explained rather than the elasticity of it. In kitchen-garden vegetables this rigidity has come about, but it is the direct result of a long effort at selection and breeding until the elasticity of the type has been largely bred out. . . . There has been, to be sure, an occasional direct attempt to produce new varieties, but there has been very little definite plant-breeding of the type which sets an ideal before the mind and then tries to attain to it. . . ." In budded and grafted tree varieties, in cuttings and tubers, and the like, less variation appeared than in seed-propagated plants. "Yet," in his address, "The Fact and Philosophy of Variation," he noted, "we have seen that no two Baldwin apple trees—all of which are but divisions, more or less remote, of the one original tree—are alike, and now and then one branch of a fruit tree may 'sport,' or develop a strange bud-variety." Fruit trees take on new characters in "different geographical regions, so that the Greening apple is no longer the Greening of Rhode Island in the West and South." Potatoes "in ten years or less, become so mixed in their characters, through rapid variation and deterioration, that we must return to seedling productions for a new start. . . . The Trophy tomato is not the Trophy tomato which was introduced over twenty years ago, although it bears the old name and is a direct descendant of the first stock." Ninety-nine of every hundred varieties "which are habitually propagated by seeds, like the kitchen-garden vegetables and the annual flowers," showed this history. The permanent amelioration and improvement of the vegetable work was to be realized from man's skill and science, but since man "only rarely [was] the direct means of originating variations," his skill and science were "exercised in the selection and so-called breeding of the offspring, more than in the original genesis of the new form." In his article, "Variation After Birth," Bailey stressed that the "whole structure of agriculture" could be interpreted with reference to plant adaptations, those forced upon it by the life struggle and the physical conditions of soil, temperature, and moisture, and those in which more especially man played a part—tillage, fertilizers, pruning, and the like.

Bailey knew that the hybridist's greatest work was to develop specifically sought quantity and quality ideals. In the production of races, not varieties, of plants—as worthy as the variety was—there could be sought what would be termed within a few years "efficiency ideals." Science could make possible more increased plant yields, more improved plant qualities, changes in late or early ripening of the season, and specifically sought physical conformations. Nor did Bailey exclude production of plants which met regional requirements in respect to climate, altitude, soil, and other features; or, plants resistant to harmful insects, disease, cold, and other elemental destructive agencies. "The slow and repeated amalgamation or blending of types," said he, "is the consummation of plant-breeding. The production of a single hybrid which may be named and sold brings more present glory, but it is only an isolated fact. The best results come when species have been so completely blended that we cannot say which are hybrids and which are not."

In 1900, in a review of "Hybridization in the United States" for the English *Journal of the Royal Horticultural Society*, he pointed commendingly to the work of John Craig on the apple at Iowa Agricultural where S. A. Beach with his wide horticultural background and his creative scientific resourcefulness was also to do outstanding apple breeding for hardiness and quality just as he had done with the entire range of horticultural plants at the New York station at Geneva; to the work of Frank A. Waugh on the plum, first at the University of Vermont and later at Massachusetts Agricultural; to the work of Webber and Swingle in Florida on the orange and pineapple; to the original breeding in corn initiated as early as 1896 by Cyril G. Hopkins at the University of Illinois, a breeding for chemical—oil and protein—content; to work in maize also at Kansas Agricultural, and elsewhere; to the work in wheat of Willet M. Hays at the University of Minnesota, begun quite early in the 1890's, selecting plants at harvest and testing them by what was called his "centgener behavior" method (on other occasions Bailey included reference to Hays's important breeding work in flax for seed and fiber and height); to the work in cotton in Alabama and Georgia; to the work in strawberries at the New York station at Geneva; and to the work at Cornell in cucurbitaceous plants. Bailey did not omit reference to the salient Canadian work in many fruits, especially apples, under William Saunders and later, his son, Charles, and the Macouns, at Ottawa and other stations. Nor did he omit reference to the spectacular work along commercial lines being done by Luther Burbank at Santa Rosa, California, nor to the important contributions of T. V. Munson of Denison, Texas, who in 1905 was to report on "Improvement of Quality in Grapes," saying: "In two generations I have raised the sugar content of Scuppernong 40 to 50 per cent, greatly thinned the skin, reduced the seeds, increased the clusters and productiveness, without getting any susceptibility to disease. . . ."[2]

In Georgia under Dr. Stuckey improvement in this variety was to continue. "While the Grape has been the most prolific field of hybridization experience in the western world," said Bailey, "it is difficult to say what fruit occupies the second place in this respect. The most marked departures have occurred in the Plums. . . ."

The extended horticultural activity in improvement by cultivation, by selection, and by hybridization very much complicated the work in "horticultural botany" and "horticultural nomenclature." As L. C. Corbett reported some years later, "Horticultural nomenclature has become endlessly mixed because many of the horticulturists are not systematic botanists" and because horticulturists themselves, for commercial or other reasons, affix "high-sounding and catching names for plants in order to sell them. . . ."[3] Corbett pointed to the fact that when Bailey had begun to describe systematically the plums, finding only three or four botanically recognized species, he had been compelled to erect a number of new species and classify many varieties under new divisions. In 1897, as to the cultivated brassicas, Bailey had said, "The conviction is growing upon me that our manuals contain too few, rather than too many species; at all events, the miscellaneous dumping of Ruta-bagas, Turnips, Rape, and other plants into *Brassica campestris* is unnatural,

[2] *Proceedings of the Society for Horticultural Science,* 1905, pp. 19-24.
[3] *Idem,* pp. 40-45.

and therefore unfortunate. . . ." Similarly, when W. W. Tracy studied
the culture forms of lettuce, he found it necessary to describe distinct
sorts, many more than eight species recorded by botanists. The same
was to prove so in Irish's study of beans, in Waugh's studies of lilies,
and Beach's study of the apples of New York. Practically all horticultural varieties were in need of systematic study.

Bailey years before had seen what was needed—a *Cyclopedia of
American Horticulture*. This monumental task covered four large volumes, consumed many years in preparation, included the labors of a
multitude of correspondents and collaborators, and was under the associate editorship of Wilhelm Miller. The volumes were completed in the
first years of the century by the indefatigable Cornell professor of horticulture. Corbett, by then affiliated with the United States Department
of Agriculture, who urged its adoption as a nomenclatural model, saying:

> . . . It is my belief that in general we would be safe in following the
> nomenclature adopted in Bailey's *Cyclopedia of American Horticulture*.
> This work has the advantage of being new and up-to-date, and purely
> American. True, it does not go into details in all cases to the extent that it is
> frequently desirable for students of cultivated plants to carry their studies,
> but when it comes to the consideration of varieties, if one will take the
> trouble to search out the introducer and determine the name under which
> any variety was introduced, this will form a safe basis for the study of all
> cultural varieties. . . . In cases where botanists are in dispute over the
> correct authority, it would in my judgment be wise to follow the precedent
> established by Bailey in his *Cyclopedia*, and use both names so that no matter
> what the, final decision of the botanists may be the book or writing will
> stand the test of the decision. . . .

Obviously, horticulturists were not trying to displace botanical sys-
tematizations. But they were insisting that taxonomy and nomenclature
of cultivated plants be enlarged to include the whole of domestic varieties
susceptible of intelligible and orderly organization. "To the botanist,"
said the *Botanical Gazette*, "the *Cyclopedia* is a mass of most valuable
information, bringing together as it does, into available and properly
edited form, the immense contribution of facts from horticulturists to
the whole evolutionary doctrine, and enabling the morphologist to know
what form he is handling and what has been done with it. The work
should find its place in the libraries of all botanical laboratories as well
as in those of practical horticulturists."

About 1902, Bailey began writing correspondents and collaborators
with reference to a Cyclopedia of American Agriculture. On August 25
of that year he addressed a letter to Joseph Charles Arthur:

> I am now making the preliminary survey of the "Cyclopedia of American
> Agriculture" which is to be made in the nature of a popular reading treatise

on the subject. There is need for a work of this kind if comprehensive and well done. I hope to have the cooperation of the leading workers in the agricultural field and am, therefore, asking you if you would like to contribute to it. . . . We can offer a small honorarium of $4 a page for the work. This is not a large amount, I am aware, but we do not see how we can offer any greater remuneration. I am taking up the work, not for pecuniary profit, but as a labor of love and for the good of the cause.

For the *Cyclopedia of American Horticulture*, Bailey had not only secured contributions from the best known and most authoritative specialists on given subjects of horticultural significance. He had also engaged the services of outstanding authorities on the larger horticultural divisions. For instance, when it was found that Charles Edward Faxon's services could not be obtained for plant drawings, on Faxon's recommendation, Alfred Rehder, who had done pen and ink drawings for a flora of Germany, was engaged to write all the articles on hardy trees and shrubs. For almost two years—1898-1900—Rehder worked almost exclusively for Bailey. In addition, not yet having moved into his Sage Place home, Bailey set up *Cyclopedia* quarters in the university buildings where a large staff of teachers and students aided him and Miller in the work.

In preparing the *Cyclopedia of American Agriculture*, Bailey pursued similar methods. His aim was always to educate. He selected as his secretary a most promising agricultural college graduate, Albert R. Mann. Mann had been born in Pennsylvania, educated in the Pittsburgh schools, and completed brilliantly his college work at Cornell in three years. Together they prepared their cyclopedia to project an agricultural vision for the future. Agricultural possibilities seemed limitless. The great field of future agricultural policy was open to all students.

In the writing of the *Cyclopedia of American Agriculture*, Bailey was not being the research scientist but the interpreter. The *Cyclopedia* epitomized an interpretation of the American agricultural scene. It sought to improve and safeguard the human values of farm life. It sought to improve the living conditions of the farmer. The farm individual and the farm product were central. Agriculture was individualistic at that time. Group concepts developed with the maturing of the academic subject of rural sociology. But who paved the way for the rural sociologist and presented the farm problem to the nation?

When in 1907-1909 the *Cyclopedia of American Agriculture*, a popular survey of agricultural conditions, practices, and ideals in the United States and Canada, was presented in four volumes to the American public, one volume stressed the farm; another, crops; another, animals; and the last, the farm and community. Naturally, the work did not have the taxonomic importance the *Cyclopedia of American Horticulture* had. The latter contained "suggestions for cultivation of horticultural plants, descriptions of the species of fruits, vegetables, flowers and ornamental plants, sold in the United States and Canada, together with geographical and biographical sketches." Reprints and "new editions" were required almost every year for the *Cyclopedia of American Horticulture*. The *Cyclopedia of American Agriculture* also found immediate favor. The combined works interpreted in magnificent fashion the whole of the business phases, and many of the biological phases, of American plant science study. Never before had such colossal undertakings been brought to completion. Since agriculture and horticulture have enormously expanded during the last three decades, such accomplishments again will probably never be possible. To the worker in the history of American plant sciences, their biographical sketches are of much value. Moreover, horticulturists and agriculturists, even to the present, attest to the value and need of frequent use of these volumes. From the *Cyclopedia of American Horticulture* has also come *The Standard Cyclopedia of Horticulture*: a discussion for the amateur, and the professional and commercial grower, of the kinds, characteristics, and methods of cultivation of the species of plants grown in the regions of the United States and Canada for ornament, for fancy, for fruit, and for vegetables; with keys to the natural families and genera, descriptions of the horticultural capabilities of the states and provinces and dependent islands, and sketches of eminent horticulturists; illustrated with colored plates, four thousand engravings in the text, and ninety-six full-page cuts; all in six volumes, by Bailey, and published from 1914 to 1917.

About 1901 a Bureau of Plant Industry of the United States Department of Agriculture, an agency created to study plant life in relation to agriculture, was constituted. One of four bureaus organized in accordance with an act of Congress, it was to become the leading institution of its kind in the United States. Recommended by James Wilson, for many years the federal Secretary of Agriculture following J. Sterling Morton who had recently died, the congressional act authorized the bringing together of plant physiological and pathological investigations, botanical, grass, and forage investigations, work in pomology, and of the experimental gardens and grounds. During the year, by executive order, the work of the Arlington experimental farm, the investigations in domestic tea production, the work on foreign seed and plant introduction, and the congressional seed distribution were added, making nine branches of the bureau. B. T. Galloway was constituted chief of the new organization. Men of the highest caliber, in charge of the various branches, were associated with Galloway. A. F. Woods, who had taken charge of the Division of Vegetable Physiology and Pathology when Galloway had become chief of the Division of Gardens and Grounds on the death of William Saunders, continued as administrative officer in charge of vegetable physiology and pathology.

Woods became assistant chief of the bureau and, in his official capacities, supervised the work of the divisional laboratories. The men in charge of the bureau's branches were of unusual ability: Coville in botany; Corbett in horticulture; W. J. Spillman in agrostology; and with them in every section or division were a large number of able assistants and field and laboratory investigators. In pomology, the notable systematic work of G. B. Brackett, a nurseryman from Denmark, Iowa, and collaborator with Charles Downing in pomological study, had gotten under way. Brackett was a leading authority in the identification of fruit varieties.

Throughout this chapter, we will devote considerable attention to the work of the Laboratory of Plant Breeding in the immediate charge of Herbert J. Webber and the Laboratory of Plant Pathology in the immediate charge of Erwin F. Smith. Webber in 1896 had written,[4] "The improvement of plants by careful selection and fixation of variations, crossing, hybridizing, etc., while in one sense a well-worn field of practical investigation, is in another sense new and promising. The demand for novelties is constantly increasing, and at no previous time have results in this direction met with so ready appreciation. The diversification and extension of fruit and vegetable industries into new regions creates a demand for varieties adapted to various conditions. As the conditions are numberless, the field for improvement seems almost inexhaustible. No branch of horticulture or agriculture promises more important and remunerative results than may be attained by intelligent plant breeding. . . ." The following year Webber was constituted investigator in plant breeding at Washington. In July, 1899, he represented the United States Department of Agriculture at the first International Conference on Hybridization and Cross-breeding, held at London, England; and that year, being placed in charge of plant breeding investigations of the department, corn breeding to secure earlier maturity, drought resistance, resistance to smut, increased protein content, and increased yield, had been inaugurated. Another industrial improvement was sought in efforts to select and breed races of cotton with a longer and finer staple than those of the upland sorts. Webber's and Swingle's orange hybrids of hardier quality were being tested at a number of state experiment stations.

Smith, with the most exacting standards, was elaborating model research, which with every year brought increasing world renown to the Department of Agriculture. With almost a decade of experience in

[4] "Influence of Environment in the Origination of Plant Varieties," *Yearbook of the U.S. Department of Agriculture* for 1896, pp. 89-106, at p. 106.

bacteriological investigation, with fully a decade and a half of close study and experimentation in a wide range of plant pathological research, in laboratories equipped for these purposes, Smith had written and elaborated the results and conclusions at which he had arrived so effectively, particularly with reference to the comparatively new subject of bacterial plant diseases, that when in 1899 the Society of American Bacteriologists was organized, he represented the study of bacteriology in relation to plants. Nor was this the most important recognition. During this period was prepared a "Primer of Laboratory Work in Bacteriology," a mimeographed set of directions concerning apparatus, chemicals, rules and exercises to be utilized in learning how to perform technical investigations. Veranus A. Moore authored the work to which Smith supplied many constructive criticisms. Smith prepared for students, teachers, and experiment station workers an "Outline of Methods for the Study of Bacterial Plant Diseases in Use at the United States Department of Agriculture," and a few years later this formed a partial basis for volume I of his great work, *Bacteria in Relation to Plant Diseases*. American bacteriological texts for medicine were few; for study of animal bacterial diseases, even fewer; and for plants, none. Smith aimed to coordinate and apply in plant bacteriology the best research techniques, both principles and practice, thus far developed by authorities in animal and medical bacteriology. Gradually he interested leading medical schools, public health institutes, and state and municipal laboratories of health and hygiene in the new branch of bacteriology. He lectured before scientific societies, at the Marine Biological Laboratory, and elsewhere. His work was followed preponderantly and almost as a pattern in plant pathological study at state experiment stations, and stimulated plant bacteriological investigation not only in America but also in Europe where his controversy with Alfred Fischer of the University of Leipzig was silencing what doubt remained as to the existence of bacterial diseases of plants.

One of the first strong centers of plant pathological investigations established in an American department of botany was at the University of Vermont under Lewis Ralph Jones. Smith for many years had hoped to become a doctor of medicine. Jones, during his first years of undergraduate study at Ripon College, Wisconsin, had definitely decided to be a medical doctor. Going to the University of Michigan in 1886, however, he had been influenced by Spalding and Smith to devote himself to plant pathology. During the second semester of the year, 1888, Smith, although previously employed at the United States Department of Agriculture and commissioned to study and investigate the peach yellows disease, had charge of the microscopical laboratory at the University of Michigan. For a while, by reason of a failure to secure necessary appropriations, the peach yellows investigation had been discontinued. Smith had always wanted a graduate degree, at one time considering studying for one at either Harvard University or Johns Hopkins University. In the autumn of 1888, the University of Michigan again granted Smith leave to work in absentia for a degree, this time for a Doctorate of Science. Early in 1889, his peach yellows commission was renewed, special attention being directed to examining microscopically healthy and diseased tissue to determine, if possible, a parasitic origin of the disease; and the university faculty allowed this to be made the subject of Smith's doctoral dissertation. Jones was still at the University of Michigan when Smith's doctoral examination took place, and was invited by Spalding to sit with the examiners. "The glimpses thus given me of the significance of and opportunity for research in the field of plant pathology," Jones has written,[5] "were most inspiring. . . . In conference with my wise and revered counselor, Professor Volney M. Spalding, the decision to turn to plant pathology was promptly reached and never since regretted." In 1898, the University of Vermont gave Jones a leave of absence on salary of one half year every other year for study and investigation. "Plant physiology and pathology are what I am most after," wrote Jones to Smith, and Smith, after letters and conference, invited Jones to study with him, in his laboratory at Washington, the bacterial soft rot of vegetables. Jones accepted, and after six months spent in Smith's laboratory during the year 1899 and further study at the University of Vermont, Jones published his celebrated studies on the *Bacillus carotovorus*, in which he showed that the rotting mechanism was incited by the production of the enzyme, pectinase, which dissolves the middle lamellae of the cell walls of the host plant. Throughout the preparation of his publications on this bacteriological subject, Jones remained in correspondence and consultation with Smith.

This was but one study which originated in Smith's laboratory at Washington during this period. Smith's own fundamental and important research which took form in a number of publications issued from his laboratory at this time must be elaborated in another book. Suffice it to say now that the importance of Smith's laboratory research and accomplishments, in these and other directions, brought about the realization that the laboratory personnel and scope of the work should be increased. In 1899 the appropriation for vegetable pathological investigations amounted to $20,000. By 1900 the appropriation reached $26,000; by 1901, $28,000; by 1902, $60,000; and by 1903, $110,000.[6] Not the whole of these amounts went to Smith's Laboratory of Plant

[5] G. W. Keitt and F. V. Rand, "Lewis Ralph Jones," *Phytopathology*, xxxvi, 1 (January, 1946), pp. 1-17, at pp. 2, 3, 5.
[6] *Yearbooks*, for 1899, p. 670; for 1900, p. 636; for 1901, p. 614; for 1902, p. 664; the appropriation for 1903 is shown in the 1902 volume.

Pathology, officially established in 1901. These sums do illustrate, at least, the astonishing growth of awareness of the importance of plant pathological investigations.

Smith's Laboratory of Plant Pathology and also Webber's Laboratory of Plant Breeding were special agencies within the larger unit, the Bureau of Plant Industry. Practically all federally financed agricultural work was expanded during these and following years. Some idea of the tremendous expansions which took place may be gathered by observing that within a decade appropriations for the larger bureaus went from sums aggregating between twenty and thirty thousands of dollars to sums ranging in hundreds of thousands and eventually millions. Forestry provides an outstanding illustration. During these years there emerged into greater national prominence than ever before, the principal bureaus, not only of plant industry but also animal industry, chemistry, forestry, soils, statistics, the weather bureau, and numerous lesser divisions and offices.

Smith and Webber were prominent among those who between the years 1898 and 1901 helped to secure appropriations to finance adequate experimental field investigations to breed orchard fruits, cereals, tobacco, and other plants, to improve varieties, and to secure varieties and stock resistant to disease; moreover, to investigate the principles of plant physiology underlying these.

It is not the purpose of this book to deal with the work of each scientist who contributed to the upbuilding of the department's various bureaus and laboratories. In this chapter, we must confine ourselves to the work in plant breeding, and laboratory investigational work in plant physiology and pathology incidental to the larger intention of ameliorating the cultivated crops used by the nation. Accomplishments, and sometimes then only a few, of some of the leading workers must be chosen to illustrate the period's research trends and triumphs.

Plant work more and more became organized on the basis of industrial crops. At the outset, perhaps by referring to the work of Charles O. Townsend in the sugar beet industry, we may effectively illustrate the unity of purpose which grew between various phases of endeavor, notably in breeding activities and pathological research. Townsend was brought in 1901, largely through the efforts of Smith, into the Department of Agriculture from the department of botany and plant pathology of the University of Maryland. His correspondence with Smith, begun at least as early as 1898, shows that he was to conduct experimental investigations and economic surveys of the sugar beet industry throughout the nation. For a number of years, conditions within this and the tobacco industries had been objects of special attention on the part of department officials. In August, 1901, after spending some time in experimental laboratory study of sugar beet diseases, Townsend wrote to factories and growers in various sections of the country and elicited information concerning the industry and matters most in need of immediate attention. This done, he went west and studied diseases in the field. In 1899, in California, curly top of sugar beet (*Beta vulgaris* L.) had been recognized as a disease of alarming proportions. This disease, or one like it, had been studied by a number of scientists. Arthur had prepared a bulletin on the subject, issued by the Indiana Experiment Station, but a belief of a bacterial origin of the disease had not been conclusively established. This was so of a number of diseases now classed in the virus group. New discoveries in Europe did not reach scientists in America with the same facility in the 1880's and 1890's as later when more journals and publications came into being. Botanical journals seldom referred to plant bacteriological investigations, except occasionally by way of notes, since the interest in plant physiology and plant pathology was still subordinated to taxonomy. Furthermore, laboratories in America were not equipped either in apparatus or personnel to confirm or keep pace with the more advanced laboratories of Europe. Even then, not until it was shown by Iwanowski and Beijerinck that the agent causing mosaic disease of tobacco could be passed through a filter with pores so minute that bacteria present would be held back, did scientists have a way, or the means of knowledge, to differentiate virus diseases from bacterial diseases. Quite often therefore, virus diseases, as known today, were then ascribed to bacteria.[7] Curly top of sugar beet had an additional complicating factor—its transmission by the beet leaf hopper, *Eutettix tenellus* (Baker), and almost a whole decade of the new century passed before this knowledge was communicated formally. A considerable portion of the history of plant pathology in America would have to be explained, were we to attempt in this book a complete presentation of the scientific work done with this disease.[8] We may only suggest in outline form the notable development in plant pathological research which was foreshadowed during the first decade of the twentieth century, a part of which would include the differentiation of bacterial diseases from fungous diseases, and still later, differentiations of virus diseases from those caused by fungi and bacteria.

One of, if not the first, virus diseases studied was discovered through the work in plants.[9] Virus diseases, as such, in the literature of plant

[7] L. O. Kunkel, "Virus Diseases of Plants: Twenty-five Years of Progress, 1910-1935," *Brooklyn Botanic Garden Memoirs*, IV (May 7, 1936), p. 51.

[8] Should the reader be interested in procuring a presentation of this subject, reference may be made to Technical Bulletin No. 360, issued May, 1933, by the United States Department of Agriculture, prepared by Eubanks Carsner et al., and entitled, "Curly-top Resistance in Sugar Beets and Tests of the Resistant Variety U. S. No. 1."

[9] Simon Flexner and James Thomas Flexner, *William Henry Welch and the Heroic Age of American Medicine*, op. cit., p. 295.

pathology, were not definitely recognized until almost, perhaps after, the beginning of the second quarter of the century.[10] About the middle of the first quarter, a number of scientists (prominently in America: H. A. Allard of the Office of Tobacco and Plant Nutrition Investigations of the United States Bureau of Plant Industry; Ivan C. Jagger of Cornell University and the University of Rochester; S. P. Doolittle of Michigan Agricultural College; and within a very few years James Johnson; at leading research centers, (including the University of Wisconsin, the Missouri Botanical Garden, Columbia University), experimentally investigating mosaic and other diseases now placed in the virus group, studied the nature of the infective principle, its incubation and sources, distribution and effects in plant tissues, modes of dissemination and what plants are affected, its thermal death-points and overwintering, transmission to progeny, and other phases of full disease study. Early a conflict in interpretation between a parasitic and an enzymatic origin was indicated. As early as 1913, W. A. Orton, in a paper read before the American Phytopathological Society, referred to a mosaic disease of potato apparently similar to the mosaic disease of tobacco and tomato. Proof of transmissability of mosaic diseases of tobacco and cucumber was made available. But inability to cultivate the causal organism on artificial media, in other words, demonstrate the visible growth of a parasitic organism, created skepticism toward these diseases as a separable group, notwithstanding that Beijerinck in 1899 had confirmed Iwanowski's finding that the virus of tobacco mosaic could be passed through a Chamberland filter and not lose its capacity to infect, and furthermore, showed that within ten days the virus was observed to pass from the upper to the lower layers of an agar plate, thus giving rise to an inference of a living parasitic organism as the cause of the disease. More than this, Iwanowski observed and described cell inclusion bodies associated with tobacco mosaic disease, corpuscular bodies which since have been found in other diseases, by L. O. Kunkel and other workers.[11] Virus disease research was fortunate in having available the laboratory and field research techniques of fungology and plant bacteriology. When during the years 1905-1915 Smith presented

---

[10] The year is given as 1927 by Dr. C. E. A. Winslow, "The First Forty Years of the Society of American Bacteriologists," *Science*, n.s., XCI (January-June, 1940), no. 2354, pp. 125-129, at p. 127.

[11] L. O. Kunkel, "Virus Diseases of Plants," p. 53. See also, Erwin F. Smith, "Fifty Years of Pathology, pp. 35-36. See also, S. P. Doolittle and H. H. McKinney, "Intracellular Bodies in the Phloem Tissue of Certain Plants and their bearing on the Mosaic Problem," *Phytopathology*, XIII, 7 (July, 1923), pp. 326-329, and citing references to the work of Ray Nelson at Michigan Agricultural Experiment Station on "The occurrence of protozoa in plants affected with mosaic and related diseases." Bulletin 58 of the Michigan station, in which Nelson's article is published, was replied to by Charles A. Kofoid, Henry H. P. Severin, and Olive Swezy in an article, "Nelson's Spiral Bodies in Tomato Mosaic Not Protozoans," *Phytopathology*, XIII, 7, pp. 330-331.

his monumental three volume work, *Bacteria in Relation to Plant Diseases*, large sections of this dealt with laboratory technique and bibliography and coordinated a great deal of the work in plant diseases with progress made in animal and medical bacteriology. The comparatively new science of plant bacteriology, a part of plant pathology but distinctive in many particulars, was placed in organized literary form before the world, and focused attention upon the importance of studying the host plant as well as the parasite, functional physiology as well as morphology, structural changes induced by disease, and the environmental relations necessary to complete understanding of disease. In a few words, the efforts more and more were directed toward tracing diseases through stages in their physiological development, from their origins through their consequences.

During the first years of the century, five principal branches of activity dominated plant pathological research: spraying with fungicides; disinfection treatments by germicides and fungicides; eradication methods where no cure, control, or other preventive could be utilized; regional studies of cultural methods with regard to both soils and crops, especially with respect to the most advantageous schemes of crop rotation; and, last but not least, breeding disease resistant varieties. Research accentuated discovering introducible varieties and breeding resistant plants to root-rot diseases. Notable productions in cotton, cowpea, oranges, flax varieties, and tobacco, we shall see, were bred. It was realized that research in plant reproduction and heredity would promote effectiveness of the work in plant breeding and that studies of the life histories and ecology of principal crops were highly desirable. Fundamental physiological research promised to link diverging lines of research and supply needed unity in the study of plants and plant life as a whole; and to provide also new, profitable practical applications. Oscar Loew's studies of fermentation in the tobacco leaf brought forth the isolation of enzymes, made possible new methods to control organic action so as to improve the aroma of the tobacco product, and supplied the basis for a new industrial development. At the turn of the century, the concept of the enzyme in plant physiology, and plant pathology, attracted wide attention. It was believed that Albert Frederick Woods' study of mosaic disease of tobacco, attributing the disease to enzymic action, that is, to an inhibitory action upon the "availability of reserve food to the growing cells"[12] (starch hydrolysis and translocation), in-

[12] *Science*, n.s., XIII, no. 320, p. 246, reviews of papers presented at the meeting of the Society for Plant Morphology and Physiology, held at Johns Hopkins Medical School, Baltimore, Maryland, December 27-28, 1900, "Observations on the Mosaic Disease of Tobacco," by Albert F. Woods. The quotation is taken from a quotation from the author's paper, appearing in the abstract. The issue of *Science* is dated February 15, 1901.

duced by an excess of oxidizing enzymes, had brought into economic plant pathology a new group known as enzymic diseases, "an entirely new type of physiological disease."[13] At the turn of the century, too, definite light was being shed on pyocyanase, and the role and value of research in antibiotics.[14]

Nevertheless, selection and cross breeding experiments as methods to solve some of the more difficult problem of disease occupied and maintained leadership in field research. Not all projects produced the results hoped for. For example, Townsend in 1902 began selecting sugar beets for resistance to curly top. At that time, the relationship of the beet leaf hopper to the disease and its transmission had not been established, and his efforts were impeded for lack of complete knowledge of causation and spread of the disease.[15] Though in 1907 he reported progress, Townsend became convinced that until the real cause of the disease was known, that is, until the disease symptoms could be reproduced by inoculation with artificial cultures, "faint hope of solving the more important economic problem of its control" could be entertained.[16] The presence of bacteria, indeed of lesions or pockets containing bacteria, in diseased beets, was not sufficient, since inoculations with pure cultures of the bacteria yielded negative results. Decades later, after Lewis Ralph Jones had performed his brilliant piece of work, developing—by selection over a number of years and breeding of resistant plants—cabbages resistant to *Fusarium conglutinans*, Eubanks Carsner, his student, together with others working on the Pacific Coast, evolved a similar method of controlling curly top by producing the noted sugar beet resistant variety U. S. No. 1; and still later, an even more efficient variety, among a number of others developed.

Later in this chapter we shall consider the production of maize hybrids, the results of years of conscientious, brilliant research in fundamental plant genetics. Similarly, reference might be made to cane-breeding work in Java extending over more than twenty years, which produced yields of sugar per acre three times that of the canes of the original crosses.[17]

The first years of the century loomed bright for the future of plant breeding. "There is no reason why Americans may not develop as re-

[13] Merton Benway Waite, "Vegetable Pathology, an Economic Science," *International Congress of Arts and Science*, Universal Exposition, St. Louis, 1904, Houghton, Mifflin and Co. (Boston and New York: 1906), 1, p. 165.

[14] Samuel Epstein and Beryl Williams, *Miracles from Microbes* (New Brunswick, New Jersey: Rutgers University Press, 1946), pp. 62-68, in which appears a description of this, together with a historical study of the development of antibiotic research.

[15] Eubanks Carsner, "Curly-top Resistance in Sugar Beets and Tests of the Resistant Variety U. S. No. 1," p. 4.

[16] *Phytopathology*, v, 5 (October, 1915), p. 282.

[17] William Crocker, "Botany of the Future," *Science* 88, no. 2287 (October 28, 1938), pp. 387-394, at p. 4 of the reprint of the address.

markable ability in originating new varieties of plants and superior new breeds of animals," wrote Willet M. Hays in 1901, "as they have already displayed in inventing machinery and processes of manufacture."[18] He pointed to the fact that in Europe the sugar content in sugar beets had been increased 100 per cent in the last century. Hays found that in America already a pleasing list of accomplishments could be cited. He suggested a number of fields—sugar beets, timothy, field peas, soy beans, red clover, and alfalfa—where definite results in several directions were further to be expected. "Many thousands of new varieties of potatoes have been originated during the past few centuries," he wrote, "and as a consequence the potato crop has greatly increased in value. Varieties especially bred for large content of starch, to be used in the manufacture of starch and starch products, have recently enhanced the total worth of the potato crop." Corn breeding increasing yield and extending its northern habitats in the northwestern states and Canada, moreover, was regarded as of extensive importance; also, the Minnesota work in flax for height and length of fiber. More principal basic industries were involved. "The chief cereals, including corn, wheat, oats, barley, rye, and rice," wrote Galloway, "constitute nearly 50 per cent of the total value of all plants grown in this country." As to rice, he suggested that no more striking example of a new industry could be found than in its spread from South Carolina, Georgia, and adjacent states to Louisiana and Texas. Hays counseled that those "acquainted with the achievements of breeders of pansies, chrysanthemums, and violets can not doubt that plants are mobile in their characters," and that, under the hand of a master of the art of flower breeding, most beautiful colors and forms might be evolved.

Bailey was always in thorough sympathy with all moves to improve flower and vegetable crops. In the *Yearbook of the United States Department of Agriculture* for 1896, he himself had written on "The Improvement of Our Native Fruits," a plea to augment the amelioration of types already domesticated rather than introduce wholly new types. Of course, plant introduction work was of the greatest importance. But in order of importance, he urged attention to the grape; the plum; the raspberries, blackberries, and dewberries; and the amalgamation of western crab apples with domestic apples. A score of native fruit types, he said, cried out for improvement work—the chestnuts, pecans, goose-

---

[18] See Hays's article, "Progress in Plant and Animal Breeding," *Yearbook of the United States Department of Agriculture* for 1901, Washington, Government Printing Office, pp. 217-228; also B. T. Galloway's article, "Industrial Progress in Plant Work," *Yearbook* for 1902, *ibid.*, pp. 219-228. Attention may also be directed to an article by H. J. Webber and E. A. Bessey, "Progress in Plant-breeding in the United States," *Year Book of the Department of Agriculture* for 1899, pp. 465-490; also an article by B. D. Halsted, "Plant-Breeding and Improvement in our Experiment Stations," *New Jersey Experiment Station Report*, 1901, pp. 411-419.

berries, currants, cranberries, huckleberries, juneberries, cherries, mulberries, elderberries, and all the tribes of hickory nuts and walnuts. Best results should be expected "by working with the highly improved forms rather than with the original wild stock." No perfect all-around varieties were to be sought, because it was "becoming more and more apparent that it is impossible to combine all the varied and contradictory specific desires of men into one plant form. There must be a best variety for every particular use and locality and soil," he maintained. "The cosmopolitan variety must become more and more restricted in range and usefulness as time goes on and as more refined and specific needs arise." A wider range of variation was needed—more divergent and unlike varieties. However, too many experiment station workers conceived of their tasks as efforts to reduce the number when, as a matter of fact, what they might be doing was determining the merits of varieties for specific uses. The greatest effort, said Bailey, should be centered in preserving and intensifying those desirable attributes which are characteristic of the wild species, the attributes of virility and permanence. For quantity and quality production meant little without these.

Bailey seldom omitted reference to the values of historical and geographical study. "Most of the forms are random or chance discoveries," he argued, "and they show that the natural tendency toward progressive variation in the indigenous fruit species must be great, else the domesticated forms could not have reached their present state. If so much has been done by mere chance, so far as the horticulturist is concerned, there is certainly reason for believing that the rewards of plant breeding must some day be great."

This theme appeared in 1896, in his address, "The Survival of the Unlike," delivered before the Philosophical Club of Cornell and also presented that year before the American Philosophical Society in a triangular discussion on the "Factors of Organic Evolution" participated in by E. G. Conklin, D. G. Brinton, and Bailey, with general remarks furnished by E. D. Cope. Bailey deplored the comparatively little plant breeding being done, notwithstanding the fact that the evidence of breeding was to him the strongest proof of evolution. He said:

But the proof which appeals to me most strongly is the fact that gardeners and breeders have it in their power to make new forms and that they have been making them since man began to deal with plants and animals. The palaeontological and embryological records do not appeal to me with such force as the experience of breeders and gardeners, who for ages have been modifying plants and animals almost to suit their will. This, of course, suggests that I am not skilled in palaeontology and embryology; but have given more attention to gardening.

I assume you all believe in evolution. Heredity is not a necessary attribute of the theories of evolution. It is a matter for the physiologists and the embryologists to discuss rather than for one who looks broadly at nature and tries to discover some of the general and fundamental facts which have determined the onward progress of creation. . . .

Nevertheless, Bailey was familiar with the results of paleontological and paleobotanical researches. He had studied the writings of Gray on the subject, based though they were largely on the work of Charles Leo Lesquereux, Oswald Heer, Sir Joseph Dalton Hooker, and other investigators of both America and Europe. In general evolutionary thought, Bailey had been much influenced by Edward Drinker Cope and his belief in a constant, determinate, definite direction in evolution as opposed to the spontaneous variation school, in part that of Darwin and Wallace. The general Lamarckian assumption of the inheritance of acquired characters—an inheritance not only of direct but also indirect environmental action—were premises of Cope which influenced Bailey.[19]

In those years of much theory and finding facts to fit the theory, botanists were not altogether proceeding on the basis of facts first, and theories made accordingly. Nor were paleontologists for that matter. Confusion between the processes of ontogenetic and phylogenetic research persisted. Indeed, ontogenetic and phylogenetic study in American laboratories was not fully developed. More extensive research would point up new truths. Theories would be modified. Scientists, nevertheless, were doing magnificent pieces of work with the facilities at hand. Embryological investigations were penetrating the realms of undiscovered knowledge brilliantly. But it was still taking the results of European study and refining and revising the conclusions. A whole new view of life and its materials was being shaped. The work required the theorist and the man of practical experience.

Bailey had more than passing acquaintance with the most up-to-date paleontological literature. No one could understand intelligently the factor of climatic influences, for example, without having some knowledge of environic conditions in preglacial and postglacial times. No one could comprehend the involved theories of geographic plant distribution without knowing the productions of paleobotanic research, as immature and principally systematic as these still were.

For the 1894 *Yearbook of the United States Department of Agriculture,* Bailey wrote a "Sketch of the Relationship between American and Eastern Asian Fruits," a sort of horticultural counterpart of Gray's historic study which had been more limited to strictly botanical aspects. Bailey listed twenty-two species of fruits which had come from Europo-Asian areas; and twenty-one species from Eastern Asia, and commented:

[19] Henry Fairfield Osborn, *Cope: Master Naturalist, The Life and Letters of Edward Drinker Cope* (Princeton University Press, 1931), pp. 527-534.

The facies of the Japanese, northern Chinese, and Himalayan floras are strikingly those of our Allegheny flora. . . . We all know that the horticultural flora most resembling that of Europe is upon our Pacific Slope; there the European wine grape, the olive, the citrous fruits, the walnut, the fig, and the prune and raisin industries are already well developed. In like manner we may expect that in the course of time the horticultural industries of eastern America and eastern Asia will acquire the similarity of facies which the floras of these regions now enjoy. . . . The most promising field for horticultural exploration and for the study of the ancestry of our fruits is now in the interior of China. . . .

One of the reasons why study of plant antiquity and history was important was its bearing on the tremendous subject which evolutionary inquiry had opened anew. Heredity, viewed ancestrally and as transmissions of environmental modifications, was a question of the hour in plant breeding. Most effective methods of study could not be agreed on until, by more than experimental observation, some more exact knowledge of the mechanism of plant breeding, and the survival of modifications, was established. The essential inquiry still was as to the origins of variation in animals, but more especially for the horticulturist and botanist, the variety origins in plants. Concepts, found applicable in the study of animal variations, were not being found of the same significance in the study of plant variations. In an address before the Biological Society of Washington on January 12, 1895, on "The Plant Individual in the Light of Evolution," Bailey remarked, "If I were a zoologist, and particularly an entomologist, I should hold strongly to the views of Lamarck; but, being a horticulturist, I must accept largely, for the objects which come within the range of my vision, the principles of Darwin. In other words, I believe that both Lamarckism and Darwinism are true; and, in this connection, it is significant to observe that Lamarck propounded his theory from studies of animals, whilst Darwin was first led to his theory from observations of plants." Lamarckism, as Bailey defined it, was a functional hypothesis, while the Darwinian belief was selective. "It is important," said Bailey in an address in 1894 on "Neo-Lamarckism and Neo-Darwinism" before the Philosophical Club of Cornell, "that I still repeat Lamarck's belief in the transmission of a character obtained by any individual during its own lifetime, for this is the starting point of the definition of an 'acquired character,' concerning the heritability of which the scientific world is now rent. . . ." Current doctrine only can be indicated here. The reader, interested in the entire discussion, must be referred to Bailey's writings in full. After discussing Darwin's theory of pangenesis, a hypothesis, which, he said, had "never gained wide support," he turned to a third hypothesis, observing:

For the present purpose, we need consider but one other hypothesis of heredity—that advanced in 1883 by Weismann, which has given rise to the philosophy now called Neo-Darwinism. Weismann's point of view is interesting and unique. He places himself at the threshold of organic life, and contemplates what takes place in the reproduction of one-celled organisms. These organisms multiply largely by simple division, or fission. . . . In time, however, there came a division of labor—cells living together in colonies, and certain cells performing one function and certain other cells other functions. This was, perhaps, the beginning of the many-celled organism, in which certain cells developed the specific function of reproduction, or eventually became elements of sex. . . . There are . . . according to this hypothesis, two elements or plasms in every organized being, the germ-plasm and the somaplasm or body-plasm; and every organism which procreates thereby preserves its germ-plasm to future generations, while death destroys the remainder. A vital point in this hypothesis is the method by which the soma-plasm, or the organs and body of the organism, can be so impressed upon the germ that they shall become hereditary. At first it would seem as if some assumption like that of Darwin's might be useful here—that this germ-plasm is impressed by particles thrown off from all the surrounding or soma-cells; but this Weismann considers to be too unwieldy, and he ascribes the transfer of these characters through the medium of the germ-plasm to "variations in its molecular constitution." In other words, there can be no heredity of a character which originates at the periphery of the individual, because there is no means of transferring its likeness to the germ. All modification of the offspring is predetermined in the germ-plasm; and if the new organism becomes modified through contact with external agencies, such modification is lost with the death of the individual. . . . It is admitted that the continued effect of impinging environment may, now and then, finally reach the germ-plasm, but not in the first generation in which such extraneous influence may be exercised. In other words, acquired characters cannot be hereditary.

This was the point. Although Bailey believed the concept of the non-transmissibility of acquired characters unnecessary to a proper evaluation of Weismannism, answering the question whether plant unlikenesses in their characters survive, he had said as a *gardener*, who, like Darwin, had studied plants with his own eyes, mind, and hands: "Yes, verily! The greater part of the amelioration of cultivated plants has come about in just this way—by gradual modifications in the conditions in which they are grown, by means of which unlikenesses arise, and then by the selection of seeds from the most coveted plants. . . . The cultivated flora has come up with man, and if it has departed immensely from its wild prototype, so has man. The greater part of all this has been unconscious and unintended on man's part, but it is none the less real." On another occasion, he said: "It is not necessary to combat this philosophy, for we know, as a matter of common horticultural experience, that every change or variation in any organism—unless it proceeds from mere accident or mutilation—may become hereditary or be the beginning of a new variety; it is only necessary, therefore, for the Weismannians to assume—as they are always ready to do—that any variation which has become fixed or permanent has already affected the germ. Their assumption needs only another assumption to prove it, and, therefore, when we are considering merely plain matters of fact and experience, we need give little attention to the subtleties of this Neo-Darwinian philosophy." As to whether the "acquired character"—some variation acquired from environment in some period of the plant's life —arose in the first generation or accumulated in other generations, proof to answer was not available. What Bailey objected to was that part of the theory which said that the variation had to affect the reproductive substance to survive.

Bailey accepted Weismann's variability concepts but denied his theory that variations are the sole result of sex. "To my mind," he said, "it is a more violent assumption to suppose that [the] first unspecialized plasma should exactly reproduce all its minor features than to suppose that it had no distinct hereditary power, and therefore, by the very nature of its constitution, could not exactly reproduce itself. The burden of proof has been thrown upon those who attempt to explain the initial origin of differences, but it should really be thrown upon those who assume that life-matter was originally so constructed as to rigidly recast itself into one mould in each succeeding generation. I see less reason for dogmatically assuming that like produces like than I do for supposing that unlike produces unlike." Whether or not all progressive or permanent variation is the result of sexual union, Bailey urged strongly "that modification and evolution of vegetable species may and does proceed wholly without the interposition of sex—that is, by propagations through cuttings or layers of various parts. This proves either one of two things—that the germ-plasm is not necessary to the species, or else that it is not localized but distributed throughout the entire body of the individual . . . and either horn of this dilemma is fatal, it seems to me, to Weismannism. If the germ-plasm is not necessary to this reproduction, then we must discard the hypothesis of the continuity of the germ-plasm; if the germ-plasm is distributed throughout the plant, then we are obliged to admit that it is not localized in germ-cells beyond the reach of direct external influences." He pointed to the asexual or leaf-propagation of the begonia, brought to Weismann's attention by Strasburger, in which "plants thus asexually multiplied afterward produce flowers and seeds, or develop germ-plasm." He pointed to "sports," to isolated tree branches susceptible of propagation, to roots which continue to live although severed from the plant, moreover, reproducing its kind. Bailey believed that if the germ-plasm exists at all, it exists throughout the entire structure of the plant. "This conclusion—that the germ-plasm resides throughout the soma," he said, "is also unavoidable from another consideration: the fact that plants are asexual organisms at all time previous to flowering, and that the germ-plasm must be preserved, in the meantime, along with the soma-plasm." Illustrating the point, he asked, "Where does the germ-plasm reside in the sporophyte?"

Bailey did not deny the continuity of the germ plasm—a concept which today is regarded an established fact. But, as to its localization in the reproductive parts, he was in disagreement with Weismann. A few illustrations used by Bailey in support of his belief may be selected from a number:

. . . Asexual modification is not confined to domesticated plants. Any plant which is widely distributed by man by means of cuttings or other vegetative parts may be expected to vary in the same manner, as much experiment shows. . . . I need only cite a few instances of habitual asexual or seedless distribution of wild plants to recall to your attention the fact that such means of distribution is common in nature, and that in some cases the dispersion over wide areas is quite as rapid as by means of seeds; and some plants, as various potamogetons, ceratophyllums and other aquatics are more productive of detachable winter buds and other separable vegetable organs than they are of seeds. The brittle willows drop their twigs when injured by storms of ice or wind, or by animals, and many of these cuttings take root in the moist soil, and they may be carried far down streams or distributed along lake shores; the may-apple and a host of rhizomatous plants march onward from the original starting-point; the bryophyllum easily drops its thick leaves, each one of which may establish a new colony of plants; the leaves of the lake-cress (*Nasturtium lacustre*) float down the streams and develop a new plant while they travel; the house-leeks surround themselves with colonies of offshoots, the black raspberry travels by looping stolons, and the strawberry by long runners; the tiger-lily scatters its bulb-like buds, and all bulbiferous plants spread quite as easily by their fleshy parts as by seeds. Now, all these vegetative parts, when established as independent plants, produce flowers and good seeds, and these seeds often perpetuate the very characters which have originated in the asexual generations, as [in] the case of many bud-varieties; and it should also be remarked that these phytons usually transmit almost perfectly the characters acquired by the plant from which they sprung. . . .

Now, where is Weismann's germ-plasm? One of the properties of this material—if an assumption can receive such designation—is its localization in the reproductive organs or parts. But the phyton has no reproductive parts; or, if it has them, they are developed after the phyton has lived a perfectly sexless life, and possibly after generations of such life, in which it and its progeny may either have remained comparatively stable or may have varied widely, as the circumstances may have determined. If the sex-elements of any flower, therefore, contain germ-plasm, they must have derived it out of the asexual or vegetative or soma-plasm. And I will ask where the germ-plasm is in ferns. These plants are fertilized in the prothallic stage, the plant enjoys only one brief sexual state, and then the sex-organs die and wholly disappear. . . . Or, if the Weismannians can locate the germ-plasm in all these instances, pray tell us where it is in the myriads of sexless fungi! There is no such thing as continuous localization of the germ-plasm in plants!

Weismann himself admits that the germ-plasm must be distributed in "minute fraction" in all "somatic nuclei" of the begonia leaf. . . . It would seem that this admission undermines the whole theory of the localization of the germ-plasm in plants, for one exception in the hypothesis must argue that there are others. . . .

If, however, said Bailey, the theory of the continuity of the germ-plasm—the passing down from generation to generation of a part or direct offspring of the original germ-plasm—is true for plants, "this element must of necessity be intimately associated with every particle of the plant body, even to its very periphery, and it must directly receive external impressions; and this concept of Weismann—the continuity of the germ-plasm—becomes one of the readiest means of explaining the transmission of acquired characters." Bailey believed, presumptively, that the weight of evidence was against the doctrine that immediate influences are without permanent effects. Variations useful to the species live, and the harmful are destroyed, with the result that "newly appearing forms tend to become permanent, sometimes immediately." The longer the transforming environments are present, the more is the probability that the resulting modification will persist.

And whether the modification is directly visible in the body of the organism, or is an intangible force impressed upon the germ, it is nevertheless of an environmental character, and was at first acquired. If this is not true—that the changed conditions of life exert a direct effect upon the phylogeny of the species—then no variation is possible save that which comes from the recompounding of the original or ancestral sex-elements; and it would still be a question how these sex-elements acquired their initial divergence.

Bailey's concern was with the *results* of embryological and physiological investigation. Never once did he characterize himself as an embryologist or physiologist. His philosophy, constructed on the results of experimental investigation as far as such had advanced at that time, and tested by observation and experimentation in the garden and laboratory, was his own as every philosophy must always be. Its value, however, was tested by its leadership. No one in American horticulture voiced a more prevalently followed structure of beliefs. Scientists then, as they do now, held discussions. But, then as now, no one's position was so strong that his simple statement was tantamount to the expression of a law. Probably Gray's leadership was the strongest that America will ever know in any branch of plant study. Yet Gray insisted that all laws of plant life, all beliefs, all doctrine, be subjected to rigid experimental laboratory investigation. Probably Bailey's position of leadership in horticulture came nearer Gray's position in American botany than the position of any other American horticulturist. While Bailey has always insisted upon the maintenance of qualitative and quantitative standards in all plant science study, his energies, like that of every other leader, were spent in increasing the effectiveness of the American plant science laboratory. Bailey had always been more a man of the garden than the herbarium, more of the field than of the laboratory. Yet strong, efficient laboratory technicians have always been associated with him. Perhaps this was why he cautioned: "All these conclusions prove the unwisdom of endeavoring to account for the evolution of all the forms of life upon any single hypothesis; and they illustrate with great emphasis the complexity of even the fundamental forces in the progression of organic nature."

It was well that he said this in 1894. For a few years more and the tremendously important revelations of Mendel and De Vries would arrive on the American scientific scene.

To dramatize in fairly comprehensive measure the sudden and epoch-initiating appearance of the work of the studious monk, Gregor Mendel, and the scientific genius, Hugo De Vries, one should pay heed to the fact that in Bailey's book, *The Survival of the Unlike*, published in 1897, not a single important reference to any conclusion of either man was made. Similarly, in *Plant Breeding*—first presented in book form in 1895, translated into French in 1901, and containing the author's two lectures given before the class in biology at the 1895 meeting of the American Society for Extension of University Teaching, the still earlier 1891 lecture on "Cross Breeding and Hybridizing" (published in 1892 with bibliography), and a lecture on "Borrowed Opinions," based on writings of Verlot, Carrière, and Focke—Bailey made no reference to the stimulating researches of Mendel and De Vries, which were performed in quiet, unostentatious fashion over years in a cloistered monastery garden of Brünn, Austria (Brno, Czechoslovakia), and in the historic botanic garden of the University of Amsterdam, Holland. The reasons for this were plain—the researches were then not known.

It is, of course, commonly known that the seemingly embalmed paper, "Plant Hybrids," quietly submitted in the year 1865 and buried as part of the Proceedings of the Natural History Society of Brünn—the results of Mendel's classic garden experiments upon the common pea—lay, like a literary corpse, for thirty-five years, unnoticed except for a very few small allusions published elsewhere in Europe, and overshadowed by the great surging sweep of Darwinian evolutionary study. De Vries, however, was the discoverer who, almost simultaneously with two other botanists, C. Correns of Leipzig and E. von Tschermak of Vienna, brought forward in 1900 the staggeringly potential Men-

delian analyses—studies significant from the standpoints of both heredity and hybridization—and the story of De Vries's find was related in a
letter to Bailey: "Many years ago you had the kindness to send me your
article on Cross Breeding and Hybridizing of 1892; and I hope it will
interest you to know that it was by means of your bibliography therein
that I learnt some years afterwards of the existence of Mendel's papers,
which now are coming to so high credit. Without your aid I fear I
should not have found them at all." Bailey had not examined Mendel's
paper. His bibliographical reference had been culled from Focke's writing.

In 1902 a second edition of *Plant Breeding* was required by extensive demand. Bailey changed the text very little, but he again included
a bibliography, enlarging it and purposely confining it to literature
which English speaking horticulturists would be most likely to find. To
some it may seem strange that the text was not revised to incorporate
the new knowledge. They forget that for many years after publication
of Darwin's *Origin of Species*, Gray did not revise any of his texts to
include the theory of natural selection, and for a good reason—adequate
interpretation required years of further study and investigation. De
Vries himself had gone to Mendel's paper—not to evaluate the ideologi-
cal worth of a new writing—but to test the validity of some of his own
hybridization conclusions. There he found that Mendel had given to
the world a body of amazingly new and valuable theory and data.

Moreover, in making known Mendel's and De Vries's theories, some
two years were required for America to import adequately, intelligibly,
and generally, the Mendelian and De Vriesian results. In 1900 an abstract of Mendel's paper was made in England by William Bateson.
Soon afterward, the Royal Horticultural Society of England published
a translation of the paper. In 1902, at the Graduate School of Agriculture assembled and organized at Columbus, Ohio, by Dean Thomas F.
Hunt of the college of agriculture of the Ohio State University, an
organization having a membership of leading agriculturists of the nation, Herbert John Webber and W. J. Spillman (both of the United
States Bureau of Plant Industry, the former in charge of the Laboratory of Plant Breeding and the latter, a mathematician and former professor of agronomy at Washington State and then agrostologist of the
Bureau) lectured on this subject.

William Jasper Spillman, a graduate of the University of Missouri
and after 1894 a scientific agriculturist, was employed by the United
States Department of Agriculture as agrostologist in 1902, and in 1915
became chief of the office of farm management. An authority on breeding and heredity of plants, Spillman, independently and it is believed
while at Washington State College at Pullman, discovered Mendel's

law of recombination, or, at least, arrived at conclusions very closely resembling those of Mendel; sufficiently so that no less an authority in scientific agriculture than Dean Eugene Davenport has written that "he practically discovered Mendel's law." This was announced in a paper, "Quantitative Studies on the Transmission of Parental Characters to Hybrid Offspring," presented at the fifteenth annual convention of the Association of American Agricultural Colleges and Experiment Stations, meeting at Washington, D.C., November 12-14, 1901, and was published in Bulletin 115 of the Office of Experiment Stations, a report of the convention, at pages 88-101. (See "William Jasper Spillman," *Who's Who in America* xiv, p. 1790.) Substantially the same discovery has been attributed to Edward Lewis Sturtevant—a study on which he published while connected with the New York Agricultural Experiment Station at Geneva.

That Webber immediately should have come into prominence and been chosen as a lecturer was not surprising. During 1901, as a part of his work in charge of the federal government's laboratory of plant breeding, he had been carrying forward cotton breeding at Columbia, South Carolina, the work in citrus at Miami, Florida, and Santa Ana, California, and the work of testing and conducting selection experiments in Egyptian cotton at localities which eventually ranged from South Carolina to Arizona. The special regions of these years were in Georgia, Texas, and Louisiana, but these were soon extended to embrace Arizona, Florida, South Carolina, and other southern states. On August 31, 1901, Webber sent a notable letter to Albert F. Woods at the Bureau of Plant Industry in Washington:

Eureka Woods. I have two hybrids. First bolls opened today which if we can reproduce true in the 3rd generation will beat any Upland varieties known. Big Boll like Upland, small black seed, an abundant lint equal in quality to Egyptian or low grade Sea Island [cotton]. Just the type I have been working for and hoping for but which I feared was unattainable. Wish I could show you these cottons. You could see more cotton by coming to Columbia [South Carolina] now than you could probably see anywhere else in the World. . . .

The possibility of long fiber strains of cotton was almost beyond belief, and on September 4, Webber enthusiastically suggested to Woods many other "important breeding problems that [should] be pushed." Again, he wrote from Columbia, South Carolina:

We seem to be in luck down here this year. You have probably already received the specimens of Cow peas which I sent you this morning containing one resistant to Root Knot Worm [Heterodera nematodes]. This is no fake but a genuine out and out discovery which is a grand thing. . . .

On July 24, 1901, Webber had revealed he had laid out "crossing experiments in detail." Pleased that his cotton hybrids that year had turned out as he expected, valuable "from both Scientific and practical standpoint," he and his aides had selected "the best plants in many series and [were] inbreeding as many bolls of them as possible." While many were variable, in fact, the great majority "light fruited or sterile," many were "fine fruitful plants" and they were "inbreeding these as extensively as possible to get seed to plant isolated patches next year. If the fiber holds up on the fruitful plants this year," he told Woods, "we will know about what to expect next year." Their variety plats, for which he was indebted to Orton, he said, contained "about 60 races all of the standard sorts" and furnished a "good opportunity to study the varieties." Some disappointments had occurred. A field of two and one-half acres of Egyptian cotton and two acres of open fertilized hybrids had been drowned out.

But the new cotton hybrids of which he wrote in August, and the disease-resistant cowpea had overcome every disappointment. Excitedly he must have written Woods immediately, "You no need fear for the breeding work longer. I think we can soon fight our own battles." Webber was urging a $40,000 appropriation for plant breeding purposes. This cowpea, found suitable as a cover crop to be rotated with cotton, and also like the "Sea Island" cottons, resistant to wilt—together with the astonishing, new, experimental cottons—attracted nation-wide interest, enlisted the aid of Congressmen to help secure additional appropriations, furthered cooperative arrangements as to other crops with more experiment stations, and forwarded progressively the bureau's entire work.

On September 20, 1900, Thomas H. Kearney, Jr., assistant botanist of the division of botany under Coville, applied to Galloway to be transferred to the division of vegetable physiology and pathology. He would become one of Webber's assistants and by 1902 special attention was being given to procuring alkali-resistant crops. Kearney, for a time, helped make up the famous corps of agricultural explorers which the department sent to various parts of the world, including such celebrated names as Fairchild, Swingle, and Carleton, and Frank N. Meyer, a former gardener of Hugo DeVries in Holland. Other explorers were sent out by the department. Reference to them and their work appear elsewhere in this book.

Through the medium of plant introductions, the nation's agricultural economy was already enriched by such valuable additions as Jannovitch Egyptian cotton resistant to wilt and requiring a minimum supply of water to mature a crop; Turkestan alfalfa more resistant to drought, winter cold, and alkali, more able to grow and produce a crop with less water than the common strain; and, to illustrate the progress made with the more widely known introductions prior to 1897 when the department placed the work on a systematic basis, it was estimated in 1900 that "600,000 acres [were] planted to Kafir corn in the State of Kansas alone, and it [was] predicted that within ten years at least 2,000,000 acres [would] be grown annually in that State. It is probable," observed Jared G. Smith, chief of the section of seed and plant introduction, referring to the earlier introductions of Turkey wheat from Russia, the Washington navel orange from Brazil, and sorghum and Kafir corn from Africa and China, "that any one of these introductions has more than paid the cost of the whole work of the Department of Agriculture since its inception." Smith's article on "Commercial Plant Introduction"[20] analyzed the continent-wide, diversified, cooperative work of the federal department with the state experiment stations. Varieties of field pea, date palm, cacti, lime, vetch, vegetable marrow, clover, hay, rye, bean, brome grass, cabbage, eggplant, and other plants, were being tested to combat a plant disease, advance or delay the time of ripening fruit and prevent winterkilling, increase productivity, perfect form, improve quality or taste, and, in instances, establish or improve new industries. Superior wheats were being introduced from Russia, Hungary, Australia, and elsewhere; broomcorn millet, muskmelon, corn, and other vegetables; Turkestan alfalfa; oats, notably, Swedish Select, from Sweden; hops and barleys from Bavaria; squashes from Italy; fiber plants from Egypt; a silver ribbed chard, a superior eggplant, and a French variety of edible podded peas; soy beans, hemp, rice, and a new radish from Japan. Southern agriculture especially benefited. Already we have alluded to the importation in 1898 by S. A. Knapp of Louisiana of Kiushi rice which so expanded the rice growing industry of the middle southern states that within three years more than twenty million dollars was said to be invested in the crop. The introduction of Bermuda grass, the production of experimental teas under the supervision of Dr. Charles U. Shepard at Summerville, South Carolina, and the improvement and development of disease resistant field crops, not to exclude reference to the establishment of the Smyrna fig industry in California, were recognized for their worth. In the north, among the many progressively valuable agricultural extensions, the enlargement of flax culture and its utilization, may be noticed, as of this time. For many years the mutual cooperative agricultural interests of Canada and the United States had been recognized and cultivated. Now the department had begun to examine the tropics more intensively and extensively than before to locate products which might be grown in the United States—coffee, rubber, bananas, cacao, and, among other novel and valuable introductions already or to be attempted; the sisal industry had been studied not only as a part of programs to improve

20 Yearbook of the U. S. Department of Agriculture for 1900, pp. 131-144; also pp. 32-33.

the agriculture of our insular possessions, but with a view to its possible development in Florida. The study of tropical plant diseases was also projected. And, of course, the development of grass, forage and forest crops. By 1902, the future of agricultural research fairly glowed with bright promise. The more was this so because transportation conditions were more efficient. Cooperative research of the bureau of chemistry and division of pomology in refrigeration, cold storage, including objective inquiries in the chemistry of fruit ripening and methods to eliminate waste and disease of agricultural products in transit made every branch of endeavor seem more worth while. Plant breeding as well as plant introductions, therefore, were much encouraged. For, our economy at last was prepared to absorb and use each and every improved staple crop brought in, as well as many novelties and rarities. During the first years of the century, systematic efforts were contemplated to extend the geographical boundaries within the insular possessions of mangoes and alligator pears in cultivation. Crops, such as these, in the south, as the avocado in the west, were luxuries, even when purchasable. Each has its individual history. In the west, the extension of range improvement research beyond small experimental areas, of irrigation and land reclamation, and the introduction of plants in areas where cultivated crops had not thrived, gave promise that all the land of the nation would someday be in use, and a healthier, more amply fed people, with commensurate opportunities for livelihood would be made possible. A permanent, progressively flourishing agriculture was demanded.

As another corollary, it might be added that Webber was appropriately chosen to present courses of lectures at Iowa Agricultural College and the Graduate School of Agriculture, gathered in 1902 at the Ohio State University. Certainly he, who was one of, if not the, leading authority on plant breeding throughout the nation, was thoroughly qualified to present the theoretical and practical prognostications forwarded by the new knowledge embodied in Mendel's paper.

Again, in 1902—from September 30 to October 2—at the International Conference on Plant Breeding and Hybridization held in New York City with such distinguished guests as William Bateson, Daniel Morris, William Fawcett, and George Nicholson, much discussion of the new plant science theories took place. Papers were presented by leading American horticulturists and botanists including Bailey, O. F. Cook, W. M. Hays, S. A. Beach, T. V. Munson, William Saunders, and others. Bailey's subject was "A Medley of Pumpkins," which was later published as its first memoir by the Horticultural Society of New York. The paper contained an elaboration of his years of research at Michigan Agricultural and Cornell in cucurbits. The most important papers were those of Bateson on "Practical Aspects of the New Discoveries in Heredity" and of De Vries on the subject of artificial atavism. L. C. Corbett spoke on the "Improvement of Roses by Bud Selection," and W. A. Orton, "On the Breeding of Disease-Resistant Varieties." Said *Torreya* in its review of the meetings:

Naturally the work of the earlier hybridizer, Gregor Mendel, was repeatedly referred to and was the central idea of several papers, particularly those of Bateson and de Vries.

Professor Bateson presented his now well-known views on the nature of the sex cells, or gametes, and their relation to the segregation of inheritable characters. He showed, among other things, that hybrids with certain characters fixed arise by the union of equivalent gametes (equivalent as regards the character in question), to use his terminology such are homozygotes, and that, on the other hand, unstable hybrids are produced as a result of the union of gametes unlike as being bearers of the characters in question, or such are heterozygotes. . . .

Professor Bateson speaks of two subjects, but does not discuss them at length, which are the theses of a paper by de Vries, "On artificial atavism," namely, the resolution of compound characters and the reformation of compound characters through the combination of simpler ones. . . .

Generally speaking, the plant breeders had not taken advantage of the Mendelian theory in their work, and some of them did not know of Mendel or of his experiments before the Conference. . . . Although hybridization formed the theme of perhaps most of the papers, not a little of the work was based on selection alone, or on selection as an aid to hybridization. The experiments of Orton, for instance, by which wilt-resistant varieties of cotton, watermelon and cow peas were obtained, consisted merely in the selection of individuals which were not subject to the disease in spite of the fact that they were growing in fields where it abounded. Roberts, on the other hand, succeeded in securing improved varieties of wheat by a system of crossing combined with rigid selection, and the same is true of other workers.

Interesting instances of the improvement of varieties by means of bud selection were also given. Powell, for example, selected buds from the portions of apple trees which had superior fruit and used them as scions for grafting on more hardy stock. As a result of the third selection (generation) he obtains an apple which has the excellence of flavor of the earlier fruit to which has been added greater vigor and hardiness of the tree and greater uniformity of fruit. . . .

This review was written by William A. Cannon, one of the first American students to comprehend the full significance of Mendelism. Cannon wrote for another publication of the Torrey Botanical Club, its *Bulletin*, in December of 1902, a most praiseworthy study, "A Cytological Basis for the Mendelian Laws."[21]

[21] For another valuable review of these proceedings, see the *Experiment Station Record*, xiv, 3 (November, 1902), pp. 205-222. Walter H. Evans of the Office of Experiment Stations has abstracted the more important of the 50 papers presented. An abstract of Cannon's paper, "Cytological Aspects of Hybrids," is presented at p. 215;

From Mendel's studies, mainly in species of *Pisum, Phaseolus,* and *Hieracium,* especially from the uncontradictory and uniform studies with peas, great changes in points of view concerning the nature of varieties and hybridization came about. When Bailey finished writing on September 1, 1903, the preface to a third edition of *Plant Breeding,* he said, "In the present edition I have added somewhat to [the] bibliography (to the close of 1902), and have made some changes in the text; but the leading change is the substituting of new matter for the old Lecture IV," which was "Borrowed Opinions," based on the writings of Verlot, Carrière, and Focke. In its place was substituted, "Recent Opinions; being a résumé of the investigations of De Vries, Mendel, and a statement of the current tendencies of American plant-breeding practice." In this edition, it was declared that the time could not be far distant when the subject of plant breeding would be rewritten from a new point of view. Realizing the new effort was to produce characters or units and that it conceived of "plant-breeding as primarily a process," Bailey included in the lecture two addresses made by him, one, "Some Recent Ideas on the Evolution of Plants" delivered December 29, 1902, before the Society for Plant Morphology and Physiology of which he had become a member at its first annual meeting in 1898. The second address was "The Forward Movement in Plant-Breeding," read April 2, 1903, before the American Philosophical Society. The first essay, that is, parts thereof relating to the De Vriesian views was read and corrected in the manuscript by De Vries, who also supplied for the edition an article, "On Hybridization." W. J. Spillman, whose experiments in wheat—studies in wheat hybrids—were characterized by Cannon as "well known," supplied an article on "Mendelism in Wheat." Apparently, the plant breeders from the Bureau of Plant Industry were among the very first American students to become acquainted with and apply the theories of Mendelism.

Coincidentally, the first American model patterned after the work of De Vries at Amsterdam seems to have been a small experimental garden—about half an acre in extent—established in 1902 in the Bronx of New York City by Daniel Trembly MacDougal, then director of the

---

of Bailey's address, at p. 217; of Hays on "Breeding for Intrinsic Qualities," p. 212; of Bateson's address on "Practical Aspects of the New Discoveries in Heredity," p. 208; and at other pages reviews of J. B. Norton's paper on improvement of oats at U. S. laboratory of plant breeding; a résumé by William Saunders of forty years of Canadian work in fruit, cereal, and other crop improvements; C. E. Saunders on variation in the second generation of berberis hybrids; Burbank on plant breeding principles; Hansen on breeding of native northwestern fruits; H. F. Roberts on cereal breeding in Kansas; Munson on grape selection and hybridization; W. Van Fleet on hybridizing gladiolus species; Beach on form, color, and other characteristic correlation of plant parts; W. W. Tracy on varying tendency and individual prepotency in garden vegetables; and O. F. Cook on evolution under domestication.

laboratories of the New York Botanical Garden. There, and in the larger gardens of the New York botanical institution, he sought, by his own efforts, and the aid of other botanists of eminence, to confirm and further the experimental inquiries of De Vries as well as conduct researches of his own. Finally, with his editing of an important series of lectures delivered by De Vries on occasion of his first American visit in 1904, *Species and Varieties* (1905), MacDougal placed squarely before the American public—some say for the first time clearly—the new theory of an origin of species by mutation.

For almost twenty years, De Vries had been working in comparative secrecy, studying hybridization of plants. Phenomena, characterized under the more inclusive concept "mutability," fascinated him, as for years the work, and this interpretative concept, had influenced Bailey. In 1895 Bailey gave expression to his belief that in plants "natural selection is the chief agent of progression," and that all theories of evolution seemed to teach that "the final result of our domestication of plants [would] come as a result of unobtrusive forces working slowly through the years, not from summary and brilliant creations. . . ." This, however, did not imply an intention to discourage the most ambitious efforts in plant breeding. Rather, it was an interpretation of the broad subject of evolutionary understanding. The study of "sports" in plants —accidental changes attributed to unknown causes and not clearly understood in Darwin's time—provided a practical and profitable source of academic perusal of contrasting elements. Sometimes found developing in a useful direction, these formed the bases of new plant races and new varieties. Individual differences in plants were always present. When discovered to usable advantage, these, too, supplied sources of new plant creations. These could be selected, accumulated, and heaped up until a new race was created from the original plant strain. De Vries, moreover, was exploring yet another method of species-origination, one which heightened discussion. No distinct examples were at hand of "mutations," a name applied even before Darwin's time to sudden and accidental changes of one species into another. For instances of these, he had searched not only in Europe but also other countries and found one, *Oenothera Lamarckiana*, or "Lamarck's evening primrose," which he believed should lead the way of a new mode of scientific research.

One of the weightiest objections to Darwin's theory of species-origin by natural selection, by slow and gradual changes, had been the large discrepancy between concepts of the "gradual evolutionists" as to the time range of evolutionary development from its beginning to the appearance of man, and concepts of the same nature formulated from evidence of physicists and astronomers. It was the incompatibility of results concerning the age of life on this earth, as propounded by physicists and astronomers, and the demands made by the theory of descent, that had given opponents of evolution a real weapon. De Vries described the issue clearly:

The deductions made by Lord Kelvin and others from the central heat of the earth, from the rate of the production of the calcareous deposits, from the increase of the amount of salt in the water of the seas, and from various other sources, indicate an age for the inhabitable surface of the earth of some millions of years only. The most probable estimates lie between twenty and forty millions of years. The evolutionists of the gradual line, however, had supposed many thousand of millions of years to be the smallest amount that would account for the whole range of evolution, from the very first beginning until the appearance of mankind.

De Vries said, therefore, that something more than the evidence of natural selection was needed to explain the origin of species. There were, to be sure, the evidences of sudden changes. "Color changes in flowers, double flowers, regular forms from labiate types, and others," said De Vries in an address at the University of Chicago, "have been produced more or less at will in my garden, and under conditions which allowed of a close scientific study. The suddenness of the changes and the perfection of the display of the new characters from the very beginning were the most striking results." Horticulturally, however, these experimental forms, these phenomena, had been known always. "They threw light," said he, "upon the way in which cultivated plants usually produce new forms, but between them and the real origin of species in nature the old gap evidently remained." Darwin had only supplied an analogy of "sports." But, said De Vries:

If such strains can be proved to offer a better analogy to real systematic species, and if the sudden changes can be shown to occur in nature as well as they are known to occur in the cultivated condition, then in truth Darwinism can afford to lose the individual variations as a basis. Then there will be two vast dominions of variability, sharply limited, and sharply contrasted with one another. One of them will be ruled by Quetelet's law of probability, and by the unavoidable and continuous occurrence of reversions.

Cope in America had been most prominent in placing Darwin's theory of descent on an even firmer foundation. But what of natural selection? De Vries did not conceive of himself as substituting a new conception or idea for the old. He did believe that he had opened the door whereby no longer the origin of species was to be regarded "as something beyond our experience. It reaches within the limits of direct observation and experiment. Its only real difficulty is the rarity of its occurrence; but this," he concluded, "may be overcome by persevering research. Mutability is manifestly an exceptional state of things if compared with the ordinary constancy. But it must occur in nature here and there, and probably even in our immediate vicinity. . . . New lines of work and new prospects will . . . be opened, and the application of new discoveries and new laws of forage crops and industrial plants will largely reward the patience and perseverance required by the present initial scientific studies." In other words, the study of the origin of species was to become an exact experimental science. Genetic differences in plants were to be closely studied.

It was Bailey's opinion that the production of unit characters by breeding rather than the production of varieties, the production of races of plants rather than novelties—as important as varieties and novelties still were—was the new plant breeding. As for the study of the origin of species as an exact experimental science, Bailey years before had observed the rarity of hybridization in nature. In an address before the State Board of Agriculture of New Jersey on January 16, 1895, "Some of the Bearings of the Evolution-Teaching upon Plant Cultivation," he had said:

Hybridization is normally rare. Nature rarely does things by jumps. There is no proof that she ever made a species or a potent form in this way. But she mildly crosses one species with itself, and out of the slightly variable offspring selects those which are best adapted to the place in which they live, and uses them for the subjects of another congenial cross; and so the family marches on from generation to generation, each step slow but each one sure. If man makes hybrids, he must generally propagate them by buds, or parts other than seeds, to keep them "true," as in the few hybrid grapes, pears, raspberries and blackberries which we have and in various hybrid ornamental plants; and as a rule these varieties are less adapted to wide ranges of conditions than are those which spring from legitimate sources. Change of seed and crossing between the different stocks are far more important agencies of the evolution of our field crops than hybridization or other forced effects. . . .

He had also maintained that "all sudden and spasmodic attempts at the amelioration of the vegetable kingdom" were discouraged by evolutionary understanding; yet, within five years, De Vries was announcing the discovery of a sudden origination of Oenothera species by mutation. De Vries had not proceeded on the basis of cytological investigation. Like Bailey, he, too, had been a man of the garden. So had Mendel, for that matter.

In 1902, in his address, "Some Recent Ideas on the Evolution of Plants," incorporated in subsequent editions of *Plant Breeding*, Bailey gave expression to his reactions to De Vriesian claims:

It will now be seen that the mutation theory of DeVries, which is in some respects a rephrasing and an extending of the old idea of sports, does not of itself introduce any new theory of the dynamics of evolution. It is not a theory of heredity nor of variation. His hypothesis of "intracellular pangenesis" carries the explanation of these phenomena one step further back, however. The plant cells give off pangenes. Each of these pangenes divides into two. Ordinarily, these two resemble the parent; but now and then one of them takes on a new character—the two become unlike—and gives rise to a mutation. This hypothesis, like Darwin's pangenesis, is useful as a graphic basis for discussion, whether or no it has real physiological foundation.

The most emphatic points of the mutation theory as they appeal to me are these: (1) It classifies variation into kinds that are concerned in evolution and kinds that are not; and thereby it denies that all adaptation to environment makes for the progress of the race. (2) It denies the power of natural selection to fix, to heap up, or to augment differences until they become truly specific. (3) It separates the results of struggle for existence and survival of the fittest into two categories, only one of which has an effect on phylogeny. (4) It asserts that evolution takes place by steps, and not by a gradual unfolding of one form into another—that it is discontinuous rather than continuous. (5) It enforces the importance of critical comparative study of great numbers of individuals. (6) It challenges the validity of the customary conception of species as competent to elucidate the method of evolution. . . .

From an argumentative point of view, it will be difficult to determine, in a given case, just what are variations and what mutations, for these categories are separated not by any quantitative or qualitative characters— the "step" from one to the other may be ever so slight—but by the test that one kind is fully heritable and the other only partially so. If a mutation is to be defined as a heritable form, then it will be impossible to controvert the doctrine that evolution takes place by mutation, because the mutationist can say that any form that is inherited is by that fact a mutation. This will be equivalent to the position of those who, in the Weismannian days, denied the transmission of acquired characters, but defined an acquired character to be one that is not transmissible. However, it is to be hoped that the discussion of the mutation theory will not degenerate into a mere academic debate and a contention over definitions. Professor de Vries himself has set the direction of the discussion by making actual experiments the test of the doctrine. . . . DeVries's work will have a profound and abiding influence on our evolution philosophies. For myself, I am a Darwinian, but I hope that I am willing to believe what is true, whether it is Darwinian or anti-Darwinian. My own belief is that species do originate by means of natural selection, but that not all species so originate.

In 1906, in Bailey's new lecture, "Current Plant-Breeding Practice," contributed to the fourth edition of *Plant Breeding*, he advised his readers:

It matters not whether the breeder is Darwinian or DeVriesian, the methods are practically the same. Even if varieties are mutants, as DeVries supposes—forms small or great that originate full-fledged—we may still need to practice selections as between mutants; and if any varieties turn out to be amenable to further separation by means of selection, it only proves that these particular forms are not mutants. If a form is so well marked and so valuable and so constant that it needs no selection, then the breeder may rejoice that his task is so easy, and he should have sufficient time and enthusiasm left to cause him to desire to repeat the experience. Howbeit, if the plant-breeder's realm lies with plants that he must propagate by means of seed, selection is usually the one essential to success.

Mendelism embraced two ideas or theories: one, hybridizational, involving the famous "3 to 1 ratios" on which were predicated production in successive generations of character units—tallness or dwarfness, smoothness or wrinkles, vigor or weakness, color qualities, and the like —and with which breeding objectives could be correlated; and, second, a theory of heredity which probably Mendel did not plan intentionally. Mendel's aims seem to have been to study plant hybrids and learn the parental contributions made in different generations to their progeny. However, on discovery of Mendel's paper, Bateson, Saunders, and others were quick to seize on the heredity theory. Bailey quoted their epitome of it, and commented:

Mendel's law of heredity is recently stated as follows by Bateson and Saunders: "The essential part of the discovery is the evidence that the germ-cells or gametes produced by cross-bred organisms may in respects of given characters be of the pure parental types and consequently incapable of transmitting the opposite character; that when such pure similar gametes of opposite sexes are united together in fertilization, the individuals so formed and their posterity are free from all taint of the cross; that there may be, in short, perfect or almost perfect discontinuity between these germs in respect of one of each pair of opposite characters."

This, in barest epitome, is the teaching of Mendel. This teaching strikes at the root of two or three difficult and vital problems. It presents a new conception of the proximate mechanism of heredity, although it does not present a complete hypothesis of heredity since it begins with the gametes after they are formed and does not account for the constitution of the gametes, nor the way in which the parental characters are impressed upon them. This hypothesis will focus our attention along new lines, and I believe will arouse as much discussion as Weismann's hypothesis did; and it is probable that it will have a wider influence. Whether it expresses the actual means of heredity or not it is yet much too early to say; but this hypothesis is a greater contribution to science than the so-called "Mendel's law" as to the numerical results of hybridization: the hypothesis attempts to explain the "law."

Cannon described the essential conception of Mendel in his article on "A Cytological Basis for the Mendelian Laws":

When one pure form (*A*) is crossed with another form (*a*) the hybrid of the primary cross shows the *A* characters only. When, however, the hybrid plants of this generation are fertilized among themselves and produce offspring the *a* characters are first seen, and in a definite proportion to the form bearing the *A* characters. These constitute the hybrids of the second generation. If now the hybrids of the second generation are fertilized in such a manner that plants with *a* characters are crossed with those bearing the same characters, and likewise plants bearing the opposing characters with forms like themselves, the resulting hybrids will behave in a manner characteristic of the respective cross. That is (1) The plants with *a* characters will be found to transmit those characters only, i.e., they are "fixed"; and (2) When the plants with *A* characters are fertilized with other plants with the same characters, that is to say, if inbred, two sorts of hybrids will result: one portion will bear only the *A* characters, which may be demonstrated by inbreeding as before, and one portion, apparently also with *A* characters only, will be found to vary just as the hybrids of the primary cross varied, i.e., this portion is really mixed or hybrid. The hybrids that bear the *a* characters are known as the "recessives"; they do not appear in the first generation, and those with the *A* characters are called the "dominants," and they mask in the first generation the recessives. . . .

Cannon pointed out that not only do hybrids vary in a regular manner but there is also a definite proportion of *a*'s or recessives, and *A*'s or dominants. That is, in the second generation one-fourth of the offspring is recessive and three-fourths apparently dominant only, "but really composed," said Cannon, "of the two sorts $(A(a))$ one third of these being dominant (pure), and two thirds mixed $(A(a))$. The latter continue in the succeeding generation to vary just as the hybrids of the primary cross varied, i.e., one fourth of their off-spring bearing recessive, one fourth bearing dominant characters, and one half being both dominant and recessive." There were other complexities of the theory. But for purposes of this book, the fact that two laws—the "law of dominance" and the law of the "splitting of the hybrid race"—were formulated is sufficient. Cytology would immediately interest itself in the second law. Breeders and geneticists would examine carefully the workings of the first law.

Bailey said, "Mendel's work is important because it cuts across many of the current notions respecting hybridization. As De Vries's discussions call a halt in the current belief regarding the gradualness and slowness of evolution, so Mendel's call a halt in respect to the common opinion that the results of hybridizing are largely chance, and that hybridization is necessarily only an empirical subject. Mendel found uniformity and constancy of action in hybridization. . . ." Bailey realized that Mendel regarded hybridization a "complex and intricate subject," and agreed, "that if we are ever to discover laws, we must begin with the simplest and least complicated problems." He regarded important the fact that real morphological units were made available. He urged that study proceed as to how far Mendel's law applied—explaining away exceptions, if possible, and finding the law's place in the evolutionary scheme. Which plants would "Mendelize," and which would not, must be found. Of course, he saw the effect the theory had on the taxonomic idea of species as a basis of study. "The experimental method has finally been completely launched and set under way," he concluded. "Laboratory methods, comparative morphology, embryological recapitulation, life-history studies, ecological investigations—all these means are likely to be overshadowed for a time by experiments in actually growing the things under conditions of control." Statistical methods were to be employed but he looked with skepticism on the wild prophecies that all breeding practice would be reduced to mathematical precision—at least, such views found him waiting for proof. "My own feeling," he said, "is that the greatest benefit of Mendel's work to the plant-breeder will be in improving the methods of experimenting. We can no longer be satisfied with mere 'trials' in hybridizing: we must plan the work with great care, have definite ideals, 'work to a line,' and make accurate and statistical studies of the separate marks or characters of plants. His work suggests what we are to look for. . . . Beyond this I do not see how the original Mendelian results will greatly modify our plant-breeding practice." In 1903, writing on "The New Ideals in the Improvement of Plants" for *Country Life in America*, he summarized:

The modern methods of plant breeding demand, first, that the breeder shall familiarize himself thoroughly with the characteristics of the group of plants with which he is to work. He must have very specific and definite knowledge of what makes the plant valuable and what its shortcomings are. Then he must secure, as starting points, plants that give promise in the desired direction. Thereafter his skill will be taxed in selecting along responsive lines, in making accurate and significant statistical measurements, in devising workable systems of testing. He must grow large numbers of plants, if he is working with farm crops, in order to multiply his chances of securing desirable variations and to minimize the errors.

That same year, in June, he appeared before the American Association of Nurserymen meeting at Detroit and discussed "The Whole Question of Varieties." The transition from seedling propagation to graft propagation, he said, had been important for every tree fruit. It had, recently, marked the rise of the orange industry in Florida. The work in grains in Illinois and Minnesota, the work of the United States Bureau of Plant Industry in cotton, citrus, apples, pineapples, oats, tobaccos, and other crops, in fact, all theoretical breeding that made for efficiency and practical ideals—producing lines of plants "having superior efficiency for some specific purpose"—and not the production or introduction of new varieties, was to make possible the "new agriculture." The new order would arrive as a result "of greater and better crop yield and greater and better animal production," combining, also, better care. Incidentally, the trades and horticulture itself would, likewise, benefit. "I believe," said Bailey, "the time has come when nurserymen must cease to propagate indiscriminately from stock merely because it belongs to a given variety. He should propagate only from stock or trees that he knows to have direct merit for efficiency."

The basic work of Mendel, Weismann, and De Vries, built upon the fundamentals revealed by Koelreuter, Knight, Naudin, Vilmorin, Van Mons, Darwin, Wallace, and others, gave rise to the development of a scientific agriculture and horticulture. Moreover, the work laid the foundation for the evolution of the immensely important adjunct to plant breeding; namely, plant genetics. Genetics, as a formally organized branch of science, was not accorded substantial recognition until about the year 1906—at the International Conference on Genetics which met in London in the summer of that year—although three years earlier in America a committee of the American Association of Agricultural Colleges and Experiment Stations invited those interested to meet and discuss problems in the "Improvement of Plants and Animals and in Studies Related to Breeding." From a gathering in St. Louis held in conjunction with the American Association for the Advancement of Science there was organized the American Breeders' [Genetic] Association which met again at the University of Illinois.

A theory that genetics as a formal science in America originated with the plant breeding work of the United States Department of Agriculture is not without some justification. Plant breeding became much more than a practical art and improved its scientific stature brilliantly during the years 1892-1906 under scientific scholars not only of the federal government but also of the state experiment stations and their extension work with many individual breeders of plants. A leadership in this regard of the United States Department of Agriculture is somewhat indicated by the fact that Herbert J. Webber was asked to speak on this subject at the International Conference of 1906. He had attended the first International Conference of 1899, also held in England, and, of course, many leading American scientists had been honored at the second conference held in the United States and already considered in this book. William Bateson, believed by Erwin F. Smith to be England's "most outstanding figure in Genetics and experimental evolution," has described the transitional years between the first and third conferences in his inaugural address, "The Progress of Genetic Research,"[22] delivered at the 1906 Conference:

It is just seven years since, on the hottest day of a very hot summer, the first Conference devoted to Hybridisation and Plant-breeding assembled at Chiswick. Looking back on that occasion we realise what some of us even then suspected that we were concerned in a remarkable enterprise. No such conference had taken place before, and our proceedings were of the nature of experiment. That definite results might come from that beginning we

[22] Report of the Third International Conference 1906 on Genetics; Hybridisation (The Cross-Breeding of Genera or Species), The Cross-Breeding of Varieties, and General Plant-Breeding, edited by Rev. W. Wilks, secretary, and printed for the Royal Horticultural Society, 1907, pp. 90-91.

Erwin F. Smith in His Laboratory, 1895

naturally hoped, but of those who endured the heat of that stifling marquee, or inspected the plants exhibited in that tropical vinery, not one, I suppose, anticipated that in less than a decade we should have such extraordinary progress to record. The predominant note of our deliberations in 1899 was mystery. In 1906 we speak less of mystery than of order.

When formerly we looked at a series of plants produced by hybridisation we perceived little but bewildering complexity. We knew well enough that behind that complexity, order and system were concealed. Glimpses indeed of pervading order were from time to time obtained, but they were transient and uncertain. As casual prospectors we picked up occasional stray nuggets in the sand, but we had not located the reef, nor had we any machinery for working it if discovered.

Then came the revelations of Mendel's clue, with all the manifold advances in knowledge to which it has led. The most Protean assemblage of hybrid derivatives no longer menaces us as a hopeless enigma. We are sure that even the multitudinous shapes of the cucurbits, or the polychromatic hues of orchids—though they may range from one end of the spectrum to the other—would yield to our analysis. Methods for grappling even with these higher problems have been devised. The immediate difficulties are chiefly of extension and application. Thus the study of hybridisation and plant-breeding, from being a speculative pastime to be pursued without apparatus or technical equipment in the hope that something would turn up, has become a developed science, destined, as we believe, not merely to add new regions to man's knowledge and power, but also to absorb and modify profoundly large tracts of the older sciences.

As a name for the new science which was "devoted to the elucidation of the phenomena of heredity and variation: in other words, to the physiology of Descent, with implied bearing on the theoretical problems of the evolutionist and systematist, and application to the practical problems of breeders, whether of animals or plants," he suggested "the term *Genetics.*"

Urgent Departmental work in the United States prevented Webber from attending the International Conference of 1906. Erwin F. Smith was in Europe that year studying plant pathological research at leading laboratories and gardens of the continent, and he was delegated to address the conference in Webber's stead on the subject, "Plant Breeding in the United States Department of Agriculture."[23]

Many honors had been Smith's in recent years. At the seventh annual meeting of the Society of American Bacteriologists, held at the University of Michigan December 28-29, 1905, he had been elected president for the ensuing year. Previous to that, he had served as chairman of Section G, Botany, of the American Association for the Advancement of Science. Smith had been asked to represent plant pathology at

[23] *Idem.* pp. 301-309, also printed separately, pp. 301-309. An important address was presented by Sir Rowland Biffen on wheat breeding experiments in England. A rust-resistant variety, and some products of sugar cane breeding by selection and hybridization, also explained, appealed to Smith as of practicable use in the United States. These topics will be more fully discussed in a biography of Smith.

the 1904 International Congress of Arts and Science, at the Universal Exposition held in St. Louis. This he declined. On January 1, 1902, he had spoken on "Plant Pathology: a Retrospect and Prospect." He was requested to name "three or four men eminent in this line who might be asked to deliver the address in question." Arthur and Waite presented addresses, one from the historical, the other from the economic, vantage points.

Smith in his address before the 1906 International Conference on Genetics discussed, showing evident familiarity and breadth of knowledge, four principal types of plant breeding: (1) for resistance to disease, in which he detailed the story of his South Carolina researches in the middle 1890's, how in 1899 he selected William A. Orton of the University of Vermont to solve the problems of disease ravages in the south, how Orton demonstrated alertness and skill and about 1900 began to breed by selection his famous "Sea Island" and "Rivers" cottons resistant to soil Fusarium, and crossed watermelon with a plant known in the United States as the "citron," obtaining from a thousand or more resultant varieties six which were worth while and one which proved commercially satisfactory. Turning from the Atlantic to Pacific coast, Smith, picturing how the Anaheim disease in California within four or five years had destroyed vineyards, caused winepresses to be sold, and the land devoted to other crops, told the story of Pierce's restoring faith in the industry's future between the years 1892-1894: first, by using cuttings from healthy vines and by importing cuttings from disease-free regions, second, by grafting varieties and crossing stocks of raisin grapes to combat another very serious disease known as *coulure*.[24] The second principal type of plant breeding considered was illustrated by Webber's and Swingle's crossing "choice oranges and other citrous fruits sensitive to frost with the extremely hardy *Citrus trifoliata*, which stands the winters well as far north as Washington and is occasionally cultivated as far north as Philadelphia. . . ." By budding the many seedlings obtained from these crosses and thereby

[24] In the *Yearbook of the United States Department of Agriculture* for 1908 (Washington: Government Printing Office, 1909), pp. 453-464, W. A. Orton presented a study, entitled, "The Development of Farm Crops Resistant to Disease," in which, after discussing and illustrating the subject, including the important phase of inheritance of disease resistance and its transmission in Mendelian proportions, he cited nine outstanding examples: (1) wilt-resistant Sea Island cotton; (2) wilt-resistant Upland cotton; (3) wilt-resistant cowpeas; (4) wilt-resistant watermelon; (5) Carleton's rust-resistant wheat; (6) Bolley's wilt-resistant flax. These, in one connection or another, have been mentioned in this book. A seventh example was found in L. R. Jones's and William Stuart's disclosures concerning "varieties of the potato partially resistant to late-blight and probably also to scab." Eighth, at the Tennessee Agricultural Experiment Station, Bain and Essary were said to "have made marked progress in developing strains of clover resistant to anthracnose, a fungous disease. . . ." Lastly, at the Colorado Agricultural Experiment Station, P. K. Blinn had "been propagating a resistant strain of cantaloupe called the Pollock . . . partly resistant to leaf-blight and also [capable of enduring] infection on account of its firmer leaf."

hastening fruiting, plant fruits were obtained within three or four years, and Smith testified, "a dozen or more proved of much interest, the quality of the fruit in some cases being excellent," and promising even better improvement in the second generation from the hybrid. Thus, the deep freeze which Swingle and Webber encountered at Eustis, discouraging as it was in 1894-1895, summoned into action resourcefulness which brought about citrous fruit creations cultivatable possibly as far north as the Carolinas. Later in the course of his address, under "Breeding for Greater Productivity," Smith considered Swingle's and Webber's cross-bred pineapples, some of which, he said, had proved to be "remarkably good," many of "excellent flavour," with specially desirable qualities—medium size, shallow eyes, juiciness, absence of hard core, attractive top, good shipping and keeping qualities—and of increased vigor, with resistance to disease, and absence of spininess in the foliage. This work indicated, Smith pointed out, "that one can obtain almost any sort of pineapple he desires by persistent cross-breeding." Moreover, Swingle's introduction of date palms to cultivation on alkali lands, so-called, had proved successful. They grew "satisfactorily in several places in Arizona and California. Many of these palms," Smith observed, "have already fruited heavily, yielding dates of excellent quality, and there is not the slightest doubt but that we shall within a few years be growing our own dates—at least all of the finer table varieties." This was one way by which thousands of acres of dry and waste land in the west were being reclaimed or utilized by planting crops cultivatable there. Some lands were permeated by "harmful alkaline and neutral salts," some had little rainfall and no irrigation, and some with rainfall were badly eroded, and the alkali washed in or off the surface. The date palm flourishes in "soils," Smith said, "that contain so much alkali that ordinary plants cannot grow at all. . . ."

This work was a part of the third principal breeding type which Smith elaborated—the breeding of plants for resistance to alkali and drought—a work somewhat tardily developed but of proven effectiveness when placed with the scientists the department was fortunate to secure for the purposes.

Thomas H. Kearney, one of Webber's assistants in the Laboratory of Plant Breeding, had charge of other crop introductions and improvements for these regions. Notably, alfalfa which would have "a greater root resistance to alkaline water," was being sought, since ordinary varieties on these lands had failed in cultivation. The work included discovery and experimental testing and breeding of a wide variety of cultivatable species which would thrive on dry land areas, especially in the semiarid region of the Great Plains, and formed part of a movement at least two decades old seeking to promote agricultural production there and in the Great Basin. Kearney's work had been brought to a focus, in considerable part, by a visit to northern Africa with Thomas H. Means of the Bureau of Soils and under auspices of the Office of Seed and Plant Introduction. In the *Yearbook* for 1902,[25] these men presented an article, "Crops Used in the Reclamation of Alkali Lands in Egypt," and discussed practical use in the United States of various crops examined. Sorghum and berseem, a clover, were favored as beginnings for the work, and the advantages of each as to seasonal use, purposes, and regional adaptation were set forth. Gradually as exploration and study progressed, certain types of leguminous and other plants were found more tolerant of alkali than others, and by 1906 a promising number of investigations were in process. In the great over-all work of promoting dry land agriculture, scientists, in many instances, supplied the principles and farmers the practice. Galloway and Woods during the early years of the Section of Vegetable Physiology and Pathology had written on "Water as a Factor in the Growth of Plants."[26] The rise of ecology as a science in field and laboratory, and the development of experimental crop applications, advanced the study. Homer LeRoy Shantz, a graduate in science of Colorado College, Colorado Springs, the possessor of a Ph.D. degree obtained in 1905 from the University of Nebraska, and who had taught botany at both these institutions and at the universities of Missouri and Louisiana (at the last named he had also taught bacteriology), was employed during the summers of 1906 and 1907 as special agent and collaborator in alkali and drought resistant plant investigations. In 1908 and 1909 he served with the rank of expert investigator, and by 1910 was constituted plant physiologist. Together with Kearney, he prepared an article, "The Water Economy of Dry-Land Crops."[27] In this paper, considerations in determining matters of plant introduction and plant breeding, as well as other requisites to guide the student in this work, were treated. Shantz attained scientific eminence in this field which attracted much scholarly investigation. Researches were directed toward determining the agricultural capabilities of land, and the land composition as indicated by the vegetation itself. In 1911 his studious document, "Natural Vegetation as an Indicator of the Capabilities of Land for Crop Production in the Great Plains Area" was published.[28] The following year appeared another bulletin of recognized merit, prepared with L. J. Briggs, "The Wilting Coefficient for Different Plants and Its Indirect Determination."[29] Shantz later became professor of botany at the University of Illinois, taking Professor Trelease's place, and still later, president of the University of

[25] pp. 573-588.   [26] *Yearbook*, for 1894, pp. 165-176.
[27] *Yearbook*, for 1911, pp. 351-362, and authorities cited.
[28] Bulletin 201, U. S. Bur. of Pl. Indus., 1911.
[29] Bulletin 230, U. S. Bur. of Pl. Indus., 1912.

Arizona. His reputation in research in forest ecology is second only to that in agricultural crop physiology. In both, he has made lasting contributions in pure as well as applied science.

With the work in western irrigation agriculture[30] under Carl Schurz Scofield, with that of dry land agricultural investigations[31] under E. C. Chilcott, with the work of cereal improvements including the grain sorghums[32] under Carleton Roy Ball and others, and other services and research agencies of the department, scientific agriculture on a large scale and in a practical manner was developing lands for new homes and farms and improving through land reclamation and rehabilitation standards of living throughout the nation. Within the Department of Agriculture, there were a number of other special branches of investigation which, if space permitted, would merit elaborate mention and description, as, for example, the advancement of tropical agriculture under Orator Fuller Cook, junior, of forage crop investigation under Charles Vancouver Piper, of fiber investigations under Lyster Hoxie Dewey, and, of course, the entire, very important work of agrostology, forestry, and soils.

Perhaps the most celebrated large scale introductions and work of crop amelioration were those performed by Mark Alfred Carleton, already dealt with at appropriate places in this book. In Smith's address of the year 1906, he characterized Carleton's making possible the cultivation of wheat in middle United States, from the Rocky Mountain foothills to within a few hundred miles of the Mississippi River, and from Manitoba, Canada, on the north to Mexico on the south as "one of the most brilliant of our economic achievements. . . . The end is nowhere in sight," observed Smith, "From small beginnings six or seven years ago the durum wheat crop of the United States has increased steadily until last year (1905) it amounted to twenty million bushels, and this year to fifty million bushels. . . . In passing it is interesting to note that some of these wheats are also very resistant to rust (*Puccinia graminis, Puccinia Rubigo-vera*). . . ." One variety was believed to be, and was for many years, "absolutely resistant."[33] Smith enjoyed telling his audience that the American wheat belt had been extended "several hundred miles over many degrees of latitude" and had overcome many difficulties of climate and soil.

The fourth principal breeding type—for greater productivity—which

[30] Scofield, "The Present Outlook for Irrigation Agriculture," *Yearbook* for 1911, pp. 371-382.

[31] Chilcott, "Some Misconceptions Concerning Dry Farming," *Yearbook* for 1911, pp. 247-256.

[32] Ball, "The Importance and Improvement of the Grain Sorghums," Bulletin 203, 1911, p. 22. Also, "The Grain Sorghums," *Yearbook*, 1913, pp. 221-238.

[33] But see E. C. Stakman, "Plant Diseases Are Shifty Enemies," *American Scientist*, summer issue, 1947, Vol. 35, no. 3, and reprint, pp. 324, 326, 336, 345.

Smith described has, in part, been discussed. Smith, of course, singled out as a leading instance Webber's crossbred cottons which he had seen have "two or three times as great an amount of fruit on them as the ordinary varieties, and others in which the fibre was at least one-third longer than the ordinary fibre." Willet Martin Hays, whose accomplishments at the Minnesota Agricultural Experiment Station also have been alluded to, was now Assistant Secretary of Agriculture. Smith pointed out that he had "bred wheats very diligently, and among other striking results he succeeded in increasing the yield of the best strains of 'blue-stem' spring wheat, on an average, two to five bushels an acre by simple selection."

The University of Minnesota, and its University Farm at St. Anthony Park, has been the scholarly workplace of a number of noted American agriculturists, prominent among them being: Samuel B. Green, whose life and work already has been considered; Theophilis Levi Baecker, leading authority in dairy husbandry, director of the Minnesota Dairy School for many years after 1893, and said to have been a stanch opponent of the doctrine of the dual purpose animal for milk and beef; Andrew Boss, authority in farm management and agronomy, pioneer in agricultural economics, a level headed man, whom Dean Davenport of the University of Illinois has said had much to do with making western farmers economically minded; Edward Monroe Freeman, who, after earning three degrees at the University of Minnesota, studied at the University of Cambridge under Harry Marshall Ward, celebrated English pathologist, worked during the years 1905-1907 with the office of cereals investigation of the United States Department of Agriculture at Washington, had published in 1905 *Minnesota Plant Diseases*, was recalled by his alma mater to study the wheat rust problem of the state and to organize a department of plant pathology and botany in the college of agriculture, forestry, and home economics, and was later constituted the college's dean; and Willet M. Hays, recognized to have been among the very first agriculturists of the world to cross wheat for varietal improvement. In 1902 Galloway regarded as outstanding the systematic enterprise of this university and experiment station in originating new varieties of crops by breeding and improving yields and quality of grain by selection of seed from races or types. In the early 1900's,[34] this institution's wheat varietal improvements, its production of taller flax with longer fiber, its historic "Minnesota 13" corn produced by selection with the distinguishing

[34] 1900-1912. Since years of selective effort went into each of these creations, it is difficult to fix any one year. Some of the work began in the late 1800's. In the *Yearbooks* of the U. S. Department of Agriculture, notices of these achievements are found most prominently in 1902, 1906, and 1912. The quotation of Galloway is taken from his article, "Industrial Progress in Plant Work," *Yearbook* for 1902, p. 223.

character of high yield-capacity, its winter rye bred hardier and with better yielding capacity than ordinary varieties, as well as oats and other commodities, placed it in the front ranks of scientific agricultural investigation. Its prestige has gained steadily, especially in its preeminently scientific and economically indispensable work in cereal pathology. Vexatiously variable rusts, smuts, scab, and other forms of disease symptomatology in grains have been studied in laboratory and field with the utmost technical proficiency and progressive ingenuity. Causal agencies, multitudinous biologic forms, have been found; control and eradication measures have been elaborated with such favorable results that enormous epidemics of the most serious and widespread nature have been brought under control, and, in instances, eliminated, at least for a while;[35] cooperative and individual accomplishments in the selection and development of rust resistant varieties of grains, as well as objective researches in disease resistance and its inheritance, have greatly added to purely scientific knowledge, benefited human and national economy, and contributed with a quality of leadership to similarly progressive and noteworthy work in other agricultural crops. It should be pointed out that at this university, and, also, at Cornell, as will be shown, the departments of plant pathology and plant breeding cooperated in much of this very important work. Moreover, comprehensive programs of scientific research were maintained with the United States Department of Agriculture and, when to advantage, with the Dominion Experimental Farms of Canada. In Minnesota, rust and wilt resistant varieties of flax have been produced. Notably valuable have been its stem rust resistant varieties in wheat. Much more might be written concerning the achievements of this university and experiment station. Elvin Charles Stakman, for many years at this institution, is today one of North America's foremost scholars of agriculture. His elaborate systematic study of pathogenic fungi, and the role of physiologic specialization in plant disease research, seems certain to have earned an enduring place in the history of the American plant sciences.[36] From

[35] Read the entire address and article, by Dr. Stakman, "Plant Diseases Are Shifty Enemies," *op. cit.*

[36] Some idea of this can be gained from Dr. Stakman's address as vice president of Section G, AAAS, Boston meeting, December 27, 1946, "The Nature and Importance of Physiologic Specialization in Phytopathogenic Fungi," published in *Science* 105, no. 2738 (June 20, 1947), pp. 627-632.

NOTE: Should the reader wish to pursue further the work of the agricultural experiment stations and colleges of agriculture, reference may be made to an article by W. H. Beal, chief of editorial division, office of experiment stations, "Some Practical Results of Experiment Station Work," *Yearbook* for 1902, pp. 589-606. In this, accomplishments of the Wisconsin station and others including Illinois, Connecticut, Ohio, South Carolina, and Rhode Island, are discussed, and consideration is given to the Minnesota wheat breeding, p. 596. Especially important is the discussion of the Wisconsin work.

1910-1917, Albert F. Woods served as dean of the college of agriculture and director of the experiment station.

Smith next told how Galloway and Dorsett, both graduated from the University of Missouri and associated together in many research projects while with the department, had increased by simple selection the yield of violets from an average of fifty to ninety flowers a plant, also breeding plants against an *Alternaria* leaf spot. Dorsett was now in charge of the department's introduction garden at Chico, California. Moreover, Galloway had found that by planting the heaviest radish seeds more uniform and much more abundant crops could be grown. Galloway had done much to forward study of the effectiveness of fungicides, as early as 1890, with Fairchild, demonstrating how grape crops could be saved from grape rot almost entirely by copper fungicides. Dorsett and Woods had explored the possibilities of hydrocyanic acid gas against insect pests in greenhouses.[37]

Hereafter we shall elaborate more fully the prominent places in breeding programs occupied by corn and tobacco. Smith pointed with pride to accomplishments of departmental workers under Webber in both plant species. As to maize, he said:

For a number of years the Department has been greatly interested in increasing the productivity of the maize plant, and has had good success.

We have shown that by simple selection the yield of maize can be increased, over large districts, an average of 10 per cent; and, in isolated cases, as much as 20 per cent. These experiments have been in the hands of Mr. C. P. Hartley. . . .[38]

With the following paragraph, Smith concluded his address:

. . . We have bred tobacco very diligently during the last few years in order to obtain a uniform quality of wrapper leaf of high character, and in this we have been remarkably successful. This work has been largely in the charge of Mr. A. D. Shamel. . . . Starting out with an arbitrary standard of perfection, he has worked steadily towards producing plants having the desired qualities, and has now obtained many such plants, a portion of which I have seen. I have also seen photographs made by him showing whole fields of tobacco in which each plant looked exactly like every other plant; the leaves, when cured having the right length, breadth, and thickness, the right texture, and the proper burning quality to make a first-rate wrapper leaf. All this has been accomplished within the last four or five years by diligent in-and-in breeding and careful selection. The tobacco has proved as plastic in our hands as the pineapple, and almost anything can be accomplished in the way of obtaining a desirable wrapper leaf by persistent endeavour.

[37] Part of this material is based on "Fifty Years of Pathology," *Proc. of the International Congress of Plant Sciences*, 1:13-46 (1929), at pp. 21, 29, 30.

[38] See an article by Hartley, "Progress in Methods of Producing Higher Yielding Strains of Corn," *Yearbook* for 1909, pp. 309-320.

Between the years 1898-1903, tobacco improvement had received special industrial attention within the department. Requests from editors of industrial journals and also from manufacturing companies had prompted the Secretary of Agriculture, so Woods had written Smith on October 7, 1898, to request an appropriation of $12,000 to study tobacco problems, and Smith was asked to write on what was known of bacteria in relation to fermentation and the curing of the tobacco leaf. At this time Webber and Woods were much discouraged at an unfavorable turn in appropriations for plant breeding. Great good could be done with $5,000. Within a few years, the merit of plant breeding research would be so firmly recognized that appropriations for the work would involve sums far in excess of $5,000 or $12,000. Indeed, amidst a growing recognition of the need and value of pathological research in not one but several agricultural crops, of the need of research in marketing, transportation, and distribution facilities, amidst a growing realization of the financially profitable and nation-wide availability of the new plant introductions, and the potentialities of further research in such subjects as industrial bacteriology, the movement to establish a United States Bureau of Plant Industry found strong arguments and friends. Shamel published in the *Yearbook of the United States Department of Agriculture* two important articles on tobacco breeding: one, "The Improvement of Tobacco by Breeding and Selection" (1904),[39] and the other, "New Tobacco Varieties" (1906),[40] in which four varieties of cigar-wrapper tobacco were described, the results of experiments in the Connecticut Valley begun in the fall of 1903. From about 750 hybrids and selections, four proved valuable. This by no means describes all of Shamel's work. The foregoing is included to illustrate in part the breeding work in this industrial crop during the first years of the century.

Inestimable in economic value as were these and other breeding achievements in America and other places of the world, genetics, as a laboratory science investigating indoors and out-of-doors both cultivated and wild plants on the bases of their heredity and evolution, with particular reference to the Mendelian and multiple factor hypotheses, began to serve agriculture and horticulture still more profoundly. It must be remembered that when the Mendelian and De Vriesian results were given to the scientific world, the concept of the gene, later used with much precision and effectiveness by geneticists, had only been anticipated. Well defined and experimentally established laws of heredity were still few. Practically all remained to be either conclusively proven or organized in intelligible theory and intelligent practice, incorporating the new and coordinating with it the old. The chromosome theory—

[39] *Yearbook* for 1904, pp. 435-452.   [40] *Idem*, for 1906, pp. 387-404.

chromosomes as unit bearers of hereditary characters, or, as differential factors in heredity—was not fully developed, although chromosomes were recognized and, in some quarters, much energy was expended in counting the number of these structures in plants. Theories of sexual differentiation and determination were still in the making. It was, in fact it had already begun, to be the fundamental school-laboratory-training in physiology, cytology, and anatomy, building on sound and well established taxonomy and morphology, that distinguished the work of a rising generation of geneticists from that of the plant breeders of the former generation. Rigid, scientific experimentation under controlled conditions performed through years of unpretentious toil the work of confirming what was true and discarding what was not. Great were the elders, great their experiential wisdom, their foundations, and their triumphs. But each generation and its order yields to the next. As John Merle Coulter once said, the self-gratulation of one generation is always the wonder of the next.

During the first decade of the new century, experimental research in America in the more scholarly subjects, plant morphology, physiology, and anatomy, would not bring forward an astonishing number of great discoveries, or attain zeniths such as Europe had known. But time and brilliant, creative effort have yielded returns. In considerable part, these conclusions were true of American horticultural research although some highly significant physiological disclosures had been made—for illustrations, Goff's studies in flower bud formation in the cherry, plum, apple, and pear; J. C. Whitten's plant temperature studies proving atmospheric warmth and not soil temperature, combined with stored physiological content, opened buds in spring; Whitten's experiment whitewashing peach tree trunks to retard activity of tissues and consumption of stored starches and sugar in older tree parts and terminal branches, to delay early blooming and insure against the harm of late frosts; Blair's studies in greenhouse glass physics; G. Harold Powell's refrigeration and storage studies for the California fruit industries and east of the Mississippi River in the apple, pear, and peach belts; general studies of winter quiescence; and other investigations of like character. Plant behavior studies under varying conditions; study of plant nutrients; diagnoses of symptoms and needs; studies aiming at indicated performances in accordance with defined objectives; analyses of chemical make-ups, their ratios, and relations to other constituents; regulating, increasing, or diminishing concentrations of elements; all had been given starts, but progress along other than practical lines had not been great. Pure science work, so-called, was not at a low ebb. Pure science in an exact sense had only begun. It had been *the* ideal toward which Bailey, Goff, and other leading horticulturists had been projecting their strongest efforts for many years. Something truly great is usually years in attainment. Realization of this in American horticulture was no exception. Pruning, grafting, all the attributes of horticulture were to be studied with more exactness through the years in the light of new experimentation. Many of the techniques employed would come from botany. The application, however, would be horticulture's. Bailey's intention and desire was to remain in research. Mendelian and De Vriesian investigations as well as the multitude of other inviting and alluring fields appealed to his imaginative and research instincts. He loved plants. Moreover, the study of the rapidly growing science of cultivated plants fascinated him. Nevertheless, as has been so often the consequence of being a strong man of unusual mind and caliber, Bailey's services were more and more demanded by administrative duties.

In September, 1903, at the Twenty-eighth Biennial Session of the American Pomological Society, meeting in Boston, Bailey spoke on "The Attitude of the Schools to Country Life." This was important since in the address was embodied a forecast of his agricultural vision:

There are three things to be considered in the agricultural teaching of the future: the teaching of the university and the college student (and I will never lower the standard); the developing of agricultural science; the reaching of the common people in their own schools. The greatest unsolved education problem today is that before the agricultural colleges, because one-third of our people make their living by the plow and the others live because these follow the plow. All this multitude of rural people must be reached in terms of their own lives. . . . For the past years the colleges have put the emphasis on how to grow products; the next ten years will see the interest shifted to the farmer himself, how to reach the man who grows the crops. And every school must be the center of interest of its community. . . .

Bailey's thinking in terms of a ten-year period had a particular significance. Furthermore, his promise to maintain standards for agricultural college students shed light on a recent event of great consequence in his life. On the previous June 19, Dean Roberts, reaching the professorial age limit, had been retired.

In his final report as director of Cornell's experiment station, Roberts reviewed the accomplishments of the years of his deanship. He expressed his confident belief that, "The greatest and most beneficial feature of the Station's activities is found . . . in the phenomenal awakening of the rural population. History furnishes no other such educational advancement and improvement of methods among the rural industrial class, or any other class of people, as has taken place in America in the last quarter of a century. The agricultural experiment stations, working patiently and quietly and almost unnoticed by the liberally educated professional classes, have taught the reading farmer much of the sciences and of their economic application to the production of plants and animals. . . . It is certain . . . that the last quarter of the nineteenth century will be referred to by those who come after us as the great epoch-making period in the development of American agriculture." He referred to the fact that the station bulletins, at first "despised or neglected," had become "highly prized" and were studied almost as textbooks. During fifteen years and two months of his directorship, there had been published 211 such bulletins—begun with editions of about 5,000 copies and in recent years attaining editions of 20,000 copies. When viewed with the fact that because of money limitations their mailing lists had been restricted to those promptly acknowledging their receipt, there was a practical certainty each copy had been read many times. Additionally, sixteen annual reports (counting one in manuscript) had contained a "vast compendium of valuable knowledge related to rural affairs." These covered 7,838 pages with 1,949 illustrations. About the beginning of the century, the Home Nature Study courses for rural families had begun their effective program. Approximately 18,000 "Junior Naturalists" were enrolled in clubs for nature study. So effective had the Farmers' Reading Courses proved that a circular letter had been sent to their wives asking if they would not like a course related largely to matters of rural home economics. The Farmers' Wives Reading Courses had been organized in response to the ready interest shown. When in 1901 Bailey announced the discontinuance of the Nature-Study Quarterly and the Teachers' Leaflets—owing to the fact there were already enough leaflets published to carry on "our mission with efficiency" and funds were to be used elsewhere to intensify the work—he said:

These publications, begun in 1896, now comprise lessons on about 30 topics. These topics are sufficient in number to enable any teacher to choose lessons for a year's work, or to suggest related lines of inquiry. These Leaflets are to be kept in print. They are a part of our working capital. . . .

Our work is maintained by a State appropriation, given for the extending of agricultural knowledge. There are several lines of work conducted under the auspices of this State law, of which the nature-study movement is one. A coordinate movement is the Farmers' Reading Course, in which nearly 30,000 New York farmers are now enrolled. A Reading-Course for Farmers' Wives is lately established, and about 6,000 women are enrolled in it. The literature which all these people read is prepared and furnished by the College of Agriculture. The Farmers' Reading-Course extends through three years, six Lessons being taken up each year. The eighteen Lessons comprise series on The soil, Animal husbandry, Orcharding.

The Lessons are elementary statements of principles. . . . It is now proposed to introduce these Lessons as texts into such rural schools as desire to take up distinctly agricultural work, and this endeavor has been approved by Hon. Charles R. Skinner, Superintendent of Public Instruction.

While we desire to reach all the schools with the purpose of improving country life, we do not believe it to be wise to make the teaching of technical agriculture compulsory in any school, not even in the rural districts. To force the teaching of agriculture is to make it perfunctory and of no avail. The teacher must be trained. Public sentiment must be awakened. A desire must be created. It is a question whether any technical or professional work should be introduced into the elementary schools; but it is always advisable to awaken the pupil's interest in the things with which he lives.

How to make the rural school more efficient is one of the most difficult problems before our educators, but the problem is larger than mere courses of study. Social and economic questions are at the bottom of the difficulty....

For these reasons, the need of a vast program of agricultural education in New York State was evident. At President Schurman's persuasion, Bailey agreed to take Roberts' place as dean of the College of Agriculture and director of the Experiment Station at Cornell. What the agricultural college at Cornell University most urgently needed were buildings. Bailey divided life into three periods: preparation for a vocation; practical application of that preparation; and, third, the doing of what one most wants to do. In Bailey's life, the second period had been reached. The need of agricultural development, especially in matters of education, he realized, was more acute than furtherance of the work he had so soundly and solidly founded in experimental and practical horticulture at Cornell. He had elucidated in 1893 his vision for agricultural education at Cornell. Bailey told Schurman he would accept the new position for a period of ten years. If by that time holes had been dug in the ground and, with a great program of state support, buildings of a great American college of agriculture had been constructed—towering symbols of lives and work dedicated with earnestness to the greatest cause confronting the nation at that time, the further development of the land and its people—he would resign and return to the sciences of his deepest affection, horticulture and botany. There were no stipulations further than this. Dean Roberts, however, left recommendations. In his final report he stated:

For some time in the future two subjects might well be made prominent in the work of both the Station and the College. The lamentably low average yield of crops and the comparatively meager rewards secured by farmers should attract our earnest attention. The subject of unsatisfactory conditions should be investigated immediately and at close range. The emphasis must be laid on a better adaptation of crops, climate and locality. More rational rotations and a more liberal sowing of manurial and cover crops should be urged. No people can long maintain its intellectual standards while the land is steadily diminishing in productive power. . . .

There are many reasons why the Station should become interested and helpful in reviving sheep husbandry in the hilly sections of the State. . . .

Farm forestry could best be conducted by the Agricultural College and the Experiment Station. A nursery for raising seedling trees might be established on the College farm. Instructors should be employed to teach and practically illustrate on small spaces the best methods of reclothing . . .

nearly useless farm areas with valuable kinds of timber woods. . . . In brief, [the] method of reforesting the semi-abandoned and stony areas, the bluff and steep hillsides which border the rivers, creeks and rivulets, would be the beginning of an intelligent and practical method of instilling a love of sylviculture in the rising generation, of ameliorating floods, of taking out of cultivation thousands of acres of land which are now farmed at a considerable loss. . . .

For the purposes, he urged securing additional federal appropriations for the "experiment stations in each of the States and Territories," and for land purchases. The reason, probably, for the last recommendation, was the discontinuance of the New York State College of Forestry.

Farm forestry was to prove to be a persistent controversial issue during Bailey's administration as dean of the New York State College of Agriculture and director of the Cornell Experiment Station. Furthermore, as will be seen later, it was to be one of the reasons why, when his ten-year dean- and directorship was completed, he would return happily to horticultural research.

Horticulture, however, never permitted Bailey to abandon, even while dean and director of agricultural work at Cornell, its field and laboratory. On June 30, 1903, S. A. Beach, then still connected with the New York station at Geneva where he conducted his notable long time fertilizer orchard experiment and, as said, did much valuable breeding and variety testing and study in pomological products (especially apples) and vegetables, circulated among American horticulturists a letter proposing organization of "a society for horticultural science, the object of which should be more fully to establish horticulture on a scientific basis." Meetings would be held "in connection with those of some kindred society, as the American Pomological Society or the American Association for the Advancement of Science. The amount of scientific work being done in this country along horticultural lines," said Beach, "is not fully appreciated in the scientific world because in many cases it is obscured in presentation by a large admixture of popular features. . . . Scientific features should be brought prominently into the foreground. . . . Further, there is a large amount of general scientific work, especially in plant physiology and physiological chemistry, which has a direct and important horticultural bearing which is not making the impress on horticultural investigation that it should. This work should be reviewed from the standpoint of the horticulturist and its horticultural applications should be clearly pointed out. This service also the society for horticultural science could perform. . . . It would aim to do for horticulture in general what the Plant Breeding Conference did for one special branch—it would call forth and centralize the most advanced horticultural thought of the day. It would be a Plant

Breeding Conference generalized." On August 7 there followed another letter announcing that the "Society for Horticultural Science" had been decided on. It was announced that, in conjunction with the biennial session of the American Pomological Society to be held in Boston on September 9, an organization meeting presided over by Bailey would take place in rooms of the Massachusetts Horticultural Society.

Accordingly, on that date, a preliminary gathering assembled in the library of the Massachusetts Society. Bailey, always a standard bearer, being elected chairman, appointed a committee on organization consisting of W. N. Munson, C. B. Smith, H. H. Hume, F. W. Card, and G. H. Powell. The committee retiring, Beach was called on to state the purpose of the meeting. Discussion was elicited from Waugh, Corbett, C. L. Watrous, Craig, Bailey, Garfield, Taylor, S. W. Fletcher, Paddock, Hansen, William Stuart, W. T. Macoun, L. F. Kinney, Taft, E. J. Canning, and Rehder. At length, the committee reported the drafting of a constitution and bylaws and, following discussion, it was adopted. The Society, today the American Society for Horticultural Science, then elected officers and for many years—from 1903 to the year 1907-1908 when W. A. Taylor followed him in the office—Bailey was retained in the presidency. In its first year, the society numbered fifty-three members, with three honorary members including Secretary Wilson of the United States Department of Agriculture.

Bailey was unable to attend the society's first annual meeting held in the Central High School building of St. Louis. In his stead, B. T. Galloway presided. The second annual meeting was held in Philadelphia in December of 1904, holding its sessions in conjunction with the fifty-fourth annual assemblage of the American Association for the Advancement of Science. At this meeting the Society for the Promotion of Agricultural Science held a joint session with the Society for Horticultural Science. The president of each group spoke, Bailey's subject being "What is Horticulture?" At this time, he reported:

Practically all the fruits, particularly in temperate climates, belong to the class of non-necessitous foods; yet their consumption is increasing with enormous rapidity. All the growth of floriculture and of ornamental gardening—largely the work of one generation—stands in a very intimate relation to the broadening sensitiveness of our lives. The number of fruit and forest trees grown in nurseries in 1900 was nearly twice as great as in 1890. In 1900 there were more than 68 millions of square feet of glass in florist's establishments in the United States. The increase of the staple food-stuffs must bear a fairly definite ratio to the increase of population, but the increase in nearly all of the horticultural products is conditioned on our attainment of relative ease and the growth of ideals.

Horticulture also represents intensive tillage and high-class effort at farming. In 1900 the earning power of land devoted to vegetables and small fruits in the United States was four times as great as the average earning power of all other crops. . . .

Further, in this address, Bailey incorporated two highly pertinent observations which demonstrated his capacity for quick evaluation of relative tendencies, at least, two tendencies contemporaneously fighting for supremacy. One: "The new plant-breeding is more important than the old insistence on fertilizing of the land." The other: "I once edited a cyclopedia of horticulture. . . . One strong impression that it left on my mind is its heterogeneousness. The most perplexing problem in its preparation was what to include. No doubt the reader is impressed with what might have been omitted. My own conclusion was that we should never see another large cyclopedia of horticulture; for such a work marks an unspecialized age." Bailey was fully aware that the biological phases of plant breeding and a tendency toward specialization were the new characteristics of the age.

The third annual meeting of the Society for Horticultural Science was held in New Orleans on December 27, 1905. The subject of Bailey's presidential address this time was, "Recent Progress in American Horticulture," and he explained:

I hold . . . that the best delimitation of horticulture is to catalogue the arts that in the course of events fall to the hands of the man who is allowed to call himself a horticulturist; and this catalogue will also equally determine the field of horticultural science. It is my mind now to make a retrospect of parts of this field. This retrospect I have made primarily for the forthcoming fourth edition of the Cyclopedia of American Horticulture, which was itself a looking backward over the course of our achievements; and the remarks that I am now about to make, take a cursory view of the very few years intervening between the completion of that book and the present time. As I see it, the horticultural progress in the few years since the Cyclopedia was projected lies in the continuous steady evolution of the already established lines of development, rather than in the appearing of wholly new movements or enterprises. . . . The most distinct progress that is now making in the general agricultural field is in placing country life subjects on a true pedagogic basis and in adapting them directly to the schools and lives of the people. In this general progress, horticulture partakes.

Bailey referred later in his address to the many attractive periodicals and books on horticulture that had appeared. In this, of course, he had played a prominent part. In 1901 he had been chosen editor of the newly organized Country Life in America. Ever since the loss of the American Garden as a popular medium for disseminating modernized agricultural and horticultural information he had been looking forward to the establishment of a magazine that would take its place. However, he did not hold his place on Country Life in America for more than two years for the purpose of the magazine—which was to portray fashionably wealthy estates and the nation's most famous gardens, a city man's country life—did not coincide with his own. He was afraid that this association might impair his relationship with the trades and the schools which meant a very great deal to him and also felt that it was not furthering his ideal of gradually improving by science and practice all simple agrarian life. Consequently, he resigned in 1903.

Bailey contributed some new books of rare value to agricultural and horticultural science. In the early 1900's *Gray's School and Field Book of Botany, Consisting of "Lessons in Botany" and "Field, Forest, and Garden Botany"*—the second part revised and extended by Bailey—was published by the American Book Company. In 1900, although copyrighted and put into circulation two years before, *The Amateur's Practical Garden-Book*, containing the simplest directions for the growing of the commonest things about the house and garden, made its appearance, with Bailey and Charles Elias Hunn as coauthors, and became another of the Garden-Craft Series. Bailey's texts proved especially valuable, not only for their substance, but also for special features therein contained. To illustrate, *The Principles of Fruit-Growing* contained in its appendix a bibliography of "American Books on Fruit-Growing." *The Principles of Vegetable-Gardening* contained a similar book inventory of its subject and, also, a list of the American experiment station leading bulletins related to vegetable growing, issued from January, 1897, to December, 1899. *The Forcing-Book* contained a bibliography of Cornell station bulletins devoted to vegetable-forcing under glass and a chapter, "Summaries of the Management of the Various Crops." *The Pruning-Book* gave specific advice, described modes of pruning including practices followed in Europe; as to grape training there were portions relating to California practice and general glass-house practice. Philosophy, practical principle applications, and classification data were always all embraced. In 1900 was published Bailey's *The Gardener*, A Book of Brief Directions for the Growing of the Common Fruits, Vegetables and Flowers in the Garden and About the House, not essentially a textbook, not necessarily a manual, but a book of directions organized with reference to the various kinds of plants described.

Since the beginning of the century the kinds and varieties of plants, descriptively and in many instances actually, have so increased that only cross sections of them would make books of the size of Bailey's early books, excluding, of course, the cyclopedias. However, Bailey's books of this period, as well as leading works of other horticulturists of the time, were the foundation literature in many branches and divisions of American horticulture. There had been a considerable taxonomic literature before Bailey. There had been some works on plant propagation, on the "physiology" of horticultural plants, on plant culture. There had been

Lindley's *Theory of Horticulture*, Hayward's *The Science of Horticulture*, the works of Thomas Andrew Knight, Darwin, Wallace, and others. There were the books of the Downings, of Thomas Meehan, of Andrew S. Fuller, of Patrick Barry, and others. Horticultural books devoted to regions such as the Gulf of Mexico states, Maine, California, and elsewhere, had made appearances before and during Bailey's earlier years as an author. Nevertheless, except for a few books by other leading American horticulturists, notably, Goff, Bailey's books are today the classic representatives of their period. Again, in this instance, the quality and worth of his literary productions are attested to by their leadership. American horticulture, as a garden and orchard art, had a far more diverse and widespread history than American botany. The history of American horticultural science parallels, and in many instances, follows that of American botany. Bailey stands in the history of American horticulture somewhat as Gray and Torrey stood in American botany, as Lesquereux in American paleobotany, as Farlow in American mycology, as Smith in American plant pathology—not only as a taxonomist but also as an interpreter and evaluater of principles, as a visionary who himself made substantial experimental research contributions.

Modernized revisions of Bailey's books have kept them useful and practical, in a limited sense, although modern scholarship with specialization and increased knowledge has vastly extended the scope of American horticulture, agriculture, and botany. Real claim may be made that the first comprehensive book on scientific horticulture based on function and performance was *Fundamentals of Fruit Production*, written by Victor Ray Gardner, Frederick Charles Bradford, and Henry Daggett Hooker, Jr., and published in 1922. A discussion of this point would have to settle first what scientific horticulture is. The aim of Bailey's generation of plant scientists had been, and would continue to be, advancement and realization of "pure science" objectives, notwithstanding the fact that in his address, "What is Horticulture," Bailey said, "I have not the least desire to confine any person's efforts to so-called 'applied science.' On the other hand, I have no desire to confine it to 'pure science.' I object to the classification of the ideas and to what this classification connotes. All knowledge is knowledge." Bailey was not solely interested in science as a laboratory technician—as much as he was aware of the dependence of the scientific structure on the work of the laboratory. He was more the leader of a great agricultural movement. He would have liked to confine himself to research but administrative duties were an obligation, because of his abilities as scientist, writer, speaker, and leader. Of this the nature study movement was an integral part.

In 1902, Doubleday, Page and Company published his *Nature Portraits*; studies with pen and camera of our wild birds, animals, fish and insects, with the text by the editor of *Country Life in America*. In 1903, the same publishing house brought out Bailey's book on nature study, *The Nature-Study Idea*, being an interpretation of the new school-movement to put the child in sympathy with nature. Bailey supported the institution of children's gardens, the decoration and beautification of rural and city school grounds and parks, the development artistically of places of play, the furtherance of interest in horticulture and agriculture as methods of introducing people to nature, the spread of parks, the enactment of game laws and laws for prevention of cruelty to animals. These were years when railroads and interurban trolley lines were bringing together, more and more, people and products; and because of their prosperity these companies were investing in suburban and rural properties. Bailey estimated that, "Not only the half of the people who live in the country, but fully half of the other half, is interested in country life." In an editorial defining what *Country Life in America* stood for, he informed his readers:

We would preach the sermon of the out-of-doors, where men are free. We would lead the way to the place where there is room, and where there are sweet, fresh winds. We would relieve the cramped and pent-up life with visions of things that every one may have for only the trouble of opening his eyes. We would tell him where the wild geranium blows and what it means. To the person who resides permanently in the country, we would give a broader view and a closer intimacy with what he has. We would show him the dandelion. We would put him into harmony with his environment.

We intend that our work shall be more than sentiment. We believe that we have also an economic and social mission. The cities are congested; the country has room. We would check the influx into the cities by opening the eyes of the country man to see the country. We would show him his advantages. The abjectly poor live in the cities. One does not starve in the country.

We shall not make a technical agricultural or horticultural journal; yet we stand for the elevation and betterment of farming in the best and broadest sense. . . . We want to encourage home-building outside the city. . . . We desire to develop the beautiful spots in our country. We would lend our influence in the preservation of natural scenery and historic places.

Agriculture, said Bailey, was reborn every spring and, therefore, remained ever young. Mountain forests, farm forestry, horticulture, and agriculture all received consideration. Potato culture, pecan culture, rose culture, date culture, chrysanthemum culture, and many other subjects, were treated. He evaluated the movement westward of the center of nursery production. He discussed the need of teaching south, north, and west, to "spread the gospel of nature-love and of self-respecting re-

sourceful farming through all the colleges and the public schools."
Bailey loved nature as is shown in many of his poems:

> "Quick smell of the earth, I am come once more
> To the feel of th' soil and the sky before
> To the tang of th' ditch and wift of the bough
> With stamp of my team and grip of my plow . . ."

In 1903, there was published, in the annual report of the Office of
Experiment Stations, Bailey's article on "Development of the Text-
Book of Agriculture in North America," which contained a chrono-
logical bibliography of North American textbooks of agriculture. This
work was regarded as so important it was separately issued by the United
States Department of Agriculture. Bailey was scholar, bibliographer,
author, investigator, encyclopedist, lecturer, naturalist, poet, teacher,
editor, and administrator.

In his address, "Recent Progress in American Horticulture," delivered before the Society for Horticultural Science in 1905, Bailey
alluded to the almost 600 experiment station bulletins of horticultural
significance in America from 1900 to 1904 inclusive. By far the largest
number pertained to fruit; the next in importance, to pests and diseases;
about one-sixth to vegetable gardening; and some to greenhouse subjects. Ornamental gardening had as yet comparatively few bulletins,
numbering in Bailey's list only 19. Of course, Bailey saw the greatest
progress—the most definite progress—in technical horticultural practice
in plant breeding. Moreover, in other respects, there had been notable
development. He related:

In distinctly commercial directions, there has been a remarkable era of
development of horticultural regions. This is particularly true of what we are
in the habit of calling "the South," comprising the great area from the
Atlantic coast to eastern and southern Texas. Peach-tree planting has proceeded on a scale of unprecedented magnitude. The strawberry is also par-
taking in this extension, particularly in those regions that hope to supply
the great eastern markets before the New York and New England fruit is
ripe. Strawberry planting is developing with great rapidity in Texas,
Arkansas and Missouri, notwithstanding the risks attendant on efficient
refrigerator car and transportation service. The interest in pecan culture
is extending very rapidly in the Gulf States. Trucking is extending farther
and farther southward with the construction of better transportation
service. This is well illustrated in the growing of Bermuda onions in Texas,
a business that is now assuming large proportions. Extreme southern Florida
is developing with remarkable rapidity; the orange region is moving farther
south; the grape-fruit interest is enlarging; winter trucking is becoming
still more important. A few years ago, there was an area of new development
in the interior West and on the Central Pacific coast; later came the development of the Atlantic seaboard region; now the farther South (southern and
eastern Texas, Louisiana, the Gulf coast) is undergoing great exploitation.

With this development in the Gulf region, there, has continued a steady filling up and maturing of the great horticultural Northwest (Oregon, Washington and contiguous regions). The governmental control of irrigation work will no doubt still further accelerate the remarkable development in the arid region states. The great Canadian Northwest is developing with remarkable enthusiasm, and much of this area, in British Columbia, is already coming to be known for its fruits. Fruit-growing can be extended 300 or 400 miles north of Vancouver. There is no part of the continent which, so far as my knowledge goes, is falling away in its general horticultural activities.

Coordinate with the development of great horticultural regions has come an enlarged and quickened knowledge of the principles underlying the handling and transporting of fruits and vegetables. The relation of cold storage to the handling of fruits has taken on new significance. . . . The general propaganda for better quality and choicer packing in fruits is beginning to have its effect, aided by the gradual increase of wealth and the elevation of taste on the part of consumers. . . .

This growing demand for better individual quality is also well exhibited in the flower and plant trade. The increasing importance of the best grades of flowers in the flower stores is evidence of this. The cut-flower trade is now seeing a remarkable development, also, of the wholesaling business. Probably three-fourths of all the cut flowers reach the retailer, at least in the East, through the commission houses.

Distinct advance has been made in the treating of insects and diseases. Sterilizing the soil in greenhouses has come to be a practicable process. The fumigation practices have been steadily perfected. Increased attention is being given to the introduction of beneficial insects of predaceous or parasitic habits. In California, experiments are being made with a parasite of the codling moth. San Josè scale continues to spread with virulence along the Atlantic seaboard, but the first fear of this pest is beginning to pass away. In sprays, the lime-and-sulphur mixture has come into use over a great expanse of the country. It is doubtful, however, whether this material will gain or hold a paramount place. It is relatively expensive, hard on pump and operator, and difficult to make. There is a marked rise of confidence in the ability of man to control pests and diseases.

A good many special methods and special crops have come to the fore. The growing of plants under shade of cheese-cloth has received much attention. The growing of dwarf apples and other special forms of garden fruits has aroused new interest. The interest in ginseng continues to spread. Golden seal and snakeroot have come to rank as commercial plants. The whole subject of specialty-farming seems to be receiving increased attention.

It is evident that there is a growing taste for ornamental plantings and a rising appreciation of what constitutes intrinsic beauty in plants. This progress is of course most marked in what we formerly considered as the West—the states of the prairie and the plains. These countries are maturing; the epoch of pioneering has passed; physical wants are being met; the old residents are being replaced; consequently, there is reason and opportunity for giving attention to the environs of the home-seat. Throughout the country I think I see a distinct tendency to better treatment of the home-grounds—the gradual giving up of mere "beds" and meaningless scattered plants, and the making of an open-centered lawn with attractive border planting. There is increasing appreciation of our native plants, as distinguished from imported "novelties" and from merely curious and striking horticultural varieties. The interest in native plants is well illustrated in the great attention that has been given recently to the hawthorns. . . .

The most distinct and methodical effort now making to enrich our cultivated flora is that of the Office of Seed and Plant Introduction and Distribution of the United States Department of Agriculture, under the charge of David Fairchild. The office has been organized under Mr. Fairchild since 1897. Over fourteen thousand selected entries appear on the inventory of the office, the majority of them representing new or untried varieties, or strains, of species already in America. Agricultural explorers have been sent to Africa, Asia, South America, Europe and the Pacific Islands, and Mr. Fairchild himself has made a tour of reconnaissance of the whole world and has established correspondents for the office in all the most important countries on the globe. Every new plant is properly catalogued and numbered, and of every seed or plant sent out to the thousands of experimenters through the country a careful record is kept for reference in future years.[41]

Bailey paid high compliments to the work of the Arnold Arboretum of Jamaica Plain, Massachusetts. Charles Sprague Sargent, its director, had gone two years before to Peking, China, and had secured for cultivation trees and shrubs indigenous to northern China or cultivated in the region of Peking. Bailey admired the work of the American botanical gardens, the United States Department of Agriculture, and several establishments of men of wealth who had commenced plant introduction and variety test studies. He referred to Luther Burbank,[42] whose breeding work was characterized as "remarkable and significant" but often "sensationalized and over-stated." Especially did he evince pleasure that the Missouri Botanic Garden and the New York Botanical Garden were doing "horticultural work of the greatest value." "There has been a steady increase of good horticultural novelties," said Bailey, "although I do not recall the introduction within the last three or four years of any botanical species not heretofore in our trade that promises unusual results." During the past two or three years, an unusually large number of novelties had been received from Manchuria and efforts were being made to increase the collections of Chinese plants which promised to be "more successful here than any other exotic trees or shrubs." Within the first years of the century, American horticulture had lost two of its greatest men—Thomas Meehan and William Saunders (of the United States Department of Agriculture). The venerable T. T. Lyon was also dead. While Bailey was editor of *Country Life in America,* Meehan was

[41] A recent book of interest which deals with this among other subjects is *New Crops for the New World*, edited by Charles Morrow Wilson, The Macmillan Company, New York, 1945. 295 pp.
[42] For a recent and thoroughly prepared evaluation of the contribution of Burbank to progress in the plant sciences, see a study made by Walter L. Howard, "Luther Burbank, A Victim of Hero Worship," *Chronica Botanica,* x, 5/6, 1945/1946 (Waltham, Mass.), pp. 301-506.

described by that magazine as "a 'horticulturist of the old school,' being one of those Kew-trained men known for their great stores of botanical and horticultural knowledge—a combination which is unfortunately too rare in this age of specialization."[43] However, in his address, in 1905, Bailey did not seem to entertain the same viewpoint. He concluded by saying:

This running sketch is sufficient to show the remarkably wide scope of the field that, by common consent, lies within the domain of the American horticulturist, and it also exhibits some of the activities that are just now in the ascendency. Within this great field there are hundreds of groups of subjects sufficiently large to occupy a man's entire attention, and of sufficient practical importance to warrant the work of a lifetime. There are problems of strict science, applied and unapplied, that will inspire a lifelong quest. Even the most cursory observer must see that the field is yet scarcely touched in any abiding and thorough-going way.

Indeed, by 1905, Bailey seemed to have endorsed without qualification the tendency toward specialized research. A knowledge of both botany and horticulture was indispensable to a complete knowledge of either subject. The two sciences were separable, however, and probably always will be. That Bailey's utterances were always regarded as words of authority, and that he led both scientific and popular opinion, may be inferred from the facts that *Country Life in America* in its first year attained, it is said, a larger circulation than any magazine in the field ever had and, from the scientific standpoint, his books were always commendably appraised. In the *Botanical Gazette's* review of *The Survival of the Unlike*, when several of Bailey's other books had either appeared or were in process of being written, Charles R. Barnes said, "Professor Bailey is a living disproof of the doctrine that overproductiveness is at the expense of the quality of the fruit." In *Torreya* F. E. Lloyd, reviewing in 1904 the third edition of *Plant Breeding* had the following to say:

Although Professor Bailey confessedly takes a conservative attitude, he is eminently fair minded, and states all the aspects of a question dispassionately. His attitude also toward the practical problems of horticulture is clearly and uncompromisingly scientific. The more we know about the behavior of plants, and the closer we follow the indications of nature, the more successful will our efforts be to ameliorate plants. The principle of the scientific method is thus adhered to. . . .

Perhaps these are the underlying reasons why Bailey proved so capable in a task of leadership that required acute skill and stupendous energy and strength: the task of transforming the College of Agri-

[43] The article was signed with the initials, "W. M." It contains some interesting comments on some of Meehan's accomplishments. Meehan came to America to become superintendent of Bartram's Garden of Philadelphia.

culture of Cornell University into an institution supported by the State of New York—a thoroughgoing state institution in all respects—and the procurement from the state legislature of a $250,000 appropriation to build agricultural college buildings worthy of the great state's name. When Bailey became a professor in Cornell University, he had been assured that a new building for agriculture and horticulture would be built the next year. The next year arrived and it was decided in the University Council that a chemistry building was more needed, and Morse Hall was built. On January 14, 1890, the Court of Appeals of New York State decided that Cornell University was entitled to claims against the State of New York on account of interest accruing from that part of the federal land-grant scrip fund of which the state was the depository. The decision was styled *People ex rel. Cornell University, appellant, versus Ira Davenport, Comptroller, respondent.* In accordance therewith, the state enacted in 1891 a law which required the comptroller to pay to the university the sum of $89,385.66, less $3,096.25. The college of agriculture and the department of horticulture thought surely then they would get a new building. But the school of law needed a building. A $110,000 edifice, Boardman Hall, for the law school, was the result.

The agricultural faculty as one mind and heart fought for equality of academic recognition. They urged their claims before university groups. They went to the public and demonstrated the value of their teaching and research. Why shouldn't "ag" students have equal academic and social status? Why shouldn't "ag" college courses be accredited equal rank toward higher degrees in other colleges and departments? President Schurman reported each year the agricultural college's increasing influence in New York state and the nation. But the view prevailed that agriculture was only for the man who tilled the soil.

On Governor Flower's recommendation, the New York legislature had appropriated $50,000 for a dairy husbandry building. In so doing, a nucleus of the state's agricultural work had been centered at Cornell. President Schurman was disappointed that a larger sum had not been obtained, though he considered that a new state policy had been "at least initiated." The president of Cornell University had the enormous task of raising funds for the entire university and he was happy to find, therefore, that Bailey's steady and unique ability to secure money appropriations from the state could be utilized.

For several years following 1903 Bailey had taken the leading responsibility in obtaining appropriation increases for horticultural and agricultural extension work. He had established many useful contacts among the people of the entire state rural area. Impressive and picturesque figure that he was, his influence was also not unknown in the cities.

In 1903, when he assumed directorship of the Cornell station, one of his administration's first accomplishments was the acquisition of more than 220 acres of new land—some of which had been arranged for by Dean Roberts, now retired—which made possible in comparatively quick time new cultivated fields, pasture land, a forestry experimental tract and, especially, the historic "Caldwell Field"[44] named to honor George C. Caldwell, first director of the faculty-organized station and author of "the first, and for many years the only, textbook on agriculture in this country. . . . The appearance of this book," wrote Dr. A. C. True, chief of the Office of Experiment Stations, was "of special significance historically because in its earlier stages of development agricultural research was almost exclusively based on chemistry, and chemists were as a rule the pioneers in such research in America as abroad."[45] According to True, beginning with this book, Cornell University had started a "library of the best agricultural literature the world has ever seen. . . ." In it were one "of the first American books of high authority and influence regarding animal diseases" by Dr. James Law; "the early work in economic entomology by Comstock and his associates, the systematic horticultural studies, plant breeding, and forcing-house work of Bailey and his associates; investigations in dairying by Wing and others; demonstration of efficient means of spraying for insect pests and plant diseases; investigations on animal diseases; and investigations on the use of, and best methods of preserving manure."

One of Bailey's first appointments was Thomas F. Hunt as professor of agronomy. Hunt was a thorough student of soils. Bailey regarded him as one of the greatest teachers of agriculture he had ever known. On Hunt's arrival from the Ohio State University, notable soil studies and a much needed, elaborate program of timothy and pasture grass experimentation were instituted. Hunt directed his inquiries toward studies of functions and behavior responses under differing conditions, and inaugurated large scale selection and breeding work. Clovers were experimented upon to increase yields and resist winterkilling. Projects to secure increased yield and shorter ripening period in corn later came into prominence along with cereal breeding in wheat and oats. Hunt's researches formed the basis for the even more notable experimental work of Herbert John Webber who took Hunt's place after the

[44] See the "Historical Number," *Cornell Countryman*, XII, 3 (December, 1914), articles by Comstock and Stone, pp. 210, 215.
[45] See the same, article by True on "The New York State College of Agriculture in its Relation to Agricultural Progress in the United States," p. 200. See also article by Thomas F. Hunt on the farms, *Cornell Countryman*, II, 3 (1905), pp. 169-174.

latter left to accept a position at Pennsylvania State College. Webber was brought by Bailey to the New York State College of Agriculture on April 1, 1907, to organize a new department of experimental plant biology—a department "made for the man," Bailey announced, "rather than the man procured for the department." Experimental plant biology, as the department was conceived, preserved the work in the art and science of plant breeding but went deeper than theretofore into the study of sex, fecundation, heredity, evolution, environmental influences and effects and physiological factors in plant variation. To use Webber's description, it was science for science's sake. Since 1897, when Webber's paper on "Fecundation of Zamia" had appeared, Bailey had watched the progress of this student, who, in addition to numerous triumphs in citrus—the Colman, Savage, and Rustic citranges, the Thornton orange, limes, tangerines, and other productions already discussed—and fifteen new varieties of pineapple, had evolved valuable long fiber cottons as a part of his famous work in charge of the laboratory of plant breeding of the United States Department of Agriculture. Webber planned to begin work immediately on promising new corn varieties for New York state, to set out 1,200 oat hybrids, and increase the number of investigations in forage plants. Though he did not take over Hunt's work in agronomy he did continue the latter's experimental plant breeding.

Dean Hunt remained five years at Pennsylvania State College. In 1912 the college of agriculture at Berkeley, California, was reorganized. Hunt went to the university there to become its dean, a position which also was offered to Bailey. In California Hunt effectively expanded the splendid agricultural teaching and research traditions which had been founded there by Hilgard and Wickson.

Poultry experimentation was another valuable expansion arranged for by Bailey. James Edward Rice had graduated in 1890 from Cornell. One of Bailey's students, he was an ardent admirer of the new dean. When an assistant and instructor during Roberts' deanship, he had given "the first definite course in poultry husbandry ever given in an American agricultural college."

Raymond A. Pearson was another Bailey selection, who became a nationally known authority in his subject. He became professor of dairy husbandry.

George N. Laumann, another Cornell graduate who had been taught by Roberts and Bailey, became secretary of the college faculty and Bailey's "general factotum." Lauman organized America's first course and department of rural economy or agricultural economics. He, while a student, had browsed, outside the classrooms, among French, German, and other foreign literature, and envisioned this new phase of knowledge as a teaching course. Because of a rule, Bailey was once styled professor of rural economy. But he did not teach the subject. Director Whitman H. Jordan of the New York station at Geneva, as part of a program of closer contact between the Geneva and Cornell stations, also held the title. Nevertheless, the honor of being the subject's first professor was Lauman's. Bailey always wanted agricultural problems studied statistically. Valuable research originated from the creation and development of this subject, and its derivative, farm management.

John Craig, professor of extension teaching in agriculture and horticulture and supervisor of the Farmers' Reading Course, took Bailey's place as professor of horticulture. The aggressive Cornell extension work continued, with an added feature of cooperative experiments in field crops extended over many counties of the state. In 1903 there were nearly 300 experiments distributed over 44 counties and these were being supervised by John L. Stone. In 1904 Stone went over to agronomy as an assistant professor. Stevenson W. Fletcher was added to the horticultural and agricultural extension work. Jay A. Bonsteel in soils investigation, John W. Gilmore and Samuel Fraser in agronomy, Robert S. Northrop and Charles E. Hunn in horticulture, John M. Trueman in animal husbandry and dairy industry, and Herbert Hice Whetzel in plant pathology, supplied able investigation and instruction, additional to others already mentioned.

Conditions at the beginning and end of Bailey's administration have been interestingly contrasted by Albert R. Mann. "When he [Bailey] became Director in 1903, the buildings were valued at about $60,000, the faculty consisted of nine persons, twenty-five courses were offered, the total enrollment of students of all grades was 252. In 1913, the buildings were valued at about $1,125,000; the faculty consisted of 104 persons, two hundred and twenty-four courses were offered, and the total enrollment was 2,305 students of all grades." What accounted for this tremendous expansion and growth?

Since 1900 agricultural development in the United States has loomed as one of the great historical attributes of the first half of the twentieth century. Whereas appropriations for expenditures of divisions, sections, or bureaus of the United States Department of Agriculture, during the last decades of the nineteenth century were figured in five and six digits and embraced at the most sums in the hundred thousands of dollars, with the turn of the new century appropriations for the same agencies climbed, steadily and in a general sense proportionately, in figures embracing seven digits and millions of dollars. Indeed, as the decades of the new century have elapsed, total appropriations for the same bureaus and new agricultural and forest services have ascended into hundreds of millions of dollars, and departments of agriculture of the federal and state governments have been firmly and permanently established as among the strongest, most influential and worthwhile agencies of government. Accomplishing great good for the public this then last of the departments of the executive branch of the federal government to be given official status in the President's cabinet has established beyond cavil or question its own justification and enduringly imperative need. In 1904 college instruction in agriculture was being given in sixty-five colleges and universities. Every state and territory, except Alaska, Hawaii, and Porto Rico had at least one institution which gave agricultural instruction, although in twenty-one states the agricultural colleges were still departments of state universities. Sixty-three institutions maintained agricultural courses of instruction, the great preponderance embracing four years of study leading to degrees, and many provided graduate work. About forty-five institutions provided special, short, and correspondence courses in various branches. With few exceptions the agricultural experiment stations were departments of the colleges or universities. "The total number of persons engaged in the work of education and research in the land-grant colleges and the experiment stations in 1904," reported the *Yearbook of the United States Department of Agriculture* for that year, "was 4,666; the number of students in these colleges, 56,226; the number of students in the four-year college courses in agriculture, 4,640; in short and special courses, 5,281. With a few exceptions each of these colleges offers free tuition to residents of the State in which it is located." Organizations interested in rural matters had also grown. In addition to the Association of American Agricultural Colleges and Experiment Stations and farmers' institutes, there were the American Association of Farmers' Institute Workers, a number of national dairy associations, the National Live Stock Association, the American Association of Live Stock Herd Book Secretaries, the National Wool Growers' Association, a number of stock breeders' associations, several forestry associations and forestry schools, a National Good Roads Association, a National Bee Keepers' Association, a National Association of Economic Entomologists, an Association of Official Agricultural Chemists, a large number of horticultural and kindred societies, organizations for protection of birds and game, the Farmers' National Congress, and, of course, the national and local granges. Quite obviously, one approaching a state legislature asking for an appropriation to advance agricultural interests had, even in the early 1900's, substantial support from a large organized and generally distributed stratum of society.

Notwithstanding this, however, in New York state there existed a unique situation educationally. Over the nation all of the colleges of agriculture except those of Michigan and Maryland, were land-grant founded and all were governed by provisions of the Morrill and Hatch Acts of Congress. These laws were so written, read, and construed that no specific provision authorized moneys realized from land sales to be used to construct buildings for such colleges. In fact, it was provided that specific sales of land should finance the maintenance of the schools. The Cornell college of agriculture, to build new buildings, could go to the people and secure an endowment. But, unfortunately, the rural people had not conquered their seemingly ever persistent depression. Indeed, a strong argument for development of the college was still the needs manifest on every side in the rural areas. Control of the affairs of the college of agriculture at Cornell, especially in the matter of securing legislative appropriations, had been placed more and more with its faculty, although officially and in a strict sense it was not a college but a department of the university. Bailey thought that New York state should have its own college of agriculture. What was needed now was the creation of an official state college of agriculture with its own buildings and a well defined jurisdiction. This meant making it a state-built-and-maintained institution. The matter of agricultural education of college grade, thereupon, came into widespread discussion among the populace of New York state and the nation.

People of the western states, which had state universities or whose state constitutions provided adequate procedure to raise funds to build and finance public education, could not grasp the perplexing situation which confronted New York state. States of the classic Ordinance of 1787 with its educational provisions drafted by Thomas Jefferson had all but settled the foundation of their legal structure for educational development. But in New York no analogy to these circumstances existed. New York had a nonteaching institution patterned after Alexander Hamilton's idea—the New York State University at Albany. Agriculture at Cornell, therefore, had to be taught according to the arrangements made by Ezra Cornell. When in 1893 Bailey's address, "Agricultural Education and Its Place in the University Curriculum," had been printed and sent to former President Andrew Dixon White, then ambassador to Russia, White wrote Bailey that the address to all practical intents and purposes envisioned an agricultural college like that Cornell had dreamed and believed would come to pass. Bailey, consequently, was aware of the obligation imposed on him. He assumed leadership of the movement. There was no escape from it.

But a bitter fight ensued. When a first move was made to get a $250,000 appropriation from the state to build Roberts Hall and a proposed legislative enactment was drawn for the purpose, Bailey called meetings of agricultural leaders, and having the confidence of members of both political parties, went among members of the legislature and interviewed them. In response to the request for $250,000, one senator asked: "Bailey, why don't you move the capital right down on the shore of Cayuga Lake?" Another insisted that large initial and long-continued maintenance appropriations, which Bailey forthrightly stated would have to be made, would bankrupt the state. Another legislator asked, "Professor Bailey, what are you drinking this year?" The answer was, "I am drinking good cold water." The legislator assured him, "Your bill is lost." But the quick and good-humored reply gained the legislator's support. Bailey maintained headquarters in Albany at his own expense. A trainload of delegates arrived as part of the proceedings. At one time a group came to Bailey and announced that plans were being drawn to place a state agricultural college in Schoharie County. Bailey was to be made its president. Bailey calmly retorted, "Gentlemen, I am not for sale." The most serious opposition to Bailey's plans came from colleges of the state.

At a hearing before the finance committee of the senate on February 23, an address was made by Chancellor James R. Day of Syracuse University, a tall, strong, and alert man. Soon, a pamphlet printed by its university press styled, "A Protest and Some Proposals Concerning Agricultural Education," was given such wide circulation that on March 18 Bailey replied with a counterpamphlet, "Agricultural Education in New York State," a statement concerning charges made against Cornell University. Bailey did not charge Chancellor Day with untruths but he answered each protest and accusation. He avowed he would not "engage in any contention between educational institutions. I am proud," he said, "of all the Colleges and universities of the State. They are doing excellent work for education, in many fields. It should be the policy of such institutions to fight ignorance, not to fight each other." Three courses were open to the state: one, distribute state money to several institutions, no one of which had sufficient funds to equip adequately an agricultural school; second, establish a separate college of agriculture at an enormous cost, requiring years to build efficient work; and, third, continue the policy on which the state had already embarked, and of which farmers and agricultural societies approved, in fulfillment of which Cornell University could conduct a program in harmony with "any and every institution in the State." The essential question, said Bailey, was not whether any one institution was favored over another but what was to be done for agricultural education in New York state. Cornell University had a history in agriculture education almost four decades old. It had a state experiment station and not far distant at Geneva was the other state station. Ezra Cornell had made certain arrangements with the state by which the university was bound. The Cornell college of agriculture received support from three classes of funds: federal, for part of which the state was trustee; private endowment, that arranged for by Ezra Cornell and others; and funds from the state itself. Certainly it seemed that Cornell University's request was in the interest of state agriculture, and in the interest of the people. The granting of it would not prejudice any other interests. The legislature saw things Bailey's way. By chapter 655 of the laws of 1904 New York state's law-making body passed with three-fifths of its members present an act to establish a state college of agriculture at Cornell University, appropriating therewith $250,000 for buildings and equipment and retaining control over only the land conveyed and the buildings when erected. When Speaker Nixon had made his opening address before the assembly, he reminded his audience that New York had been "the only state in the Union in which an agricultural college of high rank [had] been founded and developed from the first without direct backing of the state." Early in the fall Governor Odell had inspected the college and in his message to the legislature clearly stated his appreciation of the need of agricultural and scientific training in the state.

On May 9, when the bill was signed, Cornell students celebrated with a parade, bonfire, fireworks, and a banquet. No longer would it be necessary to stack the agricultural library in the business office or to house 200 dairy students in a space intended for fifty. The dairy industry was to have a new building and more equipment. Soils work would no longer be confined to the assay laboratory or the voluminous work of the Farmers' Reading Course and Farmers' Wives' Reading Course have to be done in the basement of Morrill Hall. New York could now look forward to agricultural buildings rivaling those of other states—Pennsylvania, Iowa, Illinois. Iowa had just enlarged its building program. Ohio had a $120,000 building.[46] Only a few years would pass before New York state could compare its buildings and its building program with states which already had invested hundreds of thousands of dollars in buildings, notably, Minnesota, Massachusetts, Michigan, and Wisconsin.

On April 27, 1907, there was celebrated the 100th anniversary of the birth of the founder, Ezra Cornell, the man who at the insistence of President White had acquiesced to the university's bearing his name. At the ceremonies Governor Charles Evans Hughes delivered the custody of the new buildings to President Schurman on behalf of the university. Believer in progressive agricultural education that he

---

[46] *Cornell Countryman*, I, no. 3, pp. 82 ff.

was, Governor Hughes proudly told his audience that recently the state had appropriated $100,000 to maintain the college.

With almost seeming suddenness, the New York State College of Agriculture from every standpoint stood as perhaps America's greatest institution devoted to the promotion of agricultural knowledge. Bailey always was an ardent believer in democracy. In 1906, by a Reorganization Act, the membership of the university board of trustees was, among other things, reconstituted. Democracy—equality of representation for the university, the alumni, and the state—was achieved by giving equal voice to the members who represented each division or group. Bailey was principally responsible for this. He believed that the state's interests were not sufficiently safeguarded by continuing a system which embraced ex-officio membership.

Bailey, of course, also spoke at the dedication ceremonies. He was accorded applause "of such duration that it had to be stopped in order to close the exercises of the morning."[47] His heart warmed as he beheld the university Armory decorated with national flags and Cornell University's colors. After the keys of the buildings had been delivered by Governor Hughes, Bailey spoke to the assemblage on "The Outlook for the College of Agriculture." After introductory remarks, he recited at once a statement of the college's purposes which he had written and which by that time had been made a part of the laws of New York relating to the college.

He, then, accepted the tremendous responsibility of the college's leadership. He spoke as a dean who knew whereof he spoke. The dubious agricultural situation of New York state, in relation to the nation, absorbed his entire attention. With an amazing amount of factual and statistical matter he elaborated the points of agricultural decline, their true significance, why New York state "should be first in agricultural activity." Increased production was not the only agricultural theme. Redirections of effort were to be toward rural organization, better communication facilities, rural entertainment, schools where agriculture would "be as much a part . . . as oxygen is a part of the air," effective rural government, rural banks, and generally revitalized institutions. Bailey refused to be a pessimist. As to New York's economic condition, he said, "In the face of all this statistical decline three facts stand out prominently: (1) markets are as good as ever, for there is no decline in the purchasing power of the people (rather there is a reverse tendency); (2) the land is still productive, notwithstanding a popular impression to the contrary; (3) good farmers are better off today than they ever were before."

[47] *Ibid.*, IV, no. 9, p. 286.

But he called for educated leadership, urging "I should like to see on every important four corners in the open country four buildings— on one a general assembly place, as a town meeting hall or a grange hall; on another corner I should like to see a building into which the products of the community, historical mementos, books, biographies of the inhabitants, and the like could be collected and preserved. . . . On another of the corners I should like to see a redirected rural school devoid of all fidgets and fads, which should be as much a native expression of the community as are the farms and the homes themselves. On the other of the four corners I should like to see a country church which would stand for aspirations and ideals, but which should have its roots, nevertheless, run deep into the indigenous affairs of the country. Everything with which men have to do needs to be spiritualized. This is much more effective for our civilization than merely to spiritualize things that we hope for." Bailey predicted that, "Some man some day will see the opportunity and seize it. The result of his work will be simply a new way of thinking, but it will eventuate into a new political and social economy. When his statue is finally cast in bronze, he will not be placed on a prancing steed nor surrounded by any symbols of carnage or of war. He will be a plain man in citizen's clothes, but he will stand on the ground and his face will be towards the daylight."

The college of agriculture had been removed from the old campus along the shore of Cayuga Lake, and placed to the east of the state veterinary college. The new site was elevated, on a hill, still part of the old Ezra Cornell farm. It had been an open field used for field crops and test-plats. Near the grounds the only agricultural building had been the old dairy building which was now the north wing of Goldwin Smith Hall, a new structure named to honor one of the university's early faculty members. On May 1, 1905, at the breaking ground ceremony preliminary to the building of Roberts Hall, ex-President White had spaded the earth and Bailey guided the plow, turning the first furrow. When on October 10, 1906, the first class was held in the new buildings, celebration exercises included speeches from members of the New York State Society for the Promotion of Agricultural Education and Research. Bailey made the opening address, recalling the years when the old college of agriculture had struggled vainly but arduously for an agricultural building. However, said Bailey, he was glad now that the old college had never gotten its building. For, a "thirty thousand dollar building would be all right for a new barn or equipping a poultry plant, but not for a College of Agriculture. If we had been given a building," he said, "we would be surrounded and cramped in by the other buildings on the Campus. Now we are right next to the farm, out in the edge of the country, as it should be. We now have a building with a floor space of more than three acres, and the best buildings in the United States, if not in the world, for a College of Agriculture." That same month, *Cornell Countryman*, the college's journal which Bailey had named, exulted editorially on the subject, "Our College Still Growing":

The eyes of the agricultural colleges of the country are turned on Cornell as it bursts from its chrysalis of years and emerges with an equipment and development which will be equalled by but few agricultural colleges, if any. The teaching work of the college with its new teachers, new buildings, and new equipment has expanded enormously. . . . The extension work of the college is being enlarged and rejuvenated. The winter courses are being strengthened and perfected. And, last of all, the investigational work is to be greatly aided and improved by the money placed at the disposal of the college by the Federal government. Much interest has been manifested in the development of fundamental research which this money has made possible. Director Bailey, when asked concerning this said:

"The federal funds are to be used exclusively for researches in underlying questions pertaining to agriculture. These funds are derived from the Hatch Act of 1887 and the Adams Act of 1906. It is the intention to secure the services of a very few high-class men, whose entire energies will be devoted to these fundamental and continuing investigations. These persons will not teach under-graduates, and will not be called on to engage in other and irrelevant work. This arrangement will in no way lessen the amount of experimental work of the regular departments of the college. These departments will pursue their accustomed work on the state extension funds, publishing bulletins as rapidly as their experiments and tests mature."

Beginning with the year 1906 the financial support and physical equipment of the New York State College of Agriculture grew steadily. The same year that the new buildings were formally dedicated the state of New York appropriated $50,000 for completion of building equipment, and $25,000 for barns. That year, also, the maintenance fund was enlarged to the unprecedented sum of $150,000. In 1908 the maintenance figure remained the same but in 1909 it was increased to $175,-000, and in 1910 to $200,000, and by 1911 had reached the almost unheard of sum of $225,000.

In 1908 $30,000 was allowed by the state for greenhouses, and $10,000 for extension work. In 1909 the same amount was authorized for extension work and the sum was not increased until 1910 when, as a part of a huge expansion program—which made provision for an auditorium, poultry husbandry building, and home economics building, together with, in 1911, a heating plant and $20,000 for a barn—the allowance made for extension work became $12,000. The year 1912 was to see authorization of construction of two animal husbandry buildings, a forestry building, and a building used by 1914 as a soils building. The year 1913 would bring legislative appropriations for greenhouse extension, for barns, for model school houses, for extension of the poultry plant, and other equipment and additions. And the maintenance appropriation figure would approximate in round figures a half million dollars.[48] Seldom, if at any time, in as many years, has an American agricultural college experienced such growth. Furthermore, all of it took place under Bailey's administration as dean and director—except complete realization of the 1910 building expansion program which was authorized while Bailey was on sabbatical leave and Herbert John Webber served as acting dean and director. However, Bailey had planned this program and, upon returning to the university from his leave, put into working operation a strong, flexible, and substantial ten-year plan for the college's future growth and development. Under Bailey's administration, the farm holdings of the New York State College of Agriculture, exclusive of those of the New York State Veterinary College of 100 acres, were increased to 579 acres for farming purposes. These purchases were completed as early as 1908; and later the college obtained, by gift and otherwise, title to other lands.

The demonstrated value of research to agriculture, of course, was the root source of the college's power. Research, however, was not altogether "pure science." It also embraced statistical and economic studies of social and agricultural conditions in selected regions, not entirely alike, but similar in methods and techniques employed, to Bailey's earlier horticultural surveys. Progress in American science since its transition from almost solely taxonomic investigations to studies of processes within materials has involved largely refinements of methodology and techniques and the discovery of new phenomena. Statistical studies have aided the new work. The most immediate and popular results were obtained by agriculturists from surveys which at Cornell embraced four general types: (1) a survey of agricultural resources and needs of a particular region or area, a part of the country-life movement, based on statistical rather than observational inquiry of farm experience and experiment, and illustrated by the university's Tompkins County survey initiated by George F. Warren and others in 1906 and continued several years; (2) pomological inquiries initiated by Bailey years before and elaborated by a statistical or census method and calculation of results (a method begun as early as 1903-1904 by Warren and Craig, and others, and illustrated by studies of apple-growing in Wayne and Orleans counties, in which it was believed "the

[48] These facts and figures are mainly taken from Bailey's article, "The Later Financial and Physical Development of the College of Agriculture," *Cornell Countryman*, XII, no. 3 (December, 1914), pp. 196-198.

first attempts to determine the average profits as a basis of comparison of the numerous methods of raising crops" were made) ; (3) the soils or farm management surveys, methods of work which were perfected by 1908 and aimed to study conditions from the profit standpoint "to find what conditions and types of farming result in the largest profit, or labor income" (a method which inquired into all physical and biological factors but, more, which based the calculations on statistical data, as illustrated by the Livingston and Montgomery counties' surveys) ; and (4) study of the trucking interests of Long Island where years later Cornell University would maintain a vegetable research farm. Bulletins of these studies were immediately in widespread demand and their value to the college's agricultural work, and that of the state, was inestimable. To say the least, evaluation was difficult because of their breadth and many avenues of influence.

Sound research was predicated also in more "purely" scientific, experimental investigation. There, too, new channels of exploration and vistas for future accomplishment were so numerous that exact appraisals, except inferentially, were exceedingly difficult, if not impossible. Measurements by dollars and cents standards might convey some notion of the value of what had been accomplished, or, what was possible for the future. Such prognostications were few in numbers, especially from the workers themselves. Intelligent estimates and forecasts were made, but, generally to inform the public and the sciences of what was being done, and its probable and possible values and uses. Today, we, having the benefit of hindsight and the results of time's tests, know that purely scientific research in plants, as in other fields of objective science, have enlarged and widened horizons beyond the dreams and predictions of these years. Agricultural and horticultural productions have expanded the plant industries, and their value, almost beyond estimate or calculation. Presently we will examine some illustrations of this.

Of the worth of "pure science" and its researches Bailey was as much an advocate and supporter as of other types of inquiry. Researches under the federal Hatch Act, that is, those experimental investigations begun during the early years of the American experiment stations dealt largely with practical and more immediate problems. By 1906, however, when the federal Adams Act was passed by Congress, progress in plant breeding, and the rise of theoretical studies in genetics, had established the practical worth of the study of fundamental biological problems for their own sake. For example, the delineation of laws of hybrid vigor in corn by George Harrison Shull while botanical investigator of the Station for Experimental Evolution at Cold Spring Harbor, Long Island, was of tremendous significance in the development of hybrid corn. While not the discoverer of hybrid vigor, Shull was to outline a program for its use, and Donald F. Jones would add to the program by introducing the double cross. Confining ourselves for the moment to the plant breeding-genetics relationship, one may refer to the work of Rollins Adams Emerson, Nebraska university graduate and H. J. Webber's brother-in-law, who in 1898 had begun breeding beans in the yard of Webber's Washington, D.C., residence, to test in another plant group some general conclusions of Bailey in pumpkins, melons, and cucurbits. While Emerson was naturally interested in producing new bean varieties he was much more interested in arriving at an understanding of laws of heredity. Few, if any, predecessors were ahead of Emerson in this special type of study which, to all intents, sought exclusively to investigate by exact experimental methods the genesis of plants, combining cytological, morphological, and breeding knowledge. This bean study was continued at the University of Nebraska where for a number of years Emerson taught.

One of the first formal courses in plant breeding given in an American university was presented there by Emerson in the department of horticulture. It will be remembered that, by 1899, plant breeding had become a dominant theme in scientific scholarship. Students were returning from study abroad to coordinate their newly acquired scholarship in physiology, morphology, and cytology, with the progressive research being furthered in America in a number of centers, principally, so far as the plant sciences were concerned, in the universities and experiment stations. By this time, although at first the work suffered at the hands of an agricultural committee a disappointingly small appropriation, the United States Department of Agriculture was expanding its plant breeding activities by a planned program under Webber. The federal workers continued to disseminate knowledge of what had been and could be accomplished. Activity was widespread. Many scholars were engaged in various crop specializations. Perhaps a few, certainly not every one, however, realized that two new scientific departments were being nurtured among the branches of plant science study in America. Authorities for some time to come may differ as to when the sciences of genetics and ecology attained maturity in this country. Certainly, although neither had risen to the stature of independently organized subjects of knowledge, the origins of each were being developed on this continent. In each, progress in Europe was advanced considerably over America. But Americans were learning and, even as they already had done in a few special ways in plant pathology and physiology, in taxonomy, and in other fields of greater or less specialization, they would soon be supplying new leadership, both in work and men, in genetics and ecology, and rival effectively the decades-long supremacy and prestige of Europe, whether in animal or plant study.

The United States Department of Agriculture had begun to enter into cooperative agreements with state agricultural experiment stations —agreements analogous to arrangements established by the division of forestry and state stations. One such was negotiated with the Nebraska agricultural experiment station. On May 30, 1899, Emerson at Lincoln reported to Webber at Washington:

> . . . The corn has not been all planted yet. Part of it is up and doing well. I was delayed in getting the work started on account of the late spring and because the Director did not decide what department should do the work until recently. The spring is nearly a month late. Very little corn is more than two inches high. I think the season will be long enough for the corn to mature all right even though the planting has been done a little late. I presume also that you will be home [from Europe] before the corn blossoms. If you are not however, I shall be glad to attend to the crossing personally. I am much interested in the work and shall see that it goes along all right.
>
> I am crossing plants rather promiscuously this year. I succeeded in getting a very few crosses of the common cherries with Sand Cherry pollen but failed in the reciprocal crosses. Yesterday and today I have been crossing Loniceras, of which we have three species now in blossom. I have made a collection of violets for crossing this winter if I can get them to bloom. The collection so far includes about twenty plants of each of the three species growing commonly about Lincoln, but I hope to add others. I shall also have some cultivated ones to use this next winter. If I fail to get the wild violets to bloom in the winter, I shall try them in the field next spring. One of my students is collecting for me and is becoming much interested in the work. He has had three or four years work in botany and is a good collector. He is going to work with the violets and wild roses. He will also do something with nasturtiums, of which I have about sixty varieties. His work is for university credit in my course in plant breeding. . . .
>
> I am getting some peculiar things in my bean work. One cross of two white-pod beans, one having white seeds and the other red seeds, is giving a bean with seeds spotted white, red, and purple and with pods very nearly the color of the seeds. . . .

On June 1, 1900, Emerson again told Webber of results with his bean experiments:

> . . . I have some very interesting things in the way of bean hybrids to show you when you come this summer. I find that the first generation of hybrids behave just as we should expect hybrids of distinct species to behave, that is, all the individuals of the first generation are, as a rule, intermediate between their parents and resemble each other very closely. In the second generation I get all sorts of variations including forms like both parents, intermediate forms, and forms that resemble neither parent. I am endeavoring to learn all I can of varieties of beans this year. You remember that I grew some forty varieties last year. This year I have secured over two hundred varieties including synonyms. Some fifteen or twenty of these are from British seedsmen and three from Japan. I did not get any varieties

from France, but shall endeavor to do so next year. Some of the varieties secured from England are the same, so far as I can see, as some varieties grown commonly in America. If the English seed has been grown there for several generations I shall have a chance to study the effect of two climates on the bean.

That same year, on October 16, melon hybrids were made the subject of another letter which Emerson sent to Webber:

. . . The first generation of melon hybrids behave practically the same as the first generation of bean hybrids, that is, individuals are more or less intermediate between the parents and are practically uniform in character, fully as uniform as well fixed varieties. . . .

Emerson had found "some interesting things . . . about corn [that] summer. Last year," he wrote, "I selected an ear of red corn from the field of yellow corn here on the farm and this spring planted the seed or a part of it. I was surprised this fall to find how strong the tendency is in this corn to produce red ears. . . ." During the previous March, he had told Webber, "Of course, we have many problems, but the one in which I am now especially interested is this: we want more varieties of hardy winter apples of good keeping qualities. The question is, how and where to get them. I expect to begin work in hybridizing sorts which are available for work here. . . ." Pomological matters, therefore, were combined with numerous special investigations in wheat culture, corn, potatoes, and other crops, and, in each, Emerson found some special problem of interest—the study of the effect of climate, of different soils, their propagation. Then, too, in addition to field work, greenhouse research required attention.

Emerson in 1898 had learned "something" of P. H. Dorsett's "work in selecting violets." On June 8, 1899, Galloway wrote him concerning violet crossing and selection and about a forthcoming study on violet culture being prepared by him. Emerson replied:

. . . I must confess that I am starting to cross violets with very little knowledge of what practical growers are doing or of what the public demands. A curiosity to know what I could do with the wild violets we have here is really responsible for my starting the work. Our native violets, like yours, are odorless so far as I know at present. This however does not deter me from attempting to breed from them. It is, you know, barely possible that the odor of some of our cultivated forms may be combined with the good features of some of our wild forms. If this proves impossible, it may be still possible to improve the wild violet in productiveness etc. by crossing with other kinds. One of our species is now used to a considerable extent in out-door gardens. . . . I presume I shall spend more time in trying to develop something from our wild violets that will prove hardy for outdoor growth than I shall in attempting to improve for cut flowers. . . .

An answer to a controversial issue current in many universities was incidentally contained in this letter. In larger scope, the question of whether pure or practical science should dominate research was not new but the urgent need of delimitation of functions and of some definite settlement of the question itself in university laboratories and experiment stations was becoming more evident with each passing year. In those universities where there was no agricultural college and to which no experiment station was attached, the subject was of particular moment. An agricultural college and an experiment station were part of the University of Nebraska however. Director Charles Edwin Bessey's motto, "Science with practice," a decade or two before had done much to shape a new course of study in botany. Emerson seems to have believed that pure science would win out. But he was not in a vast company of workers who interested themselves primarily in fundamental studies in crop biology.

The influence of Bailey's instruction and writing on Emerson was shown in the latter's letter to Webber dated December 18, 1899, concerning a plan of Webber's for the conduct of a "corn experiment" at the University of Nebraska the next year:

. . . I have a copy of Bailey's "Evolution of Native Fruits" and have read a considerable part of it. I find it interesting and full of suggestions. I shall be very glad to have you suggest any lines of work that you think I can carry on profitably here. I am always glad of suggestions, and know of no one who is better able to offer them along lines of plant improvement than you.

Dr. Clements and I have just started some work in the greenhouse that will probably be interesting to you. We are growing five cultivated and six wild plants, representing many types of vegetation, under different conditions of moisture, temperature, and soil. We are keeping accurate records of the temperature and relative humidity of the different rooms of the greenhouse, of the amount of water applied to the soil and the percentage of moisture in the soil. Of course we shall watch the behavior of the plants under the different conditions very closely and note any peculiarities that they may take on. It is our intention to grow the same plants through several generations. We hope to obtain results of value to Horticulturists who are engaged in plant breeding and to Botanists who are interested in ecology.

Some of Emerson's undergraduate work at the University of Nebraska had been done under one of Bailey's early Cornell students, Fred W. Card. During the winter of 1898-1899 Emerson himself studied at Cornell, and took courses under Bailey. Although he planned to take his doctorate at Cornell University, because of circumstances extrinsic to college work, he later went to Harvard and acquired his advanced degree under Edward Murray East, one of America's first great geneticists.

It is unnecessary to elaborate each of the progressive differentiations which developed between the work of the plant breeder, more interested

Plant Breeding and Experimentation 321

in the product, the end result, and the geneticist, more interested in the fundamental facts, the mechanism, of the plant. Hybrid corn provides fairly completely and demonstrably an illustration.

Since the years of Beal at Michigan Agricultural College, it had been known that vigor in corn was increased by crossing different varieties. Indeed, Darwin, and even Gray, had studied and written on beneficial results obtained from cross fertilizing plants. But neither Beal nor Darwin, nor Gray recognized the invigorating effects of cross-breeding as hybrid vigor. As early as 1881, it is said, Beal grew his first crossing plot in which one variety was detasseled and pollinated by the other.[49] During three years, crossed plants yielded more than the open-pollinated parents. G. N. Collins, in another study of the subject, "Increased Yields of Corn from Hybrid Seed,"[50] mentions that Beal demonstrated as early as 1878 that corn yields could be increased by crossing different strains. He added: "No less than four times during the thirty years following Dr. Beal's experiments the possibility of increasing the yield of corn by the crossing of two varieties was independently demonstrated, and each time without knowledge of previous demonstrations." For our purpose, the point of historical interest in the creation of hybrid corn was stated by Singleton, who commented: "Apparently the increased yields were not sufficient to create any interest in hybrid corn. Hybrid corn as we know it to-day owes its origin to an experiment in theoretical genetics."

By 1904, of course, the investigation of Mendelian phenomena in plants was on the increase. Emerson, while yet at the University of Nebraska, and as horticulturist of the state's agricultural experiment station, widened the scope of his melon and bean studies of heredity by instituting important Mendelian investigations in corn, a subject, which, when he was brought to Cornell University on the strength of recommendations from Webber and East, laid the basis for him to develop, in addition to the already thoroughly established plant breeding work of the college of agriculture, a flourishing school of genetics specializing in corn and other crops important to New York state and the nation.

The introductory years of the twentieth century were not confined to Mendelian inquiries, as has been shown. De Vries's mutation theory also had come under the scrutiny of several resourceful, careful, American workers. In 1904 George Harrison Shull had received the degree of Doctor of Philosophy from the University of Chicago and was appointed botanical investigator of the new Station for Experimental Evolution at Cold Spring Harbor, Long Island. While awaiting com-

[49] W. Ralph Singleton, "Hybrid Vigor and Its Utilization in Sweet Corn Breeding," *The American Naturalist*, LXXV (January-February, 1941), pp. 48-60.
[50] *Yearbook* for 1910, pp. 319-328, at p. 320.

pletion of the station and its facilities, Shull had collaborated with Daniel Trembly MacDougal in the work of the experimental garden, modeled after that of De Vries in Amsterdam, Holland, and directed by MacDougal, who then was director of the botanical laboratories of the New York Botanical Garden, for the purpose of studying the De Vriesian conclusions.

When the Station for Experimental Evolution was dedicated, De Vries was invited by the Carnegie Institution of Washington, under whose auspices the station was maintained, to deliver the principal address of the occasion. Coincident with the time when Shull planned his program of research while in the employ of the station, he learned that an American scientist, one whose opinion was not to be disregarded, had criticized the mutation hypothesis on the ground that De Vries had artificially self-fertilized a plant which in nature is normally cross-fertilized, and that the mutation phenomena were the response to this artificial change in breeding procedure. On this assumption that the mutations were artifacts, they could have no significance for evolution in wild nature. Shull started out to determine what effect crossing and self-fertilization has on the frequency of occurrence of mutation. He received from De Vries ten rosettes of evening primrose taken from the same abandoned potato field at Hilversum, Holland, where De Vries had gotten his materials to perform his mutation experiments in 1885. With these ten rosettes, a system of crossbreeding was established by Shull in which every pedigreed family was the offspring of four distinct grandparents. To compare with the crossbred strain, the long self-fertilized lines from De Vries' experiments were secured and grown each year side by side with the crossbred material.

Since De Vries had emphasized a distinction between mutations and fluctuations, it occurred to Shull that it would be desirable to establish a parallel experiment to determine the influence of cross- and self-fertilization in a quantitative fluctuating character. For this experiment he considered the row number on the ears of corn to be particularly suitable. Since the evening primrose experiment was started with completely uncontrolled wild material it seemed desirable that the corn experiment should be made with material which had not been a part of a formal breeding program. Consequently, the corn used to begin this experiment was that purchased in the feed market and was already on hand at the Station for Experimental Evolution when this experiment was begun.

Of Shull's experiments and their consequences, Singleton of the Connecticut station at New Haven has written:

In the summer of 1905 he made his first self-pollinations to study what effect selfing a normally cross-breeding plant would have on the inheritance of a "fluctuating" character. He found a marked reduction in vigor upon inbreeding with the subsequent increase in vigor when different lines were crossed. With comparatively few data Shull immediately made an accurate analysis of what was happening. He discovered that the inbreeding was separating the heterogeneous maize plant into a number of pure lines, or biotypes. The pure lines when crossed not only gave a vigorous hybrid, but produced for the first time a maize variety whose heredity could be rigidly controlled.

Here Shull's experiments opened a new era in maize breeding. Controlled heredity is the factor that has made hybrid corn so superior to open-pollinated varieties. Before Shull all the progress in corn breeding had been made by the use of mass selection, and with considerable success by many practical corn breeders. Shull proposed an entirely different attack—a method of first isolating pure lines, and then crossing them to give a uniform, more dependable result. His two classic papers, "The Composition of a Field of Maize" and "A Pure Line Method in Corn Breeding," outline the method in use to-day.

Edward Murray East of the Connecticut agricultural experiment station heard of Shull's paper, "A Composition of a Field of Maize," presented before a meeting of the American Breeders' Association in January, 1908, and sent for a copy. During the years 1906-1908, Shull, as a part of his employment by the Station for Experimental Evolution, had been directed to study the work of European and American breeders, and, when East's request reached him, he was at Santa Rosa, California, at Burbank's farm. Shull answered East:

I am glad to find that your extensive experiments in corn breeding might have led you to the same conclusion as that at which I have arrived, and that you are going to base your experimentation to some extent upon this view. I am convinced that there is a wide open field here which has not been touched heretofore. There is little doubt in my mind that if I had held on to my idea of the composition of a field of corn until I could have worked out some of the subsidiary problems, I could have raised a monument to myself which would be worthy to stand with the best biological work of recent times. But the matter seemed to me of too great importance in view of the value of our maize crop to selfishly keep it to myself longer than was necessary to assure myself of its correctness.[51]

The following year Shull's address, "A Pure Line Method in Corn Breeding," also given before the American Breeders' Association, conveyed by its title the name of the method he had chosen to propose the procedure in corn production which since has come to be known as

[51] The latest, and perhaps the most authoritative, discussion of this subject has been prepared by Donald F. Jones, himself an eminent contributor in the production of hybrid corn as it is known today, as a part of his biographical memoir of "Edward Murray East," written at the request of the National Academy of Sciences, and published in volume XXIII (1945), pp. 217-242. This letter, as well as others which passed between East and Shull during these years, is included and taken therefrom.

hybrid corn.[52] In this paper, Shull stressed the importance of the essential distinction of the advantages to be gained by using pure strains rather than mixed varieties. Several years later, in 1914, this was followed by an invitation lecture in Goettingen, Germany, where he specifically urged both animal and plant breeders to make conscious use of heterosis (hybrid vigor) as a source of economic gains in breeding.

From the inception of Shull's pronouncements, the possibility enunciated was specialization of the crop to attain any desired objective. World wide attention of animal breeders and breeders of other crops was attracted. The production of hybrid corn was to rank in economic merit beside any American triumph of the first decades of the century. Edgar Anderson, in his recently published study of "Maize," in *New Crops for the New World*,[53] has pictured how hybrid corn " 'caught on' slowly year by year until its great advantages for modern standardized, mechanized farming were adequately demonstrated, and then the whole corn belt switched to hybrid corn almost overnight. . . ." To Shull's work has been added the "major contribution" of Donald F. Jones of the Connecticut station—the double cross, so-called—and the practical application of principles notably by Henry A. Wallace, former Vice President of the United States and former Secretary of Agriculture and Secretary of Commerce.[54]

Shull has been happy to acknowledge that a "whole field of workers . . . each in his own way [have] helped to bring the hybrid corn program with truly amazing speed so far on its way to full fruition. . . ." In his recent address on the subject,[55] in addition to East, Wallace, Jones, and Singleton, he has named F. D. Richey, Merle T. Jenkins, "and many other workers at the Agricultural Experiment Stations, as well as at least a dozen great commercial companies," who have carried on after he had performed his part of the program.

It was Shull, however, who made the fundamental analysis, elaborated the twelve propositions or laws of hybrid vigor—though he received no monetary compensation for the product from which millions of dollars have been made by many persons. It is true also that Webber, for instance, realized little, if any, direct financial profit from his improvements in cotton, yet his productions added millions of dollars to the value of the industry. Carleton's macaroni or durum wheats en-

[52] *Science*, no. 103, 2679 (May 3, 1946), pp. 547-550, a recent address made by Shull at a formal ceremony when, because of his part in hybrid corn production, he became a recipient from the John Scott Medal Fund.
[53] New York: The Macmillan Company, 1945. Pp. 27-42, at p. 33.
[54] "Hybrid Seed Corn," *Science*, 103, no. 2679 (May 3, 1946), p. 547.
[55] As a part of a symposium on applied botanical research on maize, Secretary of Agriculture H. A. Wallace addressed the Iowa Corn Research Institute on "Six Decades of Corn Improvement and the Future Outlook," *Symposia Commemorating Six Decades of the Modern Era in Botanical Science*, I, nos. 1-3, reprinted from the *Iowa State College Journal of Science*, IX, nos. 2 and 3 (1935), pp. 347-352.

riched even more the national economy, yet it did not bring him a fortune. Other instances of a wide disparity between the magnitude and
value of a scientific accomplishment in plant study, and an inconsiderable return for, even lack of real recognition of, the fundamental initiator, exist. Their profit has been realized in the joy of knowing what
they have done. They commenced as scholars. They have been content
to remain scholars. The criticism of our social system is not that they
do not become wealthy, but that the greatness of their achievements
passes too much unknown and taken for granted by a large majority
of our people.

East admitted immediately after reading Shull's paper, "The Composition of a Field of Maize," that he agreed with the latter's conclusion,
and regretted that his depth of insight had nòt enabled him to discover
"the fact" for himself. He planned to make use of the paper, add data
of his own, in a forthcoming station report, and obtain more data the
following summer "in connection with some corn crossing experiments"
which he had planned. Moreover, after reading "A Pure Line Method
in Corn Breeding," he wrote to Shull again that the former paper had
given him his "first idea of inbreeding separating the biotypes and that
on this hinged the whole matter. . . ." Further, he had told Director
Jenkins of the Connecticut station that "Dr. Shull had just sent [him]
a paper that gave [them] the 'hunch' [they] had been wanting about
[their] inbred corn plants. . . ." East said that he had been studying
"crosses and self-fertilized maize" since 1902. Shull was not concerned
as to who had arrived at the discovery first. "What we are most concerned in," he wrote East, "is the *triumph* of the *truth* and especially of
useful truth." The test of time, however, has granted to Shull the honor
of being the originator of hybrid corn. Even though others added to
the procedure and in a sense solved "the subsidiary problems," of which
Shull wrote in 1908.[56]

For many years Shull sought to interest the agricultural experiment
stations in his pure line breeding method. He continued his corn experiments until 1916, and in that year grew his last crop. In 1914,
Professor Edwin Grant Conklin, chairman of the department of biology
at Princeton University, had chosen Shull to supply the botanical instruction at that institution. Dr. Conklin had sought a botanist who
was also a geneticist, and Shull qualified as a leading authority in both
attributes. He, therefore, left the Station for Experimental Evolution,
and, as the years have gone by, Shull has devoted his time, principally,
to genetical investigations in Oenothera and Shepherd's purse, but
many plants, and many points of research, have been dealt with by this

[56] Jones's biographical memoir of East, *op. cit.*; see introductory note to address,
"Hybrid Seed Corn," *op. cit.*

scientist. Founder of the Scientific journal, *Genetics*, and for many years its editor, defender of and possibly the first to use the word "gene" in the English language, Shull has a long list of achievements, most of which more appropriately should be elaborated in a book devoted to the history of the science of genetics in America. Today he is regarded as a leading authority on the genetics of Oenothera. He has grown more than a million pedigreed Shepherd's purse and more than three quarters of a million pedigreed evening primroses. In 1916, his discovery of a first typical gene mutation led to a very considerable expansion of Oenothera cultures. Although he has not grown as many Oenotheras as corn plants, each season from 1904 until 1943, he continued these researches of intrinsic genetical and economic value, from whence his corn work had begun.

Recommended by Bateson who had become acquainted with him while on a visit to America, East was chosen in 1909 to serve as an assistant professor of experimental plant morphology at Harvard University. East, too, turned from corn work and centered his investigations on another plant—Nicotiana. As a student of chemistry, East had been graduated from the University of Illinois at the turn of the century. For his master of science degree, obtained in 1904 from the same institution, he prepared a thesis on chemical and bacteriological studies on the self-purification of running streams. East in 1897 had also had one year at Case School of Applied Science at Cleveland, Ohio. Quite naturally, his employment at the Illinois Agricultural Experiment Station, during his years at Urbana, had been as a chemist, and he had been Hopkins' assistant. At about the time that Dr. Hopkins organized a department of agronomy at the university and Louie Henrie Smith took charge of the famous Illinois research, altering and increasing the chemical composition as to oil and protein in corn, East began dividing his time between chemical analyses as a part of corn work and took up the study of Mendelian characters in maize. By 1904 or 1905 he was selfing corn to study the effects of inbreeding. In Europe, the notable progress made in selecting beets for higher sugar content had strongly stimulated the believers in the possibility of breeding to remedy protein and fat deficiencies in corn. We have already pointed out that in the United States progress in these researches was watched with interest. A disclosure as early as 1892 by E. H. Jenkins and Winton of the Connecticut agricultural experiment station that the protein content in corn kernels ranged as much as 8.2 to 17 per cent of dry weight had suggested that the research was not without a valid basis.

By 1905 Jenkins had become director of the Connecticut station. He requested that someone be sent from the Illinois station to New Haven to expand the Connecticut station's plant improvement program. He had read several bulletins prepared by Hopkins, Smith, and East which analyzed the chemical content of individual corn ears, and he welcomed the choice of East who had been recommended. In the autumn of 1905 East went to Connecticut where he was to continue research in breeding corn, potato, and tobacco crops. The last especially was regarded as very important in view of Shamel's experimental work in tobacco breeding in the Connecticut valley for the United States Department of Agriculture. Shamel also had done some corn work at the Illinois station. He and East, therefore, had a mutual interest. Eventually, tobacco breeding in Connecticut culminated in the establishment of the Windsor Tobacco Station. East took his doctorate at the University of Illinois in 1907, and his dissertation, published as a station bulletin, was entitled, "A Study of the Factors Influencing the Improvement of the Potato."[57] East was brought to Connecticut to start a department of agronomy and officially he was listed as agronomist. The Illinois corn work, however, had grown out of that station's chemistry and soils departments, from studies in plant and animal nutrition and nutritive ratios in protein, carbohydrate, fat, vitamin, and mineral content. Jones has written:[58]

Before he left Illinois East had begun an experiment that was to have far reaching results. After the selection experiments at Illinois had been going for some time it was noted that as the percent of protein or oil was increased the yield of grain was decreased to a point where the actual amount of the ingredients was no more or even less than that produced at the start. The decrease in yield was the result of an indirect inbreeding effect. The experiment was started with several hundred individual ears. As the experiment progressed the progenies of the high analyzing ears were retained and increased in numbers and the others discarded. In a few years the lines actually being grown had all descended from only a few ears at the start. Although there was no controlled pollination the intensive selection resulted in the narrowing of the network of descent.

After an unsuccessful attempt to interest Hopkins to undertake an experiment to study primarily the effects of inbreeding, East self-fertilized a number of corn plants by bagging the ears and tassels and applying the pollen at the proper time. From these self-fertilized seeds a number of inbred lines were started and brought to Connecticut and formed the beginning of an experiment that [was] continued. . . .

East's first crosses between inbred strains were grown in Connecticut, it is said, in 1908. At first, he did not regard Shull's proposal in

[57] In 1909-1910 East also wrote on "The Transmission of Variations in the Potato in Asexual Reproduction," and in 1910 *American Naturalist* published his paper, "Inheritance in Potatoes." Attention is called also to East and Jones's *Inbreeding and Outbreeding*: Their Genetic and Sociological Significance (Philadelphia: J. B. Lippincott Co., 1919), pp. 285.

[58] "History of the Genetics Department of the Connecticut Agricultural Experiment Station," a paper presented by Jones on February 23, 1943, and which has been utilized in considerable part as a basis of the foregoing discussion.

this regard as practicable, believing more in crossing selected strains or varieties which had been reduced to uniformity.[59] East went to Harvard in 1909 and his place was taken by Herbert K. Hayes who in 1914 went to the University of Minnesota to develop further that institution's inbred studies. During the course of the next decade, many corn inbreeding programs, conducted in numerous instances under cooperative arrangements with the bureau of plant industry, were put into effect or expanded. Similar work in other crops with similar arrangements increased the effectiveness of the work for the nation enormously.

In a sense, therefore, it may be said that the work of the plant breeder laid the foundations for a science of genetics, and that genetics has refined and opened up a new science. The value of "pure science" was no more in question after genetics had proved its worth in dollars and cents. Unlimited possibilities, not to be gauged by ledger standards, were believed in by even the erstwhile skeptical. What a storehouse for man's welfare lay in solving the problems of heredity and disease, reproduction and nutrition in animals and plants, sterility and fertility, vigor and weakness, not excluding the explanation of genius in man himself.

The creation of the Adams Fund by Congress was wisdom in action. Not until the Connecticut station's 1911 report, it is said, was reference made to the use of that fund. There it was stated that the appropriation was being "devoted to a study of the laws of inheritance in maize and tobacco and a study of the comparative structure and nutritive value of the vegetable proteins." At the Cornell station, in 1909, Herbert J. Webber's department of experimental plant-breeding reported "work conducted under the Adams Act . . . to extend our knowledge of the fundamental laws of breeding." These involved studies on variation, on the laws of inheritance, of mutations and their use in breeding, on the cumulative action of selection, on correlation in breeding work, and on bud variations. To this day the New York State College of Agriculture has maintained a department of plant breeding.[60] When Emerson would be appointed to take Webber's position as head of the department, the department still would be known as plant-breeding.

The demonstration of the value to biology of research in fundamental plant problems, especially Mendelian researches, and the proof of their worth in millions of dollars to the agricultural and horticultural world, were two of the truly great accomplishments of the early decades of the twentieth century. As Webber commented in his arti-

[59] Biographical memoir of East by Jones, op. cit.
[60] For a partial summary of the work of this department, and its history, see articles, "Investigations Conducted by the Department of Plant Breeding," by H. H. Love and C. H. Myers, Cornell Countryman, xi, 1 (October, 1913), p. 11; and "Plant Breeding," by C. H. Myers, ibid., ix, 6 (March, 1912), p. 175; also numerous articles in Cornell Countryman issues by H. J. Webber, beginning about 1907 and continuing to about 1912.

cle[61] published in 1912 by *American Breeders' Magazine*, the researches on the study of hybrids "by Mendel, Bateson, Davenport, Castle, Punnett, Shull, Hurst, Correns, Tschermak, East, and a dozen of other now well known investigators have developed a science of heredity of which we had no conception a few years ago." This was in addition to a tremendously valuable increase in food production and knowledge how to obtain still larger food supplies and opportune uses. Bailey foresaw this: he predicted its coming in the last editions of his book, *Plant Breeding*, and in numerous utterances. What he had always pleaded for was a general and gradual uplifting of the vegetable kingdom. Most certainly such was being effectively and abundantly realized.

Bailey knew Senator Adams of Wisconsin very well and had many conferences with him as to purposes of his bill and the program to be adopted. Many others, naturally, had influence; since the subject was of such great importance numerous persons were consulted. Probably Dean W. A. Henry of the University of Wisconsin had had as much influence on the senator's viewpoint as anyone. Not a dozen but hundreds of leaders were in American agriculture by now. On March 16, 1906, President Theodore Roosevelt approved the Adams bill, which meant, so far as the New York State College of Agriculture was concerned, in five years an annual fund would accrue in the sum of $27,000, which would "be set aside sacredly for research on fundamental problems." Variety tests, trials, advice, and information would not be regarded as research within the meaning of this act. The fund would be devoted wholly to what Bailey termed "real investigation." With industrial fellowships and ample scholarships the college was in good financial circumstances.

In view of great progress being made in plant breeding and studies of heredity, part of the Adams research fund money went to the department of experimental plant breeding. In 1907 Bailey reported:

We have . . . organized on the Federal funds a department of soil inquiry with Dr. [Thomas Lyttleton] Lyon at its head, and a department of plant biology. . . . The only other department that receives any maintenance from the Federal fund is the entomological work in which one man is supported from these sources. The men who are employed on the Federal funds expected to give all their time to research. They teach no undergraduate students, but they may take a limited number of post-graduates, who will become practically assistants in the investigational work. For the work of these two departments two small greenhouses are now being erected and will be ready for occupancy this coming winter.

Lyon had returned to his alma mater from Nebraska where he was well known because of having introduced "dry soil" crops into arid

61 "The Effects of Research in Genetics on the Art of Breeding," III, 2, pp. 125-134.

regions. In 1908, he outlined an elaborate program to investigate "the principles of the soil that affect its productiveness" and promote "that knowledge of the properties of soils and their relation to plant growth, the possession of which is necessary for the intelligent conduct of the more immediately practical experimentation."[62]

This work in soil technology—a study of effects of particular methods of soil treatment on soil properties and plant growth—should not be confused with that of the department of soils under assistant professor E. O. Fippin. The latter was enlarging knowledge of principles such as soil granulation and movements of soil moisture, also conducting experiments with farmers in matters of tillage, fertilizers, drainage, and the like. On its own initiative and in conjunction with the federal Bureau of Soils it was pursuing the work of soil surveys covering wide areas of the state. Since the college's reorganization in 1904 there had been work in soils investigation. Jay A. Bonsteel had been assigned by the federal bureau to carry on soil study at Cornell, and for *Cornell Countryman* in March, 1904, he had prepared an article, "Soil Surveys in the United States," an illuminating discussion of the American history of this branch of agronomic study.

Soil distribution had been investigated like plant distribution. Like plants, soils had been classified in types. For more than a half-century, within the colleges, formal examinations of soils in the United States had been revealing an exceedingly complex and diversified subject, so much so that to organize a science on a continental scale promised a work which would require extensive laboratory facilities throughout the nation and a large corps of highly trained specialists. Here again, practical farmers, from the earliest years of settlement of the continent, had been supplying a body of knowledge, susceptible of being tested, organized, and extended by experimental research. State geological surveys, their history going back at least as far as the classic New York survey conducted in parts of the state by Amos Eaton, had utilized traditional and time-honored groupings indicated by mineralogy and chemistry. Soils analysis emphasized preeminently texture, organic matter, physical and chemical properties, and the like. When correlated, however, to geological formations and types of vegetation, as well as climatic influences, temperature, rainfall, evaporation, moisture, and other biologic and physical factors, soils, including forest soils, as instruments of academic study, attracted a much more substantial, although somewhat belated, scholarly adherence. As agronomic research more and more would become correlated with the sciences of plants and ani-

---

[62] For a discussion of the experimental soils work done at Cornell under Lyon and others, see his article, "Soil Experiments on Caldwell Field," *Cornell Countryman,* XI, 1 (October, 1913), pp. 4-11.

mals, there would grow and flourish a movement toward a world-wide agriculture, and experts and specialists would visit world regions, studying the older civilizations and the causes of their decline and advancements, agriculturally. On the North American continent, the scientific emphasis accorded ecologic research in field and forest, along river and lake, on the deserts and near oceans, in the mountains and on prairies and lowlands, in a few words, everywhere where plant societies could be found, extended technical knowledge greatly. For, to understand plants of cultivation, the necessity to understand growth factors and origins of all plants of nature, qualitatively and quantitatively, with exactness, was clearly realized. Coordinating vegetational areas and crop centers by mapping their ranges in the light of objective science, as, by showing a ratio between rainfall and evaporation in given regions, or, the genetic development and relationships of various plants and plant communities to environmental influences, brought ecology and agriculture, including forestry, into close harmony as working partners. Soils study figured fundamentally in arriving at verifiable understandings of plant functions and physiological processes.

Not until 1893 did the United States Secretary of Agriculture appropriate a substantial sum, $3,000, to undertake a special investigation of the different typical soils of the United States to determine their chemical character, their physical properties, and especially the nature of the nitrifying organisms which they contain. In colleges and experiment stations—prominent among them, California, Maryland, South Carolina, and Wisconsin—creative agronomic research had been in progress. Interest of students as well as practical farmers—at the Department of Agriculture and elsewhere—was strongly aroused. More and more work such as that of Charles W. Dabney, Jr., in Tennessee and Milton Whitney in Maryland came into prominence during the 1890's. Bonsteel related:[63]

In 1892 many correlations of soils with geological formations were prepared by different states for exhibition at the World's Columbian Exposition. Maryland prepared, in this year, the first soil map based on the texture and physical properties of soils. The work was done by Professor Milton Whitney, now chief of the Bureau of Soils, United States Department of Agriculture, in co-operation with the Johns Hopkins University authorities.

In 1897 Dabney of the Tennessee Experiment Station made extensive studies of the soils of that state, and published a bulletin and a map which correlated the soils with the geological formations. The bulletin gives not only chemical analyses but also mechanical analyses made by Professor Whitney.

[63] *Cornell Countryman*, I, 4, p. 108. See also another article on the same subject in the first volume of the *Cyclopedia of American Agriculture*, pp. 526-531, "Soil Surveys and Their Significance," by Milton Whitney and Bonsteel. There the work of Whitney in Maryland and Hilgard in Mississippi and California are more thoroughly described.

A year later the Division of Soils at Washington made a map of the soils of the Hagerstown valley, Maryland, which has never been published, although the text of the accompanying report was published by the Maryland Agricultural College.

With the year 1899 the work of the soil survey under federal direction began. Methods for the field determination and classification of soils had been devised. These methods were based chiefly on the physical properties of soils such as their texture or coarseness of grain, their structure or the arrangement of grains, on their drainage and to some extent upon their content of organic matter. . . .

But it should also be noticed that at first field work, save in unusual instances, did not stress mapping the boundaries of soil types, ascertaining the most fruitful adaptation of crops to soils;[64] in other words, the work was more taxonomic than physiological in its implications. Certainly one of, if not, the first soils experimental fields established at a university in the United States was at the University of Illinois —the historic "Morrow Plots," a farsighted and advanced work initiated by Dean George E. Morrow and modeled after the soil-crop researches of Rothamstead. Morrow used corn as the basic crop. "These rotation experiments," Dean Davenport, his successor, has written, "are the more to his credit because, at the time he began them, it was the current conviction that prairie soils would 'never wear out.' " The experiments were "showing a constantly declining yield at first at the rate of nearly a bushel a year as compared with rotation. . . ."

After the federal soil survey had gone west and east over large parts of the national domain, Illinois, as a state, was among the first to appropriate a large sum of money to enable its students to cooperate in field work and to follow the field mapping by experimental studies of its more important soil types.

The Illinois soil survey arose largely from the far-reaching leadership performed by Cyril George Hopkins, whose investigations and services as chemist, as specialist in soil fertility, and his vision of the soil treatment necessary to secure an agriculture of permanence, were signally outstanding. Hopkins made the first attempt to shift or alter permanently the chemical constitution of seeds, and devised plans to secure beneficial plant food elements at the least cost from leguminous crops, and in this alfalfa introductions figured. He suggested the soil survey plan. In the *Country Gentleman* (February 28, 1920) Davenport has told he suggested one evening: " 'the practice of making up a fertilizer before the character of the soil to which it is applied is known, is fundamentally and scientifically wrong.' I agreed. 'But,' he added,

---

[64] See another article by Bonsteel on "Soil Differences," *Cornell Countryman*, IV, 3 (December, 1906), pp. 68-70, where he pointed out that an increasing number of experiment stations and the Bureau of Soils were studying problems of crop adaptation and soil productivity.

'to know your soil means a soil survey not less than forty inches deep, and good enough to determine its invoice of plant food, and that is a costly undertaking.' Again I assented, but before we separated for the night we agreed to see whether we might not secure for Illinois a survey of her 'fertility invoice' sufficiently accurate and exhaustive to permit of a scientific treatment of her fertility problem."

Illinois fostered soil study with the federal government. Cornell University also was among the first state agencies to collaborate with the national government in intensive soils study.

Small wonder that by the school year 1906-1907 Bailey saw the need to split Cornell's department of agronomy into several coordinate units: farm practice, farm mechanics, farm management and farm crops, and other divisions. Adams' research funds went to experimental studies in soils. Had not Bailey been an advocate for years of practical and experimental soils investigation? Hilgard's great work on *Soils: their formation, properties, composition, and relations to climate and plant growth in the humid and arid regions*, was published in 1906. This truly great book was divided into four parts, twenty-six chapters, and, in 549 pages embodied in condensed form the essence of the author's researches and publications. Treating the origin, physics, and chemistry of soils, the volume's fourth part was devoted to a discussion of "Soil and Native Vegetation." Hilgard's work was important to practically every branch of plant science study, meteorology, physics, chemistry, geology, and even sociology, not to exclude entomology, forestry, botany, horticulture, and other studies connected with agriculture. An especially illuminating and appreciative review of this book, obviously the author's crowning masterpiece, was that published in *Science* (11, 24, pp. 681-684) and prepared by Franklin Hiram King.

King in 1901 had been appointed chief of the division of soil management in the United States Bureau of Soils, and for three years had studied crop yields and soil composition in relation to soil productivity. Author and reviewer, therefore, combined to evaluate the progress and status of American agronomic research to that time. King ranked in his own right as an authority. Having reported on matters of such fundamental importance as movement and conservation of soil water, soluble salts in relation to fertility, water requirements of crops, irrigation and drainage, protection of sandy soils from wind erosion by forest windbreaks and other agencies, and many other matters relating to good farming from the engineering, construction, and cultural standpoints, he had established for himself eminence as a founder of a science in rural engineering, as an agricultural physicist, chemist, physiographer and meteorologist, and agronomist. Not the least of his distinctions was as a geologist, in which science he had been schooled by no less a man than T. C. Chamberlin.

In his review, King pointed out: "Those who have been in the habit of attributing to Hilgard the view that physical properties and conditions of soils play but a small part in determining their productive capacity will be surprised at the amount of space devoted to soil physics. This is done, not because of any change of views. . . ." Hilgard had always insisted that "the greatest importance [be] attached to proper physical conditions as the first essential to a productive soil; and no one in America," King ventured, "has done as much as he to establish the causes of the physical differences in soils which are productive and which are unproductive, and to point out practicable methods for correcting evils when they are known to exist. It has been his strong insistence during these later years, when it has become a fashion to ignore chemical differences, that these too are very important in influencing productive capacity, that has given the impression to some that Hilgard regards physical differences as of comparatively slight moment." King concluded by unhesitatingly recommending the volume as one which "should be introduced to a much wider circle of students than those of the agricultural colleges generally. It will be found well suited to serve as the foundation of important seminars in chemistry, in geology, and especially in plant physiology and ecology." It had arrived contemporaneously "with the initiation of more rigid research work by the agricultural experiment stations, before the Bureau of Soils had been able to fully discern what should be its own precise problem, and when the materials for agricultural education have yet to be definitely brought together in proper pedagogic form." Particularly interesting was Hilgard's elucidation of plant indicators—tree growth combinations—which revealed the soil type, its value, durability, and capacity for growing crops. Nor were smaller plant forms excluded as indicators. To his credit may it be also said that most often he used the scientific designation of the plant.

Hilgard presented a mature view, several times reiterated: "the native vegetation represents within the climatic limits of the regional flora, the result of a secular process of adaptation of plants to climates and soils, by natural selection and the survival of the fittest. The natural floras and sylvas are the expression of secular, or rather millennial, experience, which if rightly interpreted must convey to the cultivator of the soil the same information that otherwise he must acquire by long and costly experience."

During the summer of 1906 Bailey's desire for research and teaching in botany which would be better adapted to the needs of agriculture was implemented by his appointment of Herbert Hice Whetzel to be assistant professor of botany in the faculty of the college of agriculture. Whetzel was an enthusiastic person, who, in the summer of 1902, had come to the botanical department of Cornell's arts and science college, after four years of study in botany at Wabash College. He had studied under Mason Blanchard Thomas (Thomas was a former Cornell student under Prentiss, Dudley, and Gage, and one of the great teachers of botany during the two decades, 1893-1912. One of America's early courses in forestry was given by him). At Bailey's request Whetzel had given, during two winters before 1906, a course in plant diseases to winter course students and the work had been conducted in laboratories of the arts college's department. He had also carried on under Atkinson's direction in the years 1903-1906 the investigations on diseases of plants for which as botanist of the Cornell experiment station Atkinson was directly responsible.

It was at this point that another real innovation in plant science study at Cornell University took place. During the acadamic year 1906-1907 Whetzel not only continued to teach a course in plant diseases for winter course students but also gave the first course in plant pathology offered to regular undergraduates. Soils work in a sense was related to pathology. In fact, during 1907 Jacob G. Lipman of the New Jersey station lectured at Cornell on soil bacteriology.[65] The work of no one department was entirely separate from another. Agriculture in the larger sense was one work. Whetzel's courses, therefore, were of immediate potential significance. Emphasizing disease symptoms in investigation, the pathological effects of disease-producing organisms on the anatomy and physiology of plants, his methods, both in teaching and laboratory study, were distinctly different from those of mycologists of those years who studied the fungi, fungal life histories, their distribution, et cetera; indeed, Whetzel's teaching methods constituted a departure from the then prevalent method of teaching plant pathological problems, namely, a primary concern with etiology of diseases. Only in the research work of Erwin F. Smith at the United States Department of Agriculture laboratory for plant pathology was there an American prototype of Whetzel's vision and conception for the teaching and investigation of a subject which was to trail human and animal patho-

[65] Much valuable research on this subject had been conducted in the laboratories of the United States Department of Agriculture. See A. F. Woods' article, "The Present Status of the Nitrogen Problem," *Yearbook of the United States Department of Agriculture* for 1906 (Washington: Government Printing Office, 1907), pp. 125-136; Karl Kellerman, "The Functions and Value of Soil Bacteria," *Yearbook* for 1909, pp. 219-226; Karl Kellerman, "Nitrogen-Gathering Plants," *Yearbook* for 1910, pp. 213-218. Kellerman was physiologist in charge of soil bacteriology and water-purification investigations of the United States Bureau of Plant Industry, and one of the bureau's ablest scientific investigators. Together with the work of Smith Laboratory of Plant Pathology, his agency had much to do with advancing bacteriological research in the federal service.

logical researches; and, of course, even the voluminous materials which Smith and his carefully selected assistants were uncovering had not been organized in teaching form, or fully elaborated in terms of principles.

When Whetzel had begun his work at Cornell in 1902, Smith was preparing the first volume of his great three volume monograph *Bacteria in Relation to Plant Diseases*, concerning the work of which Lewis Ralph Jones, who later was to establish another pioneer department of plant pathology at the University of Wisconsin, has said:

> From first to last Smith attended personally to every detail, giving exacting supervision to whatever he could not himself do. Soon after the appearance of the first volume of this monograph, Smith began the work upon crown gall, which, with the collaboration of younger associates, was to continue throughout the remaining twenty years of his life.

On July 11, 1912, congratulating Smith on one of his many celebrated publications (Bulletin 255, "The Structure and Development of Crown Gall," published by the United States Department of Agriculture) Jones told Smith, "I am convinced that you are, in these contributions on crown gall, not only giving a stimulus which must be powerful in its influence on human cancer research, but pointing to the highest plane yet attained in Plant Pathology." This expression was one of hundreds of tributes sent Smith by leaders of the plant and animal sciences, as well as of the medical profession the world over. Smith was honored on numerous occasions and by various distinctions, some of which may be set forth here: presidencies of the Society for Plant Morphology and Physiology, the Botanical Society of America, the Society of American Bacteriologists, the American Phytopathological Society, Section G of the American Association for the Advancement of Science, and the American Association for Cancer Research; by membership in the National Academy of Sciences of which he served as chairman of its Botanical Section three years; by invitations to address the first International Congress of Comparative Pathology held in Paris in 1912 and the seventeenth International Congress of Medicine held in London in 1913; by two honorary degrees from the Universities of Wisconsin and Michigan; and in 1913 the American Medical Association presented him with its certificate of honor in appreciation of the great value of his cancer research in plants. Dr. Smith's address, "Fifty Years of Pathology," delivered August 20, 1926, before the International Congress of Plant Sciences, held at Ithaca, New York—a Congress in which, we shall discover, Bailey also figured in a capacity of leadership—stands as one of the American classics in the historical literature of the plant sciences of the world, and traces in masterful, coordinated fashion the outstanding contributions (and contributors) from the plant, animal, and human sciences, which have highlighted the conquest of disease.

Smith fought almost a lone fight to advance the parasitic, as opposed to the cell anarchy and other, theories of the etiology of malignant tumors and human cancer. Never presuming to be a medical authority but a research scientist offering on a biological basis points of analogy between tumors of plants and animals, including man, he presented his findings with little realization of his greatness, refused offers of increased financial remuneration from other scientific institutions, remained in plant research until the last year of his life. Honored in the fortieth year of his scientific work at the annual dinner of the American Phytopathological Society, Smith was told by Dr. William H. Welch, pathologist of Johns Hopkins University: "While your name is associated especially with the championship of the parasitic theory of the origin of tumors, your studies of the mechanism of tumor formation, of problems of histogenesis, of formative stimuli and inhibitions of growth, and other kindred subjects, are scarcely of less importance. It would lead far to tell of the whole debt which medicine and pathology owe to you."

In 1917, when *Plant World* asked some fifty American botanists what they considered to be one or two most important botanical contributions of the last three years, Smith's work on crown gall, it was said, received at least twice as many votes as any other important work. That same year in June, President Charles H. Mayo, before the American Medical Association convening in New York City, observed: "We are proud of our Agricultural Department and its investigations as to the causes, control, and cure by serums of the diseases of animals and the destruction of parasitic hosts. The work of Erwin F. Smith on plant diseases is monumental, especially his discoveries as to the causes of certain plant tumors which show again that our bacteria and insect chemi[cals] are the prime offenders through the development of their varying acids, which may be stimulating or destructive to other cell life, causing tumors or decay. We should appreciate and aid the work of these departments."

If during these years Smith's crown gall work signified and symbolized new Olympic heights to which plant pathology with new years might ascend, it may be also said that the new reaches were being built on substantial substrata. On August 31, 1926, William A. Taylor, chief of the United States Bureau of Plant Industry, prepared a report, "A Quarter Century of Service," which reviewed outstanding accomplishments of the bureau since its establishment in 1901. The campaign against destructive plant diseases, including the development of methods for their partial or complete control, demonstrated of itself the value and efficacy of the bureau's activities. "Principal" among the bureau's research phases, which numbered sanitary improvement of water supplies, especially in dairy regions, the establishment of new industries, development of new methods of plant culture or handling, and other directions of scientific research, disease study and control combined with cooperative efforts to eradicate sectional or national disease scourges, presented an admirable adjunct to the also immensely valuable foreign cereal introductions—wheats, oats, and barley varieties—the development of sorghums, citrus improvement by bud selection, improved cotton production, the introduction of Sudan grass, and the bureau's recognized leadership in advancing the soybean industry within the United States. Dry farming on the great plains had been aided by determining first the possibilities and limitations of agriculture in each section, and by aiding individual farmers in all matters pertaining to crop production and utilization, not excluding, of course, the advancement of irrigation projects, and the spread of knowledge of fundamental laws and principles in areas where moisture conservation was an "all-important major problem."

No one could deny the tremendous worth and importance to the national economy represented by 65,000 different plants procured by agricultural explorers within the quarter century sketched, especially in view of the fact that these plants brought from foreign countries were distributed to botanic gardens, state experiment stations, and specialists.[66] No one could deny the extraordinarily creative accomplishments of the federal workers in the production and distribution of new plant varieties by hybridization and selection. Since 1892, when Swingle had been more or less permanently located in Florida after Smith and he had been sent to investigate prevalent diseases in Georgia and Florida, and Pierce had been given a similar commission to study California plant diseases, an interest in plant breeding and its utilization had steadily heightened. Pierce's new grape crosses, hardy and to resist *coulure*, were made no later than 1894. Other disease-resistant hybrids may have been achieved as early as 1892. Inspired partly by Millardet's paper on vine hybridization for disease-resistance and quality improvement, these may have been a pioneer breeding triumph. Pierce, after completing work under Spalding and Novy at the University of Michigan, including a course in bacteriology, had gone to California. But convinced that more study in Mediterranean vineyards was needed, he financed in 1890 a trip to Europe where in France and Italy he met many plant scientists. Savastano, Briosi, and Cavara showed him the bacterial tubercle of the olive,

[66] At this time, Taylor listed as "especially promising" such plants as "the Deglet Noor, Thoory, Saidy, and Zahidi dates, an unusually complete collection of avocado varieties, the Chinese dry-land elm, the Meyer lemon, the Capulin cherry, the Barouni olive, the dasheen, the mango, and the litchi. . . ."

and on this and his vine disease study he reported after his return. From Europe he wrote to Smith of plant bacterial study. While there he may have studied work in plant hybrids.

Smith ranked Pierce's raisin grapes resistant to *coulure*, the ragged bunch disease, and his partial success with walnuts resistant to a bacterial disease, with other such notable achievements as Galloway and Dorsett's accomplishment overcoming the *Alternaria* leaf spot of violets, J. B. Norton's asparagus plant resistant to a destructive rust fungus, L. B. Smith's spinach resistant to a destructive mosaic disease, Burkholder's white marrow bean resistant to anthracnose, and other creations already or hereafter to be discussed.

By 1926 Smith's Laboratory of Plant Pathology had to its credit the discovery and working out of about half of the bacterial diseases of cultivated plants, which were then recognized as serious. In basic industries concerned with producing truck, cereal, fruit, forage, and miscellaneous crops, losses from bacterial and fungous diseases were commonly estimated at from two to ninety-five per cent. Preventive and control procedures, recommended by the laboratory, substantially, sometimes almost completely, reduced these losses among many of the nation's most valuable crops. Smith estimated that the annual saving to the nation made possible by the laboratory's work could conservatively be placed at half a million dollars. Nonbacterial plant diseases were studied. Plant tumor investigations other than crown gall constituted another main branch of activity. And plant breeding for disease resistance was either directed, financed, or aided. We have presented here facts which tend to substantiate his claim that from the laboratory's early principal studies of fusarium diseases of cotton, watermelon, cowpea, cabbage, and banana, there grew the work of Orton in the control of cotton wilt and melon wilt in the southern states, of Bolley in flax wilt in North Dakota, of the United Fruit Company in the control of the fusarial disease of the banana in the West Indies, of Jones and Gilman in Wisconsin in cabbage yellows, and other extensions hereafter referred to. Most important of all, nevertheless, was Smith's establishment of a model pathological research laboratory and techniques of investigation which have influenced the development of departments of pathology, as illustrated in many experiment stations and research institutions of the world, in the department of pathology at Cornell University and in the work of Jones in Vermont and Wisconsin.

Whetzel was influenced by the fact that Smith cut into the plant and studied effects and symptoms, seeing precisely how the disease producing organism had affected tissues and structures, and rechecking his conclusions again and again. Smith was not the first to use photography in disease study, but he developed the art to a high degree, photograph-

340   Liberty Hyde Bailey

ing effects and comparing data time after time to promulgate or substantiate conclusions. Whetzel, partly emulating Smith's work and partly following a European treatise, Küster's *Pathologische Pflanzenanatomie*, began organizing courses with use of mimeographed sheets—there being no adequate texts available at the time—and thus laid the groundwork for what is today known as a Cornell school of plant pathology, an institution which has had as much of an effect on the teaching and general trend of organization in plant pathological investigation as any other in the United States. For it was among, if not the first established and has always maintained its standards. Within a space of two years, 1907-1909, at least three departments of plant pathology at great American universities were created—at the University of Minnesota, a division of plant pathology and botany, within the college of agriculture and distinct from the botany department of the college of science, literature, and arts, was authorized by the board of regents in 1907, commenced in 1908, and Professor Freeman's appointment became effective August 1, 1907; at Cornell University, a distinct department of plant pathology was established under Dr. Whetzel in the autumn of 1907; and soon thereafter, in 1909, the University of Wisconsin announced the inauguration of a department and Lewis Ralph Jones, as professor of plant pathology, began his work there February 1, 1910.[67] It must be remembered, also, that by this time a number of experiment stations, realizing that in terms of dollars and cents saving crops from destruction was as important as adding new ones, had appointed plant pathologists to their staffs.

In the summer of 1907 Whetzel determined to ask Bailey to relieve him of general botanical teaching and research and permit him to devote his entire time and efforts to plant pathology. "Do you know of any professorship of plant pathology in any university?" Bailey asked. "No," was Whetzel's quick, earnest reply. "Well, do you think the trustees of Cornell University will establish a new such chair just for you?" Bailey rejoined, his eyes twinkling. "Well, I think they will if *you* ask them," came Whetzel's prompt, confident response. And they did. At Bailey's urging, the chair was founded and Whetzel began immediately a work which has been profoundly beneficial to all growers of plants in New York state and the nation. By 1908, the demand for research in

[67] These facts were told the author by Dr. Elvin C. Stakman and Dean-Emeritus E. M. Freeman of the University of Minnesota in conferences. Some years ago the author conferred on this and other subjects with Dr. Whetzel and Dr. Jones. See the section, "The Establishment of Chairs of Plant Pathology in Universities and Colleges of Agriculture," in Dr. Whetzel's *An Outline of the History of Phytopathology*, p. 109. Also, *Who's Who in America*, XI, 1920-1921, as to Freeman, p. 1011, as to Jones, p. 1532, and as to Whetzel, XIV, 1926-1927, p. 2012. Dr. Whetzel became a full professor of plant pathology at the New York State College of Agriculture, according to this account, in 1909. Prior to that year, he had been an assistant professor of the subject.

plant disease control had become so pressing, Whetzel conceived an idea of applying the principle of financial cooperation in research as well as in extension. In line with Bailey's idea that New York state's people should share in the college's research program, Whetzel in 1909 proposed the creation of industrial fellowships and that year the board again approved a proposal, the result of Whetzel's initiative and Bailey's endorsement, by accepting from the Niagara Sprayer Company of Middleport, New York, a sum of $750 to investigate the use of lime sulfur as a summer spray—a research which demonstrated the advisability of changing from the almost universal use of bordeaux mixture for spraying apples and other fruits to lime sulfur. By January 1911 no less than eight such fellowships established chiefly by fruit farming and vegetable growing groups would be in operation in the department of plant pathology, and provide during these two years not less than $8,000 for investigations on the control of destructive crop diseases within the state. Within two decades, that is, by 1929, a total of forty-three such fellowships representing more than $120,000 would be invested by growers and commercial concerns interested in plant disease investigations, pomological, floricultural, and vegetable crop inquiries. The graduate student or instructor having charge would inquire into the disease in all its phases and explore the entire pathological field to find applicable principles and practical and efficient solutions. In 1916 would appear *Laboratory Outlines in Plant Pathology*, prepared by Whetzel, Lex R. Hesler, Charles T. Gregory, and W. Howard Rankin. Lewis Ralph Jones, reviewing the book in *Phytopathology*,[68] regarded this as ". . . a most important and valuable contribution to educational advancement in phytopathology [and] another welcome piece of evidence of the prominent and permanent place plant pathology has come to occupy in American schools." Although Jones criticized the book in certain particulars, he referred to the senior author as "the pioneer of America—perhaps . . . of the world—in the practice of intensive teaching methods in that field. . . ."

Thus, from a staff consisting in 1907 of Whetzel and one assistant, Donald Reddick, with an annual appropriation of $300 (excluding salaries) for all expenses of teaching, extension, and research, the department of plant pathology of the New York State College of Agriculture within a little more than two decades would grow to have a faculty of more than forty persons with a total annual budget of over $100,000 for salaries and maintenance, and this figure excluded the sums made available by the industrial fellowships.

In 1908, Mortier Franklin Barrus, graduated that year from Wabash College, became an assistant in the department. In 1911 he was con-

[68] VIII, 2 (February, 1918), p. 60.

stituted an assistant professor, and in 1914 a full professor. During the spring of 1910, Barrus began studying resistance and susceptibility of varieties of the common bean (*Phaseolus vulgaris*) to anthracnose, caused by the fungus *Colletotrichum lindemuthianum.* Anthracnose for a number of years had menaced the bean-growing industry of the state, and its threat to the industry as a whole so increased that the department took up a special study of the disease.

In 1911 Barrus published an article, "Variation of Varieties of Beans in their Susceptibility to Anthracnose,"[69] in which, among other matters, he showed that varieties differed in their susceptibility. Varieties were resistant to one strain of the pathogene and susceptible to another. Nevertheless, while no variety had been found resistant to every strain, pessimism was not justified. He still hoped that a resistant variety would be found, "but before we can be sure of its immunity," he wrote, "it will be necessary to test its ability to withstand infection from the various strains of the organism. Simply because a plant appears to be free from disease when its neighbors of the same variety have succumbed is enough evidence to arouse suspicion but not enough to prove the case." A chance selection provided the clue for "An Anthracnose-Resistant Red Kidney Bean,"[70] on which he wrote in 1915. "Wells Red Kidney bean," so-called, was sent to Barrus in 1913 by Mr. John Q. Wells of Shortsville, New York, who had obtained it from Mr. Byron Luce of Marion, New York, who, in turn, some eleven or twelve years before, had selected a healthy plant from a diseased field, saved the seed, replanted them until he and his brothers had enough seed to plant their own fields, and, without marketing the variety, sold his interest in the farm and the variety to Mr. Wells. By 1915 Barrus had several varieties which showed considerable resistance to anthracnose, but Wells' red kidney bean was outstanding. "It," wrote Barrus, "has shown thus far a high degree of resistance to anthracnose when inoculated with the fungus under artificial conditions, as well as when grown in the field under natural conditions favorable to the extensive development of the disease and when, indeed, the common strain of Red Kidney became so badly infected as to be practically worthless."

How such a production became a part of fundamental genetic inquiry was illustrated in yet another study, performed by Walter H. Burkholder of Cornell University. In an article entitled, "The Production of an Anthracnose-Resistant White Marrow Bean,"[71] Burkholder explained that, to secure a resistant variety for the White Marrow bean growing district of New York, he planned to cross the Wells red kidney with the White Marrow. Throughout years of experimental inves-

[69] *Phytopathology*, I, 6 (December, 1911), pp. 190-195.
[70] *Phytopathology*, V, 5 (October, 1915), pp. 303-307.
[71] *Phytopathology*, VIII, 7 (July, 1918), pp. 353-359.

tigation, he consulted Professor R. A. Emerson who gave him helpful suggestions in the breeding work. Burkholder's discussion of the genetic problem involved typifies a scholarly advancement of the twentieth century in plant breeding, and illustrates its linkage to genetical and pathological research:

Although the main problem was to produce a bean resistant to this disease, records were taken of the genetical behavior of the character of anthracnose resistance. The records, though somewhat incomplete, nevertheless demonstrate the possibilities of improving our present commercial varieties of beans.

The method most frequently used in developing a disease resistant strain of a plant has been selection. Hybridization in a few cases has been resorted to, but very few data have been accumulated as to the genetical behavior of the character under consideration. [R. H.] Biffen in working with wheat believed that the character of resistance to the yellow rust followed the simple 3:1 Mendelian ratio. Susceptibility was found to be dominant. Nilsson-Ehle states, however, that this character is more complex, and considers it to be governed by multiple factors. [W. A.] Orton in crossing a wilt-resistant variety of the cowpea with a susceptible variety was of the opinion that the character of resistance behaved in a true Mendelian fashion. No data were taken concerning the ratios, however. He found the same was also true in crossing a wilt resistant citron with a variety of watermelon. [H. P.] Stuckey in 1916 found that resistance to the blossom-end rot in tomatoes is dominant over susceptibility, but he observed no segregation in the F2 generation. Recently [W. H.] Tisdale studied the results of hybridizing wilt resistant and susceptible strains of flax. Resistance, he states, is inherited and governed by multiple factors.[72]

Burkholder crossed Wells' red kidney bean, resistant to both physiological strains of anthracnose (*Colletotrichum lindemuthianum*), and a white marrow bean, resistant to one of these strains, and obtained in the F2 generation, out of a total of 473 plants tested, 362 which proved

[72] Very important researches were conducted in the selection and development, including experimental work in hybridization, of grain at the Minnesota Experiment Station, the Kansas Experiment Station, and elsewhere. This subject will be elaborated in another book. Mention, however, of a few researches bearing on the multiple factor and Mendelian ratio hypotheses may be added at this point: G. F. Puttick, "The Reaction of the F2 Generation of a Cross between a Common and a Durum Wheat to Two Biologic Forms of *Puccinia Graminis*," *Phytopathology*, xi, 5 (May, 1921), pp. 205-213, and literature cited. This was paper 245 of the journal series of the Minnesota station, and the work was done under the direction of Professors E. C. Stakman and H. K. Hayes of the plant pathology and plant breeding departments; Olaf S. Aamodt, "The inheritance of resistance to several biologic forms of *Puccinia graminis tritici* in a cross between Kanred and Marquis Wheats" (abstract) and "Correlated Inheritance in Wheat of Winter-Spring Habit of Growth and Rust-Resistance" (abstract), *Phytopathology*, xii, 1 (January, 1922), p. 32. These were cooperative investigations of the office of cereal investigations, U. S. Department of Agriculture, and the department of agriculture of the University of Minnesota; Leo E. Melchers and John H. Parker, "The Inheritance of Resistance to Black Stem Rust in Crosses between Varieties of Common Wheat" (*Triticum vulgare*), *idem*, pp. 31-32; James Johnson, "Inheritance of Disease Resistance to *Thielavia basicola*" (abstract), *Phytopathology*, xi, 1 (January, 1921), p. 49.

resistant and 111 which proved susceptible. "These numbers show almost an exact 3:1 ratio," wrote G. P. McRostie, of the department of plant breeding of Cornell University the following year,[73] "and indicate a single factor difference between the resistant and susceptible plants with respect to the one strain of anthracnose concerned in the cross." McRostie's paper had for its object a study of "the inheritance of the resistance factor of bean anthracnose and at the same time to secure a commercial type of white pea bean that was resistant to this disease." The tabulated results of each article are exceedingly interesting, but also quite complicated, and the reader must be referred to them, should he wish to follow the subject further. Sufficient material has been presented to show the coordinated research in plant breeding and plant pathology which was developed in breeding cultivated crops for disease resistance. Pure science and practical science each reaped returns. In 1918 Barrus published another article, "Varietal Susceptibility of Beans to Strains of Colletotrichum Lindemuthianum,"[74] to which he added an index of bean varieties and species inoculated and a summarized statement regarding their susceptibility to the two strains of the fungus. During the progress of these bean studies, furthermore, while Reddick was searching field bean sections of New York for selections of disease-free or disease-resistant plants, particularly with reference to root diseases, materials for selections against an observed mosaic disease of beans were gathered. When the subject was written up,[75] Barrus's and Burkholder's immune strains were held out as models of the "most satisfactory solution of disease control." Again Emerson of the department of plant breeding collaborated with the department of plant pathology. Plant pathology, modeled at first in America in considerable part after animal and medical pathology and shaped during its formative years almost entirely by mycologists, was developing a viewpoint, a doctrine, techniques and terminology, theories and practice, essentially its own. In this, as in other branches of plant science investigation, there had been a tremendous expansion since the years when scientific agriculture had struggled for recognition.

The autumn of 1907 saw also the establishment by Bailey at the New

[73] G. P. McRostie, "Inheritance of Anthracnose Resistance as Indicated by a Cross between a Resistant and a Susceptible Bean," *Phytopathology*, IX, 3 (March, 1919), pp. 141-148, and literature cited.

[74] *Phytopathology*, VIII, 12 (December, 1918), pp. 589-614.

[75] Donald Reddick and Vern B. Stewart, "Varieties of Beans Susceptible to Mosaic," *Phytopathology*, VIII, 10 (October, 1918), pp. 530-534; also, "Additional Varieties of Beans Susceptible to Mosaic," *Phytopathology*, IX, 3 (March, 1919), pp. 149-152; Donald Reddick and V. B. Stewart, "Transmission of the Virus of Bean Mosaic in Seed and Observations on the Thermal Death-Point of Seed and Virus," *Phytopathology*, IX, 10 (October, 1919), pp. 445-450. See also, Donald Reddick, "A Hybrid Bean Resistant to Anthracnose and to Mosaic," *Phytopathology*, XII, 1 (January, 1922), p. 47 (abstract).

York State College of Agriculture of a department of plant physiology, with Benjamin Minge Duggar as its head—a comparatively early recognition of this basic subject, independently and with a departmental status, in a college of agriculture. In 1898, Duggar had taken his doctorate at Cornell University under Atkinson. In 1899, after two years of teaching plant physiology in its college of arts and sciences and while yet cryptogamic botanist of the agricultural experiment station, he had begun at Leipzig and in other German laboratories some "interesting work in connection with the physiology of the fungi." This, in turn, had been followed by a decision to study some of the rhizoctonial diseases, and, still later, during a journey of 1901, by a study of mushroom culture, the spawn making and growing of mushrooms, both subjects eminently practical and scientific and of potential value, economically.

Duggar studied experimental morphology under George Klebs at Halle, with whom Whetzel also studied. Duggar's first of several trips to Europe to study under leading scholars at the universities at Leipzig, Halle, Munich, and Montpellier, including exploratory work around the Mediterranean and study at the Marine Biological Laboratory at Naples, Italy, had been made possible by a leave of absence for the spring term. He had returned to the United States, and at the fourth meeting of the society for plant morphology and physiology in December, 1900, together with F. C. Stewart of the New York Agricultural Experiment Station at Geneva presented "A Second Preliminary Report upon Plant Diseases in the United States due to Rhizoctonia." In the spring of 1901 he negotiated an arrangement with the newly formed bureau of plant industry, and in the autumn, about the same time that C. O. Townsend began for the bureau his study of sugar beet diseases in the west, he went to Texas and the southwest to study prevalent plant diseases, especially those of cotton.

During many years Duggar has contributed notably to botanical research in Missouri. First, at the University of Missouri, he organized a department of botany, and, during his six years of teaching, 1902-1908, the department's enrollment increased more than seven fold. Still later, after a further period of teaching at the New York State College of Agriculture, he returned to Missouri, and, at St. Louis, pursued very important research, including investigations of the obscure virus diseases in plants. He is today a professor-emeritus at the University of Wisconsin.

From the start his appointment as professor of plant physiology at the New York State College of Agriculture was in relation to farm crop study. While this never became officially a part of his professorial title, Duggar's appointment, made during the school year ending September 30, 1907, became effective on his arrival at the beginning of the second term of the year 1908, that is, February 1. Undergraduates were offered courses in plant physiology and crop ecology. Research investigations included observations on environmental factors in relation to growth of field crops, studies of effects on plants of environmental factors by isolation methods, shade-tent investigations, stimulation experiments using nonnutrient salts, studies of toxic relations of certain crop plants to substances which in dilute form were known to possess stimulating effects on growth processes, nitrogen fixation by fungi, enzymatic action, and many other problems. In his first report, Duggar announced that material had been collected for studies on the cytology of some hybrid agricultural plants. Within a year cell physiology was being taught. So remarkable was the graduate interest in the subject that "the facilities of the Department were severely taxed to accommodate these students" and restriction of registration was contemplated. Indeed, within a year, this department was investigating certain "physiological diseases of plants." Plant physiology was a fundamental subject and grew by the fact of its importance and the ability of its professor. He utilized, within a few years, the mass of factual data emanating from experiment station and college laboratory investigations, and wrote two much needed texts, *Fungous Diseases of Plants* (1910) and *Plant Physiology with Special Reference to Plant Production* (1911), a book of the Rural Text Book Series. The first book was commenced at the University of Missouri and finished while at Cornell. The second book was done chiefly at the Missouri Botanical Garden to which institution Duggar went as professor of plant physiology for graduate students and professor of plant physiology at Washington University in St. Louis.

At Cornell Duggar's work in plant physiology was taken over by Lewis Knudson, a Wisconsinite by birth though a graduate in 1908, in agriculture, of the University of Missouri. That year he began teaching at Cornell University, where in 1911 he obtained the degree Doctor of Philosophy. Among many researches of outstanding merit, Dr. Knudson has specialized in fermentation, enzyme production, and organic nutrition of plants. He has studied germination of orchid seeds. During the first decade of the twentieth century, Dr. Duggar was one of the leading advocates of recognizing what he called, "Physiological Plant Pathology." His address by this title was one of three papers read at a "Symposium on Some Aspects of Plant Pathology" at the Minneapolis meeting, December 29, 1910, of the Botanical Society of America. Dr. Knudson has conducted noteworthy researches on the pathological side of work in plant physiology; as, for instance, his studies in symbiosis. In 1928 he studied in Guatemala the wilt disease of banana. His work in Central America, extending over a number of years prior to that time, was credited with having saved large sums of money to the fruit industry. He was invited to establish plant physiology in Spain, and in 1920 and 1921 lectured on the subject at Museo Nacional de Ciencias Naturales, at Madrid and Barcelona. Dr. Knudson also has a historical interest, having once prepared at Cornell University "A Brief History of the Department of Botany."

With the departure of Duggar and the return in 1913 of Karl McKay Wiegand to head up a department of botany in the college of agriculture—in reality, a second department of botany established during Bailey's administration—plant physiology in the agricultural college was merged with the botanical teaching from the arts and science college, while the mycological teaching and investigations which had been Atkinson's work were transferred to the department of plant pathology. Harry M. Fitzpatrick, Atkinson's assistant, was added to the department as assistant professor in charge of the subject.

Plant breeding now meant the study under experimental conditions of all plants of the world whether of cultivated or wild floras. "Real investigation" as Bailey styled the new researches would never exclude taxonomy since first what plant was being investigated had to be known. Biologic inquiry more and more studied plants of the wild for purposes of cultivation, introduction, breeding for new races and disease resistance, and to ascertain laws of heredity. Agriculture was both scholarly and practical. Several great crop expansions were the nation's pride, each a product of scientific agriculture. For instance, in 1907, from Cornell had gone to the U.S. Department of Agriculture William Joseph Morse, agronomist, and begun a program to expand and improve the soybean industry. In 1923 Morse, with C. V. Piper, prepared a book, *The Soybean*, and a year later was made president of the National Soybean Growers Association. With time more than 150 varieties made possible by foreign introductions and selections would add renown to the department's work and Morse's leadership in this useful food industry. During 1920 to 1925, Wightman Wells Garner and Harry Ardell Allard, both of the department at Washington, published in the *Journal of Agricultural Research* their studies on photoperiodism, response of plants to relative length of day and night. Thus was elaborated another basis for possible extensions of plant breeding knowledge, since from a discovery that growth, fruiting, and flowering characteristics vary with the light or day-length of regions, it became possible not only to adjust greenhouse illumination to the long or short day required by plants for best development and growth but also to breed plants for photoperiodic objectives.

CHAPTER VIII

THE COUNTRY-LIFE COMMISSION

Passengers on the cosmic sea
We know not whence nor whither:
'Tis happiness enough to be
In tune with wind and weather.

WITH this stanza Bailey concluded a book dedicated to his more than ninety-year old father who had always lived on a farm—"naturalist without knowing it"—*The Outlook to Nature*, a book consisting of four lectures given in January, 1905, in the Colonial Theatre of Boston, Massachusetts, as a part of a university course, maintained under auspices of the education committee of the Twentieth Century Club. The chapters were revised in 1910 and, while the lecture forms were retained with practically the same titles, "The Realm of the Commonplace," "Country and City," "The School of the Future," and "Evolution: the Quest of Truth," the author restated simply and sincerely the basic social and scientifically philosophical views he had so long advanced. "The evolution-conception of the universe," he urged, "bids us come and stand on a high place. It magnifies individual effort, kindles the inner light of conscience in distinction from authority, lessens belief in mere wonders, stimulates the reason, and emancipates the man. It asks us to lay aside prejudice and small dogmatisms. It impels us to a new and great reverence for the Power which has set in motion that stupendous enterprise which unfolds itself without a break or change of purpose, setting the stars in their courses and molding the strawberry into its new environments, losing no detail in its mighty swing and running on to destiny in ages hence of which we cannot yet perceive the meaning. It bids us put ourselves in line with the movements of the ages, to throw aside all mental reservation and oppositions to truth, and to do our little, with sympathy and inspiration, to forward the creation. All beliefs, all doctrines, all creeds are mine," said Bailey, "I want only the truth and the privilege to live in the great good world. Truth, and the quest of truth, are always safe. It is not my part to be anxious about destiny or about the universe. If my tiny opinions are outgrown, I shall wait, in patience and in hope. There is grateful release in letting the universe take care of itself. The universe is in better hands than mine. . . ."

Years before, in the February 2, 1899, issue of *The Independent*, Bailey had written an article, "An Evolutionist's View of Nature and Religion." Adding to an article of the previous issue on "The Evolution of a Strawberry," he said, "The true originality is not the collection of facts, not the piling up of intellectual cord wood, but the discovery of the meaning of facts. The same is true of the race. . . ."

For a number of years botanists, and presumably also horticulturists, had interested themselves in constructing a hypothetical "genealogical tree" showing plant groups in their true evolutionary relationships and perspective. The "genealogical tree" concept did not last. Evolution was found more and more to be too great and broad a disclosure to sustain such a simple effort at organizing, descriptively, the multifold forms of plant life. Nevertheless, in the study of plant origins and stages of development, the genealogical concept proved useful and invaded the perplexing and similarly abundant subject of taxonomic classification. Bailey was a student of the origins of cultivated crops. In these articles he narrated in part the history of an effort to "reconstruct the genealogy of the garden strawberry," how in his garden he had planted roots of wild strawberries sent to him from the far west and studied these plants under conditions of domestication—new conditions of light, space, soil, and moisture. He confessed he was not half as interested in whether he had developed a new species, either for botanical or horticultural classification, as in studying the environmental modifications which the plants underwent after being brought from a western wood to a sunny knoll in his garden, or, said in another way, from a natural state to a condition of cultivation. Nor were his studies confined to environmental modification. On at least one occasion, in his greenhouse, he studied seed grown peas and their hereditary variability through several generations. These were questions then even as they are subjects now about which scientists are not in complete agreement.

Bailey neither regarded evolution as a faith, nor did he find that it destroyed faith except as it shattered doctrines and stripped religion of its "non-essentials." "The biological speculations are emancipating us," said Bailey. "This emancipation is not yet complete; for few of us are yet willing to believe whatever may be true, or to commit ourselves unreservedly to a quest of the truth as evidence and reason may direct us." Bailey could have revealed that eminent scientists had confessed to him they hesitated to disclose the results of certain experiments bearing on evolutionary truth. They feared that faith in God and the church might be shaken. The conflict of religion and science was strong in many places. Science was reinterpreting the church's design and teleological concepts. Bailey saw no reason to fear the consequences of any scientific disclosures. The real essence is "the spirit of the real fellowship of man and nature—that creation-spirit which will come from the full understanding of our origin and our relative place in the cosmos. We have much that we call nature poetry," he commented critically, "but most of it will not be nature poetry in the time to come. We are to pass the

Age of Doubt. . . . Faith will be direct and free, as natural as the trust of the child, as native to us as the sunshine and the air. We are coming to a religion of joy and activity, full of high spirituality, of great trust in nature, of hope in man, and of direct dependence on the Almighty." Bailey marveled "that the most advanced teaching of evolution should so fully confirm the sequence of Genesis" in the holy scriptures. But where is God, was asked. "I answer," said Bailey, "that he is where he always was. Nothing that man can do can make the creation any the less true or untrue. . . . Strictly speaking, evolution does not attempt to explain creation, but only the progress of the creation. Whatever its form, it begins where Genesis begins—'In the beginning, God.'. . . We are not to search for God here and there, as if we were afraid he would elude us, but we are to see him everywhere; and we must be willing and ready to see nature as it is. . . . It is to be expected that our conception of God will enlarge as our horizon enlarges.This conception is of course anthropomorphic—founded on human attributes. Evolution implies that God is not outside nature, but in nature. He is immanent, not absent. Nature must ever be our recourse; its facts and its voices must be heeded. . . ." Bailey believed "that every minister should be a naturalist —using the word in its large and etymological sense."

In 1906 was published, as part of a set of volumes of papers delivered in 1904 before the Congress of Arts and Sciences which met at the St. Louis Universal Exposition, Bailey's address on "Some Present Problems in Agriculture." Characterizing the early agricultural problems as having been treated symptomatically, rather than as studies of underlying causative factors, he noted that many Americans with real farming zeal had moved westward and taken up new and unused land rather than stay and solve problems in the eastern and southern sections. The engineer and inventor had held the foreground. They had arrived at many farm solutions. Real advancements had been made in harvesting and transportation methods. These were, however, essentially extraneous solutions to the real matters at stake, with the consequence that in many regions there were few real improvements dealing with fundamentals—making two blades of grass grow where before only one had grown, augmenting production of better plants and better animals on better soil with better tillage, and removing special disabilities such as insects, fungi, weeds, animal diseases, and the like. With the arrival of experiment stations, an epoch of fertilizer study had come and gone. For years the station problems had been really, in many instances, "vest-pocket questions," small and incidental. "Now," said Bailey, "the fundamental backbone crops and products are being investigated in their entirety—the corn crop, the cotton crop, the grass crop, the milk product, the beef product. The experiment stations are originating a kind of constructive investigational method, and the really great questions are ahead of us. Large problems come last. We are now just coming to the large question of adaptation of special areas to special purposes. In the future one of the problems will be the more perfect adaptation of the kind of farming to soil and climate." As examples, he cited the industrial developments of domestic animals for meat and wool in the West, of cereals in the Mississippi Valley, of increased tree and grass production in the Atlantic states. Many new industries were to be developed, he believed. In this the United States Department of Agriculture would aid "by giving counsel and investigating the special technical difficulties."

With all this, however, there were still great unsolved social and economic problems relating to agriculture. "The greatest problems of American agriculture," argued Bailey, "are not the technical ones, but the relations of the industry to economic and social life in general. . . ." He urged that farming stands for individualism rather than collectivism. On another occasion Bailey had said that every farm was an experiment station and in a sense every farmer an experimenter. He believed, too, that an attractive literature, technical and artistic, relating to rural life would more and more be forthcoming.

A vast array of sociological and economic questions confronted the American agricultural scene and he enumerated a large number gathered together by him, two associates, Hunt and Lauman, and a student, Charles Aronovici. The school stood foremost as a force to revitalize the country. The return of capital to the land was imperative, but, above all, a new education "must reach the farmer in terms of the whole man—his particular business, his home and its ideals, his relations to good roads, good schools, the church, the social forces, to all that makes up a broad and satisfying country life. We must give attention to the ideals of living as well as to the ideals of farming. The sanitation of the farm home, the architecture of the buildings (what silent and effective teachers buildings are!)," he exclaimed, and added, "the reading, the character of the farmyard, the questions associated with the bringing-up of children, the social and commercial organizations—these are the kinds of subjects that the rising educational impulse must attack." Bailey believed that the purpose of an agricultural college was not "to make men farmers, but to educate farmers. We are not to limit the student's vision to any one occupation," he wrote that same year, "but to make one's occupation more meaningful and attractive than it has ever been before. . . ." To make farming more meaningful and attractive carried with it the obligations of making the rural family and farm residence more pleasant and the work more productive.

At the annual meeting of the Association of American Agricultural Colleges and Experiment Stations, which met in November, 1904, at Des Moines, Iowa, Bailey became a member of its executive committee and chairman of its committee on graduate study. Higher agricultural education was not new. But its objectives were not clearly defined. Published as Bulletin 164 of the office of experiment stations at Washington and issued as part of the proceedings of the nineteenth annual convention held a year later, an answer was written by Bailey to the question, "To what extent should the degrees in land-grant colleges be severely technical and scientific?" He wrote, "The general drift of this discussion shows that the land-grant colleges, particularly on the agricultural side, do not regard the courses as professional or at least not as severely technical" but more as home-making courses, and "if that is true, I think it means a very great gain for agricultural education. This education is industrial in a broad sense. It is natural education, and is founded on general pedagogical principles and methods. I am coming to like the phrase 'education for country life' instead of 'agricultural education.' The idea no longer stands for technical agricultural instruction alone. It stands also for all the social and economic relations of the farm to its community. . . . So I like to think that the agricultural college now stands for the open country in its largest and broadest sense. . . . I think the tendency in our land-grant colleges, as in our secondary schools, is going to simplify rather than to add more. . . ."

In a 1906 speech before the annual meeting of the Farmers' League of Maryland, meeting in McCoy Hall of Johns Hopkins University at Baltimore, Bailey reasoned that the schools should be expressions of the community. When in the country they should teach things of the country, including manual training, nature study, domestic work, and school gardens. Moreover, he said, "No school is a good school, from kindergarten to university, unless it has a laboratory." He had attended commencement exercises of Tuskegee Institute, Alabama, Booker T. Washington's school, where George W. Carver was director of the experiment station, and had been much pleased with student workmanship of this advanced institution for the colored race. In fifteen states and territories were institutions giving, similarly, agricultural instruction to Negroes.

In the summer of 1905 he had gone to California and had given a series of lectures at the university there, also attending as a delegate the Irrigation Congress held at Portland, Oregon. That year, in April, he had lectured at the teachers' college of Columbia University in New York City on "The Outlook for Industrial Education," a lecture to become a part of a number of talks on contemporaneous educational problems. February 17 he had spoken at the fifth annual agricultural banquet of Cornell agricultural students. He rejoiced that the teaching of agriculture was being introduced into secondary schools alongside the cultural subjects of Latin and Greek. The day before, he had spoken at the annual meeting of the Agricultural Experimenters League of New York, whose members had instituted since 1903, the year of its organization, over sixty active private experiment stations within the state. An organization started by Cornell college of agriculture students, Bailey thought it gave great promise of helping to bind the farmers more closely together. To the Grange, he always paid tribute when the opportunity arose. At these meetings he said, "We owe much to the 'Grange,' that true coeducational agricultural institution, truly coeducational because the Grange cannot hold meetings without women." Grange meetings, institute meetings, group society meetings, crop breeders' associations, state normal schools, and many other institutions heard Bailey, whenever possible. He became well known as a speaker of rare ability, a person who not only dramatically portrayed a better country life of the future but also somehow seemed a living embodiment of a great agricultural vision.

At the Baton Rouge meeting of the Association of Agricultural Colleges and Experiment Stations held in November, 1906, Bailey was elected its president. The National Education Association of the United States, furthermore, recognized his leadership. When L. D. Harvey, the chairman of its committee on industrial education in schools for rural communities reported at the forty-fifth annual meeting of the association held in July, 1907, at Los Angeles, California, he announced that Bailey had summarized the purposes and values of industrial education for children in rural communities.

For his presidential address given before the Association of American Agricultural Colleges and Experiment Stations, on May 28, 1907, at Lansing, Michigan, Bailey chose as his subject, "The State and the Farmer." The meetings were held at the celebration of the semicentennial anniversary of Michigan Agricultural College. In addition to President Theodore Roosevelt and Secretary Wilson who gave addresses, some thirty-five presidents and directors of universities and scientific schools were present. In his address, Bailey significantly observed:

The new West is still in the epoch of self-congratulation, and a man who criticizes or who gives some other state or community the credit of more tons of produce is subject to popular disapproval. The East has reached a point when it is willing to look the facts squarely in the face.

In another address delivered at commencement exercises of the college of his graduation, "The Agricultural Status," Bailey characterized the farm condition as "Banquo's ghost of the economic world. It stalks the earth by night and day, and points its fingers to the abandoned farms of the east, the despairing unrest of the west, the depopulation of the rural communities; to the fall in prices of farm produce, to the contrasting case of the city man, and then fixes its hollow eyes upon the foreclosure of the farm mortgage and follows the halt and broken couple to the poorhouse." The argument was similar to those of other addresses he had given on the subject. While not diminishing the gravity of difficulties and discouragements, he was convinced there was no agricultural disease. That farm boys and girls flocked to the cities did not alarm him. "I do not blame the butterfly if it seeks the flower, nor the moth if it flies to the candle, nor the bird if it revels in the color and perfume of the tangle, nor the brook if it tumbles pell-mell into the sea. All things must find their level," he said, "and all must live where life is best and where struggle for existence is least. The farm no longer needed so many boys, for two men can do the haying in a week and ride to town on a bicycle after supper. But the serious part of it is, for agriculture, that the brightest and most ambitious boys went to town."

This was the situation before schools of mechanics arose. Depleting farm ranks so that for many years few agricultural colleges were needed, the migration continued, even though few farm boys became city executives. "When men and industry went to the city, capital went too, and the country was like the shell of the cocoon when the butterfly has flown. . . . [But contrast] the average John who went to the city with the average John who stayed on the farm, and the farmer will not suffer thereby. And the average Jane—well, when John went, Jane went, too. . . . All the shifting unrest of this transition period was intensified by the sudden opening of the virgin lands of the west." From this period, more or less contemporaneous with the Civil War, conditions had been aggravated until "agriculture went under the wave, and she is just now," Bailey observed, "emerging, dripping with the tears of her sorrows, but with her face towards the rising sun." Arriving then at the "new birth," at the "time of hope in knowledge and science," he asked: "Are the conditions of agriculture so bad as they have been pictured to be? No, not to my thinking. There are unusual hardships in regions where there have been unusual disturbances; but, as a general statement, the farmer is as well off as any citizen who expends an equal amount of capital and effort. And if he is not, the remedy is not complaint nor recrimination, but an earnest and patient effort to undo the wrong. The cry of the hardships of agriculture is not new; its refrain wails throughout history. . . . We are measuring agriculture by wrong standards. Here is a realm of living which lies beyond gross ambition, beyond the greed of wealth, a place where unselfish patriotism may grow unchecked. The future must see comparatively fewer colossal fortunes and more financial thrift in the commonalty of the people. There is certain to be great change in society by means of gradual evolution, and those pursuits which are most conducive to useful and contented lives are certain to exert greater and greater influence. Give the farmer some leisure in which to think and then give him a desire to think, and the farm is no longer an innuendo. But at the present time the farmer may be addressed too often in the language of Ulysses to Laertes: 'Great is thy skill, oh father! Great thy toil! On every plant and tree thy cares are shown; nothing neglected but thyself alone!'

"You may think this good teaching for Sunday," continued Bailey, "but it will not raise bread and butter for the week days. You tell me that the farmer cannot make his expenses, and cite to me wheat at seventy-five cents a bushel. If the farmer cannot grow wheat and live, he should certainly spare himself the effort; but it may be profitable to examine this question, for it is the one most frequently cited in support of the assumption of an agricultural disease. The Cornell University estate was a run out hill farm not many years ago, advertising its shame by fields of oxeye daisies. It has had no 'fancy' treatment, and only small applications of concentrated fertilizers; but it has had most skillful management. For fifteen years the average wheat crop upon the regular fields of the farm has been thirty-six bushels per acre, and the cost of growing and securing an acre of wheat has run from twelve to fifteen dollars. . . . The secret of the whole matter is raising more wheat for less money, and then the securing of sufficient land to produce the desired income. This raises several serious questions, and brings us at once to the very heart of the current discussions respecting the agricultural depression. There is said to be an overproduction of wheat. If there is, surely the only remedy is to grow less wheat; and the lesser production will come when the price falls to a certain point. The whole question of production and demand is a relative one, and it may be expected to regulate itself in the long run by the natural laws of supply and demand. This is not an agricultural question, but a commercial one. . . . There cannot be permanent overproduction. Society is a self-sustaining organism. If agriculture adjusts itself to new conditions more slowly than other interests do, the adjustment nevertheless must come. . . . We need no class legislation. We cannot stem the tide which rises from the nature of things and which carries all human endeavor upon its bosom; we may only change the ripples which here and there play over the surface and obscure the mighty undercurrent. And, as for agriculture, it must pay, for there must be agriculture."

Bailey saw value in cautious mortgage statistical studies, in more investment of city-capital in the country, in bringing again into cultivation many abandoned farms, in their use as grazing ranges and country homes, in the growth of agricultural specialization, especially in horticulture where "the possibility of maintaining oneself upon a small holding while still retaining one's autonomy" was a sound guarantee against a drift into peasantry. Encouragement was to be found in mowing machines and riding plows, in the sequestration of the old red brick district school where children of this and the next generation could be taught to see and infer—understand a flower, see a bird's flight, hear its song, see a bee sip nectar and hum away "full of the riotous joy of living," know why wheat is rolled, "which is more than the farmer knows," said Bailey. He remembered that "New England suffered because its granite hills were too expensive for cultivation, and its water powers and its urban population invited manufacture. The great west suffered because of too rapid settlement. The great south has not yet recovered from the effects of war and the complete overturning of its social system. Special localities here and there suffer for special and local reasons," Bailey reminded his college audience, but "Time is slowly healing the wounds."

The eastern hills were not dead. They only waited for science. "And this very day New York," he added, "has better farms and better farmers, and a safer and thereby a better agricultural status, than it ever had before. They tell me that the wheat lands of the great west can no longer raise wheat. The sooner the fury of the gale is spent, the sooner will fall the gentle shower. . . . The one salvation of agriculture . . . is education. By education, I mean *education*—not the dispensing of facts. . . . It is better for [a man] to know how and why a clod holds its moisture than to know whole systems of irrigation. It is more profitable for him to know why we till than to know all the dates and methods and tools for all the crops. Give a man principles and he will apply them for himself. Give a man a place to stand and he will move the world. Facts are trivial as facts. They do not open the eyes of the blind, nor kindle the soul with enthusiasm. We are slaves to facts. Wake a man up. Shake out localisms and prejudices. Inspire him. Set him at work. Send him on a mission with joy." This spirit characterized the first American decade in scientific agricultural education. The Michigan Department of Public Instruction took this address, printed it, and circulated it as " a presentation of the situation produced by the mutations of time" and good for "perusal of all thoughtful observers of our economic conditions, especially those affecting our schools."

In 1907 the University of Wisconsin conferred on Bailey the honorary degree LL.D. In 1908 Alfred University did likewise. During the Easter school vacation of 1907 Bailey spoke before the Rhode Island League of Societies for Rural Progress.

That same year, on August 29, at the twenty-fifth anniversary celebration of the establishment of the New York Agricultural Experiment

Station at Geneva, Bailey spoke, along with Governor Hughes, President William Oxley Thompson of Ohio State University, a great friend of agriculture during these crucial years, and other notables. The Cornell dean's subject was "Lessons of the Day," and concluded with a stanza of a poem by him:

> So virile is this earth we own
> So quick with life its soil is stung,
> A million years have come and flown
> And still it rises green and young.

In this address Bailey stressed the results of the New York State College of Agriculture's "Tompkins County Agricultural Survey." He announced his belief that, in the hilly and remote lands of the state, fruit growing for export, a revival of animal industries, and extension of dairying, and forest growing would increase. He urged a "thorough-going survey of the exact agricultural status of the State," the establishment of "experimental apple orchards of large area on some of the higher and cheaper lands," and "a thorough-going special inquiry into the status and prospects of the animal industries, collecting data on which safe and fundamental recommendations can be made for the improvement and extension of these industries."

This year the American Society of Agronomy was organized in Chicago with Mark A. Carleton of the United States Bureau of Plant Industry as its president. During its deliberations, the society passed a resolution to aid in furthering a movement initiated by the Society for the Promotion of Agricultural Science to bring about some affiliation between the scientific agricultural groups.

At first, the choice of Carleton to lead an organization interested primarily in soils research might seem surprising. He had been appointed in 1894 to investigate cereal rusts and smuts for the division of vegetable pathology. Furthermore, by 1900, the year of the Paris Exposition, at which the United States, in competition with Canada, Russia, France, and other countries, had made an excellent showing especially in cereals, Carleton officially was known as the department's "Expert in Charge of Cereals." In 1909 he was titled "Cerealist in Charge of Grain Investigations, Bureau of Plant Industry."

Cereal crop improvement, however, has grown up in soils investigations. Therefore it was natural that the new American Society of Agronomy should interest itself in the "backbone" crops and their relations to various soils. Crop improvement, better culture methods, land utilization, some land reclamation were indicated. With this field of specialization as well as the agricultural and farm management survey, the new society concerned itself. It became another link in a chain of organizations dedicated to the advancement of one scientific branch.

But it was fully alive to the consciousness that the demonstrated fundamental unity of all conventional divisions of science is the blood-flow and strength of scientific progress, a realization which Bailey regarded an imperative necessity in all agriculture.

Talk to any student of the New York State College of Agriculture during the years Bailey was dean and director and he will tell you that Bailey's strongest hold on student life and opinion was formed at the agricultural college assemblies held at the beginning of each month for faculty and students. On the Cornell University campus a large circular white stone and brick building, with a seating capacity of more than 2,400 persons, today stands as a fitting tribute and memorial honoring the life and work of a presiding officer of years in the assemblies, the Bailey Auditorium.

On October 1, 1908, Bailey chose the assembly as the medium for making his first public pronouncement of, perhaps, the greatest single honor conferred on him—his appointment by President Theodore Roosevelt to serve as chairman of a national commission to study and make recommendations for legislation to improve country life by, to use the President's own terminology, "better business and better living." Only one other movement President Roosevelt regarded of equal or more national importance and that was conservation of the national resources. Evidently some imputed political significance of the appointment was rumored on the Cornell campus and Bailey, armed with the President's letter written to him August 10 from Oyster Bay, New York, went before the assembly to explain the commission's objectives.

What the President wished were "such information and advice as [would] enable [him] to make recommendations to Congress upon the extremely important matter" of country life. Bailey did not want the chairmanship but Roosevelt swore jovially that he had better accept the appointment. Conditioning his acceptance on the appointment also of Kenyon Butterfield as a commission member, Bailey, in an interview held at 10:30 o'clock one night at Washington, agreed to assume the commission's leadership. The reason for Bailey's insistence on the appointment of Butterfield, then president of Massachusetts Agricultural College, was that he regarded President Butterfield as the only other named member who had been trained in modern college research methods and whose viewpoint was approved by educators generally. When the constituency was announced, the commission was made up with Bailey, as chairman, Butterfield, Henry Wallace, editor of the world known agricultural journal *Wallaces' Farmer*, a member of a distinguished pioneer family of Iowa, father of the Secretary of Agriculture under President Warren G. Harding, and grandfather of the former Vice-President; Walter Hines Page, editor of *The World's*

Work, a prominent New York magazine of general circulation; and Gifford Pinchot, forester and chief of the United States Forest Service, a member of a distinguished and wealthy Pennsylvania family which endowed and founded the great Yale school of forestry.

By 1904 schools or important departments of forestry were maintained at Yale and Harvard Universities, the Biltmore School in North Carolina, Iowa and Michigan State Colleges, and the Universities of Michigan, Minnesota, Nebraska, and Maine. Forestry teaching was being given on a less formal scale at other schools from the Atlantic to the Pacific coasts. At Berea College, Kentucky, forestry education as part of the farmers' or agricultural course had been given for some time, its early course in training rangers being in every sense original. An academy concept was expanding, in 1903 the famous Mont Alto Academy having been proposed. Sponsored by Rothrock who wanted to train Pennsylvania foresters for forest management in Pennsylvania, the academy, under the able directorship of George Herman Wirt had graduated its first class in 1906.

Rothrock, as by far the Pennsylvania forestry movement's most important figure, for years had sought to establish forestry instruction on an adequate scale at either the University of Pennsylvania or Pennsylvania State College, but without success. A ranger school was needed in the East. The academy was doing excellent forest nursery investigation. Rothrock was not a technically trained forester. But he was a botanist of exceptional merit, one vitally interested in the forest and cause of forestry, one who had observed while a student abroad forestry methods in Europe. When Fernow was brought into Pennsylvania, he centered his attention on developing forestry in an agricultural school—Pennsylvania State College. Rothrock gave much of his energy toward developing Mont Alto Academy. The two men differed on certain points of forest policy, matters principally academic, but remained firm friends to their last years. On June 30, 1918, Rothrock wrote Fernow: "All right minded Americans who know of your great services to this country are glad to do you honor. You came as a Godsend, at the right time, and you, more than any other, opened up a great public interest."

In January, 1907, Fernow accepted a professorship of forestry at Pennsylvania State College, organizing a first-class undergraduate department. Long interested and influential in the state forestry movement of Pennsylvania, Dean W. A. Buckhout, before him, had taught forestry there but Fernow was the first professionally trained forester to head the department. By this time the state of Pennsylvania had set aside forest reservations to the extent of nearly one million acres and was adding annually more. Fernow's stay was only for the spring session and his group of students numbered only nine. In fact, he did not move to State College, but retained his residence at Ithaca, commuting between the two places. During the spring some forty students attended his lectures and ten students indicated an intention to follow the profession. As early as February 17, 1907, Fernow wrote his trusted friend Rossiter Raymond:

Who knows but that by the time you return from your trip your opportunity for advertising me as at work in State College will be gone, for I found a letter from another University asking to submit credentials with a view of getting a call. I do not give you the name, but it is out of the country, not very far, and certainly a more inviting place to reside in.

Fernow received an invitation to elaborate his conceptions as to the needs of a forestry department in the University of Toronto. He responded, setting forth the need of a forestry policy, including educational facilities, by and for the province of Ontario. In the course of his argument he pointed out that the Ontario Forest Reserves were "merely withdrawn from use and without any appropriate management except that settlement [was] excluded." Moreover, of course, he discussed the farm woodlot and waste land situation in the agricultural portion of the province. Technically trained men obviously were needed. Each forest situation "or class of cases require[d] a different treatment" dependent upon the results desired. "The University of Toronto being the Government's own institution of learning," said Fernow, "it should inaugurate not a mere chair of forestry, nor even a department of forestry for the higher grade foresters, but lay the foundation of an educational system which shall bring to each class interested intelligence and information, suited to its needs. University Extension work of the broadest kind is here called for. . . . In cooperation with the Agricultural College at Guelph, which is organically connected with the University, and where already a good beginning has been made, in advancing farm forestry, the farmers should be assisted in a practical manner to learn how to manage their woodlots and how to plant their waste places. . . ."

Although announcement was made on March 28 that the board of governors had decided to establish a faculty of forestry at the University of Toronto and Fernow had been elected dean, he did not take up his new work until autumn. At Pennsylvania State College Fernow's position was taken by Hugh P. Baker, formerly of Iowa State College, later dean of the New York State College of Forestry organized at Syracuse University, and now president of Massachusetts State College.

In a human sense it may be said that the old New York State College of Forestry at Cornell followed Fernow. When Fernow went to Pennsylvania State, *Cornell Countryman* announced the new forestry department was to be modeled after the one at Cornell. In 1908 Fernow, having begun work at Toronto, wrote Ernest Bruncken, "I take pleasure in sending you a calendar of our faculty, which will remind you much of the prospectus for Cornell University. I have seen no reason for changing our ways." It is not to be wondered at, that when colleges of forestry in the United States were later contemplated or organized, these institutions sought to obtain Fernow as dean.

Officially, however, the New York State College of Forestry at Cornell remained existent. The charter was not surrendered, and a member of the university board was constituted director.

Fernow's Canadian leadership in a sense interestingly paralleled his leadership in the United States. Not only did he establish the first professional forestry school north of the Canadian boundary, but, indeed, events in Canadian forestry development during his years of activity there interestingly compare with events which had taken place in the United States. Elaboration of the theme has pertinence in this book because conservation of natural resources was central. Quite obviously, this work was closely linked by President Roosevelt to country life work.

At the eighth annual meeting of the Canadian Forestry Association held the year Fernow went to Canada, there was great jubilation over passage by Parliament of the Dominion Forest Reserves Act by which twenty-one forest reserves in western Canada had been set aside. Timber surveys were in progress with an intention of inaugurating "scientific management." Even as the United States had begun by establishing national parks before forest reserves, so Canada a number of years previously had begun creating national parks. Similarly forest tree planting had preceded large scale establishment of reserves. It is true that by 1907 the Dominion government and the provinces, notably Quebec and Ontario, had instituted forest reservation policies, and the amounts of land in reserves were in millions of acres. Nevertheless, forest management was not much advanced beyond systems of fire prevention, some afforestation, and restrictive regulations on logging operations.

Immediately Fernow began firmly to advocate the creation of a really forward paced forest policy for Canada, a program which really sought to perpetuate Canada's great heritage of natural resources. Once again much the same great educational program had to be taught, despite the fact that the Canadian Forestry Association had been organized for some time and had carried on an aggressive program of propaganda. The need once again was the furtherance of real scientific methods. Reforestation of waste, cut-over, burnt-over, and barren land as a government duty had to be insisted on again. Principles for best annual sustained yield management had to be settled. Means of utilizing inferior material had to be devised. Battle with the forest's enemies, fire, animals, insects, and diseases had to be waged still more. Lands fit for timber growing had to be set apart. Lands suitable for cultivation had to be given over to agriculture. A wide field developing wood products industries was still undeveloped. Studies of the physical properties of Canadian woods were greatly needed. Statistics as to forest resources and forest areas were also wanted. Forest service organization within the provinces and Dominion needed development or expansion. There was no real forest experiment station. The Dominion experimental farms work under the able leadership of William Saunders, Fernow's close friend to whom he dedicated his book on ornamental trees, had done good work. In the forests themselves, however, there was need for study of forest types, a stock-taking of resources, and the whole placed under management. Fernow became the organizer, first president (an office he retained for many years) of the Canadian Society of Forest Engineers. Interest of the railroads in the work was to be aroused. Fernow was convincing when he said:

> The methods as they exist are of historical growth, and . . . devised for pioneering conditions . . . to secure income and to open the country for settlement, they probably were the best that could be devised. But the time is here, if I am not mistaken, or rapidly approaching, when it will be wisdom to change these methods, when a new purpose is to be substituted, when not merely present profitable exploitations, but the future needs are to be considered, and hence new methods are in order.

When the Forest Committee of the Dominion Commission of Conservation was organized, Fernow helped to obtain forest surveys of several provinces. He himself participated in several important forest reconnaissances. Soil, water, agricultural conditions, and a number of important factors were analyzed. In a few words, the ends were rational use of the forests, and at the same time, conservation for the future. Fernow, aided by many, but especially Sir Henri, and his son E. G., Joly de Lotbiniere, William Little, R. H. Campbell, Clyde Leavitt, and others, participated in the movement which induced the Dominion and provincial governments to change radically their attitude toward their forest property. He also almost alone won over a number of large private companies, particularly pulp and paper concerns, to forestry practice. The names of Ellwood Wilson, C. D. Howe, C. A. Lyford, Judson Clark, and former Dean Cosens of the faculty of forestry at Toronto are important in this connection. Fernow knew the history of the United States and Canadian forestry movement. Arguing for Canadian changes in forest policy in 1907-1908, he summarized:

It took 30 years of persistent propaganda to advance forestry interests in the United States so far as to secure for them at least a respectful hearing, and, if it had not been for the accident of a wealthy independent idealist [Gifford Pinchot], and a fearless, independent, idealistic President [Theodore Roosevelt] coming together to Washington, the remarkably rapid progress made there during the last ten years in governmental forest administration would very likely not have occurred.

President Roosevelt, therefore, took cognizance of this widespread forestry interest, related, as it was, to country life problems, and appointed Pinchot to the Country Life Commission. Subsequently, Charles S. Barrett of Georgia, representing the South, and William A. Beard, representing the West were added to Chairman Bailey's commission.

From the White House on November 9, President Roosevelt wrote Bailey urging that the whole success of the commission's work depended on the attitude of the people in the open country. Farmers, he said, should feel a sense of ownership of the commission. Sending out questionnaires and holding meetings were valuable. But, said the President, perhaps something more can be done.

I accordingly suggest that you ask the farmers to come together in the several school districts of the country, so that they may meet and consider these matters. . . . Your purpose is neither to investigate the farmer, nor to inquire into technical methods of farming. You are simply trying to ascertain what are the general economic, social, educational and sanitary conditions of the open country and what, if anything, the farmers themselves can do to help themselves, and how the Government can help them. . . .

A secretarial staff was provided, the members of the commission entrained, and went over the national domain, holding open hearings at thirty places between November 9 and December 22, 1908: College Park, Maryland; Richmond, Virginia; Raleigh, North Carolina, and Athens, Georgia; Spartansburg, South Carolina; Knoxville, Tennessee; Lexington, Kentucky; Washington, D.C.; Dallas, Texas; El Paso, Texas; Tucson, Arizona; Los Angeles, California; Fresno, California; San Francisco, California; Sacramento, California; Reno, Nevada; Portland, Oregon; Spokane, Washington (and at Opportunity, nearby); Salt Lake City, Utah; Cheyenne, Wyoming; Bozeman, Montana; Denver, Colorado; Omaha, Nebraska; Council Bluffs, Iowa; Minneapolis, Minnesota; Madison, Wisconsin; Champaign, Illinois; Ithaca, New York; Springfield, Massachusetts; Boston, Massachusetts; and again at Washington. The first Washington hearing was had in conjunction with meetings of the National Grange, Farmers' Institutes, and the Association of American Agricultural Colleges and Experiment Stations. At Sacramento the commission divided, part proceeding east through Nevada, Utah, and Colorado, and part returning by way of Washington state, Oregon, and Montana. All members were reunited at Omaha where a hearing was held in connection with the National Corn Exposition. At Ithaca, members Wallace, Beard, and Barrett, and, of course, Bailey, inspected the facilities of the New York State College of Agriculture. Bailey was presented by students of the college with a scroll in appreciation of the honor which had been bestowed on him. Barrett, especially, must have been interested in the college plant for early in 1907 members of the board of trustees of the University of Georgia and of the Georgia College of Agriculture had inspected Cornell's new agricultural college and buildings with a view to expending wisely a legislative appropriation of $100,000.

In October, previous to its swing around the nation, the commission's plan of inquiry had been officially organized with Norval D. Kemp as secretary to the chairman. A list of questions was prepared and mailed to about 600,000 persons. Special inquiries and investigations were conducted by individual commissioners by correspondence. E. W. Allen of the Office of Experiment Stations accompanied the hearings-journey to great geographic regions of the nation. The whole mass of data and information was brought together, the commission acting as a unit and requiring no minority report, and Bailey took hold of the large task of preparing what was simply styled Senate Document No. 705, the Sixtieth Congress, Second Session, for use of the Congress, "The Report of the Commission on Country Life." Eight times, it is said, Bailey revised the report in its entirety. The Congress did not make a special appropriation for its publication. But the Spokane, Washington, Chamber of Commerce had it reprinted for use in the country life movement in the Northwest and in 1911, published by Sturgis & Walton Company, the book made its appearance.

President Butterfield has given a description of Bailey's work on the commission. Butterfield was a great rural sociologist on whom Bailey as a balancing practical humanist wielded large influence. The nation had passed a period of President Roosevelt's popular "trust-busting" movement and, attacking monopolistic control of natural resources as well as economic problems of distribution and consumption, had inaugurated, under its federal police power, by legislation and a responsive United States Supreme Court, stimulating, progressive, social reforms that were to last well into the presidential administration of Woodrow Wilson. The country life movement, confining itself in its applications to rural needs and solutions, was but a phase. Anticipating as it did much concrete rural sociological and economic improvement, it was regarded by Roosevelt and agricultural leaders as of fundamental and immediate importance. Years after the *Report of the Commission on Country Life* was published, Butterfield evaluated the worth of Bailey's contributions as chairman:

Professor Bailey brought to the chairmanship of President Roosevelt's Country Life Commission a number of highly important qualifications. The first was a point of view. As one of his friends said, Professor Bailey looks at the rural problem with two eyes. He saw the significance both of the scientific and the human, of the practical and the philosophical, of the individual and the social, of the material and the spiritual. He saw the relationships between these elements. He balanced them in a large philosophy of the whole rural question. His phrase for this question was "The building of a new rural civilization."

Professor Bailey's method of arriving at this point of view was vital and not academic. He had not gained his philosophy from books of sociology or economics. He began as a student of science; he had gained his hold upon men as a teacher of horticulture; and he had the experience of an administrator in agricultural education. These experiences had led him to see the whole breadth and scope of the rural problem. Hence, he insisted on a first-hand exploration by the Commission. Under his leadership, the Commission came into contact with men and women who were a part of the rural problem.

As Chairman of the Commission Professor Bailey not only commanded the confidence of his associates, but of the public. There were many farmers who were prejudiced against the Commission. They resented an apparent attempt to put them in the category of people to be investigated and uplifted. But all who knew Professor Bailey knew that he had no such thought, and that the work to be done was done in the spirit of service and helpfulness along important lines.

The charm characteristic of Professor Bailey's writings was an element of strength, when the Commission came to the task of preparing its report. I venture to say that no matter how much is written in the coming years on the rural problem, the report of the Country Life Commission will be one of the classics in this field, and largely because of the Chairman's responsibility for the phrasing of the report.

Professor Bailey has rendered many conspicuous services in the field of agricultural education and development. I am inclined to believe that his work as Chairman of the Country Life Commission is likely to prove the most far reaching in its effects of any of these great services.

Guidance was the great need of rural life, according to the report. Implied in this, of course, was need of leadership, and also, need of a redirected education in consonance with all new changes and developments. "The real ends of the people are not alone the arts by which they make a living but the whole range of their customary activities," it said. A type of nationwide agricultural extension work was urged. And on May 8, 1914, with the passage of the federal Smith-Lever Extension Act, providing for cooperative agricultural extension work between the agricultural colleges of the states and the United States Department of Agriculture (including the giving of instruction and practical demonstrations in agriculture and home economics), the institution of a nationwide agricultural extension program was to be realized —in the formulation of which Bailey would have some part, since one of the authors of the bill consulted him. However, the *Report of the*

Commission on Country Life contemplated vastly more than extension work. It urged, in addition, the removal of agricultural impediments and the development of resources. For resource-improvements, it stressed human and material development. The spread of cooperative societies— in instances, when needed, combinations—the strengthening of churches and semi-religious organizations with a dominating leadership, the spread of social centers, and other agencies of coordinating action, of which Bailey had so long been an ardent advocate, were elaborated. Never once, moreover, was reliance placed on the creation of farm blocs or agencies having a solely political significance. Nor was reliance placed on resort to specific legislative measures. The report seems to have proceeded on the basis that, except in instances of unreasonable abuses, matters of economics or morality were not the province of legislation. In the large, the solutions were to be found in education. Agricultural or country life surveys, embracing careful inventory of resources from standpoints of health, labor, temperance, women's work, availability of post office, parcel post, and postal savings bank facilities, and all factors promoting efficiencies, enjoyment, and comforts of farm life, generally, were recommended.

Surveys alone could not effectuate complete solutions. Granting their directive and material aid, constructive action on a large scale was still needed. The special problems still were the "more or less serious agri-cultural unrest in every part of the United States, even in the most pros-perous regions," and the continued townward movements which tended "to sterilize the open country and to lower its social status." The funda-mental problem was, as it had been, the building of a rural civilization, even more, the building of an entire social structure, which allowed the farmer a "reasonable return" on his investment and business, such as would be permanent and satisfying to an intelligent, progressive people. To accomplish this, a new agriculture and a new rural life were still imperative. Specifically, therefore, the need of material-resource-surveys was apparent—studies of soils, farm management problems, examina-tions of farm practices, diversified and rotation farming adapted to regional requirements, and the entire range of special land and farm deficiencies, including crops, susceptible of improvement, received at-tention. Nor were the much needed matters of improved highways, rural and highway engineering services, and the like, excluded from consideration. Tenantry in "one-crop regions" was considered. Bailey seldom let go an opportunity to advance rural art—an appreciation of the beautiful in special relation to farm, home, school, and village en-vironment—a subject distinguishable from the historic landscape gar-dening or landscape architecture courses given in agricultural college curricula almost from their beginning. In 1907 (Harvard University had shortly before established a professional school covering the field), at least twenty-two land-grant colleges were giving courses in these subjects, and Bryant Fleming had developed the study of rural art at the New York State College of Agriculture. Furthermore, the great importance of home economics was stressed by Bailey in the commission's report. This subject, extensively developed in American universities—particularly Iowa State College, the University of Illinois, and Ohio State University—had been initiated at Cornell almost a decade before by correspondence. Lectures were given in intervening years, in 1905-1906[1] an accredited course was given; in 1906-1907 another program of lectures as a part of the winter course; and in the fall of 1907 four-year regular instruction, a department equipped with experimental laboratories, had commenced with the able teaching of Martha Van Rensselaer, who led in the home economics movement, with Nellie S. Kedzie Jones, Isabel Bevier of Illinois, Abby Lillian Marlatt of Wisconsin, and others. Also a graduate summer school had been provided in 1908. It is an interesting fact that every constructive educational recommendation of the report was included in study-courses at the New York State College.

In the school year 1906-1907, in partial response to researches under the Adams fund, twenty-two members were added to the college's faculty. Pioneer courses such as limnology under James George Needham, which we will discuss a few pages forward, and experimental plant breeding under Webber, to which we already have referred, were started. Webber's department had been created for the man whom Bailey regarded as America's most skillful plant breeder, and researches in alfalfa, corn, potatoes, summer and winter wheat, timothy, and other products, continued. From this work issued his corn origination, "Cornell 11," which has remained a standard corn grown in New York state almost to the present time. B. M. Duggar, American spokesman for plant physiology at the 1904 Congress of Arts and Sciences and an acknowledged authority on plant nutrition, was lifting his somewhat neglected subject to high rank in botanical work of the university and claiming increased greenhouse, garden, and other facilities. Along with Whetzel's progressive instruction (establishing field laboratories and experimental gardens to study problems) there was the general botanical work of Cornell University—nationally prominent, built by men of such caliber as Atkinson, Durand, Rowlee, Wiegand,

---

[1] *Cornell Countryman,* XIV, 4. 1917, p. 314 says the first winter course and first year of an accredited course in Home Economics at Cornell occurred in 1904. Concerning "Rural Art," see the "Report of the Director for the Year 1906," dated January 14, 1907, *19th Annual Report of the Agricultural Experiment Station of Cornell University,* p. 26; *20th Annual Report, idem* (Home Economics, p. 15), (Rural Art and Rural Architecture, pp. 14, 17).

Duggar, Whetzel, and, of course, not forgetting Prentiss and Dudley. The work of other colleges acquired national eminence also as an expansive plant science and agricultural interest was discernible in all campus quarters. Rural engineering interest had noticeably quickened in 1907. In 1905 a few lectures given by prominent editors of agricultural journals had introduced the educationally shaping subject of agricultural journalism to students.

Bailey believed that both research and propaganda were necessary in furthering the country life movement. In 1908 he wrote, "Most of us must be experiment-teachers and spreaders of propaganda; a very few may be investigators. The former has been the more needed in the past few years; they always will be of equal importance with the investigators, and they represent an equally high type of effort." Of the truth of this Bailey was a living proof. He kept pace with new developments. For example, in 1906, busy as he was, he found time to inspect the new and growing orange industry in Louisiana. Never, either, were rural school interests and the college neglected. In 1907 the *Cornell Rural School Leaflets*—a publication that has grown so with the years that today between 80,000 and 90,000 rural New Yorkers receive them— were substituted for the Junior Naturalists' monthly in order that rural teachers might have leaflets dealing with practical daily problems in teaching agricultural subjects. That all students of the college might enjoy a social as well as educational life while at Cornell, clubs, similar to the horticultural Lazy Club, were provided in nearly every important division of study. A wide program of student activities, including athletics and musical entertainment, was maintained. A somewhat model prototype of an ideal country life was placed on the college's campus, not intentionally but with the desirable elements to be fostered in an ideal rural setting. On November 3, 1911, when President Roosevelt, then out of office, addressed the college he characterized the New York State College of Agriculture as "one of the institutions of the country which is at the present time doing the most vital educational work in our country. . . . Without injustice to any other institution," he said, "this college is the foremost institution of its kind, the most useful of its kind, not only in the United States, but in the whole civilized world."[2]

The *Report of the Commission on Country Life* had taken a definite position, as far as agriculture was concerned, on a subject upon which Roosevelt had always taken a firm stand—monopolistic controls. On this subject the President had wielded not only his historic diplomatic "big stick" but often, diplomatic parlance being dispensed with, he had fought monopolies with a clenched fist, jaws set firm, and no soft-spoken

[2] *Cornell Countryman*, IX, 2 (November 1911), pp. 36 ff.

words. Aware the working farmers in last analysis would solve the farm problem, he believed the nation should "render any help towards making the solution satisfactory." He said so in introductory remarks written July 21, 1910, for the book embodying the "Report," since, he reasoned: "We were founded as a nation of farmers, and in spite of the great growth of our industrial life it still remains true that our whole system rests upon the farm, that the welfare of the whole community depends upon the welfare of the farmer. The strengthening of country life is the strengthening of the whole nation."

The commission in its report directed attention to need of restoring inherent rights of land owners—the necessity of breaking up monopolistic control of streams, especially a concentration of water power which had placed "about 33% of the total developed water powers of the country under the control of a group of 13 companies or interests." It also urged the improvement of marketing conditions by removals of trade-restraints, revisions of tariff regulations and freight rates in the farmer's interest, at least to make them more understandable by the farmer. Holdings of large land areas for speculative reasons by large companies or individuals should be discouraged. Removals of monopolistic controls of forest resources and the development of further conservation measures with aggressive programs of forestry study including soils, wood-lot property, communal farming, watershed protection, reforestation, and other phases, were advocated.

Significantly, it may be noticed, in 1910 the New York State College of Agriculture announced establishment of a department of forestry and a few months later the appointment of Walter Mulford, to head the department.[3] The law authorizing creation of the old New York State College of Forestry had not been repealed and, since, in the meantime, the New York State College of Agriculture had been erected, it was necessary to do no more in 1911 than place a department in the college of agriculture. However, astonishing events in New York state occurred that year. In 1911 Governor Dix signed a bill authorizing a new State College of Forestry at Syracuse University, notwithstanding the fact that the year before Governor Hughes had vetoed the measure. This was a source of great disappointment to Bailey since now two state supported schools would compete in efforts designed to teach the same subject—a condition which the New York State College of Agriculture had been established to prevent.

[3] See *Cornell Countryman*, VIII, 1 (October 1910), p. 19; also VIII, 4 (January 1911), p. 146. The department was established the next year. In Bailey's report as director for 1910-1911, he said, "One of the most important of [the] new units has been added this past year by the establishment of a Department of Forestry and the election of Professor Walter Mulford of the University of Michigan to the headship of the work. . . ."

During the year 1909 Bailey had practically perfected arrangements to reestablish professional forestry teaching at Cornell. Had these plans been put into effect, there probably would never have been a New York State College of Forestry at Syracuse. The Cornell plan called for the use of some of the ablest forestry teaching talent in America. Among others, Filibert Roth and Herman Haupt Chapman were to be offered positions. After he became dean of the college of agriculture, Bailey had hearkened to Roberts's recommendation to reestablish forestry teaching and research at Cornell. For he was fully aware of the importance of farm forestry in New York state. His earnest belief had been expressed to President Schurman and Speaker Nixon in 1903, the year of the sudden discontinuance of the old New York State College of Forestry. When the discussion as to the old college and Fernow's clear cutting and replanting policy at the Cornell forest tract in the Adirondacks were at their height, Bailey expressed himself as being convinced that the forestry problem in New York state was essentially agricultural. Before the New York State College of Agriculture was established in 1904 he wrote that the larger part of forest lands was "probably on farms and not in forest preserves. . . . I believe," he said, "that a school of forestry should train professional foresters, for a certain number of these will always be needed." To Speaker Nixon he reported that same year: ". . . This work should be conducted by the College of Agriculture, for all forestry is an agricultural subject and farm forestry is inextricably associated with agricultural teaching." Bailey believed in forestry work and for years urged its reestablishment at the college.

No one who has studied the situation that led to the discontinuance of the old New York State College of Forestry could agree that as a matter of right or justification the school under Fernow should have been abolished. Its disbanding wrote an infamous chapter of what unintelligent political interference in educational matters may do. Bailey had pleaded with the Cornell board not to disband the institution which today might be one of Cornell University's greatest objects of pride—the first professional school of forestry on the American continent. No complaint of the *school's* work had ever been registered. Controversy had arisen in 1901. Hearings on applications to have declared void the transactions leading to the creation of the Cornell forest tract had commenced in 1902—the same year Attorney-General Davies rendered an opinion that the New York State College of Forestry had not violated any provisions of law. A special legislative committee to investigate the policy and practice on the college forest had been appointed in 1902 and reported with some criticism the following year. When, therefore, three state bills were presented to Governor Odell for signature—one, an appropriation for the forest, fish and game commission; one, for special

demonstration work on the Cornell forest; and one, the annual appropriation enactment for the college itself—Governor Odell vetoed the legislature's appropriation for the college. Evidently what the governor
wished was to do away with the demonstration forest work. Instead, by
his action, he did away with the college. Bailey urged upon the Cornell
board that all erroneous impressions, all false understandings on the part
of the governor or members of the legislature could be straightened out
the following year.

Fernow and Bailey were the closest of friends. In fact, the night the
telegram arrived announcing the governor's veto, Bailey and Fernow
were together at a dance. Interestingly enough, the dance went on, despite the bad news. Fernow and forestry students offered to carry on
the school. Indeed, later, even the governor offered to aid in the school's
reestablishment. However, by this time, another attorney-general had
come into office. He decided to bring an action to enjoin an alleged
"waste of lands," being perpetrated on the Cornell forest tract in compliance with provisions of a contract entered into by the university and
a corporation known as the Brooklyn Cooperage Company. Despite the
school's discontinuance, the Cooperage Company continued to cut and
remove timber from the forest. An analysis of the history and development of this law suit which dragged on seven discouraging years had
much to do with the Cornell board's and President Schurman's decision
not to reestablish (despite Bailey's urgings) forestry teaching at Cornell. Fernow and Roth, among others, testified in the case. Charles S.
Chapman of the United States Forest Service was also a witness. Fernow resented Chapman's testimony which said, in effect, that as between
two silvicultural methods that might have been adopted—the selection
system or the clear cutting and replanting system—Fernow had erred
in changing to the clear cutting and replanting method. Fernow viewed
the matter academically. At least thirty silvicultural methods, dependent on conditions, might have been applied.

From the beginning of the controversy when compromise was urged
on Fernow, Fernow saw involved a forestry issue of highest importance
to American study. Although it is said that he was told, if he would
compromise, forestry and his school would be put on the map in a large
way, Fernow with honesty and forthrightness characteristic of him, refused, walking away from the offerer muttering, "No compromise."
Fernow preferred to battle out the questions as to soundness or unsoundness of his policies and practice in the Cornell forest work. Fundamentally, from the legal standpoint, Fernow had conducted himself on sound
footing. The first attorney-general's opinion had held, "The lands are
the property of Cornell University" for the experimental period of
thirty years, and that, therefore, inhibitions, constitutional or otherwise,

which applied to the state's Adirondack forest preserve had no application to the Cornell forest at Axton. Other lawyers before him must have
rendered the same opinion. But when the school was disbanded, what
then? That another attorney-general held an opinion contrary to the
first one does not impugn the soundness of Fernow's actions. The other
view was in force when Fernow directed the school. Nor do business
considerations impugn seriously his soundness of program. Railroad
facilities were not provided, as expected. Milling and distillation operations had to be brought to the forest. Fires occurred. Rises in costs took
place. Fernow was always handicapped by lack of finances. None of
these facts, however, are determinative of the soundness or unsoundness
of his silvicultural policy. Fernow saw foremost the forestry principle.
He was director of a school and administering an educational project
for the benefit of the state and nation. In the law suit, Fernow hoped and
expected that the highest court of New York (and there were at least
four high court decisions rendered) would settle the issues on the basis
of forestry principles. The court, however, saw the basic legal question
and held the lands to be property of the state of New York. The last
state court decision was dated March 19, 1912, practically nine years
after discontinuance of the old school.

Naturally Bailey's attention had been centered on the nation's agricultural status. Every effort which made for agricultural improvement,
no matter where, received, when possible, his aid. As a member of the
country life commission, he, as chairman, had written into the report
commendation of the National Reclamation Act, endorsed the spread of
irrigation projects, the development of power plants over the country,
and many other enterprises of agricultural value. In somewhat an editorial style, he had said when the *Report of the Commission on Country
Life* appeared:

. . . We must in some way unite all institutions, all organizations, all individuals, having any interest in country life into one great campaign for
rural progress. . . . We must picture to ourselves a new rural social structure, developed from the strong resident forces of the open country; and
then we must set at work all the agencies that will tend to bring this about.
The entire people need to be roused to this avenue of usefulness. Most of
the new leaders must be farmers who can find not only a satisfying business
career on the farm, but who will throw themselves into the service of upbuilding the community. A new race of teachers is also to appear in the
country. A new rural clergy is to be trained. These leaders will see the great
underlying problem of country life, and together they will work, each in his
own field, for the one goal of a new and permanent rural civilization. Upon
the development of this distinctively rural civilization rests ultimately our
ability, by methods requiring the highest intelligence, to continue to feed
and clothe the hungry nations; to supply the city and metropolis with fresh
blood, clean bodies and clear brains that can endure the strain of modern

urban life; and to preserve a race of men in the open country that, in the future as in the past, will be the stay and strength of the nation in time of war, and its guiding and controlling spirit in time of peace.

When on February 9, 1909, President Roosevelt sent to Congress his special message embodying the report, he told Congress he hoped to make farming in the nation "one of the most dignified, desirable and sought after ways of earning a living."

In 1908 with Walter M. Coleman as co-author there was published Bailey's *First Course in Biology* having three principal divisions, plant, animal, and human biology, with laboratory manuals. In 1909 Bailey's volume *Beginners' Botany* made its initial appearance, in which the author made surprising observations on a trend he believed developing in secondary education:

The present tendency in secondary education is away from the formal technical completion of separate subjects and toward the developing of a workable training in the activities that relate the pupil to his own life. In the natural science field, the tendency is to attach less importance to botany and zoology and physiology as such, and to lay greater stress on the processes and adaptations of life as expressed in plants and animals and men. This tendency is a revolt against the laboratory method and research method of the college as it has been impressed into the common schools, for it is not uncommon for the pupil to study botany without really knowing plants, or physiology without knowing himself. . . .

It is much better for the beginning pupil to acquire a real conception of a few central principles and points of view respecting common forms that will enable him to tie his knowledge together and organize it and apply it, than to familiarize himself with any number of mere facts about the lower forms of life which, at the best, he can know only indirectly and remotely. If the pupil wishes to go farther in later years, he may then take up special groups and phases.

There was so much work to be done. In 1908 Bailey prepared for the Bureau of Education of the United States Department of the Interior a bulletin styled, "On the Training of Persons to Teach Agriculture in the Public Schools." In it he reviewed in addition to the nature of the problem, the means of giving instruction to teachers already in service as well as new teachers. The surprising fact was, in spite of the large number of agricultural colleges or departments established over the land, only a few were equipped to give teaching or normal school courses. He analyzed especially the content of normal work being given in Massachusetts, Illinois, New York, Missouri, Maine, North Carolina, North Dakota, Connecticut, and Washington state, and concluded that the "above examples constitute the only instances known to the writer of agricultural colleges, or agricultural departments of colleges, in the United States that have actually put pedagogical courses or departments into operation, although other colleges or departments are each cooperating more or less with the education department of the university or college of which it is a part. Several of the colleges of agriculture," he said, "are now considering the establishing of education courses. It is probable that such courses will constitute the most marked departure in agricultural college work in the immediate future. As yet the whole subject is in a formative and experimental stage. These colleges have a very large and varied constituency, and they properly represent all the phases of country life. It is incumbent on them to reach directly the educational phase, and it is incumbent on the people to see that they are able to enter this field, for this is a necessary condition to the evolution of the public schools." When Commissioner Elmer Ellsworth Brown transmitted Bailey's report for publication, he concluded by saying:

Professor Bailey is among the foremost of those who are making the new movements in agricultural education, and his suggestions will have value and interest, not only for the authorities controlling the agricultural and mechanical colleges, but also for all who are interested in these new educational undertakings.

What an overwhelming task still lay before agricultural educators! In an address delivered Farmers' Week at Cornell University February 26, 1909, "The College of Agriculture and the State," Bailey indicated just how far educational leadership, generally, had gotten:

We are conducting reading-courses with less than 16,000 farmers and farmers' wives in New York, yet there are a half million such in the State. We are reaching at this moment less than 7,000 teachers, but there are 40,000 school teachers in the State and hundreds are being prepared every year. We are reaching 65,000 children this year, out of 1½ million in the elementary and high schools of the State. We are conducting demonstration or test work on some 300 farms out of the 227,000 in the State. We are teaching one student for about every 500 farms. In this College of Agriculture, large as it has grown to be, we yet have less than one student to each rural township in the state. There are probably more farm boys and girls in any one agricultural county in the State than are now in this College of Agriculture. All this is in spite of the fact that the number of students is increasing so rapidly that we cannot properly keep up with the work. The value of farm property in New York in the last census was $1,069,723,895. The money appropriated for maintenance of college education in agriculture is about one sixty-sixth of one per cent. of this valuation.

Persons constantly express surprise that these buildings are packed to their utmost even when they are little more than completed. It is a fact that they are packed, however, and that we ought to accept no more students with the present facilities. This is only a demonstration that the people are ready. Not all the farm youth, of course, will want a college education, but enough will want it to warrant the doubling of the present plant of this College of Agriculture at once.

The mere increase in numbers of students (there are now more than 800) makes demands on teachers and equipment that very few persons understand. It is not merely a question of finding a place in which students may sit, but desks for laboratory work, microscopes and other special apparatus, animals, library facilities, and a hundred accessories that the layman knows not of. Modern agricultural education has become a very much specialized business, and each student works with the objects and things themselves and receives careful personal help from his teacher.

The special agricultural schools and the agricultural work in the public schools, and the work of this College of Agriculture should all be organized into a system or plan, the development of which should proceed in an orderly way and as rapidly as the needs of the State demand.

Bailey observed that nearly all "the most important field crops of the State have been neglected, and no crops have received the study that is required to enable the grower to get the most from them. The potato crop is more important, in value, than the apple or than poultry. Corn is more important, in value in New York, than apples or sheep. Yet apples and poultry and sheep are not minor interests, but represent great values. There is always a tendency to study local crops and specialties, to the relative exclusion of the great underlying staples. In order that you may understand how little really has been done with staple industries, I cite hay and pasture, forests, and fish as examples. Grass is the fundamental crop of this State," he affirmed. "Of the 15,599,986 acres in farms in New York, 5,154,965 are in hay and forage, and 4,366,683 acres are in all other crops. The remainder, 6,078,338, is probably mostly in pasture. The farm land is, therefore, approximately One-third in hay One-third in pasture One-third in all other crops. The value of the grass crop is no less striking. The hay crop is worth as much as all the dairy products. It is worth nearly as much as all other crops combined. It is worth over five times as much as all the orchard products. We have no estimate of the values of pastures, but the hay and pasture crops are undoubtedly worth more than all the animals and animal products sold, and are worth more than all the other plants or plant products. They constitute considerably over one-third of the total products of New York farms. The value of hay has increased 66 per cent. since these figures were taken by the last census. In spite of these facts, the State has done practically nothing to aid in grass production. The amount of money that has been spent by the State to encourage some of the minor interests would have brought much greater returns if expended on our fundamental crop. There is as much opportunity for improvement in grass production as there is in fruit production."

Of what use, however, was the development of pastures without improvement of live stock which consume the pasture product? Of forestry, "one of the greatest crops of this State," its timber being "as much a crop as corn or potatoes," without realizing its value in stream control, game protection, flood prevention, and general attractiveness of the country? Limnology, enlarging as it did the concept of farming as a "dry-land business," included also water crops. More than a knowledge of food value and the life histories of fish were to be gained from scientific study of aquatic and semi-aquatic life in relation to agriculture. New uses of marsh land, utilization of impounded waters as breeding grounds for food fish, and cultivation of valuable aquatic plants were a few gains. So new was this subject in agricultural science that Cornell University had to invent a name when James George Needham began his original studies in the land marshes at the head of Cayuga Lake. Out of this study, embracing laboratory and breeding investigations, grew Needham's and J. T. Lloyd's *Life of Inland Waters* (1915), and a new phase of nature study, since it provided an elementary textbook of fresh-water biology for American students. In 1912 or 1913, Bailey conceived of Needham's writing a book, *The Natural History of the Farm* (1913). This book became a basis of a required course for freshmen in the college. Evolutionary growth of study subjects was the one great method on which Bailey placed reliance in developing agricultural education. In this way, a college and its instruction was indeed a mirror held up to nature. Each student became a symbol of natural growth and development.

In Bailey's "College of Agriculture and the State" address, he commented that "on the college education side, there is a State College of Agriculture and a State College of Veterinary Science at Cornell University. There is agitation for other state colleges of agriculture. There should be," he pointed out, "only one State College of Agriculture, and this should be so well supported that it can gain the primacy not only in the nation but in the world. The primacy of New York is conditioned directly on the education of its citizens. It is impossible for the State to develop several colleges of agriculture of the highest rank. We have only begun to construct one such college; if the investment in it is to be the most useful, it must be developed far beyond its present size and scope. We now have provision for three schools of agriculture, one of which is already under good headway. More will be asked for. A pressing duty now before us is to determine what we propose to do with all special schools of agriculture that may now or hereafter be established, and to lay out a scheme. We are much in need of a system. These schools should have definite relation to the State College of Agriculture, with it becoming a part of an organized plan. They should not be wholly isolated and separate, or established merely because the region needs a school. They should be secondary or special in grade and regional in application."

In 1909 there had been established at Morrisville in Madison County a new school of agriculture. To its board of trustees Governor Hughes named Bailey and State Commissioner Raymond A. Pearson, formerly professor of Dairy Industry at Cornell. Governor Hughes had always had the interests of agriculture at heart. One of his last acts as governor before assuming duties of an appointment to the United States Supreme Court, where for years he exercised a liberal influence, was to sign a $357,000 appropriation bill in 1910 to build the Bailey Auditorium, the new poultry husbandry building, and a building for home economics. Among many other matters, the program for construction of these edifices was made part of a huge "ten year plan" approved legislatively during the administration of the acting dean and director, Webber.

Only when, after Bailey's return to the college to put into effect the immense program, did the legislature break all records and authorize the college of agriculture to expend $917,000 in buildings : for forestry, agronomy, and animal husbandry. Of this sum, $129,000 were to be utilized to let contracts for other buildings and improvements—greenhouse extension, barns, a model school house, poultry plant extension, and a plant industry building, plans for which, an estimated $245,000 building, received legislative sanction and authority to build in 1914. Placing the $917,000 appropriation for the agricultural college with a similar allowance of $105,000 for the veterinary college, already the New York legislature had given to Cornell University more than a million dollars, aside from the original appropriations of 1904, for distinctly agricultural purposes. In 1912, estimated appropriations involving almost a million dollars, furthermore, had been distributed in the plan, for chemistry, horticulture, entomology and zoology, dairy industry, rural art, and farm mechanics. In other words, the entire plan embraced almost two million dollars.[4] No wonder Bailey argued that the whole state program for agriculture, inclusive of special and other agricultural colleges, should become "a part of an organized State plan."

On January 21, 1910, Bailey gave before the students of the New York State College of Agriculture the provisions of a plan to coordinate all "movements for education by means of agriculture in New York State." In this was outlined an advisory board or coordinating executive body which might guide all state agricultural education and country life advancement. The board was to include in a membership of state agricultural leaders the state commissioner of agriculture and the state commissioner of education. Under a law of 1911, Governor Dix created a state advisory board of eleven leaders and educators including deans of agricultural schools at Alfred and St. Lawrence universities, Morrisville, and the veterinary science college at Cornell. Bailey was chairman. In 1913 Governor Sulzer, in a message to the legislature, urged that education be "fostered until agriculture is taught not in a

---

[4] See Dudley Alleman's article, "The Ten-Year Plan" etc., *Cornell Countryman,* IX, 9, pp. 289-290.

few colleges but in every high school in our commonwealth." On February 17 he commended to the legislature's friendly consideration the state agricultural advisory board's report and resolutions which were published by the Senate that year.[5] Early in its deliberations the board took the position that the main effort toward introducing agricultural education, whether by state or local aid, should be directed through study of agricultural and rural subjects. This position was reaffirmed. It was advanced that additional training of agricultural teachers at the State Normal College and in normal schools should be provided. The State Department of Education could give directions for obtaining adequate teaching equipment, especially for leading agricultural industries, and should do so. Home economics and agricultural technology should be developed in the special state schools. Indeed, the board went so far as to recommend that cities of the first and second classes of the state should establish agricultural public schools. This was not all accomplished in one meeting, or two meetings, or without the aid and cooperation of the state agricultural societies, and much discussion. Nor were these the only recommendations made by the advisory board.

On August 17, 1910, for instance, Bailey addressed an audience of Alfred University on "The Fundamental Question in American Country Life." There he expressed his pleasure in the fact that America now had the most highly improved agricultural education in the world. It was founded on democratic principles and it seemed at last to have emerged from a long epoch of trial and experiment. But, he reminded his hearers, it was hazardous not to evolve a harmonious plan. Danger lurked in the fact that newer agencies were not profiting from older experience. Zeal to extend agricultural education to all ages of people could be overdone. Additional to fairs, public school instruction, and government departments, there were now five institutions in New York state teaching agriculture. With a growing feeling that other universities should introduce agricultural instruction also, Columbia and Syracuse universities were making beginnings.

On May 8, 1910, Dr. William L. Bray of Syracuse University wrote Fernow concerning a curriculum in forestry. Fernow replied, elaborating his views on forestry instruction, and observed, "You are aware I suppose that Columbia University has under contemplation a faculty of forestry of the highest type." Obviously the interest in forestry was accompanying the growing interest in agriculture.

This year President Schurman changed his views as to the need of forestry instruction. He wrote Mulford, who wrote Bailey. Bailey replied and by the end of the year, December 26, 1910, Filibert Roth at

[5] *Document* XVII *of the Senate of the State of New York,* 136th Session, also Legislature, 1913. Senate Document XXXVI.

the University of Michigan, was writing Fernow, "As you probably saw from Papers, Cornell is starting up, & our old friend, Mulford, is to set things going. . . ." Forestry instruction as departments or schools extended by this time across the entire continent from the far Northwest at the University of Washington to the University of Georgia. Canada had added two more schools. Forestry, on a smaller scale, was growing as rapidly as agriculture, in educational circles.

1911 proved to be a crucial year. Creation of the New York State College of Forestry at Syracuse was authorized. Nothing underhanded is implied. In the Syracuse University catalogue for 1909-1910 Chancellor Day wrote the copy for the announcement that special courses in agriculture and forestry were to be offered. The Chancellor said, "It is proper to announce that preparations are being made for acquiring and installing the best facilities for carrying on the full work of a College of Agriculture at Syracuse University. . . ." In 1911 Chancellor Day and the board appointed Dr. Bray acting dean of the newly authorized college of forestry. Moreover, the board authorized the chancellor and acting dean to select a permanent dean. On excellent authority, it is said Fernow was sought after. So was Roth. Perhaps, also Judson F. Clark. Fernow regarded the offer as tempting. However, another offer had come to him in 1910 and he had not felt "justified in running away from the [University of Toronto] so soon. . . ." Roth may have considered the matter favorably. Possibly the offers issued from the contemplated faculty of forestry at Columbia University. In any event, Mulford took up residence at Ithaca on June 15, 1911.

It was not possible to assemble at once a sufficient staff and equipment to give at Cornell in 1911 a professional course "worthy of" the New York State College of Agriculture. Bailey, however, never desisted from planning for a full professional course. Nor did Mulford. But Mulford was only thirty-four years of age. He revived the idea of bringing on Roth, who was appointed in January, 1912.

The announcement stirred Dean Bray to action. Bray was a botanist of excellent standing, a man, whose character was above reproach, whose ability as professor of subjects such as forest ecology, silviculture, and dendrology, had been developed through years of teaching at the Universities of Texas and Syracuse, whose administrative ability was proved by the fact he next was selected to organize a college of agriculture at the latter university. In 1911 Edward F. McCarthy, a University of Michigan graduate, and for a time with the United States Forest Service, had been brought to Syracuse as the forestry school's first instructor. Together he and Dean Bray went into conclave. They decided to offer the position to Mulford. Mulford was summoned to a conference with Chancellor Day. They came to no agreement. H. H.

Chapman and Hugh P. Baker were next considered. Baker accepted and was constituted dean and director of the school.

The New York State College of Forestry at Syracuse enjoyed large money appropriations, an unexcelled building and equipment, and, most remarkable, after a fight extending over a decade, Syracuse University was enabled to develop a college of agriculture. Bailey cannot be said to have lost his fight because the agricultural work at Syracuse in large part was privately endowed. But Bailey's victory was diminishing in importance. Instead of centralization in agricultural instruction which for years the state had enjoyed and because of which great progress had been made possible, there was springing up widespread decentralization. Only the fact of the great state's wealth could justify or sustain it. Even though the work became decentralized, said Bailey, there was need of coordinate action on the part of institutions. There was need of some unifying organization.

Roth and Mulford at the University of Michigan had made an excellent pair in forestry instruction. Roth remained at Michigan. Being one of the ablest forestry teachers America has ever had, the University of Michigan improved its facilities to retain him. Michigan forestry needed his services more.

Mulford did not remain at Cornell. In August, 1913, he was invited to confer with President Benjamin Ide Wheeler and Dean Thomas F. Hunt of the University of California at Berkeley with a view to developing forestry instruction there. He accepted as we shall see later. Thus, two great schools of forestry in the United States were to develop—one at Syracuse University under Hugh Potter Baker's leadership and the other at California under Mulford's leadership. Both men were able foresters.

On May 15, 1914, at an informal dedication of the Cornell forestry building—later named Fernow Hall of the New York State College of Agriculture—distinguished American foresters, Fernow, Roth, Dean James W. Toumey, Pinchot, and others participated. During the celebration the annual meeting of the Society of American Foresters of which Fernow was now president was held. Bailey spoke at the forestry building's dedication on "The Forest," but not any longer as dean of the college of agriculture and director of its experiment station. In this address, somewhat an epilogue to a notable career, Bailey spoke feelingly of his appreciation of the forest, long loved by him. The forestry situation was not the cause of his resignation though it cannot be denied that it was one of several contributing reasons. Indeed, feeling precipitated by the special circumstances heretofore discussed and which were outgrowths of a tremendous growth and expansion in forestry education was so tense that foresters themselves that year had agreed not to discuss the New York situation at their meeting of the Society of American Foresters. The forestry situation, nevertheless, cannot be said to have been the main, or only, reason why Bailey resigned. A number of explanations have become current since. We, therefore, must give over the next few paragraphs to a further consideration of the real reason—the future well-being and greater internal development of the New York State College of Agriculture.

Early in 1913 the ten-year period which Bailey agreed to serve as dean and director had expired. On July 31 his resignation had become effective. Resigning at the height of his powers, at the end of a period he thought sufficient for administrative officers, and believing that a new, and perhaps a younger, man was needed as dean, he had retired to pursue some cherished ambitions which he knew himself capable of fulfilling. Governor Sulzer's commission of inquiry had upheld the long established state policy constituting Cornell University "the real head of the system of agricultural teaching in the state." It had commended the work of the New York State College of Agriculture with its approximately 2,000 enrolled students. It had recommended that all agricultural work be made a unified state program. In its April, 1913, issue, *Cornell Countryman* rejoiced that under Dean Bailey the school had become undoubtedly "the best College of Agriculture in the world. . . ." Isaac Phillips Roberts, "Farmer, Teacher, Philosopher and Friend" had been nobly superseded by his follower in office. Charles W. Garfield was justly proud, too.

As early as 1910 Bailey had contemplated giving all his energies to country life development. During the school year 1909-1910 when he had taken his sabbatical leave, and after the "Report of the Commission on Country Life" had been completed, Bailey considered not returning to Cornell. He went so far as to call his faculty together, announce he was leaving for a trip, and would not return for some time. Faculty members protested vigorously, some construing his action not as a wish but as something he thought necessary to promote harmony. In 1911 had been published Bailey's book on the general subject, *The Country-Life Movement in the United States*—dedicated to Charles W. Garfield, "seer of visions, prophet of the better country life. . . ." This volume, along with a revision of *The Outlook to Nature* (1905-1911), *The Nature-Study Idea* (1903-1905), and *The State and the Farmer* (1908), an enlargement of his presidential address before the Association of American Colleges and Experiment Stations, had become members of another set of books of rural importance, the Rural Outlook Series. Bailey saw value in this work. He could write more.

He did tell Acting Dean and Director Webber that he was not returning. But he also said he was not resigning. He explained to Webber the responsibilities that would be his during his absence, what he believed could be secured in the way of appropriations, and Webber, during his period of office, secured more money than Bailey had believed would be possible. Bailey knew that New York state had been primarily interested in promoting the great resources of agricultural and veterinary science. When Webber and every faculty member and student on the campus sought by every means possible to induce him to return, he was persuaded 'to continue as dean and director in order to put into effect the legislatively approved ten-year building program. He also put into action a new plan of administration for the college of agriculture which he presented before a meeting of the board of trustees of Cornell, with every member present, in October, 1911.

Former president Andrew D. White, as the board's most influential member, gave Bailey's plan his valuable support. On December 16, 1911, at a meeting held in New York City the board adopted with slight modifications the plan which in essence gave more self-government to the college of agriculture although the college still remained an integral part of Cornell University. Immediate supervision of the college of agriculture passed from an executive committee of the board to an agricultural college council composed of the five trustees appointed by the governor, the president of the university, the trustee elected by the state Grange, the state commissioner of agriculture, and the president of the state agricultural society, both ex-officio members of the board, and two trustees to be selected by the board itself, one of whom was to be an alumnus trustee. Bailey's report to the trustees presented the reasons:

To my mind the solution of the problem is one of great simplicity, and it all lies with the University itself. It is merely this: All state work at Cornell should comprise one administrative unit. The Trustees appointed by the Governor with probably those representing popular interests, or others, and the President of the University, should constitute a small council or committee to have charge of the state enterprises, reporting to the full Board, and meeting at stated times (say four times a year) of its own right and with the attendance of the Director of the given state work. This council should audit the accounts of the state moneys. The *ad interim* business of the College of Agriculture should be carried on by the Director of the College, with the advice of the President of the University.

In an immediately following editorial which accompanied printed presentation of this report by Bailey to the trustees, *Cornell Countryman* in its issue of January, 1912, announced: "In a recent conversation with the Editor of the *Countryman*, Dean Bailey, when asked if he would remain, said that the only effect the action on the part of the board of Trustees will have on his decision to sever connections with the College of Agriculture is that any action on his part will be deferred until his plan of administration has been put into operation. He added that the plan was so largely of his own suggestion that he felt it his duty to remain until the new system had been put into practical and substantial operation. How long or how short a time that would be, he was unable to say. It is a sincere cause of delight and satisfaction that Dean Bailey will remain to direct the readjustments in the College of Agriculture as he has outlined them, and it is our earnest hope that at the end of this time circumstances will be such that it will not be necessary for him to sever his connections with the College of Agriculture in order to live his own life." Bailey had told others that the third period of his life had been reached—the period of doing what one most wants to do—and that, for Bailey, was to advance the interests of country life development and devote himself to the furtherance of American horticultural progress.

On the evening of January 21, 1910, when Acting Dean Webber had announced to the students that Bailey would return to the college as dean and director, a joyful, enthusiastic, and long continued ovation was accorded Bailey and the announcement. Everywhere Bailey went in New York state and elsewhere he was always heartily greeted, whether the occasion was an extension trip, a lecture, or business engagement. Practically no congresses or conventions were held in New York state or in nearby states, pertaining to agricultural or rural matters, unless Bailey was invited and in most instances asked to speak. Enumerating all the meetings he attended would require much space. Ranging from conferences on the distribution of population to corn days and breeders' association gatherings, these encompassed a wide variety of discussions—on all phases of agricultural education and research. Even relationships with the railroads, which had begun to take an interest in developing forestry and other special aspects of agricultural endeavor, were not excluded. The country life movement and every branch of agricultural and horticultural research were recognized the nation over by corporate interests for their utilitarian and economic, as well as educational, values.

On March 5, 1912—with 350 diners packed into the large ballroom of the Hotel Waldorf—the Cornell University Club of New York City held its thirty-second annual dinner honoring the work of the agricultural college, and accorded it recognition on a par with that of the endowed schools of the campus. Bailey had been called to his feet by the university's 21 gun salute, and a tumultuous ovation. He responded that now he knew how a pancake felt when molasses was poured over it. He recited the origins and history of his vision for agricultural education. Most of all, he emphasized the need of further developing the resources of country life. Making available expert agricultural advice within the country communities by the schools and state was, aside from university extension programs, a service being developed in New York, Pennsylvania, Missouri, Nebraska, Iowa, Illinois, Ohio, Ontario, and several southern states—in fact, numerous states of the nation. Even an International Congress of Farm Women had been held. Dry Farming Congresses had been held in the East and West. Irrigation now embraced both humid and arid areas. The rural town as well as the rural country had become an object of educational concern. In January, 1913, *Cornell Countryman* observed:

The State of New York stands at the head in floriculture, olericulture, and in the production of fruits adapted to its climate. Fertile soil, favorable climate, and proximity to markets unite to make opportunities along horti-cultural lines as great in this State as in any State in the Union. Great prob-lems of transportation, marketing and other semi-public questions remain to be solved and rapid development along technical lines in all branches of Horticulture may be expected in the near future. There never were better opportunities for the well-trained horticulturist in the commercial line to produce goods of the highest quality and to market them in the most eco-nomical and profitable manner, or in technical work to solve problems of a more or less scientific nature which are ever confronting the practical grower.

Commenting generally, of Bailey's old department of horticulture, there were now departments of pomology, floriculture, vegetable gardening, soils, plant breeding, plant pathology, and other divisions.

Bailey determined that in the main his new work should espouse two great themes: country life development and his dreams of a lifetime—to further study of all the plants of creation. At the Hotel Waldorf dinner, he concluded his address by reiterating his "desire to get out of harness and give his time to studies of which he had dreamed all his life, and said that when the time came for him to resign the work of the college to other hands he hoped his friends would let him go."[6]

If only one word could be selected to explain the life of Liberty Hyde Bailey, the word "constructive" would suffice. Bailey has been construc-tive in every period of his life. He left to the New York State College of Agriculture an exceedingly valuable heritage on which the college has since thrived and extended a world-wide scope of influence.

His volume, *Plant Breeding*, had been translated into Japanese, and the Chinese had asked permission to use it in accordance with their language requirements. His cyclopedias were on the desk or in the library of every horticulturist of consequence. When, on November 3, 1911, Theodore Roosevelt spoke before the students of the New York State College of Agriculture, he turned and faced Bailey, saying, "Dean Bailey, it is none of my affair, but I should regard it as a calamity, not only to the state, but to the nation, if you do not continue to do your

[6] *Cornell Countryman*, XI, 7 (April 1912), pp. 239-240.

work at the head of this college." In 1910 Bailey had been urged to run for the United States Congress. He replied with characteristic emphasis: "I am not a candidate for Congress or any other office. I intend to exercise what capabilities I may have along different lines, and I will never violate my trust with the farmers by dragging their issues to the political arena."

Bailey had told the trustees that at fifty years of age he would retire and devote himself to horticulture and botany. He had told Albert R. Mann, "I've set age fifty as the time to cease being regularly employed by others, and give all of my time to my own interests." To others he had said much the same. Some years were to be spent in travel, and some years enlarging the scope of American horticultural study, in which he had set work patterns in almost every branch.

The university trustees had believed that Bailey would not resign. But one day the door of the dean's office was locked and no one could find Bailey. Of his own accord he had left the college. Persuasion would not induce him to return although before and on the day of his relinquishment of duties faculty members presented him with resolutions expressing appreciation of his services and an address of regret on his leaving.[7] Having taught twenty-five years Bailey was entitled to benefits of a retirement system then provided by the Carnegie foundation, not a large sum but enough to enable him with his revenue from books and other sources to live comfortably.

On July 29, 1913, the board of trustees of the university, on recommendation of the agricultural college council, appointed William Alonzo Stocking, junior, acting director of the college for one year or until a director was appointed permanently. Stocking was a graduate of Connecticut Agricultural College who also had received a bachelor of science in agriculture degree from Cornell in 1898. From 1901 until 1904, while teaching at Connecticut Agricultural College, he had been registered part of the time as a graduate student in dairy bacteriology at Cornell University. He received his master's degree from the latter named institution and in the school year 1906-1907 became assistant professor in dairy industry. When Professor Pearson resigned to become New York's commissioner of agriculture Stocking became the full professor of the subject at the New York State College.

Acting Dean Stocking was a man of recognized attainments in the scientific field of bacteriology, a kindly, considerate, sincere man with a talent for scientific objectivity. But he was not strong in health and the administrative duties of the dean-and-directorship weighed heavily upon him. He was by nature conscientious and sincerely wished to carry

[7] The resolution dated June 17, 1913, and the address dated July 31, 1913, are fully set forth in the "Bailey Number," *Cornell Countryman*, XI, 3, pp. 100-102.

on the work of the college of agriculture. More than once he lauded
the work of Bailey. But, being one of those vigorously minded souls who
at heart are professorial research men and not administrators, he did
not wish the position permanently. While Acting Dean Stocking's
services were warmly commended, his period of office lasted only a
year, and faculty and students became more insistent than ever that a
Bailey trained man be put in to fill the place.

It was, therefore, a colossal task which Beverly T. Galloway undertook, when, as the permanently appointed college dean and director, he
greeted the students at the beginning of the school year 1914-1915. He
spoke of the college of agriculture as a "tree of knowledge" well started
in its growth toward becoming the "monarch of the forest." Galloway
was a brilliant man, great with a sharp sense of the value of new research, liberal and enlightened, one who encouraged every worth while
investigation, himself one of the pioneer American plant pathologists.
Under Galloway's guidance and direction the federal division of plant
pathology had risen from a small section which employed a few men
with an annual appropriation of a few thousand dollars to inclusion in
the great federal Bureau of Plant Industry of which for more than a
decade he was chief. The Bureau incorporated many other divisions of
plant science study and investigation and by 1913 was receiving an annual appropriation of between two and one-half and three millions of
dollars and employing one of the most able and brilliant groups of plant
science investigators to be found in the world. So recognized was
Galloway's leadership that President Woodrow Wilson had appointed
him the federal assistant secretary of agriculture. His position as chief
of the Bureau of Plant Industry had been taken by William Alton
Taylor, formerly a student of Bailey in horticulture at Michigan Agricultural College and for many years connected with the federal division
of pomology (or horticulture). Galloway's leadership, however, was
not the parallel of Bailey's. Well founded and substantiated is the belief
that President-elect Woodrow Wilson considered Bailey for the Secre-
taryship of Agriculture in his cabinet. The President did not offer the
appointment solely because he was advised in advance that Bailey would
not accept it for the same reason that he had refused to run for Congress
and had silenced all urgings by both Democrats and Republicans to
seek a nomination for the governorship of the state of New York.

Under Dean Galloway's administration, "the most modern building
planned for Soils in the country, and practically in the world" was
completed. The student number increased to 2,557; the faculty membership to 142. The college year was divided into three semesters. The
college's maintenance expenditure went to $520,000, by far the largest
sum granted annually to any American college of agriculture. In

October, 1915, Galloway predicted the student enrollment would reach 3,000. It did reach 2,830 in the school year 1914-1915. Summarizing the college's ten years of development, Galloway wrote in his 1913-1914 report:

In 1904 the only class building devoted exclusively to the purposes of the College of Agriculture was the old Dairy Building, now comprising a part of the north wing of Goldwin Smith Hall. In addition to this, the College occupied quarters in the north end of Morrill Hall and at the old forcing houses. The buildings of the College of Agriculture at that time were valued at about $60,000. At the present time the value of the buildings belonging to the College is approximately $1,250,000. At the beginning of this decade twenty-five courses of instruction were offered in agriculture. There were six full professors, one assistant professor, and two instructors. During the year 1913-1914 there have been two hundred and twenty-four courses offered in the College, and the Faculty has consisted of forty-six full professors, twenty-six assistant professors, and fifty-seven instructors. In the first year of the decade the student enrollment was two hundred and ninety-six; this year it is twenty-five hundred and twenty-six. It is interesting to note the fact that at the beginning of this period approximately one half of the total student body were special students, while at the end of this period less than one tenth are specials. This enormous growth in student body, teaching staff, and material equipment, is abundant evidence of the remarkable leadership of Director Bailey.

The Faculty of the College of Agriculture has presented to the University a portrait of Director Bailey painted by Henry Salem Hubbell. This portrait has been accepted by the University and is hung in the foyer of Bailey Hall.

New members had been added to the faculty: Edward Albert White in floriculture; Maurice Chase Burritt in agricultural extension and state director of farm bureaus, a representative of a farm bureau movement which involved placement of agents in localities, a "new factor" and "a new range in the organization of rural society," Bailey said, and of which he had been an advocate ever since his years as a student at Michigan Agricultural; George Alan Works in rural education; Rollins Adams Emerson in plant breeding, taking the place of Webber who the year before had gone to California to plan and build at Riverside the now famous Citrus Experiment Station of the University of California; and Ralph Sheldon Hosmer in forestry, taking the chair of Walter Mulford who also had gone to California in a professorial capacity.

This year brought the retirement of the world-renowned authority on entomology, John Henry Comstock. Now all but one of the great early professors of the college were either retired or dead. The death of George C. Caldwell in 1907 had been a heavy loss. In 1908 with forty teaching years and more than a decade as director of the state veterinary college, James Law had retired and for him the main veterinary science building was being named. Only Henry Hiram Wing, professor and author, who had returned in 1888 to his alma mater as secretary and deputy director of its experiment station, and had become within a few years assistant professor of dairy husbandry—who had seen animal husbandry separated as a department from dairy husbandry, just as poultry husbandry, for years a subdepartment, was afterward segregated from animal husbandry—remained. And he would continue in service many more years.

During Dean Galloway's administration, also, the "new auditorium (now Bailey Hall) was practically completed and occupied during Farmers' Week in February, 1914." On October 9 its new $25,000 Raga organ was dedicated in the presence of ex-President White, President Schurman, Andrew Carnegie—whose gifts had made possible the organ's construction—and 3,000 persons. Two days later the man for whom the hall was named returned to Ithaca from a voyage to New Zealand where, under auspices of the government of that land, he delivered a course of lectures, in the interest of a Science Congress. Completion of other buildings for forestry and animal husbandry, a stock judging pavilion, quarters for the department of landscape art, commencement of a series of farm circulars and other valuable editorial work, among many other things, occurred during Galloway's regime. Galloway presented in articles and otherwise a world-wide view of agriculture. During his years the college received distinguished guests, for example, ex-President Taft and Secretary Wilson. During Secretary Wilson's long service as a cabinet member—the longest any one man had continuously served—he had seen federal agricultural work expand from quarters comprising an old brick building, dwelling houses, old stores, and rented buildings to a million and a half dollar structure.

In his sixteenth annual report (*Yearbook*, 1912, pp. 114-258), Secretary Wilson had reviewed the services of the United States Department of Agriculture to the nation since 1897, a period of sixteen years. The total amounts appropriated for the Department aggregated almost twenty-five million dollars, almost eight times as much as the appropriations of 1898. Within the historical report (pp. 117-144), the secretary reviewed the plant industrial work of the department. From 1897 to 1912, the number of employees of the Bureau of Plant Industry had been increased from 127 to 2,128 persons. The gains in appropriations for federal agricultural work during recent years, however, were proportionately not the equal of some of the states, New York particularly, where appropriations were said to have increased from 1910-1914 one hundred and eighty-one per cent. At the October 14 Assembly of the New York State College of Agriculture, Dean Galloway presented statistics which showed that New York expended vastly more money than any other state to support its agricultural college work, more than

a half million dollars. More than fifty-five thousand students were enrolled in colleges of agriculture and mechanic arts, and the total
number of all students approached one hundred and six thousand
persons. More than seventy-six hundred, 7,651 to be exact, were
specialists engaged in research, teaching, and extension activities. The
substance of this address was published in the November, 1915, issue
of *Cornell Countryman* (p. 120). In June of that year, this same
journal, in an editorial entitled, "One Year Under the New Dean," had
praised Dean Galloway for his part in obtaining another increase in
appropriations for the college:

> . . . Dean Galloway has made marked progress in working out the details
> of organization. . . . Probably the most important task undertaken by the
> new Director is the organization of the various departments along a more
> business-like basis. There is now established a uniform system of account-
> ing for all departments. . . . An Information Service has been established
> for the purpose of giving out to the press of the State timely information
> in an attractive, readable form. Already this service has reached over fif-
> teen million readers.
> By putting before every member of the State Legislature in pamphlet
> form last year's appropriations for the College and what new ones were
> asked for and to what use they were put, Dean Galloway appealed directly
> to the business sense of the legislators and secured an additional appropria-
> tion of $129,000 for the administration of the College. . . . Dean Galloway's
> genius for organization, his strong spirit of service, and his ready democracy
> assures the future of the College.

Still, neither faculty nor students were completely satisfied. Once
students did go in a body to Galloway to express their satisfaction with
him as dean and director and with his accomplishments. This happened
on the evening of October 15, 1914, several months after the students'
association of the college had memorialized Bailey as "without doubt
. . . the most useful man that American agriculture has ever produced."
As Bailey had said, the college belonged to the people of the state, not
Cornell University. With the passing of two years, therefore, the
student dissatisfaction growing, Galloway manfully summoned the
heads of various departments of the school and, asking them for a candid
answer, was told that his administration had not measured up to Dean
Bailey's standard. Whereupon Galloway announced an intention to
resign, which was at first refused by President Schurman. Before
Galloway's arrival, it is said, Schurman was defeated in an effort to
place another nationally prominent agriculturist in the position. Indeed,
it is said also that Dean Galloway, at the time of his selection, was not
the choice of the faculty of the college of agriculture.

Influential leaders on Cornell University's campus believed that,
owing to Dean Galloway's resignation, the college of agriculture was

losing the best man obtainable in the country. A man of noble and liberal ideals, able and efficient, of Galloway's ability, character, and fitness for the position there was certainly no question. Whatever the truth surrounding his appointment, the fact was that Dean Galloway resigned, and insisted that his resignation be accepted. Furthermore, the faculty of the college of agriculture wanted as dean a man schooled in the well established Bailey tradition. The confidence of the board of trustees and President Schurman in Dean Galloway was a tribute to this leader of American agriculture. The desire of the faculty of the college of agriculture to have as dean a Bailey trained man was similarly a tribute to another worker for American agricultural advancement. President Schurman asked the faculty of the college of agriculture to help name the new appointee. The man selected was Albert R. Mann, who, while a student, had served as Bailey's secretary in preparing the *Cyclopedia of American Agriculture*.

Mann was at the time a graduate student at the University of Chicago, getting an advanced degree in general sociology with a view to adapting the subject to rural needs. Influenced strongly toward sociology by Bailey, it was his plan to teach a subject, then bearing the title "Rural Social Organization." While in the 1914 report Mann was described as secretary to the college, registrar, and professor of agricultural editing, rural sociology was the title of his department after his return. Because of his acceptance of the deanship, however—an acting appointment made permanent a year later—he never taught either rural social organization or rural sociology. The latter subject was scientifically developed under Professor Ezra Dwight Sanderson, who had been appointed by Dean Mann, and, being strengthened by statistical investigations and other fundamental research, it soon acquired nation-wide prominence. Mann was confined to the work of dean and director and in the office acquitted himself with great ability. The entire college greeted his appointment with pleasure. The October, 1916, issue of *Cornell Countryman* observed:

The new year has brought us under the administration of a new dean, Professor A. R. Mann. It is not necessary for the *Countryman* to introduce our new acting dean to its readers for already Professor Mann is known and most highly esteemed by all our alumni and undergraduates. He has been with us since his graduation in '04, and has gained the very highest admiration from all who know him.

For a time after graduation Professor Mann was an Assistant Professor in the dairy department. Then for six years he acted as secretary of the College where he gained an insight into its welfare and needs. Professor Mann's natural ability, his special training and his wonderful personality well fit him for this exacting position.

To you, Doctor Galloway, a parting word: Be sure that the student body will remember you,—your simplicity and kindliness, your sympathy with our endeavours and your readiness to assist them.

Dr. Galloway returned to the Bureau of Plant Industry where he began an investigation on importation of foreign seeds and plants. His official title became "Plant Pathologist and Plant Introducer" and the main thread of his work had to do with quarantine matters—the discovery of insect pests and fungus diseases in imported and introduced seeds and plants. Though a virile man intellectually, his physical well-being had been threatened under his onerous task as dean of the New York State College of Agriculture. There was reason for believing that, when he returned to Washington, his health was imperiled. However, immediately he was placed on work which was not strenuous and combined some pleasure, and his vigor was gradually regained.

During these eventful years, Bailey had continued his writing. In 1909, in "A Statement on the Agricultural Situation in New York State," published as bulletin 12 of the New York state department of agriculture, Bailey had urged, ". . . we need *to develop pride in our opportunities, our heritage, and our resources.*" More faith in the land and a campaign of publicity would aid the state agricultural situation.

In 1909 had appeared a book published by the Century Company, small in size but mighty in content, *The Training of Farmers,* written by Bailey and giving his diagnosis and remedies for the agricultural problems in graphic and statistical fashion. *Cornell Countryman* regarded Bailey's reasoning as rivaling Edmund Burke "for sound reasoning, insight, and practicability." Approving the idea that farmers should be neighbors and cooperators rather than rivals, it quoted the author's conclusion that, "The commercial and social isolation of the farm is passing. . . . The farmer is rapidly becoming a citizen of the world. All his problems must have a larger treatment than they ever had before." In 1910 Bailey's *Manual of Gardening* was published, which combined his two well-known works *Garden-Making* and the *Practical Garden-Book.* These were revised in the main parts and "much new material and the results of the experience of ten" years were added, including contributions made by Hunn, Ernest Walker, Taft, and Waugh. This volume became another valuable Rural Manual, in which set also belonged Bailey's *Farm and Garden Rule-Book* and his still much used *Pruning-Manual* and *Nursery-Manual.* Grouped to this literary appendage to American agriculture and horticulture, and similar to the Rural Science Series and Rural Outlook Series, were manuals of farm animals, fruit insects, weeds, fruit diseases, milk products, vegetable-garden insects, tree diseases, homemaking, American grape-growing, tropical and subtropical fruits, tree and shrub insects, and vegetable-garden diseases—all by authorities of eminence.

In 1913 Bailey's *Botany*, an elementary text for schools, was re-published as *Botany for Secondary Schools*, a guide to the knowledge of the vegetation of the neighborhood. Naturally Bailey would continue to write on New York state country life. He had material from lectures delivered on the subject before the college assemblies and elsewhere. Therefore, considering in wide scope the new problems of the farm bureaus and expert services, there appeared between 1913 and 1915 two volumes by Bailey on *York State Rural Problems*, published by J. B. Lyon Company of Albany. Bailey remained very active in the New York State Agricultural Society of which he was elected president in 1914 and, although he declined this honor, he accepted the chairman-ship of the committee on agricultural education, a position he had held the year before.

In May, 1914, appeared advance copies of the first volume of *The Standard Cyclopedia of Horticulture*, a revision and rewriting of the old cyclopedia. This was made possible, in part, by a trip to England from May until October in 1912 when Ireland, Wales, Scotland, the Orkney Islands, and the Shetland Islands were visited. Nearly two months were spent in studying cultivated plants in the herbarium of the Royal Botanical Gardens at Kew. The last part of the trip was devoted to touring the Caribbee Islands including St. Thomas, the island of Dominica, and Trinidad. At the time, Bailey had renewed an active correspondence with the Gray Herbarium.

On April 13, 1912, he had written Dr. Benjamin Lincoln Robinson there:

I am very glad to have your letter of April 9th saying that you are inter-ested in the new Cyclopedia of Horticulture. I am very sorry that you are not well but I hope that the southern climate will recuperate you so that you will return in good condition. We shall be very glad when you are returned to have any suggestion that you will wish to make in regard to the new book. We want to make this book authoritative and greatly to enlarge its scope and we want the help of all the botanists and the horticulturists so far as we can secure it.

I am greatly puzzled to know what to do with the nomenclature. I doubt whether we can really standardize and harmonize all the nomenclature in this work for the reason that we are describing plants that come from all parts of the world and in many cases the names of these plants have not yet been combined under any of the new rules of nomenclature and we would hardly expect to make enough original research in every one of these cultivated groups to enable us to arrive at any final conclusion. Moreover, the articles are written by many different authors following different sys-tems of nomenclature and they probably would not adapt themselves very well to a change. A good number of the botanists in this country would like to follow the American or Philadelphia code but a great many of the plants that we shall describe have never been combined under that code. There are international trade rights in all these horticultural groups that must be re-

Liberty Hyde Bailey, 1929

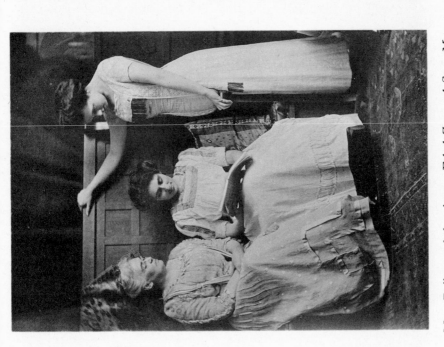

Mrs. Bailey and daughters, Ethel Zoe and Sara May, 1910

spected. Botanical names belong as much to horticulturists and to others as to the professional botanists. I want to be conservative in this regard and not upset the horticultural trade names unless in such cases in which there is fairly good indication that such changes will really be accepted and are worth the while. I am not very much inclined to make changes in horticultural groups merely for the purpose of conforming them to formal botanical standing. This may sound like heresy to a botanist but I do not see how we could take any other position in dealing with a great mass of names that of themselves do not conform and can scarcely be made to conform to any rigid set of rules. At all events we could scarcely expect to adopt the Philadelphia code for plants that come from all parts of the world and with which botanists following very different codes will be dealing. The International Congress of Horticulture at Brussels two years ago adopted the Vienna code, with modifications for cultural things. It is my desire to follow the Vienna code as far as we can follow it and make it adaptable for horticultural usage. I shall be very glad of any suggestions that you may have to make.

With Bailey in this work and as his assistant was Ethel Zoe Bailey, his daughter, who, as a botanist collaborating with her father, was to devote her life to the fulfillment of Bailey's plant science vision.

Again, on December 14, Bailey wrote Robinson concerning, among other matters, that of capitalizing specific names in the *Cyclopedia*. As to this, no statute in the Vienna Code was found, although there was a recommendation. Bailey disapproved of writing in lower case the names of persons. Furthermore, the International Horticultural Congress of 1905 had taken no action in that regard, leaving the practice as it had been. "So many of the horticultural names," he wrote, "are derived directly from persons of horticultural note and they have such great trade value that I should not be willing to presume to change the whole horticultural trade practice. Even at the best, I should never hope to bring the horticulturists into line on this question, at least not all of them, or perhaps not even any very considerable part of them in this country. In respect to the geographical names, I do not have any very strong convictions one way or another." Bailey sought the opinion of others, including many botanists. He asked Robinson to prepare Eupatorium for the cyclopedia. A letter addressed February 17, 1913, was characteristic of the difficulties and the enlarged conception of the new work. It read:

I am aware that you will have a good many difficulties and perplexities in straightening out the horticultural forms of Eupatorium. I am convinced that they are in bad shape.

The new Cyclopedia is to have a wider range than the old and it is to be under a new title as you will see by the letter-head herewith. Our national domain has extended into tropical regions so that we must introduce more of the tropical plants than we did in the old edition. Moreover, everything that is in the European trade is practically also in the American trade. Our people are buying their seeds and their plants increasingly more and more from Europe. Anything, therefore, which Vilmorin, for example, catalogues, we must describe in the Cyclopedia. I do not care to put into the cyclopedia things that are not in commerce in Europe or America. We are not attempting to describe the things grown merely in botanic gardens and practically nowhere else.

We must account for the names that have been used in horticultural catalogues and works. Many of these horticultural names do not of course represent the species that are properly described under those names. Undoubtedly in the present Cyclopedia, there are a good many cases in which the horticultural names have been assumed to represent the same plants as a similar botanical name of good standing; but without specimens and clear information, it has been impossible of course in many cases to determine whether the horticultural name has standing or not. Undoubtedly there will be a great many cases of this kind that will get into the Cyclopedia in the present edition, although we wish to reduce them in every case we can. . . .

The correspondence continued and considered many matters. In 1915, learning that the Gray herbarium was housed in a splendid, fire-proof, new building, Bailey wrote Robinson, congratulating the institution:

I have read the account in Science of your fine new buildings. I congratulate you on their completion and on the progress of the work in the meantime without loss. I am sure I shall not know the place when I sometime come back.

Bailey found that additional help was going to be necessary and so prevailed on Robinson to recommend someone with botanical training. "I am not so particular about the horticultural training as I am about the botanical," he said. "We have ways enough whereby we get cultural notes on plants from very many correspondents, but the botanical work needs special and definite training." He wanted "some one who can handle Bentham and Hooker, Engler and Prantl and the other literature of the kind and who knows the way of working these things out and following the clues. If he had a good working knowledge of German, it would be all the better because we find much of the recent publication in that language. If we had some one who had worked at the Arboretum or at some similar institution and knows something about cultivated plants, it would be all the better." Bailey also sent Robinson articles for criticism, for example, one on "Names and Nomenclature," and expressed a desire "to avoid all controversial matters of nomenclature, and to do full justice to all the codes and schools."

During the time the *Standard Cyclopedia* was being completed, Bailey began getting together material for a *Manual of Cultivated Plants*, a volume which did not make a formal published appearance for nine years, but which, when completed, enumerated and described 3,665 species and 1,246 genera in 170 natural families. *The Standard Cyclopedia of Horticulture*, on the other hand, accounted for, when completely published in 1917, 20,602 species in contrast to 8,793 fully described species (of which 2,419 were native to North America north of Mexico) included in the 1902 *Cyclopedia of American Horticulture* where 2,255 genera were systematized. A "new horticulture" had arrived. However, as late as 1924, when the *Manual of Cultivated Plants* appeared, Bailey commented, "Gray's Field, Forest and Garden Botany has been useful in the identification of cultivated plants for more than fifty years." In reality there was no saying that the old had given way to the new. But a new and wider science was being made known.

In his systematic studies of cultivated plants, Bailey had always used the garden extensively. Each and every year he had had a garden. Naturally, now, with a real return to productions in scientific horticulture, the garden became again a source of experimental studies— confined, however, more or less to taxonomic and nomenclatural investigations. Although Bailey would never abandon the greenhouse entirely—it also had been frequently used for systematic and experimental investigations—the greenhouse, more and more, would yield to the herbarium. Moreover, the horticultural laboratory in some phases of work would give way to the herbarium. Bailey never became a geneticist in the modern use of the term. Plant breeding had taken on new accessories—the theoretical and practical sciences of genetics, and biometry, although the latter was not completely and everywhere recognized. In 1915 Arthur W. Gilbert, professor of plant-breeding at Cornell, revised Bailey's *Plant-Breeding*. The original author's only function was editorial and the writing of an introduction. Gilbert, at the National Corn Exposition held in Columbus, Ohio, in 1911, reported in an address, "Present Status of Plant-Breeding Instruction in the United States," that while instruction in the principles of Mendelism and the use of biometry as an aid to the study of variation was lacking in some plant breeding courses, "over a thousand students of collegiate grade [were] pursuing plant breeding studies [and] trained each year in methods of plant improvement by breeding. . . ."[8] In 1912 Webber reported:

We can now study the characters presented by the different varieties of a plant or of different species which can be crossed with it and definitely plan the combination of characters desired in an ideal type and can with considerable confidence estimate the number of plants it will be necessary to grow to get this combination. We now know in general how characters behave in segregation and inheritance so that we can go about the fixation of a desired type, when one is secured in an orderly and intelligent way. . . . We are coming to realize that the appearance of apparently new types

[8] "Present Status of Plant-Breeding Instruction in the United States," *Annual Report of American Breeders' Association*, VII, for year ending 1910, pp. 7-11.

following hybridization is due to recombinations of different units which in their reactions give apparently new characters. . . .[9]

Naturally, such work enormously expanded systematic responsibilities in classifying cultivated plants. The value of Bailey's horticultural laboratory work has survived principally from his taxonomic studies, his great cyclopedias and manuals.

Yet, as late as 1914, Bailey's *Principles of Vegetable-Gardening* had reached its fourteenth edition and, even today, is still used in many places. *The Principles of Fruit-Growing*, with applications to practice, was for its twentieth edition, in 1915, completely revised, and in many places is also still in use. By 1916 *The Pruning-Manual* had reached its eighteenth edition, revised and reset. By 1919 *The Principles of Agriculture* reached its twenty-sixth edition. In 1920 *The Nursery-Manual* was reissued. In 1925 the *Manual of Gardening* attained its twelfth printing revision. Of all the original principal classics, however, *The Principles of Vegetable-Gardening* was to stand time's test the longest, being remade and reset in its eighteenth edition in 1921. In this Bailey "worked over the systematic botany of [the] vegetables from good material in [his] herbarium. . . ."

To be sure, most of Bailey's early laboratory experimental work has been displaced or outmoded. None may gainsay the fact, however, that practically all of it laid groundwork. Bailey's electro-horticultural findings have little practical significance today. Nevertheless, supplementary light is used experimentally and commercially in controlling bud formation, time of flowering and general plant performance. To Bailey's work may be traced a realization that, aside from, of course, a chief dependence on sunlight, additional light aids growth and development. Homer C. Thompson years ago began writing a book on vegetable crops making use of experimental studies. More was derived, he has said, from a study of the work of Bailey and his associates than all other sources combined. To illustrate, Bailey had called attention to an enhancement of growth produced when an arc light was used. These experiments of Cornell's first full professor of practical and experimental horticulture were made twenty or thirty years before discovery at the United States Department of Agriculture laboratories of the phenomena of photo-periodism. On nearly every subject Thompson found that Bailey had done some experimental work anticipatory of subsequent and more highly developed and fundamental investigations.

In 1917 the University of Chicago would confer doctoral degrees in

[9] "The Effect of Research in Genetics on the Art of Breeding," *American Breeders' Magazine* A Journal of Genetics and Eugenics, III, 2, pp. 125-134, in which the author called attention to the need of establishment of more professorships in genetics or breeding, and also described his work of some four years, including his study of pepper hybrids, and generally the development of the science of genetics in America.

botany on two skillful scientists, Ezra Jacob Kraus and Henry Reist Kraybill. They, by an epoch-making study of the carbohydrate and nitrogen relation in plant tissues, were, in a very real and exact sense, to take horticulture into an experimental laboratory entirely its own. The original source of the idea had come from a botanist, the great European botanist Klebs, who, as it happened, had not applied to horticulture certain conclusions at which he had arrived in a botanical study of nitrates as nutrients. Klebs's treatise, one of the first written in objective plant physiology, had stimulated American workers. Kraus saw what Klebs had not seen—an undeveloped application of a hypothesis. In 1918 Kraus and Kraybill issued a bulletin, "Vegetation and Reproduction with Special Reference to the Tomato,"[10] which announced their discovery that the flowering and fruiting of the tomato occurred only when the carbohydrate and nitrogen ratio varied within a certain range of relationship. Almost a decade before, in 1909, John Merle Coulter, writing on "Recent Advances in Vascular Anatomy,"[11] had urged: "With the vascular system brought into the morphological perspective, the first step was taken toward the inclusion of vegetative as well as reproductive structures. It now remains for some one to begin the organization of the remaining vegetative regions upon the same basis; and then morphology will have its facts fairly before it. . . ." Elaborating principles of investigation, Kraus and Kraybill stressed functions more than structures of plants, under what conditions a supplementary or antagonistic function expresses itself, under what conditions plant performances and behavior responses may be induced. Immediately horticultural investigation was set to work studying chemical relationships in all phases, within the plant and in relation to external factors such as soils, climate, and diverse elements of environment.

Kraus was graduated in science at Michigan Agricultural College in 1907. While he majored in horticulture, he had not immediately chosen plant research as a career. He accepted a position as scientific assistant to Dr. A. D. Hopkins in the federal forest entomological service at Washington, D.C., over an offered scholarship at Cornell University; and, in entomological investigations he remained a year. Entomology was one of several sciences in which Kraus had acquired proficiency, thanks, in part, to a provocative suggestion of Professor Beal.

Beal, advanced in years but still wise, and probably recognizing ingenious capabilities in the youthful product from Ingham County, Michigan, told him: "So, Kraus, you want to study botany. Well, you can't right now. You get over to other departments and take any courses

10 "Vegetation and reproduction with special reference to the tomato," *Oregon Agricultural Experiment Station Bulletin*, 149: 1-90 f. 1-22 (January 1918).
11 *American Naturalist*, XLIII, pp. 219 ff.

you do not like." Ezra Jacob took him at his word and for some time never went near the botany department. First trying veterinary science, and later entomology, he had a basic training in certain of the animal sciences before he took up extensively the study of horticulture, and botany, at the college. Plant research won out finally and enduringly. In 1909 Kraus accepted a professorship in horticultural research at Oregon Agricultural College, located at Corvallis. Ostensibly, his employment was to pursue horticultural researches—studies in fruit pollination—under provisions of the Adams fund allowances. On this campus, in the midst of another rich horticultural region capable of further development, Kraus's creative genius for biological research expressed itself so promisingly that the college and experiment station authorities encouraged him to stake out his own career.

En route to Corvallis, Kraus delivered at Berkeley a paper on gross morphology of the apple, a research which demonstrated the essential oneness of botanical and horticultural investigation. The bringing together again of horticulture and botany was a subject which interested him from his earliest years in plant study and which, later, he discussed with Dr. William Crocker of the University of Chicago. Crocker answered that, while this would be desirable, more fundamental applied knowledge was still needed.

Kraus had never subscribed to the old botanical notions that horticultural plants are abnormalities and not worth investigating, that they are man-made selection instruments incapable of existing or persisting without man's care and preservation. All cultivated plants, he knew, are not hybrids, and not all are special forms. Even if some are abnormalities, the word "abnormal" must be carefully limited in science, if, in the plant sciences, it has any application at all.

At Corvallis, he commenced a series of papers dealing with the structure and development of pomaceous fruits. Developmental morphology was enjoying distinctive prominence in botanical research during these years. On completing his first paper, he concluded that more work had to be done on plant structure. He continued his research and wrote papers. But he found the structural side insufficient to account for all phenomena. In one location a plant would set fruit and would not in another. Fruitfulness was perceived as something more than vegetativeness. Plant physiology, he saw, held the answer to most of the deepest problems, the study of functions, and processes, their relationships in conflict and harmony, as supplements or antagonists, externally and internally. In this, analysis reduced study to mineral or organic nutrition and the elements that enter into each or both. Finding the means of balancing or coordinating functions, study gradually opened the vista of the relation of chemical constituents.

Therefore, while at work in Oregon, almost a decade of diligently pursued research made him aware of his need for graduate study in botany. The botanical "Olympians" of North America, he had been told, were at the University of Chicago. So there he went, and, studying mostly under Doctors William Crocker, Charles Joseph Chamberlain, and William Jesse Goad Land—each, a skilled laboratory technician in botanical research—he produced, in conjunction with Kraybill, the doctoral thesis, already mentioned, published in January, 1918, as bulletin 149 of the Oregon Agricultural Experiment Station[12] and which has found a permanent place among the few great classics of American horticultural and botanical research. Graduate work in organic chemistry at the University of Chicago increased the merit and significance of the revolutionary, yet evolutionary, researches which Kraus initiated at Oregon State College, deepened at the University of Chicago, and continued after he returned to Oregon State and became Dean of the College of Letters and Science during the years 1918-1919.[13]

Many investigators have followed up these researches, applying, and discovering new truths embodied in, the set of principles enunciated by Kraus—rules of an applied botany, yet distinctly horticultural when dealing with cultivated plants. From 1919 until 1927 Kraus served as professor of applied botany at the University of Wisconsin. There, while a member of the botany department in the college of letters and science, he worked with all of the coordinate departments of the plant sciences related to agriculture. In Wisconsin, in Arizona, in the Hawaiian Islands, in Nebraska, in New York, and, of course, in California, investigators have carried forward the proposal, now recognized as a formal type of research among various plants of economic and horticultural significance, and have interpreted vegetative behavior, showing the interrelationship of fruiting and vegetation. Evaluation of the total results still belongs to science. Only the story of the origins of the work has become part of the history of science. Scientific treatises, such as H. E. Hayward's *Structure of Economic Plants*, have been written and have evaluated trends and accomplishments. The work is a growing subject of doctoral theses in universities.

In 1927 Kraus became a professor of botany at the University of Chicago and, in 1934, chairman of the department. Certainly one of the great biologists of this or any other generation, Kraus is recognized as one of the first American scientists to deserve the unquestioned distinction of being both an authority in experimental morphology and experimental physiology. In the generation of Coulter, Chamberlain, and other

[12] Pages 1-90, f. 1-22.
[13] See also notes, *Botanical Gazette*, LXIV (December 1917), p. 526; LXVII (May 1919), p. 446.

leaders of the immediately preceding historical period, leadership in either research field was sufficient for one man.

Today the horticulturist, among many divergent lines of work, has become a specialized botanist and chemist dealing with the plants of economic and horticultural significance. Research from the colleges and experiment stations has created whole new industries devoted to the seeding, growing, marketing, preserving, storing, and consumption of horticultural products. Research has increased the plant population and improved both quantity and quality; so much so that the land yields may be greater though the cultivated area may be smaller. Horticulture today postulates the concept of the plant hormone to define growth accelerating, growth inhibiting, and growth regulating substances, which induce various specific physiological processes, tropisms and movements, within differing environmental ranges of plants. Origins of plant growth hormones trace to the work (1910-1911) of P. Boysen Jensen, and beyond; animal hormones to the beginning of the century—modern, more specialized and definitive industrial science built on a foundation of former generations. Horticulture today can analyze, isolate, and vary chemical content in plants, including vitamins and other constituents, control growth, control the functioning of processes, control, intensify, and regulate their concentration and elemental composition—all work toward which the horticulturists of Bailey's generation were aiming but approaching their objectives by different methods and different principles. This does not imply that botanical physiology had not gone a long way toward these solutions. No one was more aware of the value of physiological research than Bailey. But Bailey was not a plant physiologist, nor was he a plant morphologist although he knew a type of botanical morphology and early in his years as a professor of horticulture at Cornell, when abroad, he took a course of lectures under the great European plant morphologist, Goebel of Munich. Bailey was a horticulturist interested in developing a science of horticulture. In a period of horticultural scientific immaturity, he could do no more than aid its development, both practical and experimental, to the limit of his ability. He did a magnificent job of doing what had to be done first. Before the really fundamental investigations could begin, the groundwork had to be laid.

At the thirty-eighth Convention of the American Pomological Society held at Toledo, Ohio, in December, 1921, Bailey presided as president of the society. At one of the meetings, William H. Chandler spoke on "The Trend of Research on Pomology." Bailey characterized this address as "a very stimulating paper looking to the future." Chandler was professor of pomology at the New York State College of Agriculture at the time. That fact, however, could not have influenced Bailey's judgment since Bailey no longer was connected with the college of agriculture. Chandler's appointment as professor of investigation in pomology became effective under Acting Director Stocking's administration. In the course of his address, Chandler said, "We can be certain . . . that in the future field experiments will be of a different type. First the problems investigated will almost certainly be of a more limited nature." General studies of tillage, mulching, pruning, and all distinctly horticultural activities would probably be displaced by more specific field experiments "done with very much more care than was thought necessary at the time the earlier field experiments were planned. These earlier field experiments," said Chandler, "have given us valuable results only because in the problems studied the differences were very large. As we narrow the problems down to questions involving more minute details of orchard practices we must so refine our experimental methods that smaller differences will be significant." He pointed to methods of reducing experimental error and to the necessity of obtaining "as complete knowledge as possible concerning the nature and behavior of . . . trees regardless of whether or not that knowledge may be of practical value"; and of planning wisely, interpreting wisely, until greater supplies of knowledge concerning the fundamental nature of trees and plants were available. "The greatest contribution to the fruit grower, and probably to the farmer generally, that has been made by the scientist," he said, "has been in the control of diseases and insects and this has been done by the botanist or the entomologist whose point of view was generally that of the scientist seeking the truth for sake of truth." Perhaps the most highly significant portion of the entire address were the paragraphs:

It is highly probable . . . that an increasing proportion of the research with fruit trees in the future will be physiological studies, that is studies pursued in the hope of learning more about the fundamental nature of the tree itself, or of the fruit. The phase of pomology in which our knowledge is now growing most rapidly concerns the storage of fruits and these problems are now being solved largely by physiological methods. Thus, studies in the respiration of fruits and the chemical substances formed by respiration at different temperatures is of the greatest importance concerning the influence of storage temperatures on flavor. You may expect to see very few bulletins reporting simply results of various storage temperatures of fruits with no effort to explain *how* the temperature influenced the keeping. More fundamental details will be studied in order that the results may be more safely applied to different conditions.

Such fundamental studies of the trees seem as necessary for safe conclusions as to cultural problems. The emphasis that Kraus and Kraybill give to the relation of carbo-hydrates and nitrogen in the tissue is certain to interest many workers. We are interested to know what effect on fruit bud formation a high proportion of nitrogen with a low proportion of carbohydrates may have, and we shall want to know this for every portion of the growing period. . . .

So went the discussion, describing phases of plant growth and activity, and elaborating "specific examples, out of many physiological problems that will engage the attention of the scientist in pomology."

American horticulture today possesses the names of many able and distinguished men. Among them, certainly one is William H. Chandler, and for the purpose of delineating the following point, he is selected as representative. How essentially different has been his point of view from that of Bailey? Granted that facilities were more abundant in Chandler's time than in Bailey's, granted that Chandler's and Kraus's generation began with a scientific groundwork strongly supported by public confidence, how different were the ultimate objectives of the scientists of the older and newer generations? Granted that the men of Bailey's generation had to develop the work of applied and practical science as well as "pure science," that with few exceptions scientists of Bailey's generation had to be administrators and propagandists as well as research men, how different in ultimate scientific objectives were the generations of which each man is a representative? This discussion implies no conflict or discord between the points of view of either generation. Rather, the view is taken that the present generation's work has been a continuation of the work of the past in large measure—the differences reposing in improved facilities, improved methods, improved general and special conditions, and, of course, the greatest factor, improved and increased knowledge. Bailey's generation approached a disorganized body of horticultural knowledge, a heterogeneous mass of facts based on an art, with only beginnings of a real accumulation of scientific generalizations. Chandler's and Kraus's generation began work in an era of specialization, with laboratories and experiment stations established, with a science of American horticulture organized and approaching fundamental problems, with knowledge expanding on every side, and with opportunities so great that probably their equivalents only rarely will be offered again. Both generations have encountered great tasks to be performed. Both have earned and deserved their nation's and the world's commendation.

Chandler, a native of Missouri, had obtained three degrees from the agricultural university of his state; Bachelor of Science in 1905, Master of Science in 1906, and Doctor of Philosophy in 1914. He had served his university as an assistant in horticulture, as an instructor, and as assistant professor until the year 1913. In February, 1915, a year and a half after he had become professor of pomology at the New York State College of Agriculture, he wrote an article for the *Cornell*

Countryman: "What Science Is Doing for the Fruit-Grower." As early as this year he found that conclusive results had been obtained in efforts "concerned with combatting insect pests and fungous diseases" and much value in studies in fruit culture—especially that done by workers in "pure science" without first concern for practical results. The substance of his article ably proved that "all plant science is related, and no results of experiments concerning practical methods of fruit-growing can be usefully interpreted except by making use of very many scientific facts." That long periods are required in scientific investigation, each making way for further planning of experiments, each bringing forth some knowledge of error or some fundamental discovery, seemed demonstrated by the results of years past and the prospects of years ahead. True, phases needing more adequate study were singled out—pruning, for example. Concerning tillage, there was demonstrated need of more exact experimentation. Concerning the results of fertilizer studies for orchards, the results were contradictory. It seems difficult to find any point considered in which the point of view of Bailey and that of Chandler was discordant.

In the records of the American Society for Horticultural Science (called the Society for Horticultural Science from 1903 to 1916) in which men such as E. C. Auchter, J. H. Gourley, W. H. Chandler, E. J. Kraus, H. B. Tukey, and others, have been leading figures, may be found the story of the rapid development of American scientific horticulture in specific studies in the whole broad field of horticulture, including deciduous tree fruits, grapes, small fruits, citrus, subtropicals, vegetable crops, floriculture, ornamental plants, soil science, fertilizers, water relations, genetics, plant breeding, morphology, rootstocks, plant propagation, storage, handling, and fundamental problems of physiology and development.

In 1903 at the first meeting of the society, 10 papers were presented, 38 pages in the *Proceedings*, centering around the shading of plants and recent progress in scientific horticulture. In 1913 at the tenth meeting there were 22 papers, occupying 154 pages in the *Proceedings*, dealing primarily with pomological problems. In 1923 at the twentieth meeting there were 60 papers occupying 319 pages in the *Proceedings*, dealing mostly with tree fruits, breeding, pollination, and fruit set, but now including more of vegetable crops, nursery stock, floriculture, and the propagation of ornamental plants. In 1933, at the thirtieth meeting, there were 165 papers, occupying 625 pages in the *Proceedings*. Because of the large number of manuscripts received during the year, the society published a supplementary volume of 25 papers (176 pages) making a total of 190 papers and 802 pages for the year. In 1943, at the fortieth meeting, the publication of papers in the *Proceedings* was no longer restricted to presentation at an annual meeting. The society had outgrown this method of presentation. The *Proceedings* had become virtually a journal issued in two bound volumes each year, totaling 213 papers and 993 pages of *Proceedings* for the year.

The expansion in the new phases of scientific horticulture is shown also in the steady rise in membership in the society, composed almost entirely of professional horticulturists at experiment stations and colleges, and with Federal and state agencies. The membership was 53 in 1903, 172 in 1913, 506 in 1933, and 807 in 1943.

That Bailey has continued to wield a strong influence to further scientific interests in horticulture might be illustrated in a variety of ways. An especially interesting instance may be found in an article, "Some Fundamental Considerations in the Prosecution of Silvicultural Research," by Richard H. Boerker (*Journal of Forestry*, XVI, 7, November, 1918, pp. 792 ff.) in which the author commended to the Society of American Foresters the creation of a committee on research in forestry similar to a committee of the American Society for Horticultural Science of which Bailey was chairman in 1916.

Bailey had said at the beginning of the century that there could be an overemphasis of fertilizer experimentation. Even before the beginning of the century Bailey had urged repeatedly on botanical study the importance of mycological, physiological, and systematic investigations of horticultural plants. Even before the beginning of the century he had brought to his garden and laboratories plants of the wild to study their behavior and responses, the sources of plant variations and their relations to climate, soils, and all environic factors. A study of nutrients, diagnoses of symptoms and needs, many phases of the modern points of view were initiated by Bailey in experimental studies. True, there was little direct emphasis on plant chemical composition, still less of efforts to establish ratios and relations between those elements. But there were studies of functions and processes, and, definitely, efforts to induce desired performances by plants in their growth, development, and fertilization. In evaluating Bailey's experimental studies, emphasis must be directed to his early recognitions, which are modern viewpoints, that, excluding the business phases of horticultural science, the horticulturist is a botanist working with horticultural species and that extension work, in agriculture and horticulture, whether by county agent or school, is research investigation and teaching.

CHAPTER IX

POINTS OF VIEW FOR SCIENCE AND THE
BACKGROUND PEOPLE. BASED ON THE HOLY
EARTH AND OTHER WRITINGS

IN HIS book, *The Outlook to Nature*, Bailey had stated a creed, characterized as preachments, but used in his teachings: ". . . I preach the things that we ourselves did not make; for we are all idolaters—the things of our hands we worship. I preach the near-at-hand, however plain and ordinary—the cloud and the sunshine; the green pastures; the bird on its nest and the nest on its bough; the rough bark of trees; the frost on bare, thin twigs; the mouse skittering to its burrow; the insect seeking its crevice; the smell of the ground; the sweet wind; the silent stars; the leaf that clings to its twig or that falls when its work is done. Wisdom flows from these as it can never flow from libraries and laboratories. 'There be four things,' say the Proverbs, 'which are little upon the earth, but they are exceeding wise: The ants are a people not strong, yet they prepare their meat in the summer; the conies are but a feeble folk, yet they make their houses in the rocks; the locusts have no king, yet they go forth all of them by bands; the spider taketh hold with her hands, and is in kings' palaces.'" In his volume, *The Nature-Study Idea*, he had said: "In the increasing complexities of our lives we need nothing so much as simplicity and repose. In city or country or on the sea, nature is the surrounding condition. It is the universal environment. Since we cannot escape this condition, it were better that we have no desire to escape. It were better that we know the things, small and great, which make up this environment, and that we live with them in harmony, for all things are of kin; then shall we love and be content. All men love nature if they but knew it. The methods and fashions of our living obscure the universal passion. . . ."

In 1915 was published a book by Bailey, of enduring worth, the ripened and seasoned philosophy of *The Holy Earth*. "We can be only onlookers on that part of the cosmos that we call the far heavens," said Bailey, "but it is possible to co-operate in the processes on the surface of the sphere. . . . What means this contact with our natural situation, this relationship to the earth to which we are born, and what signify this new exploration and conquest of the planet and these accumulating prophecies of science? Does the mothership of the earth have any real meaning to us?"

All this does not imply a relation only with material and physical things nor any effort to substitute a nature religion. Our relation with the planet must be raised into the realm of spirit; we cannot be fully useful otherwise.

We must find a way to maintain the emotions in the abounding commercial civilization. There are two kinds of materials—those of the native earth and the idols of one's hands. The latter are much in evidence in modern life, with the conquests of engineering, mechanics, architecture, and all the rest. . . . We come out of the earth and we have a right to the use of the materials; and there is no danger of crass materialism if we recognize the original materials as divine and if we understand our proper relation to the creation, for then will gross selfishness in the use of them be removed. This will necessarily mean a better conception of property and of one's obligation in the use of it. We shall conceive of the earth, which is the common habitation, as inviolable. One does not act rightly toward one's fellows if one does not know how to act rightly toward the earth.

Nor does this close regard for the mother earth imply any loss of mysticism or of exaltation: quite the contrary. Science but increases the mystery of the unknown and enlarges the boundaries of the spiritual vision. To feel that one is a useful and co-operating part in nature is to give one kinship, and to open the mind to the great resources and the high enthusiasms. Here arise the fundamental common relations. Here arise also the great emotions and conceptions of sublimity and grandeur, of majesty and awe, the uplift of vast desires—when one contemplates the earth and the universe and desires to take them into the soul and to express oneself in their terms; and here also the responsible practices of life take root. . . .

Man finds himself upon it, with many other creatures, all parts in some system which, since it is beyond man and superior to him, is divine.

Yet the planet was not at once complete when life had appeared upon it. The whirling earth goes through many vicissitudes; the conditions on its fruitful surface are ever-changing; and the forms of life must meet the new conditions: so does the creation continue, and every day sees the genesis in process. All life contends, sometimes ferociously but more often bloodlessly and benignly, and the contention results in momentary equilibrium, one set of contestants balancing another; but every change in the outward conditions destroys the equation and a new status results. Of all the disturbing living factors, man is the greatest. He sets mighty changes going, destroying forests, upturning the sleeping prairies, flooding the deserts, deflecting the courses of the rivers, building great cities. He operates consciously and increasingly with plan aforethought; and therefore he carries heavy responsibility. . . . Man is given the image of the creator, even when formed from the dust of the earth, so complete is his power and so real his dominion: And God blessed them: and God said unto them, Be fruitful, and multiply, and replenish the earth, and subdue it; and have dominion over the fish of the sea, and over the fowl of the air, and over every living thing that moveth upon the earth. . . . We have assumed that there is no obligation to an inanimate thing, as we consider the earth to be: but man should respect the conditions in which he is placed; the earth yields the living creature; man is a living creature; science constantly narrows the gulf between the animate and the inanimate, between the organized and the unorganized; evolution derives the creatures from the earth; the creation is one creation. I must accept all or reject all.

The earth is good. It is good to live. We talk of death and of lifelessness, but we know only of life. Even our prophecies of death are prophecies of more life. We know no better world: whatever else there may be is of things hoped for, not of things seen. The objects are here, not hidden nor far to seek: And God saw everything that he had made, and, behold, it was very good. . . . To every bird the air is good; and a man knows it is good if he is worth being a man. To every fish the water is good. To every beast its food is good, and its time of sleep is good. The creatures experience that life is good. Every man in his heart knows that there is goodness and wholeness in the rain, in the wind, the soil, the sea, the glory of sunrise, in the trees, and in the sustenance that we derive from the planet. . . . We are so accustomed to these essentials—to the rain, the wind, the soil, the sea, the sunrise, the trees, the sustenance—that we may not include them in the categories of the good things, and we endeavor to satisfy ourselves with many small and trivial and exotic gratifications; and when these gratifications fail or pall, we find ourselves helpless and resourceless. The joy of sound sleep, the relish of a sufficient meal of plain and wholesome food, the desire to do a good day's work and the recompense when at night we are tired from the doing of it, the exhilaration of fresh air, the exercise of the natural powers, the mastery of a situation or a problem—these and many others like them are fundamental satisfaction, beyond all pampering and all toys, and they are of the essence of goodness. I think we should teach all children how good are the common necessities, and how very good are the things that are made in the beginning.

> The soft, gray rain comes slowly down,
> Settling the mists on marshes brown,
> Narrowing the world on wood and hill,
> Drifting the fog down vale and rill.
> The weed-stalks bend with pearly drops,
> The grasses hang their misty tops,
> The clean leaves drip with tiny spheres,
> The fence rails run with pleasant tears.
>
> Away with care! I walk today
> In meadows wet and forests gray;—
> 'Neath heavy trees with branches low,
> 'Cross splashy fields where wild things grow.
> Past shining reeds in knee-deep tarns,
> By soaking crops and black-wet barns,
> On mossy stones in dripping nooks,
> Up rainy pools and brimming brooks
> With waterfalls and cascadills
> Fed by the new-born grassy-rills;—
> And then return across the lots
> Through all the soft and watery spots.
>
> Away with care! I walk today
> In meadows wet and forests gray.

The earth is also kindly, said Bailey.

We hear much about man being at the mercy of nature, and the literalist will contend that there can be no holy relations under such conditions. But so is man at the mercy of God.

It is a blasphemous practice that speaks of the hostility of the earth, as if the earth were full of menaces and cataclysms. The old fear of nature, that peopled the earth and sky with imps and demons, and that gave a future state to Satan, yet possesses the minds of men, only that we may have ceased to personify and to demonize our fears, although we still persistently contrast what we call the evil and the good. Still do we attempt to propitiate and appease the adversaries. Still do we carry the ban of the early philosophy that assumed materials and "the flesh" to be evil, and that found a way of escape only in renunciation and asceticism.

Nature cannot be antagonistic to man, seeing that man is a product of nature. We should find vast joy in the fellowship, something like the joy of Pan. . . . It is true that there are devastations of flood and fire and frost, scourge of disease, and appalling convulsions of earthquake and eruption. But man prospers; and we know that the catastrophes are greatly fewer than the accepted bounties. We have no choice but to abide. . . . The contest with nature is wholesome, particularly when pursued in sympathy and for mastery. It is worthy a being created in God's image. The earth is perhaps a stern earth, but it is a kindly earth. . . . To live in right relation with his natural conditions is one of the first lessons that a wise farmer or any other wise man learns. . . . Our pictures of heaven are of the opposites of daily experience—of release, of peace, of joy uninterrupted. The hunting-grounds are happy and the satisfaction has no end. . . . But we begin to understand that the best dealing with problems on earth is to found it on the facts of earth. This is the contribution of natural science, however abstract, to human welfare. . . .

The earth is holy. . . . Verily, then, the earth is divine, because man did not make it. We are here, part in the creation. We cannot escape. We are under obligation to take part and to do our best, living with each other and with all the creatures. We may not know the full plan, but that does not alter the relation. When once we set ourselves to the pleasure of our dominion, reverently and hopefully, and assume all its responsibilities, we shall have a new hold on life.

We shall put our dominion into the realm of morals. It is now in the realm of trade. This will be very personal morals, but it will also be national and racial morals. . . . The sacredness to us of the earth is intrinsic and inherent. . . . To live in sincere relations with the company of created things and with conscious regard for the support of all men now and yet to come, must be of the essence of righteousness. . . . The usual objects have their moral significance. An oak-tree is to us a moral object because it lives its life regularly and fulfils its destiny. In the wind and in the stars, in forest and by the shore, there is spiritual refreshment: And the spirit of God moved upon the face of the waters. . . .

This is a larger and more original relation than the modern attitude of appreciation and admiration of nature. In the days of the patriarchs and prophets, nature and man shared in the condemnation and likewise in the redemption. The ground was cursed for Adam's sin. Paul wrote that the whole creation groaneth and travaileth in pain, and that it waiteth for the revealing. Isaiah proclaimed the redemption of the wilderness and the solitary place with the redemption of man, when they shall rejoice and blossom as the rose, and when the glowing sand shall become a pool and the thirsty ground springs of water. . . .

But man has been engaged in habits of destruction, has not recognized fully the injunction that he is his brother's keeper, has not divided his land for realization of the best social and spiritual results, disregarded in places needed self-reliance, waged wars for dominion, and has not kept the earth beautiful as it was made. On the contrary, he has filled it with noises of industries—though these contributions of industry have been great and needed—and has not always perpetuated or developed the great traditions of a society favored with the contributions and worth of separate souls. Bailey did not fear the practical applications of the philosophy of *The Holy Earth*.

We have been greatly engaged in digging up the stored resources, and in destroying vast products of the earth for some kernel that we can apply to our necessities or add to our enjoyments. We excavate the best of the coal and cast away the remainder; blast the minerals and metals from underneath the crust, and leave the earth raw and sore; we box the pines for turpentine and abandon the growths of limitless years to fire and devastation; sweep the forests with the besom of destruction; pull the fish from the rivers and ponds without making any adequate provision for renewal; exterminate whole races of animals; choke the streams with refuse and dross; rob the land of its available stores, denuding the surface, exposing great areas to erosion.

Nor do we exercise the care and thrift of good housekeepers. We do not clean up our work or leave the earth in order. The remnants and accumulation of mining-camps are left to ruin and decay; the deserted phosphate excavations are ragged, barren, and unfilled; vast areas of forested lands are left in brush and waste, unthoughtful of the future, unmindful of the years that must be consumed to reduce the refuse to mould and to cover the surface respectably, uncharitable to those who must clear away the wastes and put the place in order; and so thoughtless are we with these natural resources that even the establishments that manufacture them—the mills, the factories of many kinds—are likely to be offensive objects in the landscape, unclean, unkempt, displaying the unconcern of the owners to the obligation that the use of the materials imposes and to the sensibilities of the community for the way in which they handle them. . . . How many and many are the years required to grow a forest and to fill the pockets of the rocks, and how satisfying are the landscapes, and yet how desperately soon may men reduce it all to ruin and to emptiness, and how slatternly may they violate the scenery!

All this habit of destructiveness is uneconomic in the best sense, unsocial, unmoral.

Society now begins to demand a constructive process. With care and with regard for other men, we must produce the food and the other supplies in regularity and sufficiency; and we must clean up after our work, that the earth may not be depleted, scarred, or repulsive. . . . Today we are moved by impulses of trade, and we find ourselves plunged into a war of commercial frenzy; and as it has behind it vaster resources and more command of natural forces, so is it the most ferocious and wasteful that the race has experienced, exceeding in its havoc the cataclysms of earthquake and volcano. Certainly we have not yet learned how to withstand the prosperity and the privileges that we have gained by the discoveries of science; and certainly the morals of commerce have not given us freedom or mastery. Rivalry that leads to arms is a natural fruit of unrestrained rivalry in trade.

Man has dominion, he has no commission to devastate: And the Lord God took the man, and put him into the garden of Eden to dress it and to keep it.

In his volume, *The Nature-Study Idea*, Bailey had observed:

The old desire to kill—first born of necessity—still lingers. But now we kill also for "sport." Practically a new motive has been born into the world with man—the desire to kill for the sake of killing. One generation of white men is sufficent to exterminate the bison and several other species. All this needs justification. The lower creation is not the plaything of man.

We are still obliged to kill for our necessities. We must secure food and raiment. More and more we are rearing the animals that we would take for food. We give them happier lives. We protect them from the severities of the struggle for existence. We remove them from the necessities of protecting themselves from violence. We take our own. There is no question of morals. We give that we may take; and we take because we must.

To kill for mere sport is a very different matter: it lies outside the realm of struggle for existence. Too often there is not even the justification of fair play. Usually the hunter exposes himself to no danger from the animal that he would kill. He takes no risks. He has the advantage of long-range weapons. There is no combat. Over on the lake shore are great cones of ice, built up by the accretions of the waves. Several stalwart men have skulked behind them and lie secure from observation. A little flock of birds, unsuspecting, unprotected, harming no man, obeying the laws of their kind, skims across the water. The guns discharge. The whole flock falls, the mangled birds struggling and crying, and tainting the water with their blood as they are carried away on the waves, perhaps to die on the shores. There is a shout of victory. Surely, man is the king of beasts!

But there is another and fairer side than this. The lack of feeling for wounded animals is often thoughtlessness. The satisfaction in hunting is often the joy of skill in markmanship, the pleasure of woodcraft, the enthusiasm of being out-of-doors, the keen delight in discovering the haunts and ways of the nature-folk. . . . It is primarily a means of enjoying the free world of the Out-of-doors. This nature-spirit is growing, and there are many ways of knowing the fields and woods. The camera is competing with the trap and gun.

Bailey did not wish to be understood as opposing hunting with gun or rod. In the last analysis, with every man, there lay a choice of ideals. But he rejoiced that an "awakening interest in the nature-world" was being reflected in the game laws—"for these laws," he interpreted, "are only an imperfect expression of the growing desire to let everything live its own life."

In man's relation to *The Holy Earth*, he distinguished three stages— the collecting stage, the mining stage, and the producing stage.

At first man sweeps the earth to see what he may gather—game, wood, fruits, fur, feathers, shells on the shore. A certain social and moral life arises out of this relation, seen well in the woodsmen and the fishers—in whom it best persists to the present day—strong, dogmatic, superstitious folk. Then man begins to go beneath the surface to see what he can find—iron and precious stones, the gold of Ophir, coal, and many curious treasures. This develops the exploiting faculties, and leads men into the uttermost parts. In both these stages the elements of waste and disregard have been heavy.

Finally, we begin to enter the productive stage, whereby we secure supplies by controlling the conditions under which they grow, wasting little, harming not. Farming has been very much a mining process, the utilizing of fertility easily at hand and the moving-on to lands unspoiled of quick potash and nitrogen. Now it begins to be really productive and constructive, with a range of responsible and permanent morals. We rear the domestic animals with precision. We raise crops, when we will, almost to a nicety. We plant fish in lakes and streams to some extent. . . . If the older stages were strongly expressed in the character of the people, so will this new stage be expressed; and so is it that we are escaping the primitive and should be coming into a new character. We shall find our rootage in the soil.

This new character, this clearer sense of relationship with the earth, should express itself in all the people and not exclusively in farming people and their like. It should be a popular character—or a national character if we would limit the discussion to one people—and not a class character. Now, here lies a difficulty and here is a reason for writing this book: the population of the earth is increasing, the relative population of farmers is decreasing, people are herding in cities, we have a city mind, and relatively fewer people are brought into touch with the earth in any real way. . . . Agriculture makes a great contribution to human progress by releasing men for the manufactures and the trades. . . . How we may achieve a more widespread contact with the earth on the part of all the people without making them farmers, I shall endeavor to suggest as I proceed; in fact, this is my theme. . . . We are not to look for our permanent civilization to rest on any species of robber-economy. No flurry of coal-mining, or gold-fever, or rubber-collecting in the tropics, or excitement of prospecting for new finds or even locating new lands, no ravishing of the earth or monopolistic control of its bounties, will build a stable society. So is much of our economic and social fabric transitory. It is not by accident that a very distinct form of society is developing in the great farming regions of the Mississippi Valley and in other comparable places; the exploiting and promoting occupancy of these lands is passing and a stable progressive development appears. . . . My reader must not infer that we have arrived at a permanent agriculture, although we begin now to see the importance of a permanent land occupancy. Probably we have not yet evolved a satisfactory husbandry that will maintain itself century by century, without loss and without the ransacking of the ends of the earth for fertilizer materials to make good our deficiencies. All the more is it important that the problem be elevated into the realm of statesmanship and of morals. Neither must he infer that the resources of the earth are to be locked up beyond contact and use (for the contact and use will be morally regulated). . . . In the background is the countryman. . . . We are teaching him how to bring some of these things under the dominion of his hands, how to measure and to weigh and to judge. This will give him the essential physical mastery. . . .The naturist knows that the time will come slowly—not yet are we ready for fulfilment; he knows that we cannot regulate the cosmos, or even the natural history of the people, by enactments. Slowly: by removing handicaps here and there; by selection of the folk in a natural process, to eliminate the unresponsive; by teaching, by suggestion; by a public recognition of the problem, even though no one of us sees the end of it. . . . We perceive the essential continuity in nature, arising from within rather than from without, the forms of life proceeding upwardly and onwardly in something very like a mighty plan of sequence, man being one part in the process. . . . The present wide-spread growth of the feeling of brotherhood would have been impossible in a self-centred creation: the way has been prepared by the discussion of evolution, which is the major biological contribution to human welfare and progress. This is the philosophy of the oneness in nature and the unity in living things. . . . We shall produce a much better and safer man when we make him self-controlling by developing his sense of responsibility than when we regulate him by exterior enactments. . . .

The farmer and every one of us: every citizen should be put right toward the planet, should be quicked to his relationship to his natural background. The whole body of public sentiment should be sympathetic with the man who works and administers the land for us. . . . We have heard much about the "marginal man," but the first concern of society should be for the bottom man. . . . We know that the farms and the back spaces have been the mother of the race. We know that the exigencies and frugalities of life in these backgrounds beget men and women to be serious and steady and to know the value of every hour and of every coin that they earn; and whenever they are properly trained, these folk recognize the holiness of the earth. . . . The earth is not selfish. It is open and free to all. It invites everywhere. The naturist is not selfish—he shares all his joys and discoveries, even to the extent of publishing them. The farmer is not selfish with his occupation—he freely aids every one or any one to engage in his occupation, even if that one becomes his competitor. But occupations that are some degrees removed from the earth may display selfishness; trade and, to a large extent, manufacture are selfish, and they lock themselves in. Even the exploiting of the resources of the earth may be selfish, in the taking of the timber and the coal, the water-powers and the minerals, for all this is likely to develop a species of plunder. The naturist desires to protect the plants and the animals and the situations for those less fortunate and for those who come after. There are lumbermen and miners with the finest sense of obligation. There are other men who would take the last nugget and destroy the last bole. . . . All men are the same when they come back to the meadows, to the hills, and to the deep woods: He maketh his sun to rise on the evil and the good, and sendeth rain on the just and the unjust.

The lesson of the growing abounding earth is of liberality for all, and never exploitation or very exclusive opportunities for the few. Even if the weaker anywhere perish in the contest for food, they are nevertheless given the opportunity to contest on terms equal to their abilities; and at all events, we come, in the human sphere, to the domination of sweet reason rather than to competition in sheer force. When, by means of reasonable education, this simple relation is understood by mankind and begins to express itself spontaneously, we shall find our voluminous complex of laws to regulate selfishness gradually disappearing and passing into the limbo. . . .

It is well for a person to have his own plot for his life-time, with the right to use it as he will so long as he does not offend, or does not despoil it for those who follow: it steadies him, and it identifies him with a definite program in life. . . . If it were possible for every person to own a tree and to care for it, the good results would be beyond estimation.

In 1928, when Bailey produced another of the Background Books, *The Garden Lover,* he put into writing a lifelong practice he had followed, saying, "One never knows a plant until one grows it and cares for it from first to last in all vicissitudes. The satisfaction of seeing a plant spring up, grow, produce its own kind of foliage, take its place among other plants, meet the days and seasons as they pass, is beyond all measure greater and more significant than the color-sensation produced by the flower or the fruit in a decoration. The purchased plant in full bloom or mature condition is not very close to one's affections, nor is it an object to be exhibited as one's own. There is no danger," he believed, "that the amateur or plant-lover must pass, whatever may be the semblance of it for any moment. The amateur will persist as long as the mind craves variety in experience and as the seasons hold their charm." One of the greatest qualities of the Background Books, written for the background people, the farmers and gardeners, then more remotely situated and more decentralized than now, was the author's inimitable capacity to share his love of the things of nature with those people who were participating in one way or another in the new nation-wide educational enterprises. In those years, the farmers and gardeners were definitely individuals, as Bailey wished them to remain. To benefit them a wealth of scientific knowledge was accumulating. Yet, this still represented a small fraction of the sum total of human knowledge. Agricultural extension work had leaped over the boundaries of states and vigorously was becoming a national enterprise. Even as agricultural development was becoming in a sense a national policy, so was forestry. Strong voices, among them, Bailey for agriculture and Fernow in forestry, were enunciating basic philosophies. Bailey began with the human being and his outlook. The Background Books illustrated the countryman's philosophy toward his work and product. It was not the voice of the scholar but the voice of the man with the hoe and the plow.

With such books as *Wind and Weather* in verse, *Universal Service, What Is Democracy, The Seven Stars, The Harvest,* and *The Garden Lover,* Bailey presented in wide and refined compass the philosophy of *The Holy Earth.* He translated to poetic terms the experiences to be enjoyed and cultivated, the wise economies to be aimed at, all that made for enjoyment and improvement of folk life of those who lived with and by plants and animals under states of domestication. Although there were propaganda elements in his writing, the era of propagandizing on behalf

of an improved American agriculture has not yet been finished. Propagandizing has been diminished and university interest is more closely
confined now to strictly scientific phases of investigation. The philosophy
of *The Holy Earth* cannot be regarded as a religion, or even a philosophy
in the strict sense, but rather as a compendium or collection of viewpoints so truthful, so basic, and universal that as a whole the viewpoints
are tantamount to a philosophy of life. If the claim be made that
elements of both the religious and philosophical are present, then the
answer must be that such was then needed, and Bailey supplied that
need. Who more than Bailey in the entire history of American scientific
horticulture and, in a sense, American agriculture imparted more faith
to these sciences? Others have supplied research techniques which have
been refined and added to and greatly enlarged the scope of the science.
Allocating persons and their contributions to defined positions is always
dangerous. But that Bailey supplied an indisputably valuable leadership
cannot be doubted.

There is originality, applicable even to the present, in *The Garden
Lover* when he says: "But the trend of gardening enterprise runs to
roses, irises, peonies, rock-gardens and many colorful subjects and the
fruit-garden of [Patrick] Barry's day is yet essentially unrealized as a
recognized effort. This is a vast pity, for not only is the [dwarf] fruit
itself of prime interest and value but the care required in the rearing
of it brings one into the most intimate relationship with the plant and
should afford a singular mental training. Nothing more clearly shows the
skill and devotion of the horticulturist than the ability to grow good
fruit in a small space, even though the subject is not essentially difficult;
and the fact that such fruit-raising is not the vogue should be specially
suggestive to one who desires to find a personal expression." Or, considering 307 plant varieties of his "garden-patch," when he said:
"Among the three hundred and seven are some fifty kinds of grasses.
They are a fascinating lot. They bear no resemblance to the twenty-four
kinds of œnotheras alongside, although sown the same time in the same
soil and tilled by the same tools in the same hands. . . . Many choice
ornamental things are among these grasses, fit for mass-planting,
edgings and bouquets. Yet in our day the grasses will not be much
sought as ornamental subjects because not sufficiently showy. . . . The
fact that so few persons choose the modest plant-forms should make
these forms the more attractive to such as desire a more personal expression, or who are interested in minor effects."

Bailey sought to make not only the rural, and urban, home ground
and garden more beautiful, developing therewith all resources. He
sought also to make farms and all lands accessible. In *The Holy Earth*,
he stated:

We undertake great conquests of engineering, over mountains and across rivers and through the morasses; but at the last we shall call on the engineer for the greatest conquest of all—how to divide the surface of the earth so that it shall yield us its best and mean to us the most, on the easiest grades, in the most practicable way, that we may utilize every piece of land to fullest advantage. . . . Our educational effort is at present directed toward making the farmer prosperous on his existing farm, rather than to help him to secure a farm of proper resources and with proper access. . . . This is no Utopian or socialistic scheme, nor does it imply a forcible interference with vested rights. It is a plain statement of the necessities of the situation. . . . In America, we do not suffer from the holding of the land in a few families or in an aristocratic class; that danger we have escaped, but we have not yet learned how to give the land meaning to the greatest number of people. This is a question for the best political program, for we look for the day when statesmanship shall be expressed in the details of common politics. We now hear much about the good-roads question, as if it were a problem only of highway construction: it is really a question of a new map. . . . Undoubtedly we are in the beginning of an epoch in rural affairs. We are at a formative period. We begin to consider the rural problem increasingly in terms of social groups. The attitudes that these groups assume, the way in which they react to their problems, will be determined in the broader aspects for some time to come by the character of the young leadership that is now taking the field. . . . The human struggle should not be on the plane of the struggle in the lower creation, by the simple fact that the human plane is unlike; and those who contend that we should draw our methods of contest from wild nature would therefore put us back on the plane of the creatures we are supposed to have passed. If there is one struggle of the creeping things, if there is one struggle of the fish of the sea and another of the beasts of the field, and still another of the fowls of the air, then surely there must be still another order for those who have dominion. . . .

Moreover, the final test of fitness in nature is adaptation, not power. Adaptation and adjustment mean peace, not war. . . . The military method of civilization finds no justification in the biological struggle for existence.

The final conquest of a man is of himself, and he shall then be greater than when he takes a city. The final conquest of a society is of itself, and it shall then be greater than when it conquers its neighboring society. . . .

It has been persistently repeated for years that in nature the weakest perish and that the victory is with the strong, meaning by that the physically powerful. This is a false analogy and a false biology. It leads men far astray. It is the result of a misconception of the teaching of evolution.

Our minds dwell on the capture and the carnage in nature—the hawk swooping on its prey, the cat stealthily watching for the mouse, wolves hunting in packs, ferocious beasts lying in wait, sharks that follow ships, serpents with venomous fangs, the vast range of parasitism; and with the poet we say that nature is "red in tooth and claw." Of course, we are not to deny the struggle of might against might, which is mostly between individuals, and of which we are all aware; but the weak and the fragile and the small are the organisms that have persisted. There are thousands of little and soft things still abundant in the world that have outlived the fearsome ravenous monsters of ages past. . . . The struggle in nature is not a combat, as we commonly understand that word, and it is not warfare. The earth is not strewn with corpses.

I was impressed in reading Roosevelt's "African Game Trails" with the great extent of small and defenseless and fragile animal life that abounds in the midst of the terrible beasts—little uncourageous things that hide in the crevices, myriads that fly in the air, those that ride on the rhinos, that swim and hide in the pools, and bats that hang in the acacia-trees. He travelled in the region of the lion, in the region that "holds the mightiest creatures that tread the earth or swim in its rivers; it also holds distant kinsfolk of these same creatures, no bigger than woodchucks, which dwell in crannies of the rocks, and in the tree tops. There are antelope smaller than hares and antelope larger than oxen. There are creatures which are the embodiment of grace; and others whose huge ungainliness is like that of a shape in a nightmare. The plains are alive with droves of strange and beautiful animals whose like is not known elsewhere." The lion is mighty; he is the king of beasts; but he keeps his place and he has no kingdom. He has not mastered the earth. No beast has ever overcome the earth; and the natural world has never been conquered by muscular force.

Nature is not in a state of perpetual enmity, one part with another.

My friend went to a far country. He told me that he was most impressed with the ferocity, chiefly of wild men. It came my time to go to that country. I saw that men had been savage—men are the most ferocious of animals, and the ferocity has never reached its high point of refined fury until to-day. (Of course, savages fight and slay; this is because they are savages.) But I saw also that these savage men are passing away. I saw animals that had never tasted blood, that had no means of defense against a rapacious captor, and yet they were multiplying. Every stone that I upturned disclosed some tender organism; every bush that I disturbed revealed some timid atom of animal life; every spot where I walked bore some delicate plant, and I recalled the remark of Sir J. William Dawson "that frail and delicate plants may be more ancient than the mountains or plains on which they live"; and if I went on the sea, I saw the medusæ, as frail as a poet's dream, with the very sunshine streaming through them, yet holding their own in the mighty upheaval of the oceans; and I reflected on the myriads of microscopic things that for untold ages had cast the very rock on which much of the ocean rests. The minor things and the weak things are the most numerous, and they have played the greatest part in the polity of nature. So I came away from that far country impressed with the power of the little feeble things. I had a new understanding of the worth of creatures so unobtrusive and so silent that the multitude does not know them.

I saw protective colorings; I saw fleet wings and swift feet; I saw the ability to hide and to conceal; I saw habits of adaptation; I saw marvellous powers of reproduction. You have seen them in every field; you have met them on your casual walks, until you accept them as the natural order of things. And you know that the beasts of prey have not prevailed. The whole contrivance of nature is to protect the weak.

We have wrongly visualized the "struggle." We have given it an intensely human application. We need to go back to Darwin who gave significance to the phrase "struggle for existence." "I use this term," he said, "in a large and metaphorical sense, including dependence of one being on another, and including (which is more important) not only the life of the individual, but success in leaving progeny." The dependence of one being on another, success in leaving progeny—how accurate and how far-seeing was Darwin! . . .

The great issues are the issues of live and let-live. There are whole nations of plants, more unlike than nations of humankind, living together in mutual interdependence. There are nations of quiet and mightless animals that live in the very regions of the mighty and the stout. And we are glad it is so.

The genius of Bailey was his ability to get close to the lives of people, to touch inner chords in human beings which no other one had struck, to give new and revitalized meaning to casual, worn, or accustomed things, to translate old matters into new meanings, contributions as great as new discoveries. Taking the past and remolding it for the present is as great as giving to the world entirely new creations or inventions.

To illustrate—let us take his attitude toward the "daily fare" and the appreciation of nearby and good materials. He related the needed essential simplicity of our habits of life "to the righteousness of simple eating and drinking."

"Good bread and good drink, a good fire in the hall, Brawn, pudding, and souse, and good mustard withal." [Thomas Tusser] Here is the whole philosophy of the contented festival—the fruit of one's labor, the common genuine materials, and the cheer of the family fireside. The day is to be given over to the spirit of the celebration; every common object will glow with a new consecration, and everything will be good—even the mustard will be good withal. . . . Much of our eating and feasting is a vicious waste of time, and also of human energy that might be put to good uses. . . . I am afraid that our food habits very well represent how far we have moved away from the essentials and how much we have misled ourselves as to the standards of excellence. I looked in a cookbook to learn how to serve potatoes: I found twenty-three recipes, every one of which was apparently designed to disguise the fact that they were potatoes; and yet there is really nothing in a potato to be ashamed of. . . . Result is that one finds the greatest difficulty in securing a really good baked potato, a well-cooked steak, or a wholesome dish of apple-sauce that is not strained and flavored beyond recognition. . . . I sometimes think that the rise of the culinary arts is banishing this fine old appreciation of fruits in their natural forms. There are so many ways of canning and preserving and evaporating and extracting the juices, so many disguises and so much fabrication, that the fruit is lost in the process. The tin-can and the bottle seem to have put an insuperable barrier between us and nature, and it is difficult for us to get back to a good munch of real apples under a tree or by the fireside. . . .

As to this, it must be remembered that Bailey was urging only simplicity and a deeper rootage of our lives in the soil and its products. His attack was directed against increasing complexity, superficiality, and fastidiousness, unnatural affectations and postured daintiness, the unreal opposing the real. Proof of Bailey's expressed pleasure at the stupendous scientific progress achieved for producer and consumer by American horticulture during the last decades may be found in many addresses and published articles. Today on Cornell University's campus is a School of Nutrition, the first one founded in the United States. Many examples of recent progress might be cited: new labor-saving machinery, vigorous hybrid crops, marvelous inventions such as DDT and 2,4-D, improvements in assembling, transporting, and storing vegetable products, improvements of methods of freezing and storing vegetables and fruits for longer and wider consumption, of dehydrating materials for longer continued and more widespread food uses—a device used with much effectiveness in war emergency in feeding millions of troops in many far and foreign lands—and other triumphs of recent horticultural science. Many perfecting methods in the canning, evaporating, and other industries—which promote health, sanitation, and greater food consumption—have been found. With such progress Bailey never quarreled but to its furtherance gave some of the most effective years of his life. Bailey's points of view in this regard are not solely economic, not solely artistic, not solely moral, but a combination of all for better human living. He believed, and he early took this position, that the heart of agriculture is on the farm; the heart of horticulture is in the garden; the heart of botany is where the plant is; although he realized that each must summon the laboratory's aid, and that perhaps some of the greatest progress awaiting achievement would be in the laboratory. He wrote:

Not even yet am I done with this plain problem of the daily fare. The very fact that it is daily—thrice daily—and that it enters so much into the thought and effort of every one of us, makes it a subject of the deepest concern from every point of view. The aspect of the case that I am . . . to re-assert is the effect of much of our food preparation in removing us from a knowledge of the good raw materials that come out of the abounding earth.

Let us stop to admire an apple. . . . In physical perfectness of form and texture and color, there is nothing in all the world that exceeds a well-grown fruit. Let it lie in the palm of your hand. Close your fingers slowly about it. Feel its firm or soft and modelled surface. Put it against your cheek, and inhale its fragrance. Trace its neutral under-colors, and follow its stripes and mark its dots. If an apple, trace the eye that lies in a moulded basin. Note its stem, how it stands firmly in its cavity, and let your imagination run back to the tree from which, when finally mature, it parted freely. This apple is not only the product of your labor, but it holds the essence of the year and it is in itself a thing of exquisite beauty. There is no other rondure and no other fragrance like this. . . . Some time ago I visited Hood River Valley in company with a rugged potato-grower from the Rocky Mountains. We were amazed at the wonderful scenery, and captivated by the beauty of the fruits. In one orchard the owner showed us with much satisfaction a brace of apples of perfect form and glowing colors. When the grower had properly expounded the marvels of Hood River apples, which he said were the finest in the world, my friend thrust his hand into his pocket and pulled out a potato, and said to the man: "Why is not that just as handsome as a Hood River apple?" And sure enough it was. For twenty-five years this grower had been raising and selecting the old Peachblow potato, until he had a form much more perfect than the old Peachblow ever was, with a uniform delicate pink skin, smooth surface, comely shape, and medium size, and with eyes very small and scarcely sunken; and my Hood River friend admitted that a potato as well as an apple may be handsome and satisfying to the hand and to the eye, and well worth carrying in one's pocket. . . .

Place a pumpkin on your table; run your fingers down its smooth grooves; trace the furrows to the poles; take note of its form; absorb its rich color; get the tang of its fragrance. The roughness and ruggedness of its leaves, the sharp-angled stem strongly set, make a foil that a sculptor cannot improve. Then wonder how this marvellous thing was born out of your garden soil through the medium of one small strand of a succulent stem.

We all recognize the appeal of a bouquet of flowers, but we are unaware that we may have a bouquet of fruits. . . . Yet, apples and oranges and plums and grapes and nuts, and good melons and cucumbers and peppers and carrots and onions, may be arranged into the most artistic and satisfying combinations. . . .

Years later, Bailey would do some exquisitely beautiful and valuable taxonomic studies, treating garden subjects. One of these was *The Garden of Gourds*, published by The Macmillan Company in 1937. The introduction describes the aesthetic point of view with which Bailey has always enriched his garden experience:

It is the first day of October. Summer birds are gone. Frosts have signalled for winter. All tender vegetables are harvested from the garden. Marigolds and zinnias and a few other rugged things still retain the glow of warm weather, yet autumn chill is in the air, new colors are on the hills, dead leaves begin to cover the grass. It is plain we approach a great event in the progress of the year, when products and ambitions will be housed and we shall settle down to the hopeful routines of winter. Most persons will cease to regard the landscape and they will seldom go to the garden or follow the lines of the brook.

Yet even now the gourds hang on the trellises, and although blossoms are mostly gone and leaves have passed their prime, the bright green-and-yellow striped fruits in comely attractive form ask for attention. Probably in every year since my youth—and that was long ago—I have grown gourds of one kind or another and sometimes of many kinds. I have made an herbarium collection of them, for record, including foliage and flowers; and many fruits lie in boxes. I cannot remember when I did not know them. For time beyond recollection I have wanted to write a simple book about the gourds; my technical and scientific writings on the Cucurbits began nearly fifty years ago; and now, as the years are ripe, I wish to express my joy in my experiences.

Once the gourds were common objects in homes, then other blooms and fruits displaced them, and now they are back again in a new vogue of popular favor, but for myself the interest in them has never lagged. They are so shapely and so colorful, so strange in their markings, so endlessly unlike each other, so durable in winter months, so apparently unrelated to the vines that bear them, and yet so simple to grow, that they hold the interest tenaciously.

The present interest in gourds is well attested by the organizing of the International Gourd Society, headquarters in California. Semi-annually, it publishes a Gourd Bulletin. . . .

Or, in *The Garden of Larkspurs*, published in 1939, also by the Macmillan Company:

. . . The first impulse is to admire the sturdy row of Rocket larkspurs in good view from my window as I write on this sweltry August day. Three months old they are; I sowed the seeds, more than a dozen named kinds, early in May when the promise of spring was at its height and the air was filled with fragrances and music; now they stand three to four feet tall, prim in their rows, glowing in spikes of white and blue and pink and purple, a pretty sight; the family cat likes to lie among them.

Close by them and in view from my table are large azure-blue clumps of the Garland larkspur, one of them Clivedon Beauty, and another the misnamed *Delphinium Barlowii*. The Candle larkspurs are now past their bloom, but one old clump stands in front of me six and one-half feet tall, holding aloft its upright seedful pods.—Plants of Bouquet larkspurs, sown this spring, are in the planting, now coming into bloom. On my table in full flower is a complete plant of the singular *Delphinium cardiopetalum*, introducing the group of Forking larkspurs. Here, then, are all the five major groups of horticultural larkspurs, to keep my pen true to its purpose. Alongside them are several kinds of bellflower, about which we may learn in another year.

It has been a season of larkspurs, and I have lived again the joys I have had in growing them for more years than I can remember. . . .

Search through Bailey's writings reveals many passages of such abundantly joyous knowledge derived from his garden and laboratory study.

Like the love of music, books and pictures, the love of gardens comes with culture and leisure and with the ripening of the home life. The love of gardens, as of every other beautiful and refining thing, must increase to the end of time. More and more must the sympathies enlarge. There must be more points of contact with the world. Life ever becomes richer. Gardening is more than the growing of plants: it is the expression of desire. As there must be many gardeners, so there must be many books. There must be books for different persons and different ideals. . . . For myself, I have been growing plants for more than fifty years for the purpose of becoming acquainted with them and their habits and requirements.

Bailey said, "The nature-desire may be perpetual and constant, but the garden-desire returns with every new springtime."

Furthermore, he said, in *The Holy Earth*:

The admiration of a good domestic animal is much to be desired. It develops a most responsible attitude in the man or the woman. I have observed a peculiar charm in the breeders of these wonderful animals, a certain poise and masterfulness and breadth of sympathy. To admire a good horse and to know just why he admires him is a great resource to any man, as also to feel the responsibility for the care and health of any flock or herd. Fowls, pigs, sheep on their pastures, cows, mules, all perfect of their kind, all sensitive, all of them marvellous in their forms and powers—verily these are good to know. . . . As a man thinketh of his materials, so doth he profit in the use of them. He builds them into himself. There is a wide-spread feeling that in some way these materials reflect themselves in a man's bearing. One type of man grows out of the handling of rocks, another out of the handling of fishes, another out of the growing of the products from the good earth. All irreverence in the handling of these materials that come out of the earth's bounty, and all waste and poor workmanship, make for a low spiritual expression. . . . An apple day or an apple sabbath would teach the people to express their gratitude for apples. . . .

A fear seems to be abroad that the inquisitiveness and exactness of science will deprive literature of imagination and sympathy and will destroy artistic expression; and it is said that we are in danger of losing the devotional element in literature. . . . There may be inflexible souls among the investigators who see little or nothing beyond the set of facts in a little field, but surely the greater number of scientific men are persons of keen imagination and of broad interest in all conquests. Indeed, a lively imagination is indispensable in persons of the best attainments in science; it is necessary only that the imagination be regulated and trained. Never has it been so true that fact is stranger than fiction. Never have the flights of the poets been so evenly matched by the flights of science. All great engineers, chemists, physiologists, physicists work in the realm of imagination, of imagination that projects the unknown from the known. Almost do we think that the Roentgen ray, the wireless telegraphy, the analysis of the light of the stars, the serum control of disease are the product of what we might call pure fancy. The very utilities and conquests of modern society are the results of better imagination than the world has yet known. . . . It is less than forty years since Darwin and less than fifty years since Agassiz. It is only twenty years since Pasteur. It is only a century and a quarter since Franklin, fifty years since Faraday, less than twenty-five since Tyndall. It is sixty years since Humboldt glorified the earth with the range of his imagination. It is not so far even if we go back to Newton and to Kepler. Within the span of a century we count name after name of prophets who have set us on a new course. So complete has been the revolution that we lost our old bearings before we had found the new. We have not yet worked out the new relationships, nor put into practice their moral obligations, nor have we grasped the fulness of our privileges. We have not yet made the new knowledge consciously into a philosophy of life or incorporated it completely into working attitudes of social equity. Therefore, not even now are we ripe for the new literature.

We have gone far enough, however, to know that science is not unsympathetic and that it is not contemptuous of the unknown. . . . Close dissection long continued may not lead to free artistic literary expression; this is as true of literary anatomy as of biological anatomy: but this does not destroy the freedom of other souls, and it may afford good material for the artist.

Two kinds of popular writing are confused in the public mind, for there are two classes that express the findings of scientific inquiry. The prevailing product is that which issues from establishments and institutions. This is supervised, edited, and made to conform; it is the product of our perfected organizations and has all the hardness of its origin. The other literature is of a different breed. It is the expression of personality. The one is a useful and necessary public literature of record and advice; the other is a literature of outlook and inspiration. The latter is not to be expected from the institutions, for it is naturally the literature of freedom.

Quite obviously, the literary allocation of *The Holy Earth* and the other Background Books was defined. Quite definitely, the introductory descriptive remarks of Bailey's more strictly scientific studies were placed there expressive of a human spirit approaching an exacting task. Bailey never escaped the responsibilities of a task, whatever its character, if he chose to undertake it. No author could adequately interpret his life without presenting the man and his work from as many points of view as space and time permit. No book can relive the life of a man. But books, constructive in intention, may cull the essences and account for accomplishments. As emotions are the mainsprings of intellectual activity, so more often than not intellectual accomplishments reveal the man. The essential oneness of persons is true, whether of scientist or artist. Bailey could with evident genius interpret Questor of *The Seven Stars* (1923) as he became "a man from Mars amused and astonished by everything he sees, or a Rip Van Winkle coming back to a world he once knew well, or some Alastor wandering in lone and silent hours, or some meditator sitting by the wayside of life," all enjoying the bounties of nature and the joys of earth and sky in relation to the eternal and cosmic. In *The Holy Earth* Bailey wrote:

Many times in this journey have we come against the importance of the individual. We are to develop the man's social feeling at the same time that we allow him to remain separate. . . . In proportion as society becomes organized and involved, do we need the separate spirit and persons who are responsible beings on their own account. The independent judgment should be much furthered by studies in the sciences that are founded on observation of native forms and conditions. . . . As an example of what I mean, I mention John Muir, who has recently passed away, and who stood for a definite contribution to his generation. He could hardly have made this contribution if he had been attached to any of the great institutions or organizations or to big business. He has left a personal impression and a remarkable literature that has been very little influenced by group psychology. He is the interpreter of mountains, forests, and glaciers. . . .

I may also recall the great example of Agassiz at Penikese. In his last year, broken in health, feeling the message he still had for the people, he opened the school on the little island off the coast of Massachusetts. It was a short school in one summer only, yet it has made an indelible impression on American education. It stimulates one to know that the person who met the incoming students on the wharf was Agassiz himself, not an assistant or an instructor. Out of the great number of applicants, he chose fifty whom he would teach. He wanted to send forth these chosen persons with his message, apostles to carry the methods and the way of approach. (When are we to have the Penikese for the rural backgrounds?). . . .

Never have we needed the separate soul so much as now. . . .

How to strike the balance between the needful individualism and social crystallization is probably the most difficult question before society. Of the great underlying classes of occupations, farming is the only one that presents the individualistic side very strongly. If individualism is to be preserved anywhere, it must be preserved here. The tendency of our present-day discussion is to organize the farmers as other groups or masses are organized. We are in danger here. Assuredly, the farmer needs better resources in association, but it is a nice question how far we should go and how completely we should try to redirect him. . . . I do not know where the element of separateness in society is to be derived unless it comes out of the earth.

Given sufficient organization to enable the farmer to express himself fully in his occupation and to secure protection, then we may well let the matter rest until his place in society develops by the operation of natural forces. We cannot allow the fundamental supplies from the common earth to be controlled by arbitrary class regulation. It would be a misfortune if the farmer were to isolate himself by making "demands" on society. I hope that the farmer's obligation may be so sensitively developed in him as to produce a better kind of mass-cohesion than we have yet known.

All these positions are capable of direct application in the incorporation of agriculture into a scheme of democracy. A brief treatment of this subject I had developed for the present book; and this treatment, with applications to particular situations now confronting us, I used recently in the vice-presidential address before the new Section M of the American Association for the Advancement of Science (published in *Science*, February 26, 1915, where the remainder of it may be found). . . .

This address, "The Forthcoming Situation in Agricultural Work," was divided into two parts: the first part dealing with public foundations was delivered as chairman of section M at Philadelphia, December 30, 1914, and the concluding part, as to non-public foundations, was given as retiring vice-president on December 28, 1915 at Columbus, Ohio. On December 30 of the latter year Bailey as president of the American Nature-Study Society, also meeting at Columbus, gave an address on "The Science-Spirit in a Democracy," and of this Dr. Aven Nelson of the University of Wyoming commented many years later—on December 30, 1936, as retiring president of the Botanical Society of America meeting at Atlantic City, New Jersey—speaking on the subject of "Discipleship":

The Columbus Meeting of the American Association in 1915 . . . was to me one of peculiar inspiration. On my return to Laramie I gave a University Assembly Address from which I quote as follows: "Dr. L. H. Bailey in his Columbus presidential address before the American Naturalists Society, revealed anew the main spring of his power. The keynote of that address was the *Sacredness of the Soil*. He came to us not as a pessimist deploring the reckless waste and destruction far too prevalent, but with the far-reaching vision of the prophet helping us to see the time when, through the loving sympathy and the intelligent cooperation of man with the laws of the All Father, the earth shall yield her present increase many fold. In his address he made us feel the holiness of the earth, the strength of the sunshine, the uplift of the birds, the fellowship of the flowers, the wild joy of the morning hours, the inspiration of the stars. He raised neither the question of *mechanism* nor of *vitalism* but his words were vibrant with that spiritual love of Nature which leaves us not far from the Kingdom. Had nothing else come into my life on this trip, except Bailey's note of hopeful optimism and inspirational vision, I should still feel that the days were well spent."

Bailey's addresses of these years, together with another on "Efficiency and Centralization," spoken before a Four-State Country Life Conference on February 7, 1916, were bound in a small volume and published at Ithaca in 1916 under the title *Ground-Levels in Democracy*. The point of new significance was the speaker's argument for the teaching of agricultural and rural subjects as cultural subjects in institutions independent of direct state support and not at once responsible to popular will. The fundamental reason advanced was the basic training for citizenship to be found in agriculture, the study of the land from which all derive sustenance. The optimism which Dr. Nelson found so radiantly expressed was epitomized by Bailey in the happy conclusion, "Our work is well under way: the morning hours are passed, and the day is well toward noon."

On December 27, 1916, the same day the American Nature-Study Society reelected him to its highest office, Bailey spoke on the subject, "The Great Lover," developing his discourse around the "great loves" of life: for another and of one's fellows; of things; and of the earth. The title of his address was taken from Rupert Brooke's poem of the same name, and from it Bailey quoted extensively, concluding:

Ye teachers, ye who stand so close to life, ye who have so firm a hold on objects and their phenomena, here is your better half. Here are the materials, and yet here is no materialism. Here are realities to your fingers, realities to your sight, realities to your nostrils. Here are things practical, abiding within the day. . . . Not long ago, freed on the bosom of the ocean, sailing across the tropics, I found the experiences of my many crowded years overwhelming me, solidifying themselves in my mind, and I wrote. What I wrote I called The Holy Earth. To judge from what I read and what they tell me, my readers seem to find in my writing only a vivid enthusiasm for the out-of-doors, and yet I attempted nothing less than a philosophy of life. Still do I feel the responsibilities of that philosophy and still shall I write. It is difficult to open the eyes to the nature in which we live.

A year ago I gave you my estimate of the contribution that the science-spirit may make to a democracy. Those remarks must have sounded strange to those who now contend that the free introduction of natural science into schools and colleges has resulted in the deterioration of character. So far as such evils have followed, it is not that science is inadequate to the highest results in human character, but rather that we have not yet learned how to use the vast treasures of fact and application that have avalanched us. We shall learn in due time that science is not merely a handmaiden to industry but that it may expand the soul.

Today, therefore, I come with poems in my hand. Today I would hear the heart beat. Today would I encourage you to every quest of science, to every minuteness and exactness of investigation, to every effort in the teaching of the young; but I would add to this the courage of the free spirit, the hope of the high look, the uttermost call of the soul. No bounds would I set to your fancy. I give you the reins, and I let you drive. I hope that the fancy which leaps from the very concrete to the very abstract will be precious to you. Fear not to prophesy.

In *The Holy Earth*, Bailey traced generally and briefly the development of public-service institutions in the rural movement—from the establishment of a United States Department of Agriculture through the enlargement of the experiment stations and their nationalization to the signing by President Wilson of the agricultural extension act of May 8, 1914. He praised the fine spirit of fraternalism between these institutions, yet without clannishness and setting a good example for all public service. The state agencies and departments were not overlooked; and, as to the extension act, the conclusion was: "No such national plan on such a scale has ever been attempted; and it almost staggers one when one even partly comprehends the tremendous consequences that in all likelihood will come of it." With an insistence that control of policies and affairs should rest in the first principle of a democracy—with the people—he spoke his belief that he had "apprehension of the tendency to make some of the agricultural work into 'projects' at Washington and elsewhere." He maintained:

If we are not careful we shall not only too much centralize the work, but we shall tie it up in perplexing red-tape, official obstacles, and bookkeeping. The merit of the projects themselves and the intentions of the officers concerned in them are not involved in what I say; I speak only of the tendency of all government to formality and to crystallization, to machine work and to armchair regulations; and even at the risk of a somewhat lower so-called "efficiency," I should prefer for such work as investigating and teaching in agriculture, a dispersion of the initiative and responsibility, letting the coordination and standardizing arise very much from conference and very little from arbitrary regulation.

The best project anywhere is a good man or woman working in a program, but unhampered.

If it is important that the administration of agricultural work be not overmuch centralized at Washington, it is equally true that it should not be too much centralized in the States. . . .

Thus far, the rural movement has been wholesomely democratic. It has been my privilege for one-third of a century to have known rather closely many of the men and women who have been instrumental in bringing the rural problem to its present stage of advancement. They have been public-minded, able, far-seeing men and women, and they have rendered an un-measurable service. The rural movement has been brought to its present state without any demand for special privilege, without bolstering by factitious legislation, and to a remarkable degree without self-seeking. It is based on a real regard for the welfare of all the people, rather than for rural people exclusively. . . .

There is a broad political significance to all this. Sooner or later the people rebel against intrenched or bureaucratic groups. Many of you know how they resist even strongly centralized departments of public instruc-tion. . . . In our rural work we are in danger of developing a piece of machinery founded on our fundamental industry; and if this ever comes about, we shall find the people organized to resist it. . . .

We want governments to be economical and efficient with funds and in the control of affairs; this also is assumed: but we must not overlook the larger issues. In all this new rural effort, we should maintain the spirit of team-work and of co-action, and not make the mistake of depending too much on the routine of centralized control.

In this country we are much criticised for the cost of government and for the supposed control of affairs by monopoly. The cost is undoubtedly too great, but it is the price we pay for the satisfaction of using democratic forms. As to the other disability, let us consider that society lies between two dangers—the danger of monopoly and the danger of bureaucracy. On the one side is the control of the necessities of life by commercial organiza-tion. On the other side is the control of the necessities of life, and even of life itself, by intrenched groups that ostensibly represent the people and which it may be impossible to dislodge. Here are the Scylla and the Charybdis between which human society must pick its devious way. . . .

Agriculture is in the foundation of the political, economic, and social structure. If we cannot develop starting-power in the background people, we cannot maintain it elsewhere. The greatness of all this rural work is to lie in the results and not in the methods that absorb so much of our energy. If agriculture cannot be democratic, then there is no democracy. . . .

The backgrounds are important. . . . We miss our destiny when we miss or forget our backgrounds. . . . The backgrounds are the great unoccupied spaces. They are the large environments in which we live but which we do not make. The backgrounds are the sky with its limitless reaches; the silences of the sea; the tundra in pallid arctic nights; the deserts with their prismatic colors; the shores that gird the planet; the vast mountains that are beyond reach; the winds, which are the universal voice in nature; the sacredness of the night; the elemental simplicity of the open fields; and the solitude of the forest. These are the facts and situations that stand at our backs, to which we adjust our civilization, and by which we measure ourselves.

The great conquest of mankind is the conquest of his natural condi-tions. . . . But even though we conquer or modify the physical conditions against which we are set, nevertheless the backgrounds will remain. . . . When you enter a real forest you enter the solitudes, you are in the un-expressed distances. You walk on the mould of years and perhaps of ages. There is no other wind like the wind of the forest; there is no odor like the odor of the forest; there is no solitude more complete; there is no song of a brook like the song of a forest brook; there is no call of a bird like that of a forest bird; there are no mysteries so deep and which seem yet to be within one's realization. . . . There is no thing in nature finer and stronger than the bark of a tree; it is a thing in place, adapted to its ends, perfect in its conformation, beautiful in its color and its form and the sweep of its contour; and every bark is peculiar to its species. . . . Man listens in the forest. He pauses in the forest. He finds himself. . . .[1] *The open fields* [came]. Here not long ago was the forest primeval. . . . Roads betook themselves into the forest, like great serpents devouring as they went. And one day, behold! the forest was gone. Farm joined farm, the village grew, the old folk fell away, new people came whose names had to be asked. . . . Here go building-stones and sand and gravel—gravel from the glaciers. Here goes the hay for ten thousand horses. Here go the wheat, and here the apples, and the animals. Here are the votes that hold the people steady.

Somewhere there is the background. Here is the background. Here things move slowly. Trees grow slowly. The streams change little from year to year, and yet they shape the surface of the earth in this hill country. In yonder fence-row the catbird has built since I was a boy, and yet I have wandered far and I have seen great changes in yonder city. The well-sweep has gone but the well is still here: the wells are gone from the city. The cows have changed in color, but still they are cows and yield their milk in season. The fields do not perish, but time eats away the city. I think all these things must be good and very good or they could not have persisted in all this change.

In the beginning! Yes, I know, it was holy then. The forces of eons shaped it: still was it holy. The forest came: still holy. Then came the open fields.

> Come over the plains to the hilltops high,
> Come over, come over and rest;
> Stay not on the plains where the soft zephyrs lie
> But come to the heights where the clouds sweep by
> And the world-round gales through the heavens fly,
> Come over, come over and rest.

> There's wonder-strong music where the storms sweep by
> Where the forests are rent and the earth-woes cry,
> There's a grand old song where things suffer and die
> And the struggle is on 'twixt the earth and sky;
> Escape your calm levels and on to the West,
> Come out with your cares to the uttermost crest,
> Come over, come over and rest.

Finally, said Bailey, another background space is the ancestral sea. "The planet is not all land, and the sea is as holy as the soil. . . . We must reckon with the sea. . . . The sea is the bosom of the earth's mysteries." The ancestral sea is the background of the planet and has contributed mightily to the human family outlook, lending zest to the great natural struggle and blessing "with abundant benedictions."

It is not the purpose of this book to rewrite a book already in published

[1] Attention is called to an interesting chapter of this book, "A Forest Background For a Reformatory," wherein Bailey tells of his study and presentation at one time of a plan to establish a state reformatory for delinquent boys where the activities would be "largely agricultural and industrial" and located in the midst of a surrounding large farm and forest area.

form. No author can give finished form, or even adequate interpretation, to another author's writing. No attempt at criticism has been assumed, as probably has been noticed. In the spirit, however, that a poem is quoted, as a brilliant paragraph or terse and beautiful statement is made use of, ample use—a "cutting"—has been made of *The Holy Earth* and other Background Books in a humble effort to present as no other media can present, the voice, the mind, the heart, the worth of Liberty Hyde Bailey—agriculturist, horticulturist, botanist, humanitarian, philosopher, and writer.

CHAPTER X

THE BAILEY HORTORIUM OF THE NEW YORK STATE COLLEGE OF AGRICULTURE AT CORNELL UNIVERSITY

ON DECEMBER 28, 1904, Bailey had given one of six addresses of a symposium on the mutation theory. Representing taxonomy, he spoke before a Philadelphia meeting of the American Society of Naturalists on "Systematic Work and Evolution."[1] Often Bailey had discussed needed reforms in this branch of plant study. He had pleaded for a systematics more thoroughly representative of the new knowledge.

Evolution was new. The generation of the early great taxonomists, of which John Torrey was the leader, had taken a practical attitude toward the immense taxonomic challenge which confronted them, and devised rigid and more or less arbitrary methods of classification. The probability is that Torrey never read Darwin's *Origin of Species*. Torrey seldom, if ever, used the garden to study the plants he systematized. Plants gathered from wild nature were brought to him to found the early great North American herbaria. But evolutionary knowledge was not taken into account. Torrey did maintain an uncommon interest in the Elgin Botanic Garden—the historic institution established by David Hosack on land which is now in the heart of New York City, between Fifth and Sixth Avenues and Forty-seventh and Fifty-first Streets. Often doubts as to the proper classification place of many plants were resolved there. Torrey was also well acquainted with "Mr. Prince" of Flushing, Long Island, who founded a historic garden, the Linnaean Botanic Garden, which embraced a pioneer American nursery and was maintained by his family for generations. It is said, "The Princes for a hundred years sold fruits in every town and hamlet, almost to every farmer, in the Hudson River Valley. The collection of tree fruits, grapes, and small fruits in their nursery included every hardy variety to be obtained in America or Europe. They made the first attempt in America to breed new varieties. . . ."[2] To this nursery is accredited an early plum growing and an early production in America of budded and grafted tree stock, especially in peaches. Nevertheless, Torrey's knowledge of the work of the Princes seems to have been largely a catalogue interest. Search has not revealed much material which confirms this inference but, reasoning from the courses of action of his followers, Gray, Engelmann, Sullivant, and others, it seems true that the garden served

[1] *Science*, new series, XXI, no. 536 (April 7, 1905), pp. 532-535.
[2] U. P. Hedrick, *A History of Agriculture of the State of New York*. Printed for the New York State Agricultural Society, 1933, pp. 381-382.

the early taxonomists more for ornamental pleasure than scientific interest. Science apparently was principally confined to the taxonomic laboratory, the herbarium. Indeed, in the instance of Sullivant, his garden was maintained by Mrs. Sullivant, and it was the garden of greatest interest in the city of his residence. On April 10, 1845, Sullivant became a vice president of the Columbus, Ohio, Horticultural Society, one of the first, if not the first, organizations of its kind in the Middle West and among the earliest of the entire country. Recently the organization celebrated the one hundredth anniversary of its founding. Charles Leo Lesquereux had a garden, a rose garden, in which he delighted to walk during the evenings. Though strewn with paleobotanic specimens, his garden was not used to establish any relations between the floras of the past and present; at least, if he did, such a practice must have been only occasional. Furthermore, Lesquereux accepted in large part the conclusions of Darwin, being in disagreement on the subject of evolution with his great and close friend Louis Agassiz. The greatness of Gray, moreover, may be strongly argued in this particular. As Gray took up study and elaboration of the evolution hypothesis, more and more he went to the Harvard Botanic Garden and studied the plants in growth and cultivation. Scientific botanical gardens located at institutions of learning and research spread from the Atlantic to Pacific coasts and from Florida and the Gulf of Mexico states far north into Canada. At the University of California, for instance, was set out in the early 1890's a garden of native plants. In middle United States the Missouri Botanical Garden was developed, as Engelmann wished, with scientific as well as ornamental objectives in view. Today every well equipped botanical and horticultural department has greenhouse, arboreta, gardens, and laboratory facilities to enable the student to learn to investigate living plant material as thoroughly as dried herbarium specimens. Elder scientists of this generation with the fervor of missionaries vested their profession with the attributes of a solemn, sacred obligation to posterity. Marvels of modern research were made possible.

Bailey in his address, "Systematic Work and Evolution," argued that an ideal taxonomy would make little or no distinction between "natural" and "artificial" forms, and that the type of a species should be its real phylogenetic or biological type rather than the first specimen that happened to be named. "Many of us," he said, "feel that the present method of nomenclature and description will be outgrown, for these methods are made for the herbarium and the museum, rather than for the field. . . ." Even as botanists were unfamiliar with the agricultural and horticultural fields, so the gardener was unfamiliar with the herbarium. The botanist defined his concept of species largely on a

The Bailey Hortorium 431

morphological basis, whereas the gardener proceeded largely on the physiological determinants which Bailey believed nearer the truth. "I have no intention of proposing any new plan of nomenclature—that would only amuse you. I merely feel, as you do," he continued, "that a change is imminent. Perhaps we shall hold to our main species—groups for history's sake, and then designate minor groups in terms of their qualities. If we find it to be true that there are fluctuating varieties and mutations of different geneses, then we must assuredly represent these facts in nomenclature and taxonomy. . . . The question really comes to this—Shall we know two kinds of species, one of taxonomy and one of biology?" Through the years a settled solution of this inquiry has baffled taxonomists, particularly as more knowledge of plant functions and their correlations, of relative and comparative plant characters, became available.

Under Bailey's administration as dean and director of the New York State College of Agriculture and its experiment station, studies were pursued with a view to standardizing systematically American horticultural varieties. Embraced within the objectives were determinations of the horticultural status and practical value of the varieties. At times, the work was done cooperatively with another institution, as, for example, a study of bean growing begun in the summer of 1902 in conjunction with the United States Department of Agriculture. For three years exhaustive variety tests were conducted; minute botanical descriptions of good varieties made; photographs of the entire plant, the leaf, the pod (dorsal, side view, and cross section) and the dry seed, taken. In 1905 a monographic study of the genus Phaseolus was commenced by C. D. Jarvis who had had charge of the work. When in 1908 he published an experiment station bulletin, "American Varieties of Beans," he explained the enterprise's history in its preface:

> Studies of garden beans at the Cornell University Experiment Station have covered a period of more than ten years. They were commenced by Professor L. H. Bailey, who published two bulletins (Nos. 87 and 115) upon Lima beans. About this time cooperative studies were undertaken with Messrs. N. B. Keeney & Son, Le Roy, N.Y. These investigations were instituted by Professor Bailey and were continued for two years by the writer. . . .

Referring then to the work at Cornell carried on in preparation for his doctoral thesis, the collaborations with the United States Bureau of Plant Industry, and continued studies in Connecticut, Jarvis explained the purpose of his bulletin of the year 1908:

> The accompanying bulletin then represents a mass of information accumulated over a considerable period. It is an attempt to present a correct nomenclature and a key to the present-day varieties of beans based upon

the form and color of the fresh seed. How useful the key will be in determin- ing old seed will of course depend upon the stability of the markings. Fresh seed is what all seedsmen and planters should be interested in. The com- mercial and field aspects of bean growing have been already treated by the Experiment Station. This bulletin is not intended for general distribution, but rather to supply the bean fancier with technically accurate information of immediate value and service. . . .

This was but one illustration of a practical service to science and the trades which Bailey early foresaw could be performed by exact, scien- tifically conducted taxonomic studies. Many such studies in other col- leges and stations, at Washington, and by individuals—not confined to vegetables but including also pomological and floricultural subjects— had been or were being completed.

On April 23, 1915, Bailey read a discourse entitled, "Some Present Needs in Systematic Botany," before the American Philosophical So- ciety. There he urged subordinating the nomenclatural questions in the interest of giving all an equal chance to study plants—an imperative necessity in a democratic nation. Free of hindrances and arbitary domi- nation by central authorities, the public has real rights in the names of plants. Furthermore, he urged that a conservative attitude toward ge- neric boundaries be maintained and that search be directed toward "the ultimate specific units—so far as there are such units" to realize a truth- ful presentation of the vegetable kingdom while at the same time avoid- ing vast changes in nomenclature. Most especially, he pressed on his audience his belief "that a few groups [should] be worked out very carefully by growing the plants under observation and as far as pos- sible under conditions of control and always, of course, in comparison with living feral material. Such studies," he admitted, "might require some years, even in a relatively small group; very good—the results would be all the more convincing. If a half dozen groups could be worked over in this way, with discussion of the living material by standing committees of some recognized association," he argued, "we should very likely arrive at a basis of judgment such as the present collecting and incidental field notation and indoor study of dried ma- terial can never give us. . . ." Incorporation of plant-life history studies and a goal projected toward realizing synthetic rather than analytic species-values were recommended. The greatest need of all in systematic botany, however, was common understanding which implied a need of substantial agreement on some of the matters which were perplexing all systematic workers.

There was outlined a definite program which combined systematic and experimental work, there was a program dealing with certain phases of the intermediate field between taxonomy and plant genetics. Two

Bailey along the Demerara, British Guiana, 1922

years later, on November 20, 1917, Bailey had occasion to deliver another paper, this time read before the National Academy of Sciences when made an Academy member, on the subject, "The Modern Systematist." "In everything," commented Bailey, "we are rapidly becoming particularists. In the time of Gray we studied plants as aggregates, trying to make them match something else; now we study them as segregates, trying to make them differ from everything else." This diversity in process, he believed, accounted for extensions in Oenothera, Carex, Rubus, Malus, Crataegus, and other genera. Bailey refused to commend those persons who divided and redivided minutely, "and who would carry descriptive botany to such a point of refinement that only the close specialist can know the forms. Under such circumstances," he urged, "systematic work defeats its own ends. . . . Every large or variable group needs to be reworked at least every twenty-five years. . . . We must outgrow the idea that there is any finality in even the best monograph." Real systematic work, more than cataloguing, sorting, or making bibliographies, more than skill in identifying plants with a knowledge of evolution and plant geography, demanded a highly trained scientist. Nowhere was the need of systematic scientific skill more apparent than in the cultivated flora. With respect to it, the treatment was particularly traditional. Indeed, said Bailey, the cultivated plants were somewhat taken for granted, whereas critical study had shown many genera contain new species that had gone all these years unrecognized. Citing instances, he characterized a present need to be the collection of cultivated plants in their various forms from many localities and dealers, which collections should be assembled "in precisely the same spirit in which feral plants are taken for herbaria." Without such sources, neither could systematology of the plants be thoroughly understood, nor could the interests of students of heredity be properly subserved. Even among recent American plant introductions, systematic confusion already existed, as shown in the velvet-beans grown in the southernmost states. The encouraging fact, however, was that Americans had begun to respond to the need for studies in the cultivated flora. As illustrious examples of work being done he pointed to that of Joseph Nelson Rose in Cactaceae; Walter T. Swingle in Citrus; Alfred Rehder in Wisteria, Oriental Pyrus; to the work in Japanese cherries done by the great naturalist explorer of western China, E. H. Wilson; and to a work in the custard-apple family, or Annonaceae, plants mostly grown in the tropics, systematized by a ship-paymaster whose hobby was botany, one W. E. Safford.[2a] "It is not too much to say," said Bailey, "that any of

[2a] See the *Journal of Heredity* (Organ of the American Genetic Association, Washington, D.C.), XVII, 10 (October, 1926), pp. 365-367, concerning William Edwin Safford.

the important groups of cultivated plants will fall to pieces as soon as touched by the competent modern systematist." Many groups had been brought into cultivation from wild stock, some in recent years, as, for instance, the horticultural blackberries. In Primula the *Cyclopedia of American Horticulture* of 1901 had described twenty-seven species. By 1916, when the *Standard Cyclopedia* had been published, 200 descriptions were required for the same group. Some groups, as, for example, Coleus, suffered from almost a complete destitution of record, at least, as to a record adequate for modern studies. The day had arrived when the horticultural systematist was a specialist and when there was a manifest need for more herbaria and growing collections strong in special lines.

During this same year, 1917, Bailey had inaugurated a large-scale career as a plant explorer. He had gone to China. On the evening of January 12, as Bailey sat at his residence working at a new study, he heard a chorus of voices singing on the front lawn the Cornell alma mater song. Quickly he went to the door and there beheld two hundred members of the faculty of the college of agriculture, and their wives, come to wish him and his family luck and happiness on his journey to the Orient which was to include travel in China and Japan—the object of each country's visit being horticultural research. Bailey invited the guests into his home and, after social exchanges lasting the first part of the evening, Acting Dean Mann presented him with a scroll signed by all members of the party and reading, "We desire to express again our gratitude for the great work you did while with us. The inspiration of your leadership is an unfading memory. We extend our best wishes for the success of the work you now have in hand. Our hearts go with you and your family. A happy voyage, and a welcome back again." This event was not the first time a faculty group, and their wives, had visited the Baileys' Sage Place residence.

On June 6, 1908, Dr. and Mrs. Bailey's twenty-fifth wedding anniversary, sixty or more members of the instructing and investigating staff of the college, and their wives, had gathered at the corner of Stewart Avenue and State Street and gone in a body to the Bailey home. There were presented, at that time, another scroll signed by all members of the agricultural college faculty and a candelabrum of five lights— each light symbolic: the first representing Bailey's literary achievements; the second, his accomplishments as educator; the third, his administrative talent; the fourth, his ability as investigator including rare powers of generalization and formulation of principles and laws of science and life; and the fifth, his open hearth, good cheer, and warm welcome accorded faculty and students, a tribute which must have been particularly reminiscent of his traditional open house held Sunday evenings. The whole, of course, symbolized the total man, the great humanitarian who helped more than one student through turbulent or vicissitudinous years. On these pleasant Sunday evenings, Bailey often read his own poetry. His poems were so beloved by the students that on their initiative a volume of them was gathered together and published in 1907 by *Cornell Countryman*.[3]

Again, in 1916, the New York publishing house, Charles Scribner's Sons, published a volume of Bailey's poetry styled *Wind and Weather*, the second of the Background Books. *Cornell Countryman* praised this, not only in its review but also in an editorial. The opening sentences of the review read: "There was a time when Bailey verse constituted an informal but important part of a course in Agriculture here at Cornell. The students of that day heard it read on Sunday evenings at the Dean's; they read it for themselves in the *Rural School Leaflets* and in *The Countryman*. They liked it; it sang the things they felt within and strived toward. The poems they particularly liked they copied down and learned by heart."

Before Bailey's departure for the Pacific coast and China, the Ithaca Board of Commerce, of which he was vice-president, arranged a dinner in his honor. On the evening of January 29, one-hundred-and-fifty friends dined at the Ithaca Hotel and R. B. Williams, serving as toastmaster, first paid tribute to Bailey's attainments as student, teacher, scientist, citizen, poet, humanitarian, and nature lover. Then he introduced Reverend Dr. John A. MacIntosh who said:

We congratulate ourselves tonight on having in our midst an idealist who can walk with the kings of education, but who has not lost the common touch.

When I first came to Ithaca I was present in the college of agriculture one time when the director was addressing a gathering of short course students. He pictured to them an imaginary youth who wanted to do something to improve the community in which he lived. To that youth the speaker said, "Down that road and over the hill there is an old man who needs companionship. Go to him. Don't go in an automobile. Don't go in a buggy. Walk, and get the feel of the road." I am not surprised that this man who tells us to keep our feet on the ground has written a book called "The Holy Earth."

Dr. W. H. Jordan, director of the New York Agricultural Experiment Station at Geneva, followed, saying:

It is to Doctor Bailey more than to any living man that the State of New York owes its college of agriculture. He has accomplished this work because of his clear vision of what ought to be created as an educational agency and because he has been a source of inspiration. But Dr. Bailey's vision has not been confined to the walls of a college. He has seen with great clearness

[3] Done into a booklet by The Roycrofters, at their shop, which is in East Aurora, N.Y., mcmvii.

the problems of the open country, and I believe no man in the United States has done as much as he toward calling attention to those problems and the great need of the social readjustment of the rural people.

But it is to his leadership in the great problems of agricultural education and research that we owe him most. His voice and his pen have been potent during this formative period. His philosophy of education has not been that of the narrow dollar-and-cents type, but he has believed that the problems involved were human problems and that in educating young men and women for service in vocational life we must not forget their human aspirations and relations.

Senator E. C. Stewart also spoke, and also Acting Dean Mann. Senator Stewart read tributes to Bailey from Anna Botsford Comstock, President Schurman, former President Andrew D. White, Isaac Phillips Roberts, Mr. Justice Hughes, Colonel Roosevelt. Dean A. W. Smith of Sibley College of Engineering of Cornell University wrote a poem entitled, "Farewell to Dr. Bailey."

Bailey went 1,000 miles into the interior of central China—in the Yangtze River region and in parts of the provinces of Hupeh and Honan. With him was a young Chinese medical student. Bailey learned, when he contracted dysentery from which he later satisfactorily recovered, that the student's medical learning was only a kind of mummery. At the outset it should be said that Bailey's travel experiences—perilous many times, amusing at others, and all intensely interesting—must become someday parts of another story—a book of heroic travel for the sole objective of increasing man's knowledge of the world's plant resources. Neither fairness to the stories nor space permit their complete inclusion in this book. To illustrate, Bailey slept many nights in Taoist temples, far in the China interior, among beggar monks, who often locked him in rooms to protect him against the dangers of wild dogs. The important fact for our purposes is that after many months of exploring, utilizing almost every mode of conveyance in that ancient, mysterious, and generally unknown land, he returned with many plant species new to science and a rich harvest of general collections. Also, even while in China, in the land area much of which is covered by water for rice fields and a crude, primitive agriculture, he kept the promise of his youth to have a garden every year. Near the town of Zaukadoo, practically a part of Shanghai, Bailey rented a plot of land, procured seeds and roots from Chinese stores and gardens, and each morning had a Chinese boatman row him across the river to it. Returning to the United States, on August 30, 1917, he wrote Robinson of the Gray Herbarium:

I am glad to find on my table as I return from China a copy of your great monograph of Brickellia. I am glad to see the appearance of the memoirs. I congratulate you on this piece of work. It is one of my greatest ambitions to undertake a monograph of this character. . . .

He immediately began work with his plant materials. He wrote Dr. M. L. Fernald of the same institution October 16, "I am glad that you have the courage to describe a new species of Vitis from New England. I am convinced that the American material, particularly in the eastern states, needs to be carefully restudied. . . ." And on October 26, "It is big sport to get back to my herbarium work after so many years wandering in the wilderness. Among other things, I am mounting up a lot of accumulated Carex," and additionally he had begun the assortment of his China collections, ferns of which he offered a few days later to someone suggested by that institution. In December Bailey spoke at Ithaca at a food saving rally, taking as his subject, "The Food We Eat," and quoting Socrates' words, "How many things there are in the world that I do not want."

During 1918 were published two more of the Background Books. Bailey confessed these books elaborated further many ideas expressed in *The Holy Earth*. Sturgis and Walton Company of New York published *Universal Service, the Hope of Humanity* in which, prompted by the situation of World War I, Bailey developed the antithetical principles of enmity and fellow service. Both were inextricably bound with the rural and urban condition. In May, 1917, *Cornell Countryman* printed Bailey's prognostication of the next decade of American Country Life. Progress would emanate to heal all suffering:

Behind all our civilization lies the rural condition. The ultimate foundation of society is the land. As the land-people live and have their being, so will our civic and social life be conditioned and sustained. Beyond all estimate is the character of this background people. Yesterday they lived as individuals. Today they begin to be effective economic units, finding the ways for satisfactory financial support, measuring themselves against commercial interests, eliminating wasteful and incompetent methods and systems. Tomorrow they will find a new individualism and a higher range of universal service.

The Comstock Publishing Company of Ithaca produced *What Is Democracy?* in which with great force Bailey reasoned that democracy is not a form of government—no more than religion is a form of worship. It is primarily a sentiment, motivated by individualism on one hand and voluntary public service on the other. Only as responsibility, and not freedom, only as cooperation, and not competition, only as service, become dominating forces can a perfected expression tantamount to a religion be realized as man's earthly destiny. In this book, the author discussed the "permanent agriculture" of China which in his opinion had become a stationary agriculture with "no prospect of advancement and progress for the race as a whole, and no real democracy." A brilliant and nationally known agriculturist, reading this book, stated that Bailey had written it by the fireside, with his boots off. *Cornell Countryman*,[4] in its review, replied, "Doctor Bailey may have written this book without his boots on, but his feet touched the earth—his 'holy earth'—at all times."

In November, 1918, was presented the first volume of a service performed for American agriculture by Bailey, the publication of *Rus* which translated from the Latin means "rural": the rural uplook service; a preliminary attempt to register the rural leadership in the United States and Canada. After the authors had spent years gathering names from college lists, experiment station records, contributions to agricultural journals and papers, and other media, the persons were written to and asked for data concerning their work and themselves. The names and data of those replying were incorporated in a series of volumes which by the fourth issue in 1930 contained 6,881 biographical entries. That same year Bailey prepared for the American Association of Nurserymen a small pamphlet on "Home Grounds, their Planning and Planting." In 1920 was to be published *The School-Book of Farming*; a text for the elementary schools, homes and clubs, another member of The Rural Text Book Series edited by Bailey and published by the Macmillan Company, and of this book Bailey was himself the author. Current still and recently republished were *The Pruning Manual, The Principles of Vegetable-Gardening, The Standard Cyclopedia of Horticulture*, and *The Principles of Agriculture*, the last of which had reached its twenty-sixth edition. In 1920 also reappeared *The Nursery-Manual*. However, the most important event of the year 1920 was the appearance of the first of Bailey's studies, *Gentes Herbarum*, or kinds of plants, initiated with a monographic study, "Plantae chinenses," devoted to the study of his plant collections in China.

In the March 29, 1918, issue of *Science*[5] had appeared an article by Bailey on "The Indigen and Cultigen." He proposed that the term "indigen" should be used to designate species of known and recognized occurrence in nature, and the term "cultigen" to designate domesticated groups with equally good specific characters but of which the origin and nativity were unknown. On May 18 he wrote Robinson:

Very much obliged to you for your reaction on my article on the Indigen and the Cultigen. It gives me some very interesting suggestions.

One of the points I tried to make in my paper was the fact that we cannot establish these gentes on the basis of an herbarium "type." It is quite impossible to typify the cultivated canna, any more than it is Zea Mays, Triticum sativum, Oryza sativa and any number of other things. We must have names for groups. I see no other way. The real question is, therefore,

[4] xvii, 2 (November 1919), pp. 74-75.   [5] *Science*, new series, xlvii, pp. 306-308.

whether it will be allowable for us to return to the Linnean system with cultivated plants.

This is not at all a question of using a word when the idea is lacking. The idea is a very real and visible one in the case of the cultivated canna. An idea does not need to be represented in a type, in the botanical sense.

I am agreed that we should have herbaria representing cultivated plants. I am trying to build up such a collection. I think its value, however, will be rather more for purposes of description, record, and information on variation, than as a repository of "types" of cultigens that might be described at this day. I think that "the common cultivated canna" can be much more easily visualized than a type specimen representing a great line of variables. Of course I think that names for cultigens should be given with much caution and only when other means cannot be employed; yet I see no reason why a name should not be given to a group rather than to a type specimen when that group is well known and when it is not likely to be confused with any other group. If one attempted to give names to the different horticultural forms of garden cannas, he would find himself in the same predicament as did Sweet in his great monograph of the Pelargoniums. The names that he applied cannot be used now because many or most of the old garden forms are obsolete. His names, therefore, are only historically interesting and cannot even be cited as synonyms.

The problem before me is a very insistent and practical one and I should like to get your advice on it. I always prize your advice in these matters. I am working on a manual of cultivated plants: what shall I do with the garden canna? How shall I treat it?

On June 3, after receiving Robinson's reply, Bailey wrote again:

Your conception of the way in which I might treat the garden Canna is essentially that at which I have arrived. . . .

I am interested in your suggestion of names. I have been rather given to the names "hortorum" and "domesticum," as indicating clearly that they are cultivated things. . . . I rather like [Andreas Voss's] use of the word "cultorum," as in Delphinium cultorum. In some cases possibly we might use "artificialis" although as a matter of fact these things may not be artificial in the ordinary sense. They may be just as natural as certain wild groups. One difficulty is that the "type" of a new species may not be a biotype. It may be only an aberrant or outlying form or it may itself be a hybrid for aught anyone knows.

I agree with you fully that any such newly made name ought to be reinforced by specimens in an herbarium. Descriptions ought to have reference to plants rather than merely to an indefinite horticultural conception. These specimens could hardly be types in the strict botanical sense, however. I am inclined to think we are at the beginning of a new method of treating these horticultural things, in such a way as to make them more or less definite, to give them recognized standing, and to prevent the duplicate or even antagonistic practices of botanists and horticulturists.

On June 25, 1919, the degree of doctor of letters was conferred on Bailey by the University of Vermont at its commencement exercises. On this occasion he was also the speaker.

Bailey still clung to the belief that, so far as methodology in research was concerned, botany and horticulture should work as partners. With his collections from China and Japan he wanted to give a comprehensive picture of the Urasian flora. By going to Cambridge and studying several months he could both enjoyably renew years of his youth and lay foundations systematically for much of his future contemplated horticultural work; at least, he could be certain there would be no working at cross purposes. Before him were two or three months more of work at Ithaca. On August 26, 1918, he had written to Robinson:

If things come right I hope to be able to spend some time late this autumn and winter at the Gray and the Arnold working up my Chinese collection and a good number of other things. I do not wish to make my plans too definitely until I have taken the matter up with you to see whether I would be in the way if I came to the Gray or whether there would be a window in one of your rooms or basements where I could do my work. I should try not to make any trouble.

One of the difficulties in my getting away is the fact that Mrs. Bailey is deeply engaged in Red Cross work here and she would not feel right if she went to Cambridge to board and did not put her time into some war work. I remember that Mrs. Robinson was engaged in Red Cross work when I was at your home. Perhaps Mrs. Robinson would know whether there would be any opportunity for Mrs. Bailey to put in her time, or at least a good part of it, in Red Cross work in Cambridge or Boston if we were to come. I assumed that Mrs. Robinson was engaged in the Red Cross work in Cambridge. Of course my wife wants nothing whatever to do with the management, but merely wishes to work. Here she has been taking up any and all pieces of work that they have given her to do.

The Baileys went to Cambridge in the autumn and took a temporary address in Cambridge at 35 Concord Avenue. While there, part of Bailey's time was spent collaborating with William Gilson Farlow and Roland Thaxter in preparing a biographical memoir of George Francis Atkinson, who had died earlier that year. The memoir was published in the July, 1919, issue of the *American Journal of Botany*. But, except for this, all of Bailey's energies were spent in studying and systematizing his Asiatic collections. Returning to Ithaca, on February 19, 1919, he wrote Dr. Farlow, "My winter at Cambridge was not only a profitable one for me but was also delightful. No small part of my satisfaction was due to the fact that I had an opportunity to renew the acquaintanceship with you and the other botanists." About the middle of February, Bailey reached a point in his work which made evident the necessity of consulting the large scientific collections abroad, particularly the botanical material at Kew, the British Museum, the Edinburgh Botanical Garden, and several points on the continent. On account of early post-war conditions, arranging for passports was difficult. He returned to Ithaca and on February 27 wrote Robinson: "The winter at

Cambridge was a delight to all of us, and it was more profitable to me in my work than I had even anticipated. My herbarium work is proceeding again at full swing. As you know the general needs of systematic botany in this country, I shall appreciate any suggestions you wish to make me at any time as to the best disposition that may eventually be made of a collection like mine." By March 31 he had this to say: "I have now mounted all my Chinese things except the fifty or so residua that must be looked up abroad." And by April 10 he was writing: "I remember your speaking to me about the Exsiccatae Grayanae. I should prize the sets very much and could mount them at any time. I am growing hundreds of things this year of cultivated plants from many parts of the world, and I can make specimens in exchange for you. . . . I have mounted about 2000 sheets since I returned and the process still goes on rapidly." That summer Bailey and his family went to Europe, visiting, as planned, Kew, Edinburgh, Copenhagen, and many other places.

On September 4, 1919, he wrote to Robinson an account of his journey:

I have not forgotten my promise to write you about my pilgrimage. It is now closed, except getting home. Sailings from Great Britain are impossible before winter and are even then doubtful. Therefore I got a sailing from Copenhagen on the 12th (Frederick VIII). It is impossible to get to Denmark now except via Norway or Sweden, and I sail for Sweden tomorrow. Unfortunately I shall have neither time nor permission to visit Stockholm or Upsala.

I landed at Liverpool July 20, and until a week ago have been at Kew, with two visits to the National Herbarium. For the last 3 days I have been at Edinburgh, and was glad to see the herbarium of Léveillé which has just been acquired there, complete. It is in good condition and perfect order, so that it may be consulted readily although it will be considerable time before it is incorporated in the Edinburgh collections. W. M. Smith went to France to get it. The specimens are excellent, about 40,000 of them. It was purchased for the Gardens by a friend. Professor Balfour is deep in Chinese Primulas and Rho[do]dendrons. It is marvellous what he has. He has described nearly 200 rhod[od]endrons and has probably as many more. They are growing many of the S[outh] W[estern] China things with great success. The herbarium and laboratories are much overcrowded, but one gets the impression that things are decidedly on the move there. It is too bad the U[nited] S[tates] is not sharing in some of these great botanical explorations.

At Kew all is normal. Sir David Prain, Mr. Skan, Rolfe, Hutchinson, N. E. Brown (retired), Sprague, C. H. Wright, and others are hard at work. Mr. Ridley is working on his Straits Settlement things, and Mr. Gamble was there part of the time on his Madras flora, the third part of which is going into type. Dr. Stapf is well, but was on his vacation and I saw little of him. There was some pressure against him from the townspeople, but his staff stood solidly behind him and he had no real difficulty.

At the National Herbarium, Dr. Rendle is well and active, as is also E. G. Baker. I called on Mr. Baker's father (J. G.), and found him mentally alert although physically broken. I had a good visit with Arthur Bennett, the "Pot" man, and found him keen, interested and active although far along in the 70's. Other persons I met, collecting and elsewhere, and my trip has been profitable and most enjoyable. Several times they spoke of Mr. Blake's calls at the herbarium and spoke very highly of him. I am the first American who has come over specially to Kew since the War.

I have got together some 800 specimens, and several hundred more will follow. I was able to purchase a specially good collection of British Rubi (about 150 kinds) with the authentication of William Moyle Rogers, the best living authority on the genus. Mr. Rogers is now 85 and infirm, and he referred me to Mr. Riddelsdel on whom his mantle has fallen and of whom I got the specimens. As I had already arranged for Rubi named by Sudré, I feel that I shall be well reinforced on the W[estern] European species, particularly as Dr. Focke long ago gave me an interesting set. I have some interesting material in several groups.

I found little information on continental botanists. No one seemed to know of any loss in the number due to the War. Dr. Rendle is interested, as you know, in the forthcoming Congress. . . . I presume the Congress cannot be held before 1921. The country is certainly not ready for visitors.

Although considerable exception is taken to some of the American systematic work, yet I was much pleased with the very high regard in which most of it is held.

I trust that all is going well with you. If I can assist in getting material for you, please let me try.

By October 27 Bailey was again in Ithaca and he supplemented his letter:

. . . I lost my sailing from Copenhagen because of strikes and I had two weeks in Denmark. I was much interested to get in touch with the botanists there and to spend some time in the herbarium. I met Raunkiaer, Christensen, Paulsen, Rosenvinge, Lange, Ostenfeld, and others. I went back to Sweden and up to Norway and sailed from Christiania. I had a good visit with Dr. Wille and Dr. Lynge there. The new botanical quarters in Christiania are occupied and are very good. . . .

Specimens are piling on me rapidly now and I can hardly keep up with them.

I have a very few extra specimens of Chinese things, some of them new species, and I am sending them to you today for the herbarium.

By another letter Bailey pleaded with Robinson not to carry out a projected plan to put the Harvard Botanic Garden under the Bussey administration. "The garden," he urged, "ought to be put under a resident directorate and radically changed in its purpose and character. Harvard has an opportunity to do a distinct piece of work here, and I trust it will not miss the chance." Bailey had no opposition to anything which made for agricultural advancement; quite the contrary, he still gave his vigorous energies to agricultural work. However, the garden, as the living plant, was to him the heart and arterial strength of horticulture and botany. Always conscious of the garden's great historical status, he sought to preserve its integrity in perpetuity—whether concern was for the Harvard garden, or any other garden.

In 1917 there had been organized at Philadelphia the American Association for Agricultural Legislation, an institution dedicated to agricultural research. It was an expert advisory institution which frowned on the use of propaganda, a unifying and coordinating agency by which it was hoped that contradictions and confusions in agriculture might be removed and standardization of laws governing American agriculture might be obtained. It was not organized as a class association. It carried with it no political connotation, maintained no lobby. Only incidentally were remedial measures by special legislation contemplated. Confessedly it was an organization which sought to help the farmer by research. If legislative measures had to be resorted to, its aim was to afford "scientific preparation for sound agricultural legislation." A precedent for its establishment was found in the American Association for Labor Legislation. Its methods were demonstrated by its bulletins: such as its first contribution, a study on the private colonization of land by Dr. Ely, by subsequent papers on tenancy by Ely, Spillman, Galpin, and Stewart, and by a suggestive catalogue of rural, social, and economic problems compiled by Galpin and Cox. Annual reports, a journal, state and local chapters—an example was afforded by a Texas association—study programs, establishment of relations with educational institutions, et cetera, were held in view. It was a concrete realization of an organized program for which Bailey had long stood. And Bailey became one of its first presidents. On December 29, 1919, at Chicago, he delivered his presidential address, "Field and Purpose of the American Association for Agricultural Legislation." He reminded his audience that the society's nativity had been in the city of brotherly love. He called attention to its conceptions, history, and accomplishments, and observed:

The past generation has been known by the domination of the financial and corporate interests. The present generation is known by the emergence of labor organizations. The coming generation will see the rise of the farmer. . . . If we are to have investigations of subjects likely to eventuate into enacted law, we must arrive at a philosophy of agriculture and rural life, and the investigators must be trained persons in the broadest sense. We must combine the historical and scientific methods, and be capable to express ourselves in legal form. The Association should stand for the welfare of the farmer in the interest of society. . . . The investigators should have real experience of agriculture. . . .

The need, therefore, was for an intelligent agency of guidance, which would encourage study of problems affecting agriculture and rural life, and the association was to supply that need. On American history, he said,

At this point we are confronted by two theories of the development of society. One theory assumes that progress is made by war between factions or sides, one part making drives on another part and seeking for victory. The other theory assumes that progress should be, on the whole, an orderly process and proceed in a more or less consistent evolution. In the former theory, advancement depends on strife; in the latter it depends on cooperation and public service. It may be true that partisanship has effected much of our progression, but we are now ready to ask whether henceforth we should not transfer to the other basis.

Bailey regarded the farmer no longer as a small feudal master in a stratum or range by himself. Although the farmer was still an individual, he saw no reason to fear farmer solidarity expressed in a political class, for, very likely, such would and could never be. Bailey was never a believer in farm blocs or like political agencies. In an address made before the Florida State Horticultural Society in 1925 on "The Personality Phase of the Food-Production Program," he affirmed with great strength that, "The remedies for our agricultural distresses lie very little in direct legislation." Critical problems of population-increase stimulated by industrialism and accompanying new food production problems confronted America. He admitted, "We are coming to be governed by organization, resulting in a new kind of politics; we witness something like a recrudescence of medieval guilds. . . . We may deplore the existence of farm blocs, but we must remember that we have been controlled by a bloc, represented in commerce and tariff, and one bloc is as fair as another." Nevertheless, Bailey insisted, as he always had, that the great future of agriculture and country life lay "in energetic production of supplies for food, shelter, clothing and the arts. . . . Agriculture," he maintained, "is still based on the soil, and not on any philosophy of political protest or social unrest and dissatisfaction." Bailey saw danger in too much reliance on statistics. Gain and loss, and economics alone, were not regarded "the essential concern of aspiring humanity. Civilization cannot maintain itself if the care of the soil is to be relegated to cheap men. If farming settles into the small contentions of so many of the industries, we shall face disaster, for the fundamental consideration of mankind is to keep the earth fit."

During the summer of 1920, "Plantae chinenses," the first issue of *Gentes Herbarum*, made its appearance to the great pleasure of botanists and horticulturists alike. A week of the winter previous was spent in the "Puget Sound country, where the early spring flowers were out and the farmers were plowing." On August 10 he wrote Robinson:

My herbarium is growing rapidly these days, much to my satisfaction. I have purchased in England two moss exsiccatae and also from Germany a very good set of about 1200 numbers of Baenitz's Herbarium Dendrologicum. I have a lot of European material coming in this year, as well as considerable from the Pacific Coast region. It is interesting to see a little herbarium like this grow. . . .

The last of November the Baileys sailed for Trinidad and Venezuela from where Bailey wrote Robinson on January 20, 1921 :

We have had a pleasant and profitable month at Caracas, and have put about 1100 numbers to press. Within the confines of a boarding-house we cannot pay much attention to making duplicates, but of many things I have taken two or three specimens. There are a few Eupatoriums and Mikanias hereabouts, and I have remembered you with specimens, although Mr. Pittier tells me he has supplied you with them. I suppose they are all common and well known things.

I have a plan for a real botanical exploration in a certain region in Eastern Venezuela, and shall do my best to come back to it. Probably I shall not cross the llanos to the Orinoco as the dry season is well on and that country will be parched by the time I could reach it. But I hope to enter the river from the sea.

This trip will enable me to supply many blanks in my little herbarium, particularly in some of the cultivated things.

As my plans progress, I shall let you know about them. Mrs. B[ailey] (who has much enjoyed Caracas) will probably remain in Trinidad. At all events, she will not return to Venezuela. I hope the daughter may come back with me. She is an excellent scout and companion, and a good collector.

On March 7, from Ciudad Bolivar, Bailey wrote again, saying Miss Ethel and he had had "a very interesting collecting trip." They had got more than 600 numbers, although, because of the dry season, they had hoped for no more than 200. "We have been specially interested in the llanos," he said, notwithstanding the fact that fire had swept parts of them, and announced that at Trinidad, where they were going to rejoin Mrs. Bailey, they had spent three weeks and had "put in a few hundred things, getting many palms amongst them." On March 15, at Port of Spain, Trinidad, Bailey wrote Dr. Wiegand of Cornell:

As our collecting season ends today, I thought you might be interested in a brief account of the results. The young woman and myself have recently returned from the Orinoco country (Mrs. B. having been sitting on Trinidad). We went about 400 miles up the River. The country there is now very dry and the scant forests are in places as bare as winter. Many woody things in leaf but no flowers or fruit we did not attempt to get, for they would remain only bold puzzles from a region from which apparently no collections have been taken. However, we got nearly 700 numbers of identifiable stuff, under conditions of oppressive heat. In the Caracas region we got more than 1200 numbers. Our Venezuelan things run, therefore, more than 1900. In Trinidad we have taken a few hundred, and the collection here is rich in palm material. Altogether the scout and myself think we shall have a very interesting addition to make to our little herbarium.

Of course our numbers include cultivated things, and these will be of special value to me. It is much more work to get the cultivated things than the wild ones.

We have had good health and an enjoyable winter. We are now ready for home. . . .

On April 16 the party reached Ithaca with a "mountain of work" before them. The only disappointment to Bailey was that they had been unable to get to Colonia Tovar and to the towns and mountains in the hinterland from Cumanà, a great botanically unexplored mountainous region between 8,000 and 9,000 feet high. "As it is," however, he told Robinson, "we have enough to keep us busy for the next two or three years. We are now sorting our material into piles and the work ahead of us looks very heavy."

December 7, 8, and 9, 1921, Bailey presided as president of the American Pomological Society at its thirty-eighth convention, held in Moose Hall, at Toledo, Ohio. At this convention, "for his notable contributions to horticulture and his work for the Society," Bailey was awarded the Marshall P. Wilder silver medal by the committee composed of J. H. Gourley and L. R. Taft. In his acceptance Bailey, deeply moved, said:

I wish to say that I appreciate this very much. It so happens that I have been the recipient of certain medals and diplomas both from this country and abroad, and the one I prize most is the Wilder Medal which I received in 1885 for an exhibit of native nuts and fruits, and with this medal, coming at the last of my work, it is difficult to say which I will prize the more. I very much appreciate this action.

Marshall P. Wilder was the great pomological authority of his day, instrumental in the founding of the American Pomological Society, and a man whom Bailey revered.

In his presidential address, Bailey contrasted graphically the American Pomological Society of the past, the present, and the future. Portions are here quoted:

In the early years, the convention consisted of two parts—the reports of the fruit committees and the open discussions. In those days, pomologists did not come together "to hear papers." They told each other what they had learned in the two years, for the custom had not then developed of asking government for aid, of demanding redress of grievances, and of laying great plans for the securing of rights and the furtherance of trade.

For more than half a century this Society occupied a distinct field quite its own, concerned largely with amateur interests and the varieties of fruits because, at first, there were practically no other interests. Its work was associated with production. But the great State horticultural societies came into existence; large commercial interests developed; distribution and marketing took precedence, in public discussions, over production; the scientific undertakings received great stimulus and the investigators made an association of their own. The old Society came into difficulty, and almost before anyone was aware it found itself without a field of effective operation. There have now been some years of prospecting. We think we now have a program and we know the field is clear. There is nothing in the genius or even in the history of the Society to prevent it from occupying a large place in the stirring processes of the twentieth century. . . . In a peculiar sense the Society now stands between yesterday and tomorrow. It emerges from its long and honorable past into a future of a somewhat different direction. . . .

We now come to a time, nearing the end of the first quarter of the twentieth century, when the delightful subjects associated with the kinds and varieties of fruit are readily and effectively handled by State, Provincial and local societies. The production of fruit is largely a series of geographical questions, and the methods employed in one part of the country may not be applicable to remoter parts. The national fruit-growing subjects are rather those that have to do with policies and programs. How to organize and to effectualize the forces of society for the furtherance and protection of fruit-growing are problems for a national and international society to consider. The different State and Provincial societies represent political divisions of the continent. All of them, however, must consider large questions of policy associated with transportation, distribution, selling, marketing, storage, quarantine, packages, and many legislative matters that touch the fruit-growing industry. It would add much to their effectiveness without detracting anything from their initiative and integrity if they could act through a body of continental scope, including both the United States and Canada. This is the large field of the American Pomological Society.

As the address indicated, the society was not enjoying the prosperity it had once known. Viewed continentally, however, it still remained the science's principal organization and to give it new vitality and vision for the future it turned to Bailey. For pomology had been his first real horticultural interest. Bailey was concerned that the society should not become a trade organization. And he considered it important that it should not forget the amateur and small planter. The society, he said, "may stimulate all planting of fruits independently of the size of those plantings. It must encourage the growing of single trees and plants as well as of large orchards, for the interest of fruit-growing holds together from one end to the other." Membership of all persons interested in fruits should be secured. Frequent periodical issuance was needed. To furnish an adequate service to practical farmer members and to academic students required an organization as well as conventions and exhibitions. Bailey outlined a program and concluded his address by saying:

Let us keep constantly before us the three larger purposes of the Society. These purposes are: to encourage the production of more and better fruit; to increase the consumption of fruit; to enable everyone to have greater joy and reward in the knowledge and the growing of fruits.

Immediately there was a motion from the floor to adopt the president's recommendations. Bailey, however, suggested that a committee consider each point and to that end, after agreement from the members, appointed three committeemen who reported the next day commending "without reservation the forward-looking program outlined by our President, and [congratulated] the Society on the opportunities for serving the fruit industry of America that are before it." The chairman was H. P. Gould, and the committee's other members were Frederic Cranefield and M. B. Davis.

Although Bailey regarded these years as "the last" of his work, it did not turn out that way. On December 20, he wrote Dr. Robinson from the New York Botanical Garden:

I think I should let you know the different species of mischief in which I am engaged. I am now at the Bronx for two weeks or so working on Venezuelan things. Jan[uary] 14 we (Mrs. B[ailey] and daughter and self) expect to sail for Bermuda en route to Barbados. I want to get into Venezuela again (the women remaining at Barbados or Trinidad) to search for the original Oreodoxa and certain other things. I want also to go again to Bolivar and try to make the overland route to the sea across the llanos. No botanist has crossed the llanos, so far as I can find out. Even Pittier has never had a sight of them. . . . If I go to Venezuela, the women are likely to pick me up on the Coast and we can come back via Porto Rico, giving me an opportunity to get the palms of the island. . . .

Again, on January 1, 1922, Bailey wrote:

It is doubtful whether I get to Venezuela on this trip. . . . I shall be leaving here in two or three days for home. We sail Jan[uary] 14 for Barbados via Bermuda. The destination beyond Barbados is yet unknown to us. I shall be after palms specially. I think about half my Venezuelan collection is now named. . . .

Among the grasses and ferns, the Baileys had found nothing new. Among cacti, however, was "a fine new Cereus, an immense thing" collected on an island in the Orinoco. Dr. Rowlee made a new Ochroma out of the material from Caracas. Various species were published by group specialists. In 1930 as article 10, volume II, fascicle 4, of *Gentes Herbarum* were published other "South American Novelties" in the genera Rynchospora, Echeveria, Chamæcrista, Grimaldia, and Passiflora. At the Promenade Garden, Georgetown, British Guiana, Bailey had seen in 1921 a manac palm in cultivation, a tree in fruiting condition, and apparently the Jamaican species. An absorbing interest in palms—almost the equivalent of his great interest in American Rubi— had been aroused some years before by Mrs. Bailey.

While enjoying a vacation at Saint Ann's Bay on the north shore of Jamaica, the Baileys had stopped at the Bristol Hotel which was then new. They took rooms near a veranda on the second floor. One day, sitting on the veranda and enjoying the beauty of the newly planted and graded grounds, Mrs. Bailey asked, "What are those palms planted down there?" Bailey replied, "I do not know." When she answered, "I thought you were a botanist," that settled a decision permanently. Bailey long before this had had an inclination to study palms. Here, however, was a challenge from the one who had always inspired him in life the most. He resolved from that day forward to make a thorough study of the palms. When Bailey sailed for Barbados he was after palms. He had collected some at Trinidad and other tropical places. He wrote Robinson that he hoped to return by April or May; and on April 18, true to his word, he announced: "I am just returned this morning from one of my most successful collecting trips; and this is my first letter." On April 24 he wrote Fernald: "I had a very interesting collecting trip this year and got an abundant supply of palm material representing about 150 species or reputed species."

During 1922 the Macmillan Company published the first of the Open Country Books, a work by Bailey on his first real horticultural interest, *The Apple-Tree*. That same year were reprinted volumes 2 and 3 of the *Cyclopedia of American Agriculture*, those devoted to farm crops, a popular survey of crops and crop-making methods in the United States and Canada, and to farm animals. *Gentes Herbarum* in December elucidated "Two species of Hibiscus from China." It will be remembered that as early as 1897 Bailey had complained of the botanical classification of the cultivated Brassicas, stating at the time that he was not clear as to the generic merits of Brassica and Sinapis. He knew of no group in which many of the difficulties of classification vanish more quickly upon a study of the growing plants than in the Brassicas. Accordingly, in December, 1922, Bailey made "The Cultivated Brassicas" the subject of a paper of *Gentes Herbarum*. Again in 1930 there appeared a second paper, the introduction of which read:

Eight years ago I published a paper on such cultivated Brassicas as I had then grown and studied, representing the conclusions of more than thirty years of attention to the subject (Gentes Herbarum, i, fasc. ii, Dec. 18, 1922). Since that time the interest in the group has been maintained; and inasmuch as the edition of the paper is now nearly exhausted it is necessary to prepare an epitome of it together with new observations.

The plants herein discussed are those named in Brassica and Sinapis, comprising the coleworts and the mustards. In the former paper reasons were given for uniting Sinapis with Brassica, the main one being that I do not know to which group many of these plants should be assigned. I still feel that if we are to divide them we should not stop with two genera; but I yet see no compensations in having more than one for the plant herein discussed.

The utilities of the species of Brassica to human beings are not likely to be understood in any one country because the uses are so regional. Brassicas of one species or another are raised for fodder, for green leaf-food, as dried, salted and preserved foods, pickles, krauts, accessories to meat dishes, as tubers, for oil from the seed, and for table mustard from the seed. Familiar with the kales, cabbages, cauliflowers, turnips, ruta-bagas of Europe and North America, one is not prepared for the sowings of mustard in eastern Asia as if they were fields of wheat. . . .

Bailey's articles written for *Gentes Herbarum* have been of general as well as systematic value. In 1940 appeared "Certain Noteworthy Brassicas," published in fascicle 9 of volume four. There Bailey observed:

We like to hope that cytological and genetical studies may help us on the origins and definitions of the troublesome Brassicas, but the reader may see at once that records made on the usual or prevailing botanical names are of no value to these ends; and students in those fields must learn to discriminate and diagnose the plants in comparable terms, with preservation of specimens. . . . The present paper is naturally not a histological study but only an effort to employ gross seed characters in the taxonomic definition of classes and species. . . . Nativities of the five Brassicas treated . . . are unknown. The same is true of several of the accepted species of Linnæus and other early authors. These plants have been in cultivation for untold years, and undoubtedly have passed from hand to hand in many countries without notice or record. They may have been botanically described in the long course of their history although I cannot discover positive names for them; and the presumption is rather against it inasmuch as plants of long domestication are taken for granted and nobody fathers them. Whatever may be the nomenclature behind them, it is no gain to put them into species to which they do not belong. I do not know any accepted species of Brassica to which these plants can be referred without so extending the definitions of those species as to break them down. To propose a new nomenclature for some of the Brassicas now under consideration involves risk of duplication of very old names.

So went the discussion, a demonstrative proof of the need of thoroughly trained systematic students of the cultivated flora. Some of Bailey's work in horticultural classification has proved to be the finished product. Some of it has indicated challenges for the future. At all events he has laid foundations in the literature of the plant sciences. A beautiful illustration of the imperishable service he has performed for horticulture and botany may be found in his study of *The Cultivated Evergreens*; a handbook of the coniferous and most important broad-leaved evergreens planted for ornament in the United States and Canada, published in 1923, and succeeded in 1933 by *The Cultivated Conifers in North America* comprising the pine family and the taxads, well illustrated and both published by the Macmillan Company.

Moreover, Bailey's artistic genius, manifested in beautifully selected photographic half-tone pictures, has added greatly to the value of the *Gentes Herbarum* papers. Illustrative photography was a technique employed by Bailey in botanic study as early as 1888; in fact, as already indicated, he was doubtless an American pioneer in such use. Into the historic "garden herbarium" of the early horticultural division of the Cornell College of Agriculture—which herbarium was brought to his residence about 1915 at his request and made part of his collections—

he had introduced the practice of taking photographs to preserve accurate records. Years of accumulating materials during his years as professor of horticulture had enlarged the herbarium, which contained pressed and mounted specimens of all species grown in the Cornell garden. Together with other material brought in, and the photographs, this had provided Bailey with an excellent nucleus with which to continue "botanical studies of cultivated plants and to build up a considerable collection," as he expressed his intention by letter dated June 14, 1915, to Professor E. A. White. In 1923 Bailey elaborated another study begun years before, "an attempt," as he later described it, "to bring the lima beans into systematic order for purposes of discussion and for record in current literature." This study (*Gentes Herbarum*, 1, 122) being at variance with another work on the separateness or unification of the Lima and Sieva beans was continued by garden tests and study of other sources. In 1940, in an article, "Phaseolus Lunatus and Relatives,"[6] Bailey reviewed his findings and announced his arrangement, commenting:

I speak particularly of nomenclature inasmuch as it is yet impossible to determine what are the specific lines in nature. The systematic question must be worked out with abundant native plants, and such material is not assembled. The problem now is with the cultigens. . . . The Lima bean group is difficult in nomenclature both because of the complicated history and variation of the plants under domestication, and final conclusions are not to be expected. . . .

To be fair, one should read Bailey's full discussion. However, this much quoted is sufficient to indicate the perplexities of the horticultural systematist, and, most important, the need of research among the plants of our daily use.

On November 12, 1923, Bailey communicated with Dr. J. M. Greenman of the Missouri Botanical Garden of St. Louis: "We are leaving in a week for Brazil, where we hope to spend a few months collecting anything we can lay hands on but with particular reference to palms. Undoubtedly, from that collection and others, there will be things that I can send you." En route, from Barbados, Bailey sent a card to Robinson: "We are calling here for a few hours. Next stop is Rio de Janeiro." Years before Bailey had had an opportunity to go to Brazil to study and survey that country's agricultural resources. He had not gone but the movement toward agricultural betterment in Brazil had not ceased. Brazil had been one of the most progressive of the agriculturally undeveloped nations of the world. Among the peoples of foreign lands, this nation's populace had been one of the first to establish on a scientific basis agricultural colleges of growing world prominence. As it hap-

[6] *Gentes Herbarum*, IV, 9 (1940), pp. 336-338.

pened, the leadership employed to establish these colleges had been Americans. The wealthy benefactor who had formerly sought Bailey took the professor of agriculture of Michigan Agricultural College, Eugene Davenport. Bailey had recommended Davenport. The two had been close friends and schoolmates. Señor Louis Queroz told Davenport that he was "in search of a man to return with him and help found a 'Leetle Lansing' in his country, the state of São Paulo having promised to take it off his hands as soon as he should establish it after the model he had in mind." Dr. and Mrs. Davenport and family sailed in October, 1891, and returned to the United States by way of England in the summer of 1892. Shortly afterward Davenport accepted the position of dean of the College of Agriculture of the University of Illinois. The threat of one of the many South American revolutions of those years interfered with putting into effect the preliminary plans prepared while Davenport served as president of the Collegio Agronomica located at Piracicába. Later Clinton D. Smith, another professor of agriculture of Michigan State College, was convinced by Davenport and others there was an agricultural future for Brazil. He went there and, carrying out many of Davenport's plans during a stay of about ten years, placed the school on a permanent basis.[7]

In 1921, also, had been founded the Escola Superior de Agricultura e Veterinaria do Estado de Minas Geraes at Viçosa under the directorship of Peter Henry Rolfs, formerly the director of the United States Sub-Tropical Laboratory at Miami, Florida. When Rolfs received his Brazilian commission, the state had not even located land for the institution. Rolfs' only instructions practically were to locate, organize, and conduct an agricultural college on the modern plan. When he informed the people of Minas Geraes he would have to study first the agriculture and needs of the state, they listened in amazement to learn that their agriculture could be different from that of any other land. Rolfs, however, fortunately, enjoyed a wide diversity of agricultural experience. Graduated from Iowa Agricultural in a year when, it is said, only three "biologists" in the United States were given advanced degrees in botany, he went in 1891 to the Florida Experiment Station where he served until 1899 as entomologist and botanist, and professor of botany at the state agricultural college. Then he went to the South Carolina station and Clemson Agricultural College where he remained two years; and then became plant pathologist in charge of the Sub-Tropical Laboratory at Miami. In 1906 he became director of the

[7] The quotation and most of the facts just above are taken principally from an autobiographical narrative, *What One Life Has Seen. Personal Recollections of an Epochal Era 1856-1935*, prepared by E. Davenport, Woodland, Michigan, 1935, but, so far as is known, never published. Information was also supplied by Dr. Bailey and Dr. H. B. Tukey, now professor of Horticulture at Michigan State College.

Florida agricultural experiment station, was director of extension during the year 1913, and from 1915 to 1921 served the state further as dean of the college of agriculture of the University of Florida. Bailey wrote him from Rio de Janeiro on December 9, 1923:

When preparing to come to Brazil I was surprised to learn that you are in the country. I arrived yesterday, and am here on a botanical collecting trip. I may come up to Minas before we leave, and at any rate shall hope to see you. My particular quest is palms, although I am collecting everything that comes to hand. We expect to be in the country a few months.

On December 22, Rolfs replied:

. . . Well, we have finally moved into the "casa nova," and have our belongings sorted more or less into the various rooms. We should be very glad indeed if you and your ladies would come up and pay us a visit, and stay as long as you can. We have plenty of room in the "casa nova" and the weather is delightful.

Let us know long enough ahead of time so we can arrange for pack animals to make the Araponga trip. We can go by Ford to São Miguel da Anta in about an hour. From there to Araponga it is said to be six leagues. That point, São Miguel da Anta being the nearest "Fordable" place to Araponga. I have never been to that region and am anxious to see it from Dr. Alvaro Silveiro's account of it.

However, the Baileys were unable to accept the invitation immediately for the reason that Miss Ethel and Miss Emilie Perkins, a trained nurse, college chum, and now doctor of medicine, had "left for Buenos Aires en route to Valparaiso and [would] not be back until toward the end of January." As Miss Ethel and Bailey were "the ones who would like to make the trip to Araponga," wrote Bailey, "we shall be obliged to await her return before making any arrangements." Much cordial correspondence ensued between Bailey and Rolfs. Bailey continued collecting in various Brazilian regions. Finally, in February, all of the members of the party were ready (after a stop at São Paulo) for the high point of the visit—Arapongo—where at a high altitude a certain pinnate-leafed palm grew, according to a belief which Bailey wished to confirm or dispel. Miss Perkins accompanied the party to visit two hospitals of the interior—one for tropical diseases and one a charity institution. The climb of the sierra in the rainy season was believed not wise for Mrs. Bailey. So she remained in Rio. The trip proved to be a fascinating experience. They were able to view the medieval, romantic, rural interior of Brazil—the high, remote, and undeveloped areas. Dr. Rolfs' daughter, Clarissa, accompanied the party, and an enthusiastic, intelligent, and affable priest gave them aid. They found the pinnate-leafed palm. On March 16, Bailey wrote: "The Viçosa-Araponga experience will be one of my pleasantest memories, aided by the honest Araponga mud that I am taking back on some of my property," which included a box of driers, card-boards, presses and other collecting supplies, a heavy camera, and the like. Just before sailing, he bade farewell, saying: ". . . The girls and myself are glad to have the word from the good Padre, whom we shall never forget. . . . I was to send you measurements of the collecting case. Instead of that, I am sending the case itself in memory of the Araponga journey (it is the one that went thither). . . . I trust that all your work may prosper. I am convinced that you have made a solid beginning and that your plans are capable of accomplishing great good for Brazil."

Although somewhat delayed by winds and rather heavy seas on the voyage home, by the middle of April the Baileys and their Brazilian collections were safe at Ithaca. On September 17, 1924, Bailey wrote Greenman: "Since our return from Brazil in April we have mounted 8000 sheets and we still have much ahead of us. . . . Much of our Venezuelan collection of three years ago is yet undetermined." While in Brazil, weeks had been spent working at the Barbosa Rodriguez palms. "Upward of 150 species of palms are growing here, many of them magnificent specimens," he had written Robinson. When on May 17, 1924, Bailey wrote Robinson of the results of his Brazilian journey, he said:

My special quest was palms, but I tried to get everything else that came to hand but did not go to search for it. I brought back abundant palm material representing more than 170 species. It is the biggest single haul I have yet made.

And on May 31:

. . . I have perhaps three-quarters of my Venezuelan things identified, and expect to go to Washington next week with the final consignment to work for a time with Blake.

The Griffith's palms is here, and I am glad to add it to my growing collection of literature on the subject. I was able some time ago to purchase a good set of Martius, and on my last trip I picked up a complete set of the great folio in two volumes by Barbaso Rodriguez, Sertum Palmarum Brasiliensium.

My collection grows apace, and when I look at the great amount of palm material I brought back this winter I wonder where I am to find room for it.

During the winter before the Baileys' trip to Brazil, Bailey had given most of his time to completing his *Manual of Cultivated Plants*, which was published in 1924. On January 5, 1923, he had written to Robinson:

. . . I was sorry to have missed the meetings at Boston, but we are so closely engaged here now in making my manual of cultivated plants that I do not wish to be absent from it except for very special reasons or when I wish to look up puzzles in connection with it. I am accumulating a good bunch of puzzles, and probably sometime before the apple-trees blossom I shall drop around at your place to look some of them up.

In the spring of that year, 1923, Bailey prepared for *Rhodora*, the official publication of the New England Botanical Club, a sketch of the life and work of George Lincoln Goodale, who, in his eighty-fourth year, had died at Saco, Maine, honored and beloved by the entire botanical fraternity.

During 1923, Bailey incorporated as fascicle 4 of the first volume of *Gentes Herbarum* a continuation of his life-long study of the genus Rubus, an article attempting to account for the pomological varieties, entitled "Certain Cultivated Rubi." In October, 1925, this was followed by a sequential article, "The Eubati Native in North America," and this, in turn, by other papers and, at length, by a monographic—but not floristic—series of papers, "Species Batorum" on various divisions of the genus Rubus. In the Eubatus subgenus article, Bailey observed:

The present brief paper is the third attempt in modern time, to bring together all our species, but it considers only the Eubati and the territory does not extend south of the United States, nor is it the purpose to diagnose the species other than the new ones. The intervening years have brought together much new material, so that a new study is needed. My purpose in this paper is simply a tentative Enumeration or sequence, not a monograph. . . .
I have collected Rubus the length of Florida and in much of the intermediate country as far as Mt. Mansfield in northern Vermont. I have visited all the places from which Blanchard obtained the types of his Vermont and New Hampshire species, some of which places in the remote mountain parts are now overgrown and difficult of access. My herbarium contains more than 5000 mounted sheets of Rubus.

A long list of persons had furnished Bailey with specimens for study. The author urged on his readers the need of "a good iconography of the North American species, illustrations of sufficient size and skill to stand in the place of representative specimens. . . . We need, also," he wrote, "careful regional Rubus studies. The most important of such contributions in this country is Brainerd & Peitersen's 'Blackberries of New England—their Classification,' comprising Bulletin 217 of the Vermont Agricultural Experiment Station, June, 1920. The systematic part is principally the work of the late Dr. Ezra Brainerd . . . who had 'spent a considerable part of his time for the past 25 years in a critical study of this genus' and whose contributions will remain among the standard references."

On the question of hybridity, Bailey stated his position clearly:

As in my former Rubus paper . . . I am here concerned "with identification and nomenclature, not necessarily with the biological question of origins." Binomial nomenclature is not a decision on origins. We must not confuse nomenclature with hypotheses of origin, as I tried to point out in my Brassica paper . . . : "the subject has been obscured by the effort to combine an hypothesis of the origins of the forms with the identification of them." The greatest quest in biology, to be sure, is the determination of origins and phylogeny, but the immediate necessity is clear identification: we must know the objects in nature; disdain of these objects is one of the outstanding deficiencies in current biology. . . .

It will be understood that I do not take issue with European or American botanists on the broad question of spontaneous hybridity in Rubus, in Brassica, or other genera; nor is this discussion controversial; nor does it imply criticism of any published work. I am not now concerned with hybridity, but with identification and with nomenclature as a requisite to it. We must constantly test new methods and applications, hoping at each step to make the subject clearer. . . .

It is probable that we have now passed the epoch of the effort to account for the forms of plants by assuming hybridity on the evidence of superficial likenesses or intermediateness. . . . We must look for more fundamental evidences, and give up the idea that this form or that shows an "influence" or "infusion" of this or that parent because it does not conform to our conception of what the species should be. We are first to clarify our ideas as to species-types and to understand that these types may not coincide with phylogenetic lines: with these types clearly in mind, we shall be able objectively to arrange the variations in reference to them. These types are such as the founders of species have taken for the starting-points of nomenclature; they are definite, whenever the specimens still exist, and are to be substituted for whatever hazy notion a person may have in his head as to what is or ought to be "typical" of the species.

If we wait in the expectation of finding perfectly clear and definite constant differences between what, for purposes of nomenclature, we call species, we shall not understand Rubus.

Bailey raised no opposition to research along morphological, cytological, physiological, or genetical lines. However, he did insist that, "Evidence of hybridity in the wild must rest on more complete and exact evidence than we yet possess." Moreover, he admitted that probably "the study of the numbers and characteristics of chromosomes is capable of modifying opinions as to the validity of the species, but," he said, "it must be based on critical identification of the plants and the preservation of ample herbarium material for verification and record." Squarely he placed his work before the plant sciences as a voluntary service in the systematization of the cultivated flora on which, with the material known and named, research in other branches might be predicated.

Bailey realized that the era of specialization in the plant sciences had reached full maturity. In 1925 when the Macmillan Company published his work, *The Gardener*, A Book of Brief Directions for the Growing of the Common Fruits, Vegetables and Flowers in the Garden and About the House—a book which he explained bore "the same relation to the Hunn-Bailey Practical Garden-Book that the Manual of Gardening [bore] to [his] old Garden-Making"—he commented:

Many changes have arisen in the practice of gardening within the past quarter century. The attitude toward insects and plant diseases has changed radically, and direct methods of control are now matters of common knowledge. The commercializing of plant-growing has produced great changes, and many kinds are losing attention and these, unfortunately, are not always the poor ones. Of late years, specialty-gardening has made great headway. The specialties are represented by societies, and the progress in the breeding of varieties has been marked. The growers become fanciers. Such special groups are chrysanthemum, carnation, peony, iris, gladiolus, dahlia, rose. The development in these classes of plants is much to be desired; but we are not to forget that we still need the attitude of the old-time gardener, who was an all-around man and who brought to his work a devotion and general skill that gave a singular flavor to his art. It is to be regretted that in the development of the specialty-interest we have not included the home fruits. Why not an amateur apple or strawberry society?

Specialists were not confined to floriculture. In every segregate of plant science research, new and old, there were many specialists. Momentarily confining our attention to one segregate, plant pathology, some idea of the research expansion in plant study may be gained by noticing that at the fifteenth annual meeting of the American Phyto-pathological Society in 1923, one hundred and fourteen papers were presented, as opposed to forty-four in 1917. One hundred and forty-five members were in attendance. Canadian, Pacific, and Southern sections of the society had been organized. Furthermore, a well attended summer conference was held each year. Special research and investigational projects were established. A national phytopathological institute was formed, and the society was cooperating with such progressive plant research foundations as the Boyce Thompson Institute of Yonkers, New York, in the study of special problems such as the mosaic diseases. A crop protection institute and its functions were outlined. At the Cincinnati meeting of the American Association for the Advancement of Science in 1923, three joint sessions were participated in by the American Phytopathological Society: one, with the Mycological Section of the Botanical Society of America; another, with Section G at which Lewis Ralph Jones spoke on "The Relation of Environment to Disease in Plants"; and, third, with the American Society for Horticultural Science and Horticultural Section of the American Association of Economic Entomologists, a symposium on crown gall inspection was held to prepare practical rules and principles, in the light of abundant knowledge of the disease made available principally by Erwin F. Smith, and to improve methods to prevent sale and planting of susceptible stock. Papers were presented at a symposium on potato scab held by the Potato Association of America.

Jones's illustrious work on Fusarium-resistant cabbages was accomplished after more than a decade of research, and with him several of his colleagues on the faculty of the University of Wisconsin and a number of graduate students collaborated. On December 13, 1921, Jones presented at the New York Botanical Garden an illustrated lecture on "Disease Resistance in Plants," and in a published account of the meeting prepared by Marshall A. Howe, secretary, several other disease-resistant crop achievements, already considered in this book, were referred to. None, however, received the recognition for brilliant achievement which Jones's work was given. Claude Wilbur Edgerton, graduate of the University of Nebraska and Cornell, had done important breeding work in tomatoes for disease resistance at the Louisiana experiment station. Likewise, Charles Elmer Durst, at the University of Illinois and the state experiment station. By 1922 Jones reported three established strains of later cabbage varieties and two promising earlier varieties. Researches conducted independently and as adjuncts to the selection and breeding work had accumulated, moreover, much exact knowledge of the relations of various diseases and infection to soil and air temperature, moisture, climatic influences, and other environmental factors. Their influences on metabolism, chemical contents, and other physiological activity of plants were included. James Johnson, who some years before had evolved valuable root-rot resistant tobacco, utilized laboratory apparatus constructed to grow plants under controlled temperature and humidity conditions and obtained experimental evidence pointing to an inference of a parasitic rather than enzymic origin of mosaic disease. During the 1920's the phrase "virus diseases" came into common use.

The prominence given by Jones and his collaborators to environmental influences in causation and effect in matters of disease resistance and susceptibility emerged alongside of Smith's work on crown gall, Freeman and Stakman on disease resistance in wheat, and Cornelius L. Shear on Glomerella. Not to be overlooked was the work of Leonard Lee Harter, senior pathologist of the United States Bureau of Plant Industry and a graduate of the University of Nebraska and Georgetown University, in diseases of vegetable crops generally, particularly his economically valuable studies of storage rots and his elaborate studies of sweet potato diseases. Certainly of especial value to coordinated plant breeding and plant pathological study was the work of the laboratories of the New York Botanical Garden under the direction of Arlow Burdette Stout, graduate of the University of Wisconsin and Columbia University. Each man was not only a specialist, but an authority, both with regard to special crops and phases of investigation. Nor were their researches confined to plant pathological subjects. Stout, for example, spent much time in studying sterility in plants, especially flowering plants. Much more could be written about the work of each of these scientists and leaders in their fields. The work of many others also could appropriately be elaborated at this point in our narrative.

In increasing numbers scientists in horticulture, phytopathology, forestry, and other branches of plant science research, explored the tropics and established experimental laboratories there. In each of the principal United States insular possessions could be found by this time reputable scientific research. In some countries of South America, this was also true. Occasionally, a scientific investigator was sent on a special mission, as, for instance, in 1918, when Dr. William H. Weston, Jr., later professor of plant pathology at Harvard University, was sent by the Bureau of Plant Industry to study downy mildew of maize. Later, when the Tropical Research Foundation set forth a program of agricultural and forestry development in the tropics, the discovery and development of disease-resistant plants was accorded a deservingly conspicuous place. William A. Orton and Jones were leaders in advancing the work of the foundation. Very few, if any, have excelled these men as plant pathologists, Jones especially. As a founder and first president of the American Phytopathological Society, as first editor of its journal, *Phytopathology*, as a president of the Botanical Society of America, editor of the *American Journal of Botany*, and in numerous other capacities, he has exercised a valuable leadership and contributed a sound scholarship over many years. But we must discuss further the matter of disease prevention in the early decades of the century.

Progress had been made also in fungicides—the introduction of the lime-sulfur as a more effective spray for certain crops than bordeaux mixture, and the use of dry sulfur as a safe and profitable replacement of liquid sprays in the control of certain common and destructive diseases.[8] Probably because of its fundamental significance, physiology was among the last of the plant science branches to attain maturity. However, it had risen to full consciousness of its probable scope and aims, and the quantitative and qualitative methods by which to realize its ends. With the advance of specialized endeavor, physiological applications were revealing fundamental explanations in horticulture as well as botany. There then issued from the University of Missouri laboratories the text book, already mentioned, of "more than usual merit," *The Fundamentals of Fruit Production* by V. R. Gardner, F. C. Bradford, and H. D. Hooker, published by McGraw-Hill publishing company. Re-

[8] For a fuller discussion of these points, see Herbert Hice Whetzel's *An Outline of the History of Phytopathology*, pp. 112-114. Particular attention is called to the bibliography, pp. 116-126. From the section devoted to the history of the subject, attention should be directed to two articles not before cited in this book: Lewis Ralph Jones, "Problems and Progress in Plant Pathology," *American Journal of Botany*, 1 (1914), pp. 97-111; A. D. Selby, "The Future of Vegetable Pathology," *Science*, n.s., xv (1902), pp. 736-740. See also, E. C. Large, *The Advance of the Fungi*, Henry Holt & Co., New York (1940), chapters 29, 31.

viewing it for the *Botanical Gazette* Charles A. Shull said: ". . . The material is presented in seven sections, as follows: water relations, nutrition, temperature relations of fruit plants, pruning, fruit setting, propagation, and geographic influences in fruit production. The section on nutrition is particularly commendable. . . . The book is a challenge to teachers of horticulture. Few students of this subject in the past have acquired the necessary fundamental training in plant physiology to make the best use of such a text. . . ."

The University of Missouri was for many years the teaching residence of J. C. Whitten, historically and scientifically one of America's most important horticulturists. Whitten was once a graduate student under Bailey at Cornell. For a time he had taught at South Dakota State College of Agriculture. The last years of his life were spent teaching at the University of California. While at Missouri, Whitten initiated his famous plant temperature studies, studies in rest periods of plants, effects of frost, studies in the most effective methods of pruning, and much else. His work was carried on with great success in California. Inspiring as a teacher, his influence has been considerable. This does not minimize the originality and worth of Gardner, Bradford, and Hooker's book. Many able American horticulturists believe an epoch in American horticulture was commenced with the appearance of it and other new texts of the period.[9] William H. Chandler produced a text in 1925, *Principles of Fruit Growing*, which stressed the tree-as-a-whole concept rather than practical phases of production. Specialization in study had much to do with the production of new texts. Textbook changes were bound to follow in the wake of the vast knowledge developed in colleges, experiment stations, and literally thousands of individual investigations during three decades of time. The wonder is that more texts did not come sooner, responding to enlargements of understanding, refinements of techniques, and changes of methods. Chandler's last text was organized around a study of processes in the tree. In other words, the horticulturist in the biological sense had come to be a specialized botanist.

Bailey may have believed these years to be "the last of [his] work." As a matter of fact, however, these were years which brought him encomiums and recognition, unparalleled in American plant science history.

At the meeting of the American Association for the Advancement of Science held during Christmas week, 1925, at Kansas City, Bailey was elected the association's president. At the same time American botanists honored his return to the science of his early affection by electing him president of the Botanical Society of America. The following year—

[9] Joseph Harvey Gourley produced an excellent *Text-Book of Pomology* in 1922.

between December 27, 1926, and January 1, 1927—Bailey presided at the eighty-third meeting of the American Association and its affiliated societies, gathered at Philadelphia in the halls of the University of Pennsylvania. Likewise, he presided over meetings of the Botanical Society of America with section G of the Association. A registered attendance of 264 botanists were present. At the botanists' dinner Bailey spoke on the need of greater attention to and use of plant collections. The address of the retiring president was the principal one of the evening. This was delivered by Jacob Richard Schramm, formerly professor of botany at Cornell, who became in 1925 editor-in-chief of *Biological Abstracts.* He discussed, "The Attitude of Science toward Religion." Bailey was never to deliver his addresses as retiring president of these organizations. When in 1927 the Association and the Society met in Nashville for their annual meetings, Bailey was recovering from a surgical operation and found it impossible to attend or prepare an address. He, however, sent a note of greeting which was read at the opening session of the Association.

Moreover, an honor, perhaps even greater than his simultaneous presidencies of the American Association and Botanical Society of America, came to Bailey in 1926 when at the International Congress of Plant Sciences (the fourth International Botanical Congress), held at Ithaca August 16-23, he was constituted its president and presiding chairman. Up to this time international prestige and leadership had been more or less concentrated in Europe and the British Isles. Surely this was complete recognition that the mantle of American leadership which only Gray had enjoyed in a world-wide sense had fallen to Bailey.

Few Americans had shared with Europeans world preeminence in the plant sciences. Seldom had world acclaim of an American leader been made without some reservation. There are no national boundaries in science. Its orbit is the world. Yet, in plant study, groups for many years had visualized an American autonomy in investigation spheres. Bailey consistently had adhered to a world conception of natural science research. This conception applied in every segregate of the enlarging realm of plant study. He grouped the segregates in his opening address: bacteriology, cytology, histology, morphology, physiology, genetics, ecology, mycology, taxonomy, paleobotany, agronomy, horticulture, forestry, pharmacognosy, and pathology. Bailey had always favored world congress meetings of plant students to promote understanding. Had he not spoken years before in New Zealand in the interest of a science congress?

The Ithaca Congress considered proposals to amend the international rules of nomenclature. Recommendations were formulated for the London Congress to be held in 1930. The long-sought promulgation of a permanent International Code would constitute one of the significant events.

Bailey at the Ithaca Congress took advantage of his leadership to enunciate his "Statements on the Systematic Study of Variables." He called for caution and restraint in the treatment of variables, particularly in the estimates of hybridity. He saw the need of better field work, and caution in the attitude toward phylogenies. "In biology," said Bailey, "the variables are in many ways the most significant objects and they are most in need of careful study. Necessarily we must conform to the standard practices, but not to the extent that conformation obscures the truth in nature. A new approach to the whole subject of variables is now the greatest desideratum in systematic botany."

The following year, 1927, the famous and historic publication of Kew Gardens and the Royal Horticultural Society of England honored Bailey by dedicating the last volume[10] of *Curtis's Botanical Magazine*, begun in 1787, to him, "in recognition of his long devotion to the scientific training of workers in horticulture and agriculture and to the increase and spread of knowledge in these branches of science." In 1931 a volume of dedications and portraits appearing from 1827 to 1927 in the *Botanical Magazine* was published. The accounts were brief biographical sketches. The account of Bailey enjoys the distinction of being the book's last entry. Other Americans included in the volume were John Torrey, Asa Gray, and Charles Sprague Sargent. Of the four, Bailey was the only living American.

Bailey, who in 1898 had received the silver Veitch memorial medal of the Royal Horticultural Society, received also in 1927 the Society's gold Veitch memorial medal. In 1928 he was given the coveted Grande Medaille of the Societé Nationale d'Acclimation de France. Bailey was now an honorary member of the Royal Horticultural Society of London, honorary member of horticultural societies in Japan, China, New Zealand, and Norway, a corresponding member of the Royal Academy of Agriculture in Turin, a corresponding member of the Societé Lyonnaise d'Horticulture, and an honorary member of the Japanese Agricultural Society.

Likewise, there were other honors received in America. Besides American memberships already mentioned, Bailey was now a fellow of the American Academy of Arts and Sciences. Many state horticultural societies—Michigan, Massachusetts, Rhode Island, Indiana, Western New York, et cetera—had enrolled his name as a ranking or honorary member. All of the more prominent scientific societies with general memberships spread over the United States had given him a ranking, corresponding, or honorary membership. Sigma Xi and Pi Alpha Xi had

[10] Volume 153.

extended to him fraternal bonds. Before his retirement as dean and director, he had been made an honorary member of the Philadelphia College of Pharmacy, he had served as chairman of the New York State Park Commission, and was also a trustee of the American Scenic and Historic Preservation Society. In 1927 Bailey was awarded the George Robert White medal of the Massachusetts Horticultural Society, and in 1928 the gold medal of the National Institute of Social Sciences. In 1931 the Garden Club of America would confer on him the distinction of being the fourth recipient of its honorary award medal "in recognition of his outstanding contributions to horticulture"—a recognition given only three times before, once to Charles Sprague Sargent, once to Mrs. Francis King of Mt. Pleasant, Michigan, and once to the Massachusetts Horticultural Society on the one hundredth anniversary of its founding. That year the American Association of Nurserymen would select Bailey for its distinguished service award. When the new horticultural building at Bailey's alma mater,. Michigan State College, was erected, a selection, based on a wide canvass, was made to choose twelve men who had contributed most to Michigan horticulture, twelve who had contributed most to American horticulture, and twelve the most to world horticulture. Bronze plaques by names memorialized each group. The only person represented in all three groups is Bailey. At the commencement exercises of Swarthmore College held on June 8, 1931, Bailey gave the commencement address and Dr. Frank Aydelotte, the college's president, announced that for that year the Arthur Hoyt Scott gold medal and $1,000 were being bestowed on Bailey. The donee of these honors kept the medal but the money was placed in a bank where it has since drawn interest and Bailey plans someday to use the sum to further a horticultural enterprise. The next year, 1932, the University of Porto Rico chose Bailey as their commencement orator. When he delivered his address the honorary degree doctor of science was conferred on him. This listing is sufficient to characterize Bailey's great national and international prominence.

Official recognition by the United States government was shown by the appointment of Bailey in 1927 by Secretary of Agriculture Jardine to serve on the advisory council constituted to establish a national arboretum at Washington, D.C., in accordance with provisions of an act of Congress. The appointment of Bailey may have been due to the fact of his presidency that year of the Botanical Society of America. The appointments, however, were not made by the Secretary of Agriculture to accord recognition officially to organizations. Rather, the appointees were selected on the basis of their essential worth and value to the movement to establish the arboretum. Moreover, the fact that Bailey saw he could not be of real service to the enterprise, and, therefore, terminated his connection with it, does not minimize the importance of a distinction conferred on Bailey by Secretary Jardine.

There were other honors—tenders of the presidency of colleges and universities, and offers of other official positions. A governor of a prominent state pleaded with Bailey to accept the presidency of the university of his state. In truth, a movement was launched during President Schurman's administration to constitute Bailey president of Cornell University. Hearing of this, Bailey immediately required the movement's leaders to write him a letter to which he replied positively and certainly he was not seeking further administrative honors. His determination was to further scientific advancement. In this he saw his greatest opportunity for service to man.

Bailey's eager and active energies were turned toward building up his plant sciences collection. Robinson and other distinguished men visited him. On August 31, 1926, Bailey wrote to I. M. Johnston: "I am glad I had an opportunity to show you my little shop in the back woods. You now know where my puzzles originate." During May, previously, Bailey reminisced over a visit to the Gray Herbarium: "It was good to have seen the Gray Herbarium again and to have had the visit with you. It is always a great aid to me."

During the winter of 1926-1927 the Baileys journeyed to the far west. Months were spent visiting places of historic and floral interest—especially in California, places where rubi and palms were found—around San Francisco, Palo Alto, Santa Barbara, Riverside, Pasadena, Los Angeles, San Diego, and other points. While at Palo Alto, Bailey received a letter dated March 24, 1927, from Dr. Wiegand, saying that at present there was no room at the college to "house any more herbaria." Wiegand continued:

When the new building is completed we would be very glad to furnish space for housing your entire herbarium with room adjoining for your study and any other convenience that we could well provide. We would be glad to furnish labor for mounting and caring for the collection, and would be glad to do that now before the new building is occupied, if that seems desirable to you. We shall be glad to do this for the use that we may have of the herbarium, and also out of fairness to one who is still a member of our faculty (though ranked as emeritus) and, therefore, entitled to college aid. I see no reason why your research contributions, such as those published in the Gentes Herbarum, could not be entirely appropriate for our Memoir Series, if you desired to have them placed there. They are nearly all concerned with genera of economic or even "agricultural" importance, and the Memoir Series was planned for technical contributions on just such subjects. I make the above statements wholly of my own volition, following my own desire. We all wish that you might be more closely affiliated with us. These statements, therefore, are not official, but I have reason to believe that they could be made so with little difficulty, as Dean

Mann, in our casual conversation has seemed quite in accord with the suggestion as outlined above.

From the California Hotel at San Bernardino, Bailey replied:

It is good of you to write me about the disposition of my herbarium and the publication of my studies, and I keenly appreciate it, particularly as it is the expression of your own volition. The situation with me must soon require decisive action.

On the placing of my accumulations I have strong predilections.

The problem of the publication of my papers is not simple. The studies cover a wide range and some of them would hardly have "agricultural" significance. Probably my major contribution should be in the Palmaceae; I am increasingly impressed with the lack of accurate knowledge in this field and the shocking inadequacy of the preserved material. It is not to be expected that the State of New York would be interested in the publication of memoirs on palms.

There is really no agency in this country for the publication of such studies as mine, in a number of lines. I am therefore undertaking to publish in Europe; this will place the work out of reach of our people who would chiefly profit by it but of course it will be available to specializing students.

We are getting an excellent collection this winter, including an unexpected wealth of palm material. Although we have been here in the winter season and many other activities have demanded my attention, we have taken more than 1300 numbers, and Ethel and I are now on the way to Ithaca by auto and we shall collect as we go. Mrs. Bailey and her sister left on the 2nd for Chicago, but Ethel and I expect to take forty days for our journey. I have taken a large lot of good photographs.

I thank you for your offer to share space and publication facilities with me.

Dr. Wiegand showed Bailey's letter to Dean Mann and on April 20 the dean wrote Wiegand: "Thank you for letting me see the letter from Dr. Bailey. . . . It is helpful . . . to know his own present thinking with respect to his collections and his publications. What he really needs is a private grant which will enable him to work out his purposes." So matters remained until January 16, 1928, when Dr. Whetzel asserted again his great admiration of Bailey and his work by taking the initiative, this time to arrange the first meeting of a committee to consider endowing the Bailey herbarium. On April 24 Whetzel reported to Wiegand: ". . . I have had several conversations with Professor Bailey about the matter and have some hope that we can find a solution for the problem. The Dean is now working on the possibilities of finding approximately $10,000 a year for this project and until he can determine just how the land lays it seems to me there is little the committee can do but wait."

His work continued. On August 1, 1928, he wrote I. M. Johnston:

For some years I have been making a study of the cultivated Verbenas and have come to conclusions that are not orthodox. In this study of course I have gone into the identification of the related species in South America, and have photographs of a number of the type specimens from Europe and also in some cases actual pieces of the original plant. If you get into Verbena I shall want to bring my material over to the Gray and go over it with you, for as I intend to publish on the subject it would be too bad for the two pieces of work not to be harmonized.

Again, however, Bailey was forced to go to the hospital and the Verbena study was deferred. In 1929 Bailey discussed in *Gentes Herbarum* the cultivated lily-turfs (Ophiopogon and Liriope)—plants he had grown in the open and in the greenhouse, plants he had collected in China and in the United States, England, and tropical America. He had examined herbarium material in many places. Bailey also considered in the paper the bush-honeysuckles (Diervilla) and Weigelas, and the wire-plants and ribbon-bush (Muehlenbeckia), and other plants.

As the second fascicle of volume II of *Gentes Herbarum* appeared Bailey's first paper on "The Domesticated Cucurbitas." The completion of this study has occupied many years. In fact, as late as December 6, 1943, an entire issue of *Gentes Herbarum* was devoted to Cucurbita species which were known to grow wild in the United States, Mexico, Guatemala, and British Honduras. The work at Cornell in this vegetable group has continued to be of much value. It is another structure, within the larger structure which Bailey started, which has enlarged significantly.

In 1930 Bailey took up the plantain-lilies and the day-lilies, and considered various botanic and horticultural problems. Work in groups of special study—the cultivated Brassicas, for example—was continued. Trips on behalf of Rubus study were made to locations in the United States.

An enumeration of all his activities would read like a bibliography. The work was varied. But the palms held a place of dominant interest. While the year 1930 witnessed the publication of Bailey's and Miss Ethel's first edition of *Hortus*, a concise dictionary of gardening, general horticulture and cultivated plants in North America, by the Macmillan Company—a supplement to the *Standard Cyclopedia of Horticulture*—most of their time was given to palm study. During the past years, a few minor articles had been appearing in various publications and periodicals—for example, some in *Gardeners' Chronicle*. A few books, already mentioned, had been presented—for instance, *The Harvest of the Year to the Tiller of the Soil*, another Background Book, published by Macmillan Company in 1927, and *The Garden Lover*, another member of the set, published in 1928.

Before the Ohio Botanic Garden Society, meeting at Cincinnati, November 20, 1925, Bailey had delivered an address, "The Botanic Garden Idea," which had been published by the society. He included a historical study of the Cincinnati region as a setting for a Botanic Garden, and published the address as chapter 11 of *The Garden Lover*. Bailey's primary emphasis in horticulture, however, has been, "Know your plant. Identification is the primary process in education." In a Central and South American journal[11] was published in July, 1928, an article by Bailey treating "Las palmeras y su utilidad." Palms were the plants to which Bailey wished to direct his attention for a while. His earlier formed opinion as to need of their identification and systematization had been reinforced by his visit in 1927 to California and from La Jolla in January of that year he had written to Robinson:

I am much interested in the many palms introduced into California and am making many photographs and assembling a large collection. I am specially interested in the native Washingtonias, which still need careful systematic attention. Apparently the native colonies in the mountains of San Diego County have not been carefully studied. I am planning to invade some of them. One of the puzzles in this genus is Watson's Washingtonia Sonoræ. Can you tell me whether any of Watson's material is preserved at the Gray? If so, I may want to look it up sometime.

On January 3, 1931, from Ithaca, Bailey addressed a communication to Charles Alfred Weatherby of the Gray Herbarium: "We are just closing shop here for a few months: palms and things." The Baileys were bound for Jamaica. Early in the year 1929 they had made "a very interesting collecting trip in Cuba." During 1930 Bailey published a *Gentes Herbarum* paper, "Fear of Cultivated Plants," in which he explained his exploratory intention and purpose:

. . . A basic trouble is the fact that we have no consistent and adequate records of cultivated plants. . . . The botany of cultivated plants requires the same careful approach as that of wild plants, and it should not be left to the cultivator. . . .
There are two great classes of cultivated plants. (I, archeophytes). Those that are completely domesticated. These plants have mostly accompanied man so long that they go far back of dependable history. For the most part the nativities are unknown. The evolution of them as human companions goes back to archeology if in fact not sometimes into geology. We do not have definite beginnings or "types" of species. Here belong wheat, rye, apple, pumpkin, chrysanthemum, cabbage, orange, date, and others. Our "species" representing them are cultigens. . . . This group includes plants of special difficulty, and therefore of absorbing interest to the systematist.
The other class (2) comprises the plants less anciently associated with man, mostly less widespread in cultivation, and more readily identified with a wild prototype. Often the beginnings of marked variation, if in fact not of the actual introductions of the species to cultivation, are matters of record. It follows that one may see through the problem more assuredly then in the aboriginals of the other class.

[11] Bol. Union Panamer. 62: 697-708.

In the study of cultivated plants the systematic botanist misses the element of nativity, range and habitat. This lack is at first confusing. One does not know where to begin or what reference literature to consult, and the writing may not have the orderliness that one associates with systematic record. One hesitates at first if the "origin" is not evident, although we really know little or nothing about origins of any species: usually we mean nativity when we speak of origin. Often the literature is more difficult than the plants. One soon acquires the method of approach, however, and comes to depend on the characters of the plants themselves rather than on extrinsic considerations. A close personal knowledge of cultivated plants as they grow in gardens and fields regulates the judgment on the values to be assigned to variations. The confusing horticultural nomenclature then begins to organize itself and to lose its terrors. It is strange as between horticulturists and botanists that each regards the plant-names of the other with distrust, even though the plants are the same.

In many or most of the ancient groups of high modifiability it is hardly to be expected that any two independent industrious workers will arrive at the same conclusions on the systematic positions of species, varieties and races; but such disparity is not peculiar to cultivated plants.

The literature of cultivated plants is voluminous, and still the critical writing on the systematology of them is really meager beyond the range of trees and shrubs and certain special groups; yet the highest horticulture and the best plant-breeding are impossible without careful identification of species. Moreover, identification is a primary element in good education of young and old, whether of plants, birds, stones or emotions. Cultivated plants are the readiest objects with which to begin such education in home and school; to this end the identity of them should be at least as well understood as of the native plants.

It is also time that all of us begin to be prepared for the new and more fundamental studies of the origins of domestic plants and of the physiological nature of their plasticities. This general field will become one of the large botanical adventures, with marked redirection in method and mode of attack. We shall be surprised at the novelty of the subject; a good working knowledge of systematic values will be necessary to the enjoyment of it.

Exploration, therefore, embraced the laboratory, the garden, the orchard and the field. Its imperatives required not only a study of the plant growing in a state of cultivation. Adequate investigation required, moreover, the study of the cultivated plant's wild prototype, wherever and whenever possible. No one man could slay all the dragons confronting the horticultural systematist. The approach and procedure were to follow lines set forth in the orderly classification of the plants of wild nature. Bailey, from the first years of his career, had shouldered as much of the task as one man could possibly do. He had found happiness and enjoyment in the doing. Others had been welcomed and more were wanted. Whether more persons took up the study or not, to the blazing of new paths for explorers he had dedicated the last strong years of his life. Months each year were spent in the laboratory—a laboratory unique in the world since its chief concern was identification and systematization of the cultivated floral groups. Months each year were spent in the field and forest—and to invade the problems of tropical horticulture required breaking new paths in great tropical jungles by foot, by wagon, by boat, and, in these modern times, to an extent by automobile and airplane.

On March 4, 1931, at Ligaunea, Jamaica, Bailey wrote to Wiegand:

I have now had a month with the palms of Jamaica. I came here specially for one palm not recognized here, which has been much in doubt, and which I was obliged a few months ago (in anticipation of Hortus) to transfer to another genus. I have now found it and covered it completely, and it is quite distinct; but in doing so have been amazed to find that the characteristic mountain palm of Jamaica is not the plant it is supposed to be but is an unrecognized species. This is strange enough in an island with such a long botanical history; it illustrates again the fragmentary state of our knowledge about these plants.

This I think has been my most active journey, and I have had a new and interesting set of experiences. One never knows what one is to come up against.

Today I sail for Cuba Oriente, where I have some weeks of hard plugging.

I suppose you are now in the new building, and I trust it is satisfactory. You deserve it.

That year, on July 9, he wrote again, this time from the unique and intentionally preserved wild jungle island, Barro Colorado, of Frigoles, in the Panama Canal zone:

Our stay on the wild Island is now in its latter half. Unfortunately I must be in Ithaca at the time of the Country Life Conference, and this necessitates us leaving the Zone on the 29th of July for we intend stopping a week in Jamaica to complete some of my pilferings there.

We find Barro Colorado all we expected as a botanical preserve. There have been listed 862 species from the Island, which shows the wide and confused variety, and every collector adds a few more. In palms a dozen have been recorded, but we have a score, in several genera. Whether they are Central American, South American, or exclusively Panamanian, only careful study can determine; but the publication of the lot will reveal some surprises in the palm botany of this region.

We are richly enjoying the experience. It is not the best time for collecting because the daily torrents of rain cut down our available time. Moreover, the rainy season is primarily the time of vegetative growth rather than of bloom. However, we have already taken 550 numbers and most of the palms are represented by 10 or more specimens (of course not counted as numbers). The heat and wet make photography difficult, but nevertheless we shall be able to illustrate the palms in a way they have never been shown before. Most of the palms have been obtained in flower or fruit, and several of them in both which is rather unusual.

We have been here a month alone, we two, but now a third person has come.

In August Bailey spied in Jamaica the prickly-pole palm, known then as *Bactris Plumeriana* "as a great group among broad-leaved trees in a pasture near Gibraltar, St. Catherine, with dead fruit but spathes intact." Again in November, 1935, he was to visit the spot and find "the clump in good red fruit." However, this was not the great triumph of Bailey's tropical explorations.

One of his and Miss Ethel's most daring feats as explorers occurred in the Panama zone. Braving dangers of the disease-ridden and boa constrictor inhabited Mohinja Swamp which borders Chagres River, they disregarded warnings and went in search of a rare palm. Accompanied by two or three others and with two natives to cut trails, they made their way through water up to their hips amid the season's rains to photograph and describe *Raphia taedigera*—the only species native to both the old and new worlds and growing north of the Amazon. Bailey was confident that the palm would be found growing in this swamp. They found the nature hidden treasure. In a pouring rain, with the camera placed on a tripod in water almost the tripod's height, they photographed the palm. The picture was published as part of a Panama palm article written by Bailey and presented in *Gentes Herbarum*, III, 2, in 1933, where seven species were established and one transfer to another genus made. When told of the accomplishment, the natives marveled that a man could go there at all—difficult as it was even in the dry season. But a man 73 years of age! And a woman! This was unheard of. In 1943, Bailey would present in *Gentes Herbarum* another study of Panama palms, "Palmae novae panamenses, et aliae." Gradually and to much effect were the Baileys' field studies proceeding.

From the Barro Colorado exploration of 1931 the Baileys returned to Ithaca as planned and on September 5 he wrote Weatherby:

It is good of you to remember me with the Exsiccatae, and I am very glad of them. They will all be in the Herbarium before the month has passed. I am particularly pleased to find the Rubus for I am now entranced of the blackberries and do not expect to come out of the trance until I am finished—I hope by Thanksgiving time. I am buried under ten thousand specimens.

What shall I send you in exchange? When they shall have been determined I can send some of our pilferage from Barro Colorado if you would like them.

On November 9 a parcel "containing 151 of [their] recent tropical collections" was forwarded "with the hope that out of the number you may find enough desirables to balance the century of plantae exsiccatae Grayana. Of course," wrote Bailey, "one does not get as good specimens knocking about in a tropical forest in the rainy season as one obtains at home, and particularly when one or two sets already have been taken out." On December 26, "My Rubus paper is now all written and it remains to be edited and verified. I fear it will introduce a number of departures." This was fascicle 6 of volume II of *Gentes Herbarum* published on March 4, 1932, another paper by Bailey on "The Blackberries of North America." In 1933 would be added "Blackberries of the Lower South beyond the mountains and highlands of Georgia and Alabama" after a busy collecting season from the upper Gulf Coast to Vermont and Maine; and in 1934, "Certain Northern Blackberries"; and there would be other papers on the genus Rubus.

On March 17, 1932, Bailey wrote to Robinson: "I am pleased that you find something to commend in the Rubus paper."

To I. M. Johnston, a couple of days later, he said:

It is comforting to know that you have been entertained by the Rubus paper. It has been a long pull and I am glad to have it published. Yet I am not done with Rubus. Much material will accumulate this year, and probably a good number of undescribed things in my herbarium will then be made clear.

Next to Rubus, my most important collection of native stuff is Vitis. I have been accumulating material for a monograph for at least twenty-five years. Nothing has really been done with the American grapes since I worked them over long ago for the Synoptical Flora. I am completing my collections this year in the expectation of doing next year what I did this year in Rubus. It is an interesting bunch.

Just now I am fascinated of the palms of Panama and have a paper on the subject partly written. I hope to publish in summer, after I have returned from the West Indies.

Palm hunting, therefore, again took Bailey to the tropics. On April 11, 1932, he announced to Weatherby: "Now I am making ready to ship myself off to the West Indies to test some [described] and other notions with my hands on the plants." On June 25 he reported: "I am recently returned from a very interesting and successful palming trip in the West Indies, and I have a lot of work ahead of me."

In 1930 Bailey, as the most famous student, though not alumnus, of the South Haven, Michigan, schools, had delivered their commencement address. Following this, in 1933, members of the South Haven Garden Club honored again the life and work of the man who annually had made a pilgrimage to his South Haven home and garden to visit his father and friends. They planted in A. S. Dyckman Park a rugged, shapely tree.

Liberty Hyde Bailey, senior, died on January 16, 1912, at the age of 92 years. The stalwart, living memorial of this tall, rugged, proud, and restless man was an avenue of maples arching for a quarter of a mile the highway which led to the modest white residence. Liberty Hyde Bailey, senior, had been abundantly pleased with the life and accomplishments of his youngest son. How the elderly man must have loved the sight of those maples which he himself had planted! Naturalist without knowing it, his son had characterized him. Often his son had heard with pleasure of his gifts of small Arbor Day trees to South Haven children.

Not many years hence—in August, 1938—a Bailey shrine in South Haven would be established. For plant science pilgrims and all other persons, Mrs. C. B. Charles of Bangor, Michigan, purchased the historic residence and grounds at South Haven and presented it to the city. Go there today and you will see placed before a modest white home —like any average American home—a Michigan state highway sign inscribed and pointing out the "birthplace of Dr. Liberty Hyde Bailey." Then walk through the orchard and the fields of the farm and stroll into the shrine and observe the great strong timber taken from the Michigan forest of which the home was built. The strength of Bailey is there symbolized.

In 1933 the Macmillan Company published Bailey's book, *The Cultivated Conifers in North America*, and another meritorious work, *How Plants Get Their Names*. In the last are passages of beautiful and instructive writing. In it was incorporated a chapter devoted to Carolus Linnæus, who founded the binomial system of naming plants and animals. In this book, moreover, was considered the general subject of nomenclatural rules, and many other matters of general and specific systematic interest. The next year, 1934, Bailey's *Gardener's Handbook* appeared, successor to *The Gardener*; brief indications for the growing of common flowers, vegetables and fruits in the garden and about the home. In 1941 this volume was reissued in an imperial edition. As a one-volume encyclopedic manual of gardening—its subject matter arranged alphabetically and informative of every phase of growing flowers, shrubs, vegetables, and fruit—it has been especially commended for its special advice on such topics as annuals, vines, borders, rock-gardens, hotbeds, and control of insects and diseases. In the *Gentes Herbarum* papers, Bailey has done some special floricultural studies, as illustrated by "Novel Chrysanthemum species" (1940) and "Neglected Jasminums" of the same year. *Hortus*, a concise dictionary of gardening, general horticulture and cultivated plants in North America, was newly revised in 1935. In 1941 *Hortus Second*, including most of the material of the former work and plants in cultivation to the close of the year 1939, was published. Furthermore, the year 1937 produced *The Garden of Gourds*, with decorations; the year 1938, *The Garden of Pinks*, with decorations; the year 1939, *The Garden of Larkspurs*, with decorations; and, at the present writing, Bailey is preparing a similar work on the bell flower family. Beyond all doubt, Bailey has truly earned his title as Dean of the horticultural world, generally conceded him by both the science and the trades.

During 1933, Bailey was good as his word. He studied, as promised, the grapes. After giving much time in the course of that year to Rubus, adding 1,000 sheets to his herbarium, "some of it very critical material," he turned to Vitis. On October 1, he wrote to Greenman:

As I return from the Bronx where I have been going over their Vitis, I find . . . your letter of September 28th and also the parcel of Engelmann specimens. I had not expected to receive the actual specimens, but of course they are better for my work and I greatly appreciate the courtesy. I am now submerged in Vitis, having about 2300 sheets of my own and also others to name. These Engelmann things come just in time. . . .

The year 1933 saw publication in the new fourteenth edition of the *Encyclopedia Britannica* of a selection of articles by Bailey and others on botany: plants and gardening, and a separate compilation drawn therefrom. Moreover, on December 28, Bailey was able to report to Weatherby, "My Vitis paper is now written but until it actually goes to the printer it is always subject to minor changes." On March 15, 1934, as the fourth fascicle of its third volume *Gentes Herbarum* offered Bailey's article, "The Species of Grapes Peculiar to North America," a paper presented with the intention of completing "the work begun nearly fifty years ago on the botanical and horticultural identities of North American grapes, and particularly to extend the monograph prepared for Gray's Synoptical Flora published in 1897." The author had drawn from a wide variety of sources, including scientific institutions both of the United States and Europe, from many universities, from the United States Department of Agriculture, and from experiment stations, nurseries, and many individuals.

On October 1, 1934, he told Weatherby:

. . . My Sabal studies are producing results that surprise me, but this is to be expected in almost any group of palms. I know of no herbarium specimens outside my own that show generic differences which probably must be recognized.

The intention of the present biography is to produce a book confined to history. It contemplates no scientific evaluation of the material still subjects of scientific inquiry and investigation; such belongs of right to the respective branches of plant science study. Dr. Bailey's work on the palm, berry, and other plant families has not been completed, nor probably will it be during, it is hoped, many forthcoming years of a worthy and famous life. Critical evaluation and comparison of unfinished work of scientific men is, obviously, a daring task even for thoroughly trained men of science, and not part of true historical perspective. Suffice it, therefore, for our purposes, to say, that Bailey has produced a number of permanently worthy and authoritative articles on palms, all further proof of his rare ability as a plant scientist. Aside from studies already alluded to, one may refer to other *Gentes Herbarum* papers, among them: "Binomials of Certain Palms" (1930) ; "Palms and Their Characteristics (1933) ; "American Palmettoes" (1934) ; "The Royal Palms —Preliminary Survey" (1935) ; "The King Palms of Australia—Archontophœnix" and "Certain Ptychospermate Palms of Horticulture" (1935) ; "Arecastrum—the Queen Palms," "The Butias," and "Washingtonia" (1936) ; "Erythea—the Hesper Palms," "Notes on Brahea" (1937) ; "Thrinax—the Peaberry Palms," "Certain Palms of the Greater Antilles, Calyptrogyne-Calyptronoma, the Bactrides Group (Bactris), Reported Copernicia in Jamaica," (1938) ; "Various Palms, Howea in Cultivation—the Sentry Palms, Species of Raphis in Cultivation—the Lady Palms, Ptychospermate Palms—Supplement, Lucaba Palm in the New World, Coccothrinax of Florida, Geonomas in the Lesser Antilles," and "Certain Palms of the Greater Antilles—ii, New Haitian Genus, Coccothrinax in the Southern Antilles, Geonoma oxycarpa, the great Carossier: Attalea crassipatha, Royal Palm of Hispaniola, Pseudophœnix Puzzle" (1939) ; "Several Palm Problems, the Problem of Colpothrinax, Acœlorraphe vs. Paurotis—Silver-Saw Palm, Rhyticocos—the Overtop Palm, the Generic Name Corozo, Euterpe in the West Indies, Sabal princeps" (1940) ; "Acrocomia—Preliminary Paper" (1941) ; "Palms of the Seychelles Islands" and "Palms of the Mascarenes" (1942).

In 1940 a paper by Bailey on "The Rib-Seed Palms in Florida" was presented formally through the medium of "Occasional Papers" of the Fairchild Tropical Garden at Coconut Grove, Florida. This is an institution of which Bailey was early constituted a member of its governing board and which had been established by David Fairchild. During the winter of 1941-1942, in recognition of Bailey's service in systematic study of the world palms, this world-renowned institution laid out and dedicated in Bailey's honor the "Liberty Hyde Bailey palm glade," a memorial which will pay homage for many, many years to Bailey's genius in plant science study. Amid days of ceremony, at the formal dedication, Bailey was present and delivered a principal address. One questions if, living or dead, any American plant scientist has been honored with more tributes, testimonials, and objects of esteem and veneration. Genius and ability alone cannot explain this. Qualities of character have also taken a part—among them bravery, courage, and determination. To portray these characteristics, no more than three illustrations are necessary to dramatize Bailey's determination to do a thorough and lasting job of palm systematization.

Picture him, at the time 80 years of age, pack on his back, swinging limb to limb through treetops of a high, dense, dark, evergreen mountain forest on the French island of Guadeloupe in 1938-1939, in the company of an island guide and two native foresters. He was spending his strength to examine for himself a palm species in flower, an Euterpe, represented to him and believed by government authorities there to have been long extinct.

Or, visualize, if you will, a perilous ocean adventure far out from a little oceanic island beyond Andros Island of the Bahamas. There, Bailey became separated from a gasoline launch, the *Mandalay*, procured for a palm exploration, and drifted all of one night in a yawl in the midst of high winds and heavily tossed seas. On this venture Bailey was accompanied by two persons, a strong negro, and one Percy Cavel, a white man of the small island. By accident, Bailey and Cavel in the yawl became separated from the launch on which the negro was left. All through the night on a storm-ridden ocean, Cavel handled the rudder and Bailey the sails. With the break of morning, sounds of a gasoline motor in operation warned them that the negro, frightened because of the storm, was taking their launch and leaving them to any luck that might happen. Like a flying leaf across those waters they guided their yawl, sails up, and presently, fortune favoring them, the *Mandalay* became stuck, and they gained, eventually reaching her. But the negro disliked Cavel and, as they climbed aboard, put up a fight. He was armed and murder was thwarted only when Bailey broke in between them, and prying the negro's 42-caliber from him, enabled Percy to throw the glaring, mad negro to the launch floor and into the ocean until, exhausted, he begged for mercy. Two days were required to return to the little island. But, en route, at their planned destination, Bailey got the palm species he was after.

Another adventure was recorded in 1940. At the age of 82 years, he set out to reach the type station of *Sabal Mexicana*, long an enigma. It had been described by Martius from plants grown from seeds collected by the Russian collector Karvinski. Bailey chartered an airplane for the first part of his journey over the palm country of Popocatepetl. The journey was completed by truck, wagon, horseback, and dugout canoe, through one of the most primitive western hemisphere regions he had ever seen.

Expenses of these later journeys have been borne personally by Bailey. The collected materials and results of his published studies, however, have been made part of the herbarium and library of the Bailey Hortorium of the New York State College of Agriculture. On May 1, 1935, the *Ithaca Journal* and the *Cornell Daily Sun* carried news of an event of historic importance in the annals of American plant science study—one of especial significance to the state of New York and its college of agriculture and Cornell University. The *Ithaca Journal's* announcement read:

Cornell has been fortunate in receiving gift collections of various sorts. None has been more significant from a scientific viewpoint than that just made by L. H. Bailey.

The L. H. Bailey Hortorium will be of inestimable value to research and instruction in the plant sciences, and will be one of the show places of the University. The fact that a new name had to be manufactured to describe the collection is some indication of its unique importance.

Doctor Bailey spent more than thirty years in building up what is perhaps the largest record of cultivated plants in existence. Most herbaria have concerned themselves with wild, uncultivated flora. The library accompanying the gift represents a lifetime of careful selection of one of the world's most eminent scientific scholars.

Graduate students and faculty members of the State College have had access to the Bailey collection for many years. Now the donor is making it even more accessible. The modesty with which Dean Bailey made the gift, and his remark that "The value of these collections depends upon the use that is made of them," were characteristic of his life work in agriculture and country life.

When Doctor and Mrs. Bailey had reached 77 years of age, they discussed one evening what disposition to make of the institution, developed extensively during two decades. "Why should we not give it to Cornell University?" asked Bailey. Mrs. Bailey answered simply, "Yes, that is where it should go." Aside from the real estate on which the hortorium is located and which has become property of Cornell University, Bailey in 1935 had invested about $50,000 in the hortorium work. On April 6, 1935, a board of trustees' meeting was held to constitute the hortorium a department of the university. With Bailey as director and Ethel as curator—in 1941 she was elected to faculty membership of the college—an advisory board of the Liberty Hyde Bailey Hortorium was constituted. In accordance with directory provisions of the proceedings, on October 4, 1935, President Livingston Farrand of the university appointed Dr. Wiegand as chairman of the committee or board, and professors E. A. White, L. H. MacDaniels, H. H. Whetzel, A. C. Frazer, A. H. Wright, H. C. Thompson, R. S. Hosmer, and U. P. Hedrick to constitute its membership, with Bailey and Miss Ethel as ex officio members. By this time Dean Mann had become provost of the university and the college of agriculture had a new dean and director. President Farrand in his letter to Dr. Wiegand said, "Dean [Carl E.] Ladd has discussed this matter carefully with Dr. Bailey and he is very cordial to the idea."

Wiegand, the year of his election as president of the Botanical Society

of America, included in a letter his estimate of the hortorium's value
to Cornell University, saying:

. . . Early in 1935 Dr. Bailey, feeling that age and financial resources
were such that to place the herbarium on a more firm foundation by
making some provision in this direction would be wise, therefore, gave
the herbarium and the library connected with it to Cornell University with
the stipulation that it should be called The Bailey Hortorium and should
be financed from that time on by the University. The trustees have placed
it directly in charge of the College of Agriculture. The staff now consists of
a director, Dr. L. H. Bailey; a curator, Miss Ethel Z. Bailey; an advisory
committee of 10 university professors, and a research taxonomist, Dr.
Robert T. Clausen.

The objectives of the herbarium are in general as follows:

The herbarium is intended to present the cultivated flora of the world.
Nowhere else is there a place where the plants of agriculture and horticulture
can be dealt with scientifically. There are now some 25,000 species in
cultivation and this number is increasing rapidly as many more are introduced from foreign countries. The names have never been standardized.
Many are going under incorrect names. Accurate systematic knowledge of
the cultivated flora should constitute a basic consideration in investigation
and teaching of horticulture, genetics and plant breeding, physiology,
pathology, agronomy, and other branches connected with our economic
plants. It is a major requirement in the development of institutions of
learning in agriculture.

Such a development demands abundant material. Not only should the
material be in the form of herbarium specimens, but there should be a
garden for growing and experimenting on these cultivated plants. Such a
garden is connected with the Hortorium. Growers are constantly contacting
the herbarium for the proper identification of their plants. Publications such
as "Hortus" coming from the herbarium are of the utmost importance to the
nurserymen and florists.

The Hortorium is unique as a scientific institution, there being no other
of its scope devoted to these purposes from the standpoint of agriculture
and horticulture. It is a scientific institution, a scientific museum of plants
built up to help the horticulturist and floriculturist on a scientific basis.

The Hortorium is now housed in several large rooms adjacent to Dr.
Bailey's home in Sage Place, Ithaca. These rooms were donated to the University along with the herbarium. The collection is housed in new steel
cases of the most approved type. Photographic rooms are provided. There
are mounting rooms for the preparation of specimens, a room for artists,
and a number of cabinets for books. Adjacent to the building in which these
rooms are located is a garden of considerable extent, where plants from
seeds imported from abroad are growing. Many more plants are grown for
the herbarium on college land on the farm.

Altogether the Bailey Hortorium is one of the most important units added
to the university, and particularly to the College of Agriculture, in recent
years.

Wiegand's analysis of the hortorium's objectives was somewhat a
synthetic summary of Bailey's statement of "Aims, Ideals and Pur-

poses" formulated for the committee's first meeting on October 18, 1935. Bailey estimated, that not only about 25,000 species and Latin-named forms of plants were then in cultivation, with other species constantly appearing, but that "Something like 1,000 kinds are now added to the lists yearly in North America. The greater part of the 25,000 kinds of plants in cultivation are imperfectly known as to identification," observed Bailey. He continued:

The names are largely taken for granted, and they pass from dealer to dealer, from catalogue to catalogue, from nurseryman to purchaser without discriminating check. There is no recognized place in the world for the identification of all cultivated plants as such, with facilities for investigation, covering both herbaceous and woody subjects, and relating the knowledge to the needs of the cultivator and the investigator. . . . To keep in touch with cultivated plants one must be prepared to grow the novelties in species, as one acquaints oneself with the developments in any other field. Such plants are best understood if one is gardener as well as botanist; and this kind of gardening should have much effect in developing higher ideals in that craft. Gardening is now practiced in the motive of display. For very many years I have grown plants in this spirit and have added the specimens to the herbarium. In any year I may grow 200 to 800 kinds. The land on which these plants have been grown is now the property of Cornell University. Its use for such purposes should be continued. In fact, the establishing of living museums of many of the confused groups of cultivated plants is now a necessity. The work on Sedum and Sempervivum begun with R. T. Clausen is an example. A similar start in Allium is now under way by the Curator of the Hortorium; in this genus some ninety binomials are in the trade, and the species in cultivation are in utter confusion. Such museums of growing plants afford materials for record and comparison, and provide means of checking names in commerce; they may be a source of supplying properly determined stock to nurserymen; in the end they will afford herbarium exsiccatæ for other institutions. Such living collections should dissipate much of the confusion in cultivated plants, and also place new objectives before growers. I hope we foresee the beginning of an epoch in horticulture. It is the one departure in that field now most needed.

Time has come, also, for a definite organized program for the growing of cultivated plants as soon as they are introduced. There is no place where specimens may be found of all species as cultivated subjects. Presumably the woody plants may be grown for the purpose in the proposed arboretum, but special provision should be made for the herbaceous subjects, which are more numerous. This shows the need of a botanic garden at Cornell. Plants should be grown also of the kinds involved in any monographs on which members of the staff may be working. . . . Greenhouse plants grown for Hortorium purposes are specially needed. . . .

Some idea of the useful growth of the Bailey Hortorium herbarium may be gathered by noting, first, the results of Bailey's first paper of *Gentes Herbarum*, "Plantae chinenses" (1920). Among numerous concepts, this systematized 20 new species distributed among 13 genera, and 15 new varieties and forms. "Brassica cultorum" (1922) described

5 new species and 6 new varieties. However, contrast these papers with Bailey's great monographic study of the years 1941-1943, "Species Batorum the Genus Rubus in North America (north of Mexico) II Hispidi III Setosi IV Verotriviales v Flagellares," a notable elaboration of the blackberries, raspberries, groundberries, northern bristle berries, southern dewberries, et cetera, in other words, the great berry family which Bailey had begun to study as early as 1880. In 1939 the hortorium collection of the genus Rubus comprised 17,568 sheets. One may acquire some knowledge of Bailey's service to plant science study at the New York State College of Agriculture by contrasting the hortorium herbarium which now comprises about 200,000 specimens of cultivated and wild plants—on July 16, 1943, approximately 188,857 mounted specimens—with the comparatively small and almost unused "garden herbarium" brought from the college in 1915 to Bailey's home and shop. Today the total number of horticultural species and varieties accounted for approach very closely 40,000 plants, among which *Hortus second* recognized 18,447 pure species, and of which there are approximately 25,000 pure species of introduced cultivated plants which are possible subjects of experimentation. In many respects—and he so regards it—this work has been Bailey's most important service to plant science knowledge.

Bailey's has been a life granted to few men. Among botanists he stands prominent in a small fraternal circle of specially venerated members. Among horticulturists he holds the unquestioned honor of deanship. In the course of more than fifty years of residence at Ithaca, he has worked and fought and lived to see agriculture established at his beloved university on a sound, permanent basis. He has seen it grow from a small department or "college"—a courageous outgrowth of a hardy struggle against prejudice, ridicule, and scorn. Bailey has been privileged to live to see agriculture so advanced as a subject of academic prominence that in one of America's greatest institutions of learning, Cornell University, its highest honorary and administrative position, chairman of its board of trustees, is filled by a man of agricultural affiliations. In 1940 Howard Edward Babcock, of Syracuse, New York, was constituted the board's temporary chairman when, because of age, his predecessor retired. A year or so later, Babcock was elected permanent chairman. Accepting the distinction, he resigned as a trustee in the Grange. Babcock's affiliations had consisted almost entirely with organizations having to do, in one form or another, with agriculture. His election symbolized a triumph of a half-century long struggle waged by agriculture for full academic recognition. Agriculture was still recognized as America's basic industry. But its real significance was now seen in terms of both the

city and country. Far-sighted men saw a sound agriculture as impera-
tively necessary to maintain health and welfare in the cities.

Into an eminent company of scientist immortals—although still
very much alive and still accomplishing for American plant sciences—
Bailey has already entered. One finds difficulty in selecting words sufficient to characterize his accomplishments in total perspective. Moreover, he is one who prefers tribute and honor in restraint. In 1938,
when Bailey was notified of the dedication of the Liberty Hyde Bailey
Memorial Park—his old home—at South Haven, he wrote a citizen
there:

> I am glad the occasion was so auspicious. It seems strange to become
> historic at this stage in my career. The old house was built by my father
> and it should be a good memorial to him.

Bailey could not attend the dedication because that year Mrs. Bailey
—who for years had valiantly fought a serious illness—died. On July 13
he wrote his South Haven townsman and friend, C. O. Monroe:

> The sympathies of yourself and wife are appreciated. I have passed an
> epoch in my life. We have had fifty-five years together, for which I am
> thankful. Three years ago we lost our older daughter, and we have her
> children. . . .

Bailey's grandchildren are now grown: his grandson served in the
armed forces of World War II, and his granddaughter is married. At
their Sage Place residence Bailey and his daughter Ethel live quietly,
carrying on their work at the hortorium and occasionally going on exploring tours. In 1943 for a month Bailey was in Mexico, at the age
of 86 years, collecting plants with as much agility and zest as ever. Bailey's scholarly interests in the genus Rubus and the cucurbits have persisted. In January, 1944, appeared a monograph, "Quidam Rubi Tropi-
cales" (*Gentes Herbarum*, VI, 6, pp. 325-364) elaborating, among other
matters, the genus for Jamaica, Hispaniola, and Panama. On December 6, 1943, "Species Cucurbitae" (*idem*, VI, 5, pp. 267-322) was presented, purposing to account for species in the United States, Mexico,
Guatemala, and British Honduras. In consequence of these and other
papers on these subjects, many collections have been sent to him. Seeds
of cucurbits from Mexico to Argentina have been received, and he continues to grow them in his garden adjoining the Hortorium. He still
has a pronounced interest in the tropical flora, for both its systematic
and economic concerns, and his work in the palms has remained steady,
producing papers of lasting value. In August, 1943, "Studia Palmarum," elucidating, "Brahea, and one Erythea" and "New Palms in
Panama, and others," was published (VI, 4, pp. 177-264); in July, 1944,
"Revisio Palmettonum" (VI, 7, pp. 367-459); and on July 17, 1946,

"Herbarium Palmarum" (vii, 2, pp. 153-180), this paper containing remarks on certain taxonomic practices, especially that concerned with the palm herbarium—each interestingly and beautifully written. From January to March, 1946, Bailey again visited northern South America and, while in Venezuela, became a guest of the government and was presented with a scroll of honor by the agricultural college there. On the last day of his 88th year, he flew by plane from Piaraco and landed at Miami, Florida, to visit again David Fairchild. Among many other collecting journeys he, sometimes with Ethel, sometimes alone or with other accompanying explorers, has collected in California and Lower California, and in New England (1936), in Haiti and San Domingo, Nova Scotia, Cape Breton Island and Prince Edward Island (1937), the Bahama Islands, Haiti, Cuba, Virginia and North Carolina, Long Island and Connecticut, Florida, French West Indies, Guadeloupe, and Martinique (1938), in Kentucky, Missouri, the South generally, and Staten Island, Haiti and San Domingo (1939), in Florida and Mexico (1940), in Virginia (1941), on six Caribbean islands, including islands of the Dutch West Indies and Trinidad, and, obtaining permission from the Brazilian government, he spent a month exploring along the Amazon River and within the wilderness and tributaries adjacent searching for palms and rare flora (1947). The foregoing, making no pretense to completeness, is told to give some idea of the scope of Bailey's earnestness in carrying out his planned program and as an indication of his exploratory zeal. For one objective and that only— plant collecting—has every journey been taken. During her lifetime— even when invalided—Mrs. Bailey was the one most insistent he carry forward his work to completion.

A recent honor of unusual distinction was the selection of Dr. Bailey to represent the plant sciences by an address at a symposium on America's Role in the Growth of Science, held October, 1946, by the American Philosophical Society. Another honor has been the choice of Dr. Bailey to serve as chairman of the committee on policy and management of the Cornell University Plantations, the history of which has recently been written by Ralph S. Hosmer, emeritus professor of forestry of the New York State College of Agriculture, and published by the administrative committee.

The following poem "Outlook," written by Bailey in 1911, expresses his spirit of steadfastness more ably than a humble biographer:

> ... I have wandered far from homes of men
> In deep strong woods and fragrant fields
> Where every rising morning yields
> A world uncursed and new.
> The meadows green, the heavens blue,

The noonday heat, the morning dew,
The winds that roam the great groves through,
The beast and fin and feathered crew—
    They bear no mark of fateful trend
    To perdition or doom-end—
All lead me out to fearless view
A deepening hold on life construe
For what they teach I hold is true.

They teach that all the world is good
Alike for man and brute and wood
All set in one vast fellowhood,
Nor innate guilt appears;
That all the tribes are onward bound
Ascended each from lower round
Prophetic of uprising forms
That shall accord to higher norms,
And in them all no wreck inheres;
Some better man than yet may come
Old earth is still not dead or dumb—
The kinds and races are outpast
And every one unto itself is better than the last:
So,
I trust my lot
As my ways are trod,
And I blaspheme not
The perfecting works of God;
And I build my holy fires
Where every living thing aspires.

And I am I;
Dominion unto me is given
As my fertile years go by
To win my way to heaven.
Myself I must redeem—
    All nature helps me on
    And all good saints of here and yon—
My soul must be supreme.
Within myself my kingdom lies
Nor any fatal faiths shall blind my eyes
When my soul would take its wings and rise,
For all nature disregards our small philosophies
And confounds them with her everlasting silences.

The creatures live their parts complete
To them there is no blank defeat
Or canker set against the heart:
So shall I take my eager part
In the great program
And let there be no weak repine
And no self-annulment mine
Where I am—

But may there be some good conquest
That I shall win with trust and zest
Where all things are divine.

Nor are we blind
Hope lies not behind
Ever new is the language nature speaks—
We live not with the Greeks;
The earth and sky stretch on and on
With web of law and mystery
Yet bear some healing benison
To consecrate my sins to me—
We find a goodly harmony
When nature holds the mastery.

I break not with the past.
I stead myself in all the things of yore
In all mankind's long climb and all the sacred lore,
And then I outward look to what lies on before.
From first unto the last
Some mighty essence runs,
It moveth in the worlds and riseth in the suns:
Its scheme I would forecast,
For some far time will science open wide the vista vast
And let us see the chart whereon our ways are cast.—
    When I consider the heavens, the stars, and the moon
    My spirit out-wings its small forenoon
      With pride of master and man
      To partake in the plan.

We helpless gaze unto the stars;
But some great day we shall in signal be with Mars
And in a twinkling shall sense a wider brotherhood
Than any man hath ever understood—
A kinship that encompasseth the universe
Wherein will all our feeble cults disperse
And all the worlds our neighbors be
In one vast fraternity.
New visions will outlift the race
As we identify ourselves in space
And achieve the meaning of the whole
In some new splendor of the soul;
Old formulas will readjust,
And calmer still will be our trust
When our shrinking fears will cease
And we discover our release
From all vagary and caprice;
And everywhere shall God appear
In our serene abiding here.
    And closer then on earth the ties
    When free of doubt and all disguise
    Their common end men recognize
    And in one wholesome effort rise.

'Tis not for time alone I seek
'Tis not for hope or joy I speak,
I fly beyond all things we know
To understand why all is so—
I must be free:
Why should I fear to look when I have eyes to see?
Then casting all reserve aside
To know things as they are,
The order in the world's my guide
Its process is my star:
The planets and the systems ply—
If they are safe, then so am I.
I fear no ill where I shall range
Nor lose my bearings when my forms of hope shall change.
There may be worlds about us that we cannot apprehend
Existences that all our hopes and days transcend:
These may take us hence
Into some super-sense
And this may be our great sequence.
So,
I hail the brother soul
Who rides with me this whirling world
Through the waiting spaces hurled;
So let the cycles roll
While this tiny sand-grain sphere
Lives its little shining year
And so will my days possess
No aching void of loneliness
Because my world has larger grown,
But fuller be as they unfold
With the gladness lived of old
And with the ranges then unknown.
Quietly the rain-drops fall
And tirelessly the white winds call;
So,
I live and love as seasons fly
And then, O Teacher, here am I.
     I stand within the cosmic sea
     And dreadless wait my destiny—
     I stand with bird and beast and tree
     And all the things unbound and free,
     For they and I and all together
     Pass on in space and time and weather.

ACKNOWLEDGMENTS

MOST of the material contained in this book has been quoted direct— or obtained from unpublished correspondence which has never before been generally available. For information that has been previously published the most authoritative sources have been made use of and references to these have been incorporated as footnotes. For valuable assistance in securing this material and for helpful criticism afforded the author in writing this book, he wishes to express his indebtedness to the following persons and institutions.

To Dr. George Harrison Shull, Professor Emeritus of Botany and Genetics of Princeton University, to Dr. Herbert Hice Whetzel, since deceased, Professor of Plant Pathology, The New York State College of Agriculture, Cornell University, and to Dr. Harold B. Tukey, formerly chief of research, Division of Pomology, New York State Agricultural Experiment Station, Cornell University, Geneva, New York, who have read the manuscript at various stages of progress, given much helpful aid and advice, suggested corrections, and other forms of improvements.

To many persons who have been interviewed by the author, and in numerous instances have furnished documentary material and data, among them, most prominent, of course, Dr. Bailey and Miss Ethel Bailey; also, Dean Albert R. Mann, of New York City, Dr. James Edward Rice, of Mexico, New York, Dr. Herbert John Webber, of Riverside, California, Dr. Benjamin Minge Duggar, of Madison, Wisconsin, Dr. J. F. Duggar, of Auburn, Alabama, Dr. Aven Nelson, of Laramie, Wyoming, Dr. U. P. Hedrick, of Geneva, New York, Dr. Jesse M. Greenman, of St. Louis, Missouri, Drs. H. Harold Hume and P. H. Rolfs, of Gainesville, Florida, Dr. David Fairchild, of Coral Gables, Miami, Florida, Drs. Donald F. Jones and James G. Horsfall, of New Haven, Connecticut, Dr. S. A. Waksman, of New Brunswick, New Jersey, Dr. and Mrs. Frederic Edward Clements, of Santa Barbara, California, Drs. Willis Linn Jepson, Reed, and Davis, John Bennett, and Harry Morton Butterfield, and Miss Alice Hilgard, of Berkeley, California, Dr. George T. Hastings, of Santa Monica, California, William F. Pickett, of Manhattan, Kansas, Bethal Stewart Pickett, of Ames, Iowa, Dr. William R. Maxon, of Washington, D.C., Dr. Albert F. Blakeslee of Northampton, Massachusetts, Frederic William Taylor, of Los Angeles, California, Dr. Alton H. Finch, of Tucson, Arizona, Niels Ebessen Hansen, of Brookings, South Dakota, Alfred Rehder, of Jamaica Plain, Massachusetts, C. A. Weatherby and Dr. M. L. Fernald, of Cambridge, Massachusetts, Drs. William Trelease, Charles F. Hottes, Louie Henrie Smith, and Joseph Cullen Blair, of Urbana, Illinois, Drs. Albert Frederick Woods, Walter Tennyson Swingle, and Rogers McVaugh, of the United States Department of Agriculture, Washington, D.C., Drs. Wendell Paddock, Joseph H. Gourley, Edgar Nelson Transeau, Adolph Edward Waller, and William Alton Taylor, of Columbus, Ohio, Drs. George N. Lauman, L. H. MacDaniels, James G. Needham, Lawrence Palmer, Homer C. Thompson, Rollins Adams Emerson, and R. T. Clausen, and Lewis Knudson, and Dr. and Mrs. William Kelly, of Ithaca, New York, Drs. Lewis Ralph Jones and James G. Moore, of Madison, Wisconsin, Mrs. Mary Rogers Miller, of Los Angeles, California, Mrs. Harris J. Ryan, of Palo Alto, California, J. Horace Mc-Farland, of Harrisburg, Pennsylvania, John J. Dillon, of New York, New York, Jared von Wagenen, of Cobleskill, New York, Dr. Carl C. Epling, of Brentwood, California, and others. Obviously no order of importance attaches to the foregoing list. Many of these persons have given the author invaluable aid, some more than others. Especially the author wishes to acknowledge the valuable conferences had by him with Dr. William H. Chandler, of Westwood, California, and Dr. Ezra Jacob Kraus, of Chicago, Illinois. In almost every instance, the person interviewed has or has had a connection with an educational institution. The assistance of the institution as well as the individual is acknowledged. Space limitations, however, have compelled omission of the institution's name and, also, his official position.

To the Farlow Herbarium, Harvard University, Cambridge, Massachusetts, and to the Arthur Herbarium, Purdue University, Lafayette, Indiana, for permission to copy correspondence of Bailey, to the Library of Cornell University for a loan of letters of Bailey to K. M. Wiegand, to Miss Clarissa Rolfs for a loan of letters of Bailey to her father, P. H. Rolfs, since deceased, to the Gray Herbarium of Harvard University, Cambridge, Massachusetts, for permission to photostat a large amount of correspondence of Bailey with officials of that institution, to *Cornell Countryman* of the New York State College of Agriculture for a loan of a set of its issues during the period concerned in this biography, to the Bailey Hortorium of minutes of meetings, a set of *Gentes Herbarum*, and other documents, to the New York State College of Agriculture for a gift of a set of its experiment station bulletins issued during the period concerned, to Dr. Bailey for a loan of several volumes of *Country Life in America*, to Dr. Lawrence Palmer of Ithaca, New York, for materials concerning the development of the nature-study movement, to Dr. H. B. Tukey for a loan of unpublished memoirs and materials of Eugene Davenport, formerly Dean of the College of Agriculture of the University of Illinois, to Dr. Hedrick and the New York State Agricultural Experiment Station at Geneva, New York, for a loan of materials once saved and bound in volumes by Dr. Edward Lewis Sturtevant, to the Library of the Ohio State University for the loan of a set of *Garden and Forest,* to Dr. Lewis Knudson of Ithaca, New York, for a loan of an unpublished manuscript on the history of the department of botany of the New York State College of Agriculture, and to Miss Grace Howard for the loan of a manuscript prepared by her and entitled, "The Life and Accomplishments of Liberty Hyde Bailey, South Haven's Most Illustrious Son," to Dr. Donald F. Jones, for a loan of a prepared manuscript on the history of genetics work at the Connecticut Agricultural Experiment Station, to Dr. William F. Bray, of Syracuse University, Syracuse, New York, for the loan of a prepared manuscript of the history of the development of The New York State College of Forestry at Syracuse. A large amount of material has been gathered for the purpose of writing a biography of Dr. Bernhard Eduard Fernow. That biography has been written and the authorities for what is said concerning Fernow will appear appropriately there. Similarly, some materials from a collection gathered together to prepare a biography of Erwin Frink Smith but regarded more relevant for use in this book will appear here. Because of the abundance of the collections assembled for purposes of the Smith book, it was believed that a portion of the materials should and could be

Acknowledgments 87

utilized in the present book without detracting from the value of the study of the life and work of Dr. Smith. Therefore an outline story of early plant pathological research in North America has been included. Acknowledgment for the privilege of using these materials is due principally to Mrs. Erwin F. Smith, the United States Bureau of Plant Industry, and the National Archives of Washington, D.C.

To many libraries, too numerous to mention all, but especially libraries of the Gray Herbarium, the Missouri Botanical Garden, the College of Agriculture of the University of Wisconsin, the University of Illinois, the libraries of Cornell University, the Carnegie Library of Columbus, Ohio, which lent the author many of Dr. Bailey's books, the Ohio State University Botanical and Zoological Library, the University of California at Los Angeles, the Library of the United States Department of Agriculture which permitted the photostating of the card index file of Dr. Bailey's published writings, the Library of Congress, the Library of the Smithsonian Institution, which institution also permitted the author to copy letters of Bailey herein quoted, the Library of the University of Chicago, the Public Library of Buffalo, New York, and the Ohio State Library.

To the author's mother and father, Mr. and Mrs. Andrew Denny Rodgers, for much aid and encouragement, together with many suggestions for improvement.

INDEX

Index

Index